A COLLECTOR'S MOVIE STAR MEMORABILIA

Brian MILLS

B.T. Batsford Ltd, London

First published 1991

ISBN 0 7134 6612 X

Typeset by Servis Filmsetting Ltd, Manchester

Printed in Great Britain by
Courier International Ltd, East Kilbride, Scotland

for the publishers
B.T. Batsford Ltd
4 Fitzhardinge Street
London W1H 0AH

To Peter, Doreen, David, Josie and Tena, with love

ACKNOWLEDGEMENTS

My thanks to the following people for their invaluable help: David Aldridge, Gilles Bergal, Mick Brunton, Liz Connell, Roy Deeley, Patrice Duvic, Ken and Sylvia Ferguson, Joel Finler, Laura Gilfillan, Chris Golden, Ken Graham, Ian Howe, Louise Irvine, Lynn Keddie, Kristine Krueger, Val Lyon, Alan Miller, Ian Milne, Martin Murray, Liane Newton, Kevin Pearson, Irene Schubert, Maurice Speed, Gary Wallington, Martin Willoughby, Peter Woodland.

I am eternally grateful for the help and assistance I received from the staff of the following organizations: Academy of Motion Picture Arts & Sciences, British Film Institute Library, The British Library, Christie's South Kensington, Library of Congress, Lincoln Center of the Performing Arts, Sotheby's.

The following companies are gratefully acknowledged for use of material in this book: The Amalgamated Press Ltd, Argus Specialist Publications Ltd, BPI Communications Inc., *Cahiers du Cinéma*, *Cinémonde*, Cowles Magazine Inc., Dell Publishing, Fawcett Publications Inc., Flicks Publications Ltd, Globe Photos Inc., Hansom Books, Hulton Picture Library, Independent Magazines Ltd, Lawleys By Post, Murdoch Magazines, The National Board of Review of Motion Pictures Inc., Orpheus Publications Ltd, Photoplay Publishing Company, Reed Publishing, Spotlight Publications Ltd, Time Warner Inc.

Finally I would like to thank my editor Pauline Snelson for her patience, encouragement and belief in this book.

PHOTO CREDITS

American Film cover of Sean Connery, copyright of *American Film* 1989: used with permission from BPI Communications Inc.; *Life* cover of John Wayne, copyright 1965 John R. Hamilton/Globe Photos Inc.: used with permission; *Time* cover of Vivien Leigh, copyright 1939 Time Warner Inc.: reprinted with permission of *Time*.

Photographs of Bergman, Gable, Bogart, Davis, Grable, and Lollobrigida, and posters from *Rebel without a Cause*, *Jailhouse Rock* and *It Happened at the World's Fair* are from the British Film Institute. Photographs of Robert Taylor, Leslie Caron, *Time* cover of Vivien Leigh, and the posters of *Born Yesterday* and *Broken Arrow*, are all used courtesy of the Joel Finler Collection.

Picturegoer postcard of Marilyn Monroe is used by courtesy of Ian Milne; cigarette cards by courtesy of Murray Cards International Ltd, and photographs of Royal Doulton figures courtesy of Lawleys By Post, photographed by Northern Counties Photographers. Posters are photographed by Paul Turner.

Stills of *Call Northside 777*, credit to Twentieth Century Fox.

Films In Review cover of Gena Rowlands, copyright October 1980, Films In Review. Used with permission.

Premiere cover of Tom Hanks, copyright 1989, Murdoch Magazines. Used with permission.

Film Favourite cover is used by courtesy of the Patrick Robertson collection.

Photoplay cover of Marilyn Monroe is used by courtesy of the Liz Connell collection.

Most of the material used in this book is from the author's own collection.

CONTENTS

PREFACE

Did the Marx Brothers ever appear on a magazine cover? Do you know the dates of the *Picture Posts* that had uncredited Monroe covers? How many times did Garbo make the cover of *Motion Picture*? What was the picture on the missing dust jacket of the first Maurice Speed *Film Review*? What cigarette card set includes James Cagney? Was Margaret O'Brien ever in the *Picturegoer* series of postcards? Do you know what a front of house set is? Can you tell the difference between an original still and a reproduction? Who is Saul Bass? What is a one-sheet? Are you sure that the Paul Newman signature is genuine? What items belonging to Laurel and Hardy fetched over £11,000 in auction? Is there a Royal Doulton figure of Elvis Presley? Where can you buy all this movie memorabilia? How much will it cost? Questions, questions, questions. This book's intention is to provide the answers to these and many more questions that the movie memorabilia collector, and often the dealer, has asked but not found the answers to.

The largest section of this book is devoted to magazines. It lists over 20 magazines and their film star covers. Many of these are complete entries from first issue to last – movie magazines from *ABC Film Review* to *Picturegoer*, and general or news magazines from *Life* to *Time*. Space has obviously limited the selection to what I consider to be the most collectable magazines for film star cover collectors. The choice was also determined by the availability of the magazines: many issues, sometimes entire volumes, were missing. Sometimes I was offered what appeared to be very good and complete copies of a magazine, but on closer inspection found mutilated pages and covers which had been removed by over zealous readers. This has resulted in my choosing to include a few incomplete entries where I feel the magazine's inclusion is of paramount importance to the collector. Although the majority of the magazine entries are up to 1989, in the case of the American film fanzines I have stopped the entry at the end of the fifties, when their covers began to decline.

Hollywood movie magazines of the thirties and forties offered artist-drawn portrait covers beneath the magazine's logo. The covers were uncluttered and simple, with the portrait alone selling the magazine. Today we have the crowded cover with teasers and multiple pictures assaulting the eyes like a poster-plastered shop window. It is still hoped, but unlikely, that a movie magazine may be produced that will revive the perfect front page.

Movie magazines are still one of the cheapest forms of memorabilia and an old *Picturegoer* or *Picture Show* can still be bought for as little as £1 each. American magazines like *Modern Screen*, *Motion Picture* and *Photoplay* will cost a lot more, £10 or £15, depending, as in all cases, on who the star is on the cover. Monroe, Dean, Laurel and Hardy, Presley, Garbo covers will be at a premium. Copies of *Fans' Star Library* are worth £3 each, but Monroe, Dean and Presley numbers would sell for £15 per copy.

By no means overlook other magazines like America's *TV Guide*, *Screen Romances*, *Silver Screen*, *Screenland*, *Hollywood Studio Magazine*, *Ciné Revue*, *Esquire*, *Film Dope*, *Radio Times* and newspaper supplements. One of the most readable current film magazines is *Empire*, destined to be collected in bound copies.

Choosing the most popular stars was a daunting task once past the big five. The selection had to be those most popular with collectors rather than filmgoers' favourites; a decision which ruled out Bing Crosby but allowed in Ava Gardner. There are 24 actresses, 21 actors. They range from Marlene Dietrich to Madonna, Rudolph Valentino to Harrison Ford. The major test is whether the demand for a star's memorabilia is a lasting or a fleeting one. A few years ago, Matt Dillon, Brooke Shields and Richard Chamberlain material was collectable and valuable, but they were shooting stars who have since fallen and burnt out. It would seem that Tom Cruise and Arnold Schwarzenegger are going to stay the course, but time will tell. Madonna has already proved massively popular with collectors, even though her films have not been memorable.

All the beautiful Kodachrome full-page plates that appeared in F. Maurice Speed's *Film Review* are listed in the section on film annuals. From the first, Gloria Jean, in 1944, to the last, Sean Connery and Honor Blackman, in 1964–5, *Film Review* with an original dust jacket and in good condition will cost from £8; the first considerably more.

British tobacco manufacturers who issued cigarette cards relating to films are all listed. Some sets and individual cards have been identified in detail. Picture postcards of film stars have been selected to show a wide coverage of various series, emphasis being given to *Picturegoer*. The latter will sell for £2 each for the average card, £6 or more for others, a Shirley Temple for an example.

Front-of-house sets are listed to show the most popular. Some of these can be found sold as individual stills, and with patience you can build up a set this way. Most sets will be complete, that is, eight stills per set. Posters are sold rolled or folded. When a poster is expensive yet the film mediocre, it could be the artwork that accounts for this; it is often this that makes the difference. In this section of the book, an alphabetical list of the leading poster illustrators is given.

In the next two sections, Signed photographs and Props and souvenirs, I have listed all the full-page signed photographs (Gregory Peck to Luciana Paluzzi) and the star souvenir prizes (Valentino's fur hat to Elizabeth Taylor's gilt earrings) that appeared in *Picture Show*. There is also special mention of Royal Doulton character jugs and figures.

During the compilation of this book some of Hollywood's greatest stars have passed on to that silver screen in the sky: Barbara Stanwyck, Bette Davis, Rex Harrison, Paulette Goddard, Ava Gardner, Irene Dunne and the legendary Garbo. They leave us with the memories and their memorabilia.

CHAPTER ONE

A – Z GUIDE TO THE MOST POPULAR FILM STARS

WOODY ALLEN

Born: Flatbush, Brooklyn, New York, 1 Dec. 1935.
Real name: Allen Stewart Konigsberg.
Top box office ranking: 4 in 1979.

MAGAZINE	YEAR	MONTH	REF. No.
American Film	1977	May	Vol. 2, no. 7
Esquire	1987	April	Vol. 107, no. 4
Films in Review	1975	Aug./Sept.	Vol. 26, no. 7
	1977	June/July	Vol. 28, no. 6
	1979	June/July	Vol. 30, no. 6
Gentlemen's Quarterly	1986	Feb.	Vol. 56, no. 2
Life	1969	21 March	Vol. 66, no. 11
Midweek	1986	17 July	
Newsweek	1978	24 April	
Radio Times	1987	7 – 13 Nov.	Vol. 255, no. 3337
Review	1986	2 May	
Rolling Stone	1987	9 April	Issue no. 497
Saturday Evening Post	1978	July/Aug.	Vol. 250, no. 5
7 Days	1989	23 – 29 July	
Showtime	1966	Dec.	
Sight & Sound	1979	summer	Vol. 48, no. 3
Sunday Times Magazine	1986	25 May	
Time	1972	3 July	Vol. 100, no. 1
	1979	30 April	Vol. 113, no. 18
Time Out	1989	1 – 8 Nov.	No. 1002

FRONT-OF-HOUSE SETS

Original American sets of any of his films.

POSTERS

Original American one-sheets from *Take The Money And Run* onwards. The poster of *The Front* is a picture of Woody facing camera. Posters of his films bear his unmistakable individuality and are unique in their honest simplicity.

SIGNED PHOTOGRAPHS

Portraits and stills, signed 'Woody Allen', are available from bona fide dealers. Prices start from £20 for ink signed.

PROPS AND SOUVENIRS

Memorabilia is guaranteed to appreciate in value as his standing as a movie master increases.

BRIGITTE BARDOT

Born: Paris 28 Sept. 1934.
Real name: Camille Javal.
Top box office ranking: 7 in 1958.

MAGAZINE	YEAR	MONTH	REF. No.
ABC Film Review	1959	April	Vol. 9, no. 4
	1968	Aug.	Vol. 18, no. 8
	1969	Feb.	Vol. 19, no. 2
Cinémonde	1955	20 Oct.	no. 1106
	1956	19 April	no. 1132
		21 June	no. 1141
	1957	4 April	no. 1182
	1958	15 May	no. 1240
	1959	26 March	no. 1285
		13 Oct.	no. 1314
	1960	19 Jan.	no. 1328
		12 April	no. 1340
		12 July	no. 1353
	1961	28 March	no. 1390
		6 June	no. 1400
		3 Oct.	no. 1417
	1962	18 Sept.	no. 1467
	1963	5 March	no. 1491
		7 May	no. 1500
	1964	17 March	no. 1545
		22 Sept.	no. 1572

MAGAZINE	YEAR	MONTH	REF. No.
Fans' Star Library			no. 21
Films & Filming	1962	May	Vol. 8, no. 8
	1966	March	Vol. 12, no. 6
Illustrated	1955	26 March	Vol. 17, no. 5
Jours de France	1963	9 Nov.	
Life	1961	28 July	Vol. 51, no. 4
Marie-Claire	1959	March	
Photoplay (British)	1958	Oct.	Vol. 9, no. 10
	1960	Jan.	Vol. 11, no. 1
		April	Vol. 11, no. 4
Picture Post	1955	1 July	Vol. 68, no. 1
	1956	24 March	Vol. 70, no. 12
Picture Show	1960	17 Sept.	Vol. 75, no. 1947
Picturegoer	1955	23 July	Vol. 30, no. 1055
	1956	7 April	Vol. 31, no. 1092
	1958	1 March	Vol. 35, no. 1191
	1959	12 Dec.	Vol. 38, no. 1277
Screenland	1959	March	Vol. 60, no. 11

Bardot was modelling for magazine covers at the age of 15. All French magazines of the late forties and early fifties bearing Bardot covers are very collectable.

FRONT-OF-HOUSE SETS

French sets of all of her films of the fifties.

POSTERS

French posters, particularly *La lumiere d'en face, Et Dieu créa la femme, La mariée est trop belle.*

SIGNED PHOTOGRAPHS

Ink-signed photos of the fifties will fetch premium prices.

PROPS AND SOUVENIRS

In 1987 Bardot's jewels and mementoes from her film career were auctioned, raising $500,000 to create an animal protection foundation.

INGRID BERGMAN

Born: Stockholm, 29 Aug. 1915.
Died: 29 Aug. 1982.
Top box office ranking: 2 in 1946.

MAGAZINE	YEAR	MONTH	REF. No.
ABC Film Review	1958	Aug.	Vol. 8, no. 8
Cahiers du Cinéma	1953	July	Vol. 5, no. 25
	1954	July	Vol. 7, no. 37
Cinémonde	1947	5 Aug.	no. 679
	1948	17 Feb.	no. 707
		13 April	no. 715
		28 Sept.	no. 739
	1949	7 March	no. 761
	1950	9 Oct.	no. 844
	1951	9 June	no. 879
	1952	8 Aug.	no. 940
	1954	25 June	no. 1038
	1955	29 Dec.	no. 1116
	1956	24 May	no. 1137
Ciné Revue	1946	27 Sept.	
	1949	29 Feb.	
		7 Oct.	
	1950	Oct.	Special number
	1958	18 April	
Film Journalen	1935	3 March	
Films & Filming	1958	Dec.	Vol. 5, no. 3
Films in Review	1958	Dec.	Vol. 9, no. 10
	1974	Dec.	Vol. 25, no. 10
	1976	Nov.	Vol. 27, no. 9
	1979	Feb.	Vol. 30, no. 2
Illustrated	1947	6 Sept.	Vol. 9, no. 27
	1948	25 Sept.	Vol. 10, no. 30
	1949	9 July	Vol. 11, no. 19
	1952	8 Nov.	Vol. 14, no. 37
	1954	26 June	Vol. 16, no. 18
	1958	9 Aug.	Vol. 20, no. 25
Life	1945	12 Nov.	Vol. 19, no. 20
	1946	2 Dec.	Vol. 21, no. 23
	1948	15 Nov.	Vol. 25, no. 20
	1956	26 Nov.	Vol. 41, no. 22
	1967	13 Oct.	Vol. 63, no. 16
Look	1943	6 April	Vol. 7, no. 7

MAGAZINE	YEAR	MONTH	REF. No.
	1944	25 July	Vol. 8, no. 15
	1945	18 Sept.	Vol. 9, no. 19
	1947	30 Sept.	Vol. 11, no. 20
	1948	20 July	Vol. 12, no. 15
	1952	29 Jan.	Vol. 16, no. 3
		20 May	Vol. 16, no. 11
	1957	19 March	Vol. 21, no. 6
	1958	2 Sept.	Vol. 22, no. 18
Modern Screen	1943	Aug.	Vol. 27, no. 3
	1945	Nov.	Vol. 31, no. 6
	1947	May	Vol. 34, no. 6
	1948	May	Vol. 36, no. 6
Mon Film	1957	1 May	no. 558
Motion Picture	1943	April	Vol. 65, no. 3
	1945	March	Vol. 69, no. 2
	1947	Dec.	Vol. 74, no. 5
	1948	Dec.	Vol. 76, no. 5
Photoplay (American)	1943	Oct.	Vol. 23, no. 5
	1945	Jan.	Vol. 26, no. 2
	1946	June	Vol. 29, no. 1
	1947	Feb.	Vol. 30, no. 3
	1948	Feb.	Vol. 32, no. 3
	1949	Dec.	Vol. 36, no. 1
Picture Post	1943	27 March	Vol. 18, no. 13
		18 Dec.	Vol. 21, no. 12
	1946	16 Feb.	Vol. 30, no. 7
	1949	14 May	Vol. 43, no. 7
	1957	28 Jan.	Vol. 74, no. 4
Picture Show	1941	16 Aug.	Vol. 45, no. 1164

MAGAZINE	YEAR	MONTH	REF. No.
	1944	29 July	Vol. 48, no. 1242
	1946	20 April	Vol. 50, no. 1287
		10 Aug.	Vol. 50, no. 1295
	1947	19 April	Vol. 51, no. 1313
	1948	25 Dec.	Vol. 53, no. 1357
	1950	7 Jan.	Vol. 54, no. 1397
		20 May	Vol. 54, no. 1416
	1957	2 March	Vol. 68, no. 1771
		28 Dec.	Vol. 69, no. 1813
	1958	25 Oct.	Vol. 71, no. 1856
	1959	24 Jan.	Vol. 72, no. 1869
Picturegoer	1941	12 April	Vol. 10, no. 516
	1944	30 Sept.	Vol. 13, no. 616
	1948	28 Aug.	Vol. 17, no. 717
	1950	13 May	Vol. 19, no. 784
	1951	1 Sept.	Vol. 22, no. 852
Saturday Evening Post	1948	30 Oct.	
	1949	19 Feb.	
Se	1953	11 June	no. 24
	1955	28 Jan.	no. 4
	1959	19 Feb.	no. 8
Silver Screen	1945	June	Vol. 15, no. 8
	1947	March	Vol. 17, no. 5
Svensk Damtidning	1943	1 May	no. 18
	1956	13 Dec.	no. 50
	1957	25 July	no. 30
	1960	28 July	no. 30
Time	1943	2 Aug.	Vol. 42, no. 5
Vecko Journalen	1960	8 July	no. 27

Early Swedish magazines with Bergman covers are rare and collectable.

POSTCARDS

Picturegoer series 1458. W 269. W 161, W 612.

FRONT-OF-HOUSE SETS

American sets of all her films from *Intermezzo* to *Under Capricorn*.

POSTERS

Swedish posters of early films. American posters from *Intermezzo* onwards. Original American one-sheet of *Casablanca*, most valuable item.

SIGNED PHOTOGRAPHS

Early ink-signed portraits and stills.

SIGNED FULL-PAGE PICTURE

Picture Show, issues of 29 October 1949 and 24 January 1959.

PROPS AND SOUVENIRS

Any memorabilia relating to *Casablanca*.

HUMPHREY BOGART

Born: New York, 23 Jan. 1899.
Died: Los Angeles, 14 Jan. 1957.
Top box office ranking: 5 in 1947.

MAGAZINE	YEAR	MONTH	REF. No.
Film Review	1988	Sept.	Vol. 38, no. 9
Films in Review	1957	May	Vol. 8, no. 5
Life	1969	21 March	Vol. 66, no. 11
Look	1949	7 June	Vol. 13, no. 12
Picture Show	1943	27 March	Vol. 47, no. 1207
	1945	14 July	Vol. 49, no. 1267
	1950	8 April	Vol. 54, no. 1410
	1952	8 March	Vol. 58, no. 1510
Picturegoer	1944	16 Sept.	Vol. 13, no. 615
	1946	26 Oct.	Vol. 15, no. 670
	1949	12 Feb.	Vol. 18, no. 729
Screen Stories	1954	July	
Time	1954	7 June	Vol. 63, no. 23

POSTCARDS

Picturegoer series: 1139a. W 271.

FRONT-OF-HOUSE SETS

Original American sets of his films from *The Petrified Forest* to *The Harder They Fall.* Sets of *The Maltese Falcon* and *Casablanca* will fetch from £50 upwards, per set.

POSTERS

Original American one-sheets of films as above.

SIGNED PORTRAITS

A half-length film still signed on the margin 'Humphrey Bogart' sold in auction at Christie's in 1989 for £550.

PROPS AND SOUVENIRS

The Bogart cult continues. Practically anything relating to this star will be collectable.

MARLON BRANDO

Born: Omaha, Nebraska, 3 April 1924.
Top box office ranking: 4 in 1958.

MAGAZINE	YEAR	MONTH	REF. No.
ABC Film Review	1957	Jan.	Vol. 7, no. 1
	1961	Aug.	Vol. 11, no. 8
	1963	May	Vol. 13, no. 5
Cahiers du Cinéma	1953	Jan.	Vol. 3, no. 19
Cinémonde	1955	8 Sept.	no. 1101
	1956	19 Jan.	no. 1119
		12 July	no. 1144
	1957	11 April	no. 1183
	1961	19 Sept.	no. 1415
	1962	9 Oct.	no. 1470
Fans' Star Library			no. 11
Film Review	1972	Sept.	Vol. 22, no. 9
Films & Filming	1954	Oct.	Vol. 1, no. 1
	1956	Jan.	Vol. 2, no. 4
	1957	March	Vol. 3, no. 6
	1958	March	Vol. 4, no. 6
	1960	Aug.	Vol. 6, no. 11
	1962	Dec.	Vol. 9, no. 3
	1972	Sept.	Vol. 18, no. 12
Films Illustrated	1979	Nov.	Vol. 9, no. 99
Films in Review	1952	March	Vol. 3, no. 3
	1953	May	Vol. 4, no. 5
	1961	March	Vol. 12, no. 3
	1972	April	Vol. 23, no. 4
	1986	Oct.	Vol. 37, no. 10
Life	1953	20 April	Vol. 34, no. 16
	1960	4 April	Vol. 48, no. 13
	1962	14 Dec.	Vol. 53, no. 24
	1972	10 March	Vol. 72, no. 9
	1979	June	Vol. 2, no. 6
Look	1955	17 May	Vol. 19, no. 10
Motion Picture	1956	March	Vol. 45, no. 543
People Weekly	1975	13 Oct	
Photoplay (British)	1961	Feb.	Vol. 12, no. 2
	1972	Oct.	Vol. 23, no. 10
Picture Post	1955	3 Dec.	Vol. 69, no. 10
Picture Show	1952	26 April	Vol. 58, no. 1517
	1954	6 Nov.	Vol. 63, no. 1649
	1955	9 April	Vol. 64, no. 1671
	1956	22 Sept.	Vol. 67, no. 1747
	1957	1 June	Vol. 68, no. 1783
	1958	12 April	Vol. 70, no. 1828
		22 Nov.	Vol. 71, no. 1860
Picturegoer	1952	5 April	Vol. 23, no. 883
Time	1954	11 Oct.	Vol. 64, no. 15
	1973	22 Jan.	Vol. 101, no. 4

POSTCARDS

Picturegoer series: D 128.

FRONT-OF-HOUSE SETS

Original American sets from his first film, *The Men*, to *One Eyed Jacks*.

POSTERS

Original American one-sheets of *A Streetcar Named Desire*, *Viva Zapata*, *The Wild One*, *On The Waterfront*, *The Godfather*.

PROPS AND SOUVENIRS

Any memorabilia relating to above films.

CHARLIE CHAPLIN

Born: Walworth, London, 16 April 1889.
Died: 25 Dec. 1977.
One of the screen's greatest superstars.

MAGAZINE	YEAR	MONTH	REF. No.
American Film	1984	Sept.	Vol. 9, no. 10
Cahiers du Cinéma	1952	Nov.	Vol. 3, no. 17
Film Pictorial	1936	14 March	Vol. 9, no. 212
Film Weekly	1929	15 July	Vol. 1, no. 39
Films & Filming	1957	Aug.	Vol. 3, no. 11
Films in Review	1950	Sept.	Vol. 1, no. 6
	1952	Nov.	Vol. 3, no. 9
Illustrated	1940	21 Dec.	Vol. 2, no. 43
	1947	17 May	Vol. 9, no. 11
	1952	20 Sept.	Vol. 14, no. 30
		18 Oct.	Vol. 14, no. 34
Life	1966	1 April	Vol. 60, no. 13
	1972	21 April	Vol. 72, no. 15
Look	1940	24 Sept.	Vol. 4, no. 20
Motion Picture	1915	July	Vol. 9, no. 6
Picture Post	1940	14 Sept.	Vol. 8, no. 11
	1956	15 Sept.	Vol. 72, no. 11
Picture Show	1919	3 May	Vol. 1, no. 1
	1920	3 July	Vol. 3, no. 62
	1921	2 April	Vol. 4, no. 101
		30 April	Vol. 5, no. 105
		27 Aug.	Vol. 5, no. 122
		8 Oct.	Vol. 5, no. 128
	1922	18 March	Vol. 6, no. 151
		17 June	Vol. 7, no. 164
		25 Nov.	Vol. 8, no. 187
	1923	17 Feb.	Vol. 8, no. 199
		10 Nov.	Vol. 10, no. 237
	1924	3 May	Vol. 11, no. 262
	1925	22 Aug.	Vol. 13, no. 330
		7 Nov.	Vol. 14, no. 341
	1926	11 Dec.	Vol. 16, no. 397
	1927	24 Dec.	Vol. 18, no. 451
	1928	20 Oct.	Vol. 19, no. 494
	1931	4 April	Vol. 24, no. 622
Picturegoer	1936	25 Jan.	Vol. 5, no. 244
	1941	18 Jan.	Vol. 10, no. 504
	1952	18 Oct.	Vol. 24, no. 911
Time	1925	6 July	Vol. 6, no. 1
	1931	9 Feb.	Vol. 17, no. 6

POSTCARDS

Essanay: nos 1 – 4; Rotary: nos 11675, a – c; *Picturegoer* series: 336, a – b. W 936.
Other postcards include artist-drawn cards of Chaplin by Donald McGill and Louis Wain, and the Imperial Playhouse series.

FRONT-OF-HOUSE SETS

Original American or British sets of all of his films up to and including *Limelight*.

POSTERS

Original American one-sheets and British quads. A framed lithograph of Charlie, in colour, printed by L'Affiche d'Art, Paris, *c.* 1920, sold for £440 at Christie's on 20 December 1989.

SIGNED PORTRAITS

Head and shoulders portrait of Charlie inscribed 'With best wishes Charlie Chaplin, 1941' sold for £420 at Christie's on 27 April 1990.

PROPS AND SOUVENIRS

Character jugs, figurines, dolls, toys. A bamboo cane, which was allegedly given by Charlie to the manager of a London theatre, sold for £700 in auction at a Christie's sale on 27 April 1990.

JOAN COLLINS

Born: London, 23 May 1933.

MAGAZINE	YEAR	MONTH	REF. No.
ABC Film Review	1960	March	Vol. 10, no. 3
Films & Filming	1975	Jan.	Vol. 21, no. 4
Films Illustrated	1971	July	Vol. 1, no. 1
Films in Review	1956	Nov.	Vol. 7, no. 9
	1957	June/July	Vol. 8, no. 6
	1959	Jan.	Vol. 10, no. 1
	1960	Feb.	Vol. 11, no. 2
Illustrated	1951	1 Dec.	Vol. 13, no. 40
Life	1955	12 Sept.	Vol. 39, no. 11
	1985	Oct.	Vol. 8, no. 11
Photoplay (American)	1957	May	Vol. 51, no. 5
Photoplay (British)	1955	Nov.	Vol. 6, no. 11
	1959	Sept.	Vol. 10, no. 8
	1971	June	Vol. 22, no. 6
	1979	Nov.	Vol. 30, no. 12
Picture Post	1954	11 Sept.	Vol. 64, no. 11
	1957	8 April	Vol. 75, no. 1
Picture Show	1955	17 Dec.	Vol. 65, no. 1707
	1956	18 Feb.	Vol. 66, no. 1716
	1957	27 July	Vol. 69, no. 1791
Picturegoer	1953	18 April	Vol. 25, no. 937
	1956	28 April	Vol. 31, no. 1095
	1957	14 Dec.	Vol. 34, no. 1180
	1959	28 Feb.	Vol. 37, no. 1243
		21 Nov.	Vol. 38, no. 1274

POSTCARDS

Picturegoer series: D 228.

FRONT-OF-HOUSE SETS

Original British and American sets of her fifties films.

POSTERS

Original British quads of *Our Girl Friday* and American one-sheets of *The Girl In The Red Velvet Swing*.

PROPS AND SOUVENIRS

Although remembered for her part of Alexis in *Dynasty* on the small screen, it is her movie memorabilia, particularly magazine covers, that are sought after.

SEAN CONNERY

Born: Edinburgh, 25 Aug. 1930.
Real name: Thomas Connery.
Top box office ranking: 1 in 1965.

MAGAZINE	YEAR	MONTH	REF. No.
ABC Film Review	1965	July	Vol. 15, no. 7
	1969	Feb.	Vol. 19, no. 2
American Film	1986	Sept.	Vol. 11, no. 10
	1989	May	Vol. 14, no. 7
Cinémonde	1964	30 June	no. 1560
	1965	16 Feb.	no. 1593
Film Review	1976	Aug.	Vol. 26, no. 8
	1984	Jan.	Vol. 34, no. 1
	1989	July	Vol. 39, no. 7
Films & Filming	1965	Oct.	Vol. 12, no. 1
	1974	March	Vol. 20, no. 6
	1983	Dec.	Vol. 30, no. 351
Films Illustrated	1975	Dec.	Vol. 5, no. 52
Films in Review	1966	June/July	Vol. 17, no. 6
	1967	Aug./Sept.	Vol. 18, no. 7
	1972	Jan.	Vol. 23, no. 1
	1974	Dec.	Vol. 25, no. 10
	1976	April	Vol. 27, no. 4
	1979	April	Vol. 30, no. 4
Life	1966	7 Jan.	Vol. 60, no. 1
Photoplay (British)	1964	Aug.	Vol. 15, no. 8
		Nov.	Vol. 15, no. 11
	1966	Dec.	Vol. 17, no. 12
	1967	July	Vol. 18, no. 7
	1972	Jan.	Vol. 23, no. 1
	1984	Jan.	Vol. 35, no. 1
Radio Times	1961	8 June	

FRONT-OF-HOUSE SETS

Original American and British sets of all his Bond films.

POSTERS

Original American one-sheets of *Doctor No, From Russia With Love, Goldfinger, Thunderball, You Only Live Twice, Diamonds Are Forever.*

PROPS AND SOUVENIRS

A specially adapted briefcase disguising a portable telephone/recording device used on the film *From Russia With Love* sold for £420 at Christie's on 27 April 1990.

All the Bond material will be expensive, but there are other memorabilia items worth seeking: anything on *Hell Drivers*, *The Hill*, Hitchcock's *Marnie*, and *Indiana Jones and The Last Crusade.*

GARY COOPER

Born: Helena, Montana, 7 May 1901.
Died: 13 May 1961.
Real name: Frank James Cooper.
Top box office ranking: 1 in 1953.

MAGAZINE	YEAR	MONTH	REF. No.
ABC Film Review	1951	June	Vol. 1, no. 6
Cinémonde	1947	28 Oct.	no. 691
	1953	5 June	no. 983
	1959	19 March	no. 1284
Esquire	1961	May	
Film Favourite	1932	27 Feb.	Vol. 1, no. 16
Film Pictorial	1932	17 Dec.	Vol. 2, no. 43
	1934	3 March	Vol. 5, no. 106
	1935	8 June	Vol. 7, no. 172
	1936	1 Feb.	Vol. 8, no. 206
		15 Aug.	Vol. 9, no. 234
		10 Oct.	Vol. 10, no. 242
	1937	26 June	Vol. 11, no. 279
	1938	19 Nov.	Vol. 14, no. 352
Film Weekly	1930	29 March	Vol. 3, no. 76
		28 June	Vol. 3, no. 89
	1931	7 March	Vol. 5, no. 125
	1935	7 June	Vol. 13, no. 347
	1936	1 Aug.	Vol. 16, no. 407
	1937	26 June	Vol. 18, no. 454
	1938	12 Feb.	Vol. 20, no. 487
		30 April	Vol. 20, no. 498
		16 July	Vol. 20, no. 509
		24 Dec.	Vol. 20, no. 532
Le Soir Illustré	1961	18 May	no. 1508
Life	1938	7 Feb.	Vol. 4, no. 6
	1940	7 Oct.	Vol. 9, no. 15
Look	1942	28 July	Vol. 6, no. 15
Motion Picture	1939	Aug.	Vol. 58, no. 1
	1943	April	Vol. 65, no. 3
New York Magazine	1973	13 Aug	
Photoplay (American)	1932	Sept.	Vol. 42, no. 4
	1939	Oct.	Vol. 53, no. 10
Picture Show	1929	22 June	Vol. 21, no. 529
		19 Oct.	Vol. 22, no. 546
	1930	3 May	Vol. 23, no. 574
	1931	21 Nov.	Vol. 26, no. 655
	1933	28 Oct.	Vol. 30, no. 756
	1934	10 March	Vol. 30, no. 775
		23 June	Vol. 31, no. 790
		1 Sept.	Vol. 31, no. 800
	1935	15 June	Vol. 33, no. 841
		Christmas special edition	
	1936	21 March	Vol. 34, no. 881
		8 Aug.	Vol. 35, no. 901
		17 Oct.	Vol. 35, no. 911
	1937	17 April	Vol. 37, no. 938
		26 June	Vol. 37, no. 948
	1938	12 Feb.	Vol. 38, no. 981
		17 Sept.	Vol. 39, no. 1012
	1939	22 April	Vol. 41, no. 1043
		14 Oct.	Vol. 42, no. 1068
	1940	16 March	Vol. 42, no. 1090
		28 Sept.	Vol. 43, no. 1118
	1941	5 April	Vol. 45, no. 1145
	1942	14 Feb.	Vol. 46, no. 1178
	1943	13 Feb.	Vol. 47, no. 1204
	1944	29 July	Vol. 48, no. 1242
	1945	15 Dec.	Vol. 50, no. 1278
	1946	20 April	Vol. 50, no. 1287
	1949	6 Aug.	Vol. 53, no. 1375
	1951	2 June	Vol. 56, no. 1470
	1954	18 Dec.	Vol. 63, no. 1655
	1957	10 Aug.	Vol. 69, no. 1793
	1958	5 July	Vol. 71, no. 1840
	1959	17 Jan.	Vol. 72, no. 1868
		4 April	Vol. 72, no. 1879
Picturegoer	1931	29 Aug.	Vol. 1, no. 14
	1936	25 April	Vol. 5, no. 257
	1937	22 May	Vol. 7, no. 313
	1938	Summer annual	
		31 Dec.	Vol. 8, no. 397
	1940	27 Jan.	Vol. 9, no. 453
		30 Nov.	Vol. 10, no. 497
	1941	5 April	Vol. 10, no. 515
	1942	14 Nov.	Vol. 11, no. 567

MAGAZINE	YEAR	MONTH	REF. No.
Picturegoer	1946	2 March	Vol. 15, no. 653
(*cont.*)	1947	30 Aug.	Vol. 16, no. 691
	1950	21 Jan.	Vol. 19, no. 768
	1951	26 May	Vol. 21, no. 838
Silver Screen	1940	May	Vol. 10, no. 7
Time	1941	3 March	Vol. 37, no. 9

Le Soir Illustré has a tribute to Gary Cooper: a seven-page illustrated article and an excellent cover picture. Gary Cooper was one of the few male stars to appear regularly on magazine covers during the thirties and these would today, if in pristine condition, command prices of double figures.

POSTCARDS

Picturegoer series: 190. 333, a – e, 518, 531, 565, a – c, 868, a – b, 1128, a, 1300, 1347, 191, W 54, W 427. B 6; Colourgraph: c12, c117, c139, c314; 'Famous Film Partners' series: PC 134, w/ Marion Davies. PC207, w/Jean Arthur. PC234, w/Frances Dee. PC262, w/Merle Oberon.
'Famous Film Partners' were also available in sepia – the aforementioned postcards were in coloured glossy. The *Picturegoer* cards nos 190 – 91 were of film scenes.

FRONT-OF-HOUSE SETS

Original American sets from *Morocco* to *High Noon.*

POSTERS

Original American one-sheets of *Morocco, A Farewell to Arms, Mr Deeds Goes To Town, Beau Geste, The Westerner, Meet John Doe, Sergeant York, For Whom The Bell Tolls, High Noon.*

SIGNED PORTRAITS

A half-length portrait photograph, 9 × 7 in, signed and inscribed 'Sincerely Gary Cooper' *c.* 1937, with a pencil portrait of him and his dog, signed and inscribed 'Sincerely Gary Cooper', fetched £161 in auction at Christie's on 20 December 1989.

JOAN CRAWFORD

Born: San Antonio, Texas, 23 March 1908.
Died: 10 May 1977.
Real name: Lucille Fay LeSueur.
Top box office ranking: 3 in 1932.

MAGAZINE	YEAR	MONTH	REF. No.
Cinémonde	1947	21 Oct.	no. 690
	1950	15 May	no. 823
Film Pictorial	1932	24 Dec.	Vol. 2, no. 44
	1935	12 Jan.	Vol. 6, no. 151

MAGAZINE	YEAR	MONTH	REF. No.
		25 May	Vol. 7, no. 170
		7 Dec.	Vol. 8, no. 198
	1936	6 June	Vol. 9, no. 224
		28 Nov.	Vol. 10, no. 249
	1937	11 Dec.	Vol. 12, no. 303
	1939	2 Sept.	Vol. 16, no. 393
Film Weekly	1928	29 Oct.	Vol. 1, no. 2
	1929	4 Nov.	Vol. 2, no. 55
	1931	22 Aug.	Vol. 6, no. 149
	1932	30 Jan.	Vol. 7, no. 172
	1933	17 March	Vol. 9, no. 231
	1935	16 Nov.	Vol. 14, no. 370
	1936	28 March	Vol. 15, no. 389
		5 Dec.	Vol. 16, no. 425
	1937	30 Jan.	Vol. 17, no. 433
		24 April	Vol. 18, no. 445
		9 Oct.	Vol. 19, no. 469
	1938	5 March	Vol. 20, no. 490
		27 Aug.	Vol. 20, no. 515
	1939	25 Feb.	Vol. 21, no. 541
Films & Filming	1963	April	Vol. 9, no. 7
Films in Review	1956	Dec.	Vol. 7, no. 10
	1979	Aug./Sept.	Vol. 30, no. 7
	1989	Dec.	Vol. 40, no. 10
Illustrated	1955	12 March	Vol. 17, no. 3
Look	1937	23 Nov.	Vol. 1, no. 20
	1939	28 March	Vol. 3, no. 7
		26 Sept.	Vol. 3, no. 20
	1940	12 March	Vol. 4, no. 6
Modern Screen	1932	Feb.	Vol. 3, no. 3
	1933	Oct.	Vol. 6, no. 5
	1935	March	Vol. 9, no. 4
Motion Picture	1928	March	Vol. 35, no. 2
	1931	Sept.	Vol. 42, no. 2
	1932	Sept.	Vol. 44, no. 2
	1934	Jan.	Vol. 46, no. 6
	1935	March	Vol. 49, no. 2
	1936	Dec.	Vol. 52, no. 5
	1948	Feb.	Vol. 75, no. 1

MAGAZINE	YEAR	MONTH	REF. No.
Photoplay (American)	1927	Dec.	Vol. 33, no. 1
	1930	March	Vol. 37, no. 4
	1931	Oct.	Vol. 40, no. 5
	1934	Jan.	Vol. 45, no. 2
	1935	Oct.	Vol. 48, no. 5
	1936	April	Vol. 49, no. 5
	1937	Feb.	Vol. 51, no. 2
		Oct.	Vol. 51, no. 10
Picture Show	1928	7 April	Vol. 18, no. 466
	1930	18 Jan.	Vol. 22, no. 559
		8 March	Vol. 22, no. 566
	1931	23 May	Vol. 25, no. 629
		29 Aug.	Vol. 25, no. 643
	1932	20 Aug.	Vol. 27, no. 694
		5 Nov.	Vol. 28, no. 705
	1935	6 April	Vol. 32, no. 831
	1937	30 Jan.	Vol. 36, no. 927
		24 April	Vol. 37, no. 939
		9 Oct.	Vol. 38, no. 963
	1938	5 March	Vol. 38, no. 984
		27 Aug.	Vol. 39, no. 1009
	1940	21 Dec.	Vol. 44, no. 1130
	1952	21 June	Vol. 58, no. 1525
	1954	17 July	Vol. 63, no. 1633
Picturegoer	1931	26 Sept.	Vol. 1, no. 18
	1933	25 March	Vol. 2, no. 96
		2 Dec.	Vol. 3, no. 132
	1935	23 March	Vol. 4, no. 200
	1937	27 March	Vol. 6, no. 305
		26 June	Vol. 7, no. 318
	1938	3 Sept.	Vol. 8, no. 380
	1939	25 March	Vol. 8, no. 409
		2 Sept.	Vol. 9, no. 432
	1940	4 May	Vol. 9, no. 467
	1941	26 July	Vol. 11, no. 531
	1943	9 Jan.	Vol. 12, no. 571
		15 May	Vol. 12, no. 580
	1946	2 Feb.	Vol. 15, no. 651
The Picturegoer	1929	March	Vol. 17, no. 99
	1931	May	Vol. 21, no. 125.

POSTCARDS

Picturegoer series: 339, a – e, 544, a – b, 566, a – b, 661, a, 1113, a, W 327.
Colourgraph: c230, c230a.
'Famous Film Partners' series: PC76, w/Neil Hamilton. *PC227, w/Robert Young. PC228, w/Robert Young. *PC230, w/Spencer Tracy. (*also available in sepia.)

FRONT-OF-HOUSE SETS

Original American sets of *Mildred Pierce* and *Johnny Guitar.*

POSTERS

Original American one-sheets from *Rain* to *Female On The Beach.*

SIGNED PORTRAITS

A group of autographed photographs of Joan sold for $715 at a Sotheby's auction in the United States in 1984.

PROPS AND SOUVENIRS

A travelling vanity case that Joan Crawford gave to the wardrobe supervisor of Shepperton Film Studios in 1957, plus a signed photograph of the star, sold for £380 at Christie's on 27 April 1990.

BETTE DAVIS

Born: Lowell, Massachusetts, 5 April 1908.
Died: 6 Oct. 1989.
Real name: Ruth Elizabeth Davis.
Top box office ranking: 6 in 1939.

MAGAZINE	YEAR	MONTH	REF. No.
American Film	1977	March	Vol. 2, no. 5
Cahiers du Cinéma	1951	May	Vol. 1, no. 2
Cinémonde	1947	22 July	no. 677
Film Pictorial	1932	8 Oct.	Vol. 2, no. 33
	1934	7 July	Vol. 5, no. 124
	1935	6 July	Vol. 7, no. 176
Film Weekly	1935	5 July	Vol. 14, no. 351
		21 Dec.	Vol. 14, no. 375
	1939	22 April	Vol. 21, no. 549
Films & Filming	1955	Sept.	Vol. 1, no. 12
	1956	May	Vol. 2, no. 8
	1959	Feb.	Vol. 5, no. 5
	1963	April	Vol. 9, no. 7
	1968	Jan.	Vol. 14, no. 4
	1988	March	Vol. 34, no. 402
Films in Review	1978	Nov.	Vol. 29, no. 9
	1984	Nov.	Vol. 35, no. 9
Illustrated	1942	17 Jan.	Vol. 3, no. 47
Life	1939	23 Jan.	Vol. 6, no. 4
Look	1951	13 March	Vol. 15, no. 6
Modern Screen	1933	Feb.	Vol. 5, no. 3
	1938	Aug.	Vol. 17, no. 3
	1940	Oct.	Vol. 21, no. 5
Motion Picture	1933	Dec.	Vol. 46, no. 5
	1935	May	Vol. 49, no. 4
	1936	April	Vol. 51, no. 3
	1937	Nov.	Vol. 54, no. 4

MAGAZINE	YEAR	MONTH	REF. No.
Photoplay (American)	1933	June	Vol. 44, no. 1
	1936	Aug.	Vol. 50, no. 2
	1938	Oct.	Vol. 52, no. 10
	1939	June	Vol. 53, no. 6
	1940	Aug.	Vol. 53, no. 8
	1941	Feb.	Vol. 18, no. 3
	1942	March	Vol. 20, no. 4
Picture Post	1942	18 April	Vol. 15, no. 3
Picture Show	1934	14 July	Vol. 31, no. 793
	1935	23 March	Vol. 32, no. 829
	1936	19 Sept.	Vol. 35, no. 907
	1939	17 June	Vol. 41, no. 1051
		23 Sept.	Vol. 41, no. 1065
	1940	5 Oct.	Vol. 44, no. 1119
	1941	25 Oct.	Vol. 45, no. 1170
	1947	25 Jan.	Vol. 51, no. 1307
	1951	20 Jan.	Vol. 56, no. 1451
Picturegoer	1933	19 Aug.	Vol. 3, no. 117
	1935	16 March	Vol. 4, no. 199
	1937	23 Jan.	Vol. 6, no. 296
	1938	15 Jan.	Vol. 7, no. 347
		10 Sept.	Vol. 8, no. 381
	1939	24 June	Vol. 9, no. 422
		28 Oct.	Vol. 9, no. 440
	1940	18 May	Vol. 9, no. 469
		28 Dec.	Vol. 10, no. 501
	1943	25 Dec.	Vol. 12, no. 596
	1945	20 Jan.	Vol. 14, no. 624

MAGAZINE	YEAR	MONTH	REF. No.
Silver Screen	1936	Sept.	Vol. 6, no. 11
	1938	Feb.	Vol. 8, no. 4
	1939	March	Vol. 9, no. 5
	1940	June	Vol. 10, no. 8
	1941	Aug.	Vol. 11, no. 10
Time	1938	28 March	Vol. 31, no. 13

POSTCARDS

Picturegoer series: 686, a – c, 1342, W 292.
Colourgraph: c250, c345, c250a.
'Famous Film Partners' series: *PC126, w/ Charles Farrell. *PC273, w/Errol Flynn. *PC278, w/George Brent. *PC297. w/Errol Flynn.
(*also available in sepia.)

FRONT-OF-HOUSE SETS

Original American sets from *Jezebel* to *Now Voyager*, plus *All About Eve*.

POSTERS

Original American one-sheets of any of her films of the thirties.

SIGNED PORTRAITS

Ink-signed photographs from £60 upwards.

JAMES DEAN

Born: Marion, Indiana, 8 Feb. 1931.
Died: 30 Sept. 1955.
Real name: James Byron Dean.
His popularity soared after his tragic death.

MAGAZINE	YEAR	MONTH	REF. No.
Astros Estrelas	1985		no. 2
Cinémonde	1955	19 May	no. 1085
	1956	27 Sept.	no. 1155
	1957	14 Feb.	no. 1175
Fans' Star Library			no. 16
Look	1956	16 Oct.	Vol. 20, no. 21
Picture Show	1955	15 Oct.	Vol. 65, no. 1698

POSTCARDS

Picturegoer series: D 697, D 760, D 761, D 779.

FRONT-OF-HOUSE SETS

East Of Eden, Rebel Without A Cause, Giant: original American and British sets from £60 each.

POSTERS

Original American one-sheets and British quads of all films.

SIGNED PORTRAITS

Ink-signed photographs sell for from £500 upwards.

PROPS AND SOUVENIRS

All original memorabilia will fetch high prices. A worn black leather wallet, stamped inside with gilt lettering JAMES DEAN, accompanied by an affidavit confirming the provenance and a photograph of the vendor with Dean and an actress at Santa Barbara race track two months before Dean's fatal accident, fetched £5,500 in an auction at Christie's on 20 December 1990.

MARLENE DIETRICH

Born: Berlin, 27 Dec. 1901.
Real name: Maria Magdalene von Losch.
Legendary German actress at her best under the direction of Josef von Sternberg.

MAGAZINE	YEAR	MONTH	REF. No.
Cahiers du Cinéma	1965	July	Vol. 29, no. 168
Cinémonde	1948	10 Feb.	no. 706
	1949	3 Jan.	no. 752
		9 May	no. 770
	1954	20 Aug.	no. 1046
Film Pictorial	1935	12 Oct.	Vol. 8, no. 190
	1936	4 July	Vol. 9, no. 228
		19 Dec.	Vol. 10, no. 252
Film Weekly	1931	14 Feb.	Vol. 5, no. 122
	1934	7 Sept.	Vol. 12, no. 308
	1935	6 Sept.	Vol. 14, no. 360
	1936	1 Aug.	Vol. 16, no. 407
Films & Filming	1962	Jan.	Vol. 8, no. 4
Films in Review	1958	Jan.	Vol. 9, no. 1
	1985	Feb.	Vol. 36, no. 2
	1987	March	Vol. 38, no. 3
Illustrated	1944	5 Aug.	Vol. 6, no. 24
	1950	27 May	Vol. 12, no. 13
Life	1948	9 Aug.	Vol. 25, no. 6
	1952	18 Aug.	Vol. 33, no. 7
Look	1938	19 July	Vol. 2, no. 15
Modern Screen	1931	May	Vol. 1, no. 6
	1932	Nov.	Vol. 4, no. 6
	1936	March	Vol. 12, no. 4
	1937	Nov.	Vol. 15, no. 6
	1940	Nov.	Vol. 21, no. 6
Motion Picture	1931	April	Vol. 41, no. 3
		Dec.	Vol. 42, no. 5
	1935	June	Vol. 49, no. 5
	1937	July	Vol. 53, no. 6
Photoplay (American)	1933	Nov.	Vol. 44, no. 6
Picture Post	1944	10 June	Vol. 23, no. 11
Picture Show	1931	21 Feb.	Vol. 24, no. 616
	1932	23 April	Vol. 27, no. 677
		8 Oct.	Vol. 27, no. 701
	1934	27 Jan.	Vol. 30, no. 769
		15 Sept.	Vol. 31, no. 802
	1936	8 Aug.	Vol. 35, no. 901
		5 Dec.	Vol. 36, no. 919
	1938	8 Jan.	Vol. 38, no. 976
	1940	13 April	Vol. 43, no. 1094
	1941	27 Sept.	Vol. 45, no. 1168

MAGAZINE	YEAR	MONTH	REF. No.
	1945	27 Jan.	Vol. 49, no. 1255
	1950	26 Aug.	Vol. 55, no. 1430
Picturegoer	1931	30 May	Vol. 1, no. 1
	1932	27 Feb.	Vol. 1, no. 40
	1933	30 Sept.	Vol. 3, no. 123
	1935	30 Nov.	Vol. 5, no. 236
	1936	25 April	Vol. 5, no. 257
	1937	19 June	Vol. 7, no. 317
	1940	7 Dec.	Vol. 10, no. 498
	1948	20 Nov.	Vol. 17, no. 723
Silver Screen	1931	Sept.	Vol. 1, no. 11
	1932	Oct.	Vol. 2, no. 12
	1933	June	Vol. 3, no. 8
	1936	March	Vol. 6, no. 5
	1937	Sept.	Vol. 7, no. 11
Time	1936	30 Nov.	Vol. 28, no. 22

Any early German covers of Dietrich are very collectable.

POSTCARDS

Picturegoer series: 471, a – c, 504, a – c, 519, a – c, 520, a – b, 528, a – b, 529, a – b, 532, 642, a, 643, a, 644, a – b, 645, a – b, 1082, a, 1083, a, 1162. w/ Clive Brook: 603, 604, 650, 606, 607, 607a. w/ Hans Albers and Emil Jannings: 521.
Colourgraph: w/Clive Brook: c141, c142, c143, c144, c145, c165.

FRONT-OF-HOUSE SETS

Original German sets of *The Blue Angel*.
American sets of *Morocco*, *Shanghai Express*, *The Scarlet Empress*, *Destry Rides Again*.

POSTERS

Original German posters of films up to and including *The Blue Angel*; American one-sheets thereafter.

SIGNED PORTRAITS

Ink-signed photographs fetch from £50 upwards.

PROPS AND SOUVENIRS

Highest prices paid for thirties memorabilia.

CL!NT EASTWOOD

Born: San Francisco, 31 May 1930.
Real name: Clinton Eastwood Jr.
Top box office ranking: 1 in 1972 – 3 and 1983 – 4.

MAGAZINE	YEAR	MONTH	REF. No.
ABC Film Review	1970	Nov.	Vol. 20, no. 11
	1971	Nov.	Vol. 21, no. 11
American Film	1988	Sept.	Vol. 13, no. 10
Film Review	1972	Oct.	Vol. 22, no. 10
	1975	Aug.	Vol. 25, no. 8
	1976	Sept.	Vol. 26, no. 9
	1978	Jan.	Vol. 28, no. 1
	1979	Dec.	Vol. 29, no. 12

MAGAZINE	YEAR	MONTH	REF. No.
	1980	Feb.	Vol. 30, no. 2
		July	Vol. 30, no. 7
	1982	Aug.	Vol. 32, no. 8
	1984	Feb.	Vol. 34, no. 2
		Nov.	Vol. 34, no. 11
	1985	March	Vol. 35, no. 3
Films & Filming	1984	Feb.	no. 353
Films Illustrated	1979	Jan.	Vol. 8, no. 89
	1980	July	Vol. 9, no. 106
	1981	Jan.	Vol. 10, no. 112
Life	1971	23 July	Vol. 71, no. 4
Newsweek	1985	23 Sept.	

MAGAZINE	YEAR	MONTH	REF. No.
People Weekly	1975	2 June	
Photoplay (British)	1970	May	Vol. 21, no. 5
	1975	Sept.	Vol. 26, no. 9
	1978	March	Vol. 29, no. 3
	1980	Feb.	Vol. 31, no. 2
		Aug.	Vol. 31, no. 8
	1981	Feb.	Vol. 32, no. 2
	1984	Feb.	Vol. 35, no. 2
Film Monthly	1989	April	Vol. 1, no. 1
		(listed under *Photoplay*)	
Rolling Stone	1985	4 July	
Time	1978	9 Jan.	Vol. 111, no. 2

FRONT-OF-HOUSE SETS

Original American and Italian sets of the 'spaghetti westerns'. American sets of *Dirty Harry* and *Magnum Force*.

POSTERS

Italian posters of *A Fistful Of Dollars*, *For A Few Dollars More*, and *The Good, The Bad, and The Ugly*; American one-sheets of the rest.

PROPS AND SOUVENIRS

Prospective collectors should purchase this star's memorabilia now, while it is still affordable, as it is guaranteed to appreciate in value.

ERROL FLYNN

Born: Hobart, Tasmania, 20 June 1909.
Died: 14 Oct. 1959.
Top box office ranking: 8 in 1939.

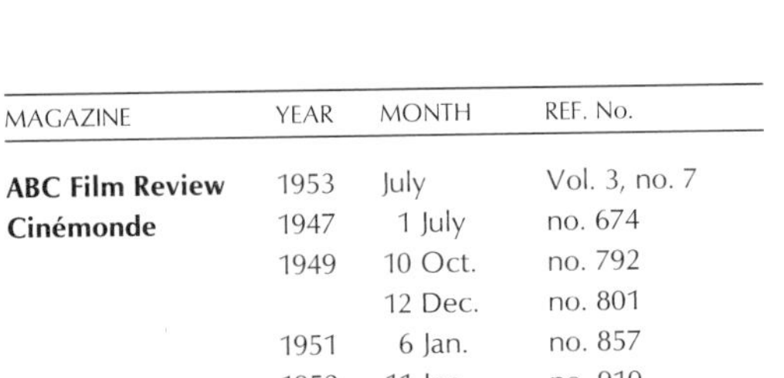

MAGAZINE	YEAR	MONTH	REF. No.
ABC Film Review	1953	July	Vol. 3, no. 7
Cinémonde	1947	1 July	no. 674
	1949	10 Oct.	no. 792
		12 Dec.	no. 801
	1951	6 Jan.	no. 857
	1952	11 Jan.	no. 910

MAGAZINE	YEAR	MONTH	REF. No.
Film Pictorial	1937	2 Jan.	Vol. 10, no. 254
		4 Sept.	Vol. 12, no. 289
	1938	31 Dec.	Vol. 14, no. 358
Film Weekly	1937	2 Jan.	Vol. 17, no. 429
		13 March	Vol. 17, no. 439
	1939	26 Aug.	Vol. 22, no. 567

MAGAZINE	YEAR	MONTH	REF. No.
Life	1938	23 May	Vol. 4, no. 21
Look	1938	12 April	Vol. 2, no. 8
Modern Screen	1943	Nov.	Vol. 27, no. 6
Motion Picture	1938	Nov.	Vol. 56, no. 4
Picture Show	1936	9 May	Vol. 35, no. 888
	1938	31 Dec.	Vol. 40, no. 1027
	1939	17 June	Vol. 41, no. 1051
		22 July	Vol. 41, no. 1056
		2 Dec.	Vol. 42, no. 1075
	1940	5 Oct.	Vol. 44, no. 1119
		2 Nov.	Vol. 44, no. 1123
	1949	12 Nov.	Vol. 53, no. 1389
		24 Dec.	Vol. 53, no. 1395
	1950	22 July	Vol. 55, no. 1425
	1951	17 March	Vol. 56, no. 1459
	1953	31 Oct.	Vol. 61, no. 1596
	1955	29 Jan.	Vol. 64, no. 1661
		30 July	Vol. 65, no. 1687
	1956	28 Jan.	Vol. 66, no. 1713
Picturegoer	1938	26 Feb.	Vol. 7, no. 353
		4 June	Vol. 8, no. 367
		8 Oct.	Vol. 8, no. 385
	1951	11 Aug.	Vol. 22, no. 849

POSTCARDS

Picturegoer series: 1043, a, 1301. W 65, W 910. Colourgraph: c296, c296a, c300, c301, c346, c347.
'Famous Film Partners' series: *PC257, w/Olivia De Havilland. *PC273, w/Bette Davis. *PC297, w/Bette Davis. (*also available in sepia.)

FRONT-OF-HOUSE SETS

Original American sets from *Captain Blood* to *They Died With Their Boots On*.

POSTERS

An original American one-sheet of *The Adventures of Robin Hood* will fetch £1,000 or more.

SIGNED PORTRAITS

Ink-signed photographs go for £75 upwards.

PROPS AND SOUVENIRS

Six autograph letters, signed, each written by schoolboy Errol Flynn to Mary White, the sister of a colleague, and dated from 1922 to 1924, were sold at Christie's on 20 December 1989 for £2,860.

The tunic that Flynn wore in *The Adventures Of Don Juan* fetched $3,500 at a Sotheby's auction in the United States in 1984.

HARRISON FORD

Born: Chicago, Illinois, 13 July 1942.
Top box office ranking: 3 in 1984.

MAGAZINE	YEAR	MONTH	REF. No.
American Film	1986	Dec.	Vol. 12, no. 3
Cahiers du Cinéma	1988	April	no. 406
Film Review	1978	Dec.	Vol. 28, no. 12
	1980	June	Vol. 30, no. 6
	1981	Sept.	Vol. 31, no. 9
	1984	July	Vol. 34, no. 7
	1989	July	Vol. 39, no. 7
Films & Filming	1984	July	no. 358
	1985	May	no. 368
	1987	Feb.	no. 389
Films Illustrated	1981	Aug.	Vol. 10, no. 119
Flicks	1989	July	Vol. 2, no. 10
Life	1984	June	Vol. 7, no. 6

MAGAZINE	YEAR	MONTH	REF. No.
Photoplay (British)	1978	Feb.	Vol. 29, no. 2
	1981	Sept.	Vol. 32, no. 9
	1982	Oct.	Vol. 33, no. 10
	1984	July	Vol. 35, no. 7
	1985	June	Vol. 36, no. 6
	1987	March	Vol. 38, no. 3
Film Monthly	1989	July (listed under Photoplay)	Vol. 1, no. 4
Premiere	1988	March	Vol. 1, no. 7
	1989	June	Vol. 2, no. 10
Rolling Stone	1981	25 June	no. 346
Starburst	1984	June	
You, *Mail On Sunday* magazine	1984	27 May	

FRONT-OF-HOUSE SETS

Original American sets: *Star Wars, The Empire Strikes Back, The Return Of The Jedi, Raiders of The Lost Ark, Indiana Jones and The Temple of Doom, Indiana Jones and The Last Crusade.*

POSTERS

Original American one-sheets of *Star Wars* are valued at £200. His roles as Han Solo and Indiana Jones have proved the most popular with his fans and collectors alike. Any memorabilia relating to these roles will appreciate in value.

PROPS AND SOUVENIRS

A hand-made sixteen-plait bullwhip, used by Harrison Ford as Indiana Jones in *Raiders of The Lost Ark, Indiana Jones and The Temple of Doom*, and *Indiana Jones and The Last Crusade*, was auctioned at Christie's on 20 December 1990. Harrison Ford donated the bullwhip to the Institute of Archaeology in London, to help raise funds for building a new Centre for Conservation and Museum Science at University College, London University. The bullwhip was sold for £12,100.

CLARK GABLE

Born: Cadiz, Ohio, 1 Feb. 1901.
Died: 16 Nov. 1960.
Top box office ranking: 2 in 1934, 1936 – 8, 1941 – 2.

MAGAZINE	YEAR	MONTH	REF. No.
American Film	1978	March	Vol. 3, no. 5
Cinémonde	1950	31 July	no. 834
Film Favourite	1932	23 Jan.	Vol. 1, no. 11
Film Pictorial	1933	26 Aug.	Vol. 4, no. 79
	1934	6 Oct.	Vol. 6, no. 137
	1936	9 May	Vol. 9, no. 220
		19 Sept.	Vol. 10, no. 239
		28 Nov.	Vol. 10, no. 249
	1938	13 Aug.	Vol. 13, no. 338
Film Weekly	1936	12 Sept.	Vol. 16, no. 413
	1937	9 Jan.	Vol. 17, no. 430
		24 April	Vol. 18, no. 445
		13 Nov.	Vol. 19, no. 474
	1938	17 Sept.	Vol. 20, no. 518
	1939	8 April	Vol. 21, no. 547
Films in Review	1960	Dec.	Vol. 11, no. 10
	1961	Feb.	Vol. 12, no. 2
	1983	Aug./Sept.	Vol. 34, no. 7
Life	1941	13 Oct.	Vol. 11, no. 15
	1961	13 Jan.	Vol. 50, no. 2
	1988	May	Vol. 11, no. 6
Look	1943	23 March	Vol. 7, no. 6
	1949	20 Dec.	Vol. 13, no. 26
	1954	7 Sept.	Vol. 18, no. 18
	1955	4 Oct.	Vol. 19, no. 20
	1956	4 Sept.	Vol. 20, no. 18
Modern Screen	1931	Dec.	Vol. 3, no. 1
	1933	Sept.	Vol. 6, no. 4
	1937	March	Vol. 14, no. 4
	1942	Nov.	Vol. 25, no. 6
	1943	July	Vol. 27, no. 2
	1947	March	Vol. 34, no. 4
Motion Picture	1938	Sept.	Vol. 56, no. 2
	1941	Feb.	Vol. 61, no. 1
		Sept.	Vol. 62, no. 2
	1943	Feb.	Vol. 65, no. 1
	1944	Feb.	Vol. 67, no. 1
Photoplay (American)	1932	Jan	Vol. 41, no. 2
	1938	July	Vol. 52, no. 7

MAGAZINE	YEAR	MONTH	REF. No.
	1940	Feb.	Vol. 53, no. 2
Picture Show	1932	9 Jan.	Vol. 26, no. 662
		26 March	Vol. 26, no. 673
		9 April	Vol. 26, no. 675
	1933	4 March	Vol. 28, no. 722
		18 March	Vol. 28, no. 724
		19 Aug.	Vol. 29, no. 746
	1935	6 April	Vol. 32, no. 831
	1936	4 Jan.	Vol. 34, no. 870
		26 Sept.	Vol. 35, no. 908
	1937	9 Jan.	Vol. 36, no. 924
		24 April	Vol. 37, no. 939
		6 Nov.	Vol. 38, no. 967
		13 Nov.	Vol. 38, no. 968
	1938	24 Sept.	Vol. 39, no. 1013
	1939	9 Sept.	Vol. 41, no. 1063
	1941	26 April	Vol. 45, no. 1148
	1943	16 Jan.	Vol. 47, no. 1202
	1947	23 Aug.	Vol. 51, no. 1322
	1948	13 Nov.	Vol. 53, no. 1354
	1950	15 July	Vol. 55, no. 1424
	1951	10 Feb.	Vol. 56, no. 1454
	1953	6 June	Vol. 60, no. 1575
	1954	9 Jan.	Vol. 62, no. 1606
	1957	29 June	Vol. 68, no. 1787
	1958	17 May	Vol. 70, no. 1833
Picturegoer	1932	26 Nov.	Vol. 2, no. 79
	1935	1 June	Vol. 5, no. 210
		21 Sept.	Vol. 5, no. 226
	1936	9 May	Vol. 5, no. 259
	1937	Summer annual	
	1938	30 April	Vol. 7, no. 362
	1940	27 April	Vol. 9, no. 466
		5 Oct.	Vol. 9, no. 489
	1941	19 April	Vol. 10, no. 517
	1942	17 Oct.	Vol. 11, no. 565
	1946	17 Aug.	Vol. 15, no. 665
	1948	17 July	Vol. 17, no. 714
	1949	17 Sept.	Vol. 18, no. 750

MAGAZINE	YEAR	MONTH	REF. No.
	1950	15 July	Vol. 20, no. 793
	1951	20 Oct.	Vol. 22, no. 859
Silver Screen	1940	Feb.	Vol. 10, no. 4
Time	1936	31 Aug.	Vol. 28, no. 9

POSTCARD

Picturegoer series: 507, a, 581, a – b, 737, a – c, 752, a – b, 1017, a – b. W 218.
'Famous Film Partners' series: *PC187, w/Constance Bennett. PC249, w/Myrna Loy. *PC288, w/Norma Shearer. (* also available in sepia.)

FRONT-OF-HOUSE SETS

Original American sets: *It Happened One Night* and *Gone With The Wind.*

POSTERS

An original American one-sheet of *Gone With The Wind* sells for $3000.

PROPS AND SOUVENIRS

Royal Doulton character jug produced for the celebrity series of 1984 and then withdrawn. Valued at £2,500.

GRETA GARBO

Born: Stockholm, 18 Sept. 1905.
Died: New York 16 April 1990.
Real name: Greta Lovisa Gustafsson.
Top box office ranking: 5 in 1932.

MAGAZINE	YEAR	MONTH	REF. No.
Cinémonde	1947	8 July	no. 675
Film Pictorial	1932	24 Sept.	Vol. 2, no. 31
	1933	15 July	Vol. 3, no. 73
	1934	*13 Jan.	Vol. 4, no. 99
		8 Sept.	Vol. 6, no. 133
		20 Oct.	Vol. 6, no. 139
	1935	13 April	Vol. 7, no. 164
		5 Oct.	Vol. 8, no. 189
	1937	30 Jan.	Vol. 10, no. 258
		27 Nov.	Vol. 12, no. 301
	1938	5 March	Vol. 13, no. 315
		12 Nov.	Vol. 14, no. 351
Film Weekly	1929	30 Sept.	Vol. 2, no. 50
	1930	26 April	Vol. 3, no. 80
		12 July	Vol. 4, no. 91
	1931	21 March	Vol. 5, no. 127
		21 Nov.	Vol. 6, no. 162
	1933	1 Dec.	Vol. 10, no. 268
	1934	31 Aug.	Vol. 12, no. 307
	1935	8 March	Vol. 13, no. 334
	1936	4 Jan.	Vol. 15, no. 377
	1937	4 Sept.	Vol. 19, no. 464
	Christmas extra		Vol. 19, no. 475a
	1938	9 April	Vol. 20, no. 495
Films in Review	1973	Dec.	Vol. 24, no. 10
	1979	Nov.	Vol. 30, no. 9

MAGAZINE	YEAR	MONTH	REF. No.
	1981	Oct.	Vol. 32, no. 8
Life	1937	8 Nov.	Vol. 3, no. 19
	1955	10 Jan.	Vol. 38, no. 2
Modern Screen	1931	Dec.	Vol. 3, no. 1
	1934	April	Vol. 7, no. 5
	1938	June	Vol. 17, no. 1
Motion Picture	1927	Dec.	Vol. 34, no. 5
	1930	May	Vol. 39, no. 4
	1931	March	Vol. 41, no. 2
	1932	Jan.	Vol. 42, no. 6
	1937	Jan.	Vol. 52, no. 6
Photoplay	1928	May	Vol. 33, no. 6
(American)	1929	Aug.	Vol. 36, no. 3
	1932	Jan.	Vol. 41, no. 2
	1934	Dec.	Vol. 47, no. 1
Picture Post	1939	15 July	Vol. 4, no. 2
Picture Show	1927	24 Sept.	Vol. 17, no. 438
	1929	12 Jan.	Vol. 20, no. 506
		2 March	Vol. 20, no. 513
		7 Sept.	Vol. 21, no. 540
	1930	25 Jan.	Vol. 22, no. 560
		1 March	Vol. 22, no. 565
		19 July	Vol. 23, no. 585
		1 Nov.	Vol. 24, no. 600
	1931	28 March	Vol. 24, no. 621
		4 July	Vol. 25, no. 635
		22 Aug.	Vol. 25, no. 642
	1932	9 April	Vol. 26, no. 675
		7 May	Vol. 27, no. 679
		1 Oct.	Vol. 27, no. 700
	1933	28 Jan.	Vol. 28, no. 717
	1934	8 Sept.	Vol. 31, no. 801
	1935	16 March	Vol. 32, no. 828
	1936	11 Jan.	Vol. 34, no. 871
	1937	2 Jan.	Vol. 36, no. 923
		4 Sept.	Vol. 37, no. 958
	1938	9 April	Vol. 39, no. 989
	1940	6 April	Vol. 43, no. 1093
Picturegoer	1931	6 June	Vol. 1, no. 2
	1932	1 Oct.	Vol. 2, no. 71
	1934	10 March	Vol. 3, no. 146
		14 July	Vol. 4, no. 164
		1 Sept.	Vol. 4, no. 171
		8 Dec.	Vol. 4, no. 185
	1935	2 March	Vol. 4, no. 197
		15 June	Vol. 5, no. 212
	1936	4 Jan.	Vol. 5, no. 241
		28 Nov.	Vol. 6, no. 288
	1937	30 Jan.	Vol. 6, no. 297
		6 Nov.	Vol. 7, no. 337
		18 Dec.	Vol. 7, no. 343
	1939	5 Aug.	Vol. 9, no. 428
	1940	6 Jan.	Vol. 9, no. 450
	1942	24 Jan.	Vol. 11, no. 546
Primer Plano	1942	7 June	
Screen Romances	1937	Oct.	
Silver Screen	1930	Nov.	Vol. 1, no. 1
	1932	July	Vol. 2, no. 9
	1935	Aug.	Vol. 5, no. 10
	1939	Oct.	Vol. 9, no. 12.

*includes 32-page supplement, 'Private Life Of Greta Garbo'.

POSTCARDS

Picturegoer series: 283, a – r, 503, a – b, 508, a, 601, a – d, 637, a – b, 638, a – b, 639, a, 640, a – b, 641, a, 798, a – c, 954, a, 1161, a – c, 1348, a, 1349. 523: w/Lew Ayres. 600, a – h: w/Ramon Novarro.
Colourgraph: c228, c228a, c267, c287, c127, w/ Ramon Novarro.
'Famous Film Partners' series: *PC145, w/Herbert Marshall. P175: w/Fredric March. *PC208, w/Robert Taylor. PC210, w/Robert Taylor. *PC299, w/Melvyn Douglas. (*also available in sepia.)

FRONT-OF-HOUSE SETS

Original Swedish sets of her early films; German sets of *Joyless Street*; American sets from *The Torrent* to *Two-Faced Woman*.

POSTERS

All films. Original American one-sheets.

SIGNED PORTRAITS

Rare, as she refused to sign pictures.

PROPS AND SOUVENIRS

Absolutely anything. Eight publicity stills by Clarence Bull of Garbo in the role of Queen Christina, 1933, were sold at Christie's on 27 April 1990 for £320.

AVA GARDNER

Born: Grabtown, North Carolina, 24 Dec. 1922.
Died: London, 25 Jan. 1990.
Real name: Ava Lavinia Gardner.
Surprisingly never made the top ten box office stars.

MAGAZINE	YEAR	MONTH	REF. No.
ABC Film Review	1951	Aug.	Vol. 1, no. 8
	1954	July	Vol. 4, no. 7
		Oct	Vol. 4, no. 10
	1956	Nov.	Vol. 6, no. 11
Cahiers du Cinéma	1958	Oct.	Vol. 15, no. 88
Cinémonde	1948	21 Sept.	no. 738
	1951	1 Sept.	no. 891
	1953	24 April	no. 977
	1954	5 Feb.	no. 1018
		14 May	no. 1032
		3 Sept.	no. 1048
	1956	2 Aug.	no. 1147
	1957	24 Jan.	no. 1172
	1962	9 Jan.	no. 1431
Fans' Star Library			no. 27
Films & Filming	1956	Sept.	Vol. 2, no. 12
	1959	Dec.	Vol. 6, no. 3
	1960	Sept.	Vol. 6, no. 12
Films in Review	1952	Oct.	Vol. 3, no. 8
	1954	Feb.	Vol. 5, no. 2
	1956	May	Vol. 7, no. 5
	1957	April	Vol. 8, no. 4
	1966	Oct.	Vol. 17, no. 8
Look	1949	22 Nov.	Vol. 13, no. 24
	1951	18 Dec.	Vol. 15, no. 26
	1953	6 Oct.	Vol. 17, no. 20
	1955	25 Jan.	Vol. 19, no. 2
Modern Screen	1949	March	Vol. 38, no. 4
		Nov.	Vol. 39, no. 6
	1950	Oct	Vol. 41, no. 5
	1952	Jan.	Vol. 44, no. 2
		Sept.	Vol. 45, no. 4
	1953	Jan.	Vol. 46, no. 2
		Nov.	Vol. 47, no. 6
Motion Picture	1948	Nov.	Vol. 76, no. 4
	1950	Jan.	Vol. 78, no. 6
	1951	April	Vol. 81, no. 3
		Nov.	Vol. 82, no. 4
	1952	Nov.	Vol. 84, no. 4
Photoplay (American)	1948	Dec.	Vol. 34, no. 1
	1951	July	Vol. 40, no. 1
	1952	Feb.	Vol. 41, no. 2
Photoplay (British)	1953	Jan.	Vol. 4, no. 1
Picture Post	1951	27 Jan.	Vol. 50, no. 4
Picture Show	1948	10 Jan.	Vol. 52, no. 1332
	1949	17 Dec.	Vol. 53, no. 1394
	1950	17 June	Vol. 54, no. 1420
	1951	3 March	Vol. 56, no. 1457
	1953	7 Feb.	Vol. 60, no. 1558
	1954	9 Jan.	Vol. 62, no. 1606
		9 Oct.	Vol. 63, no. 1645
	1956	1 Sept.	Vol. 67, no. 1744
	1957	26 Oct.	Vol. 69, no. 1804
	1959	5 Dec.	Vol. 73, no. 1906
Picturegoer	1948	31 Jan.	Vol. 17, no. 702
	1949	10 Dec.	Vol. 18, no. 762
	1951	17 Feb.	Vol. 21, no. 824
	1952	1 March	Vol. 23, no. 878
	1953	10 Jan.	Vol. 25, no. 923
		7 Nov.	Vol. 26, no. 966
	1954	12 June	Vol. 27, no. 997
	1955	19 Nov.	Vol. 30, no. 1072
Time	1951	3 Sept.	Vol. 58, no. 10

POSTCARDS

Picturegoer series: D 77. D 274.

FRONT-OF-HOUSE SETS

Original American sets of films of the fifties.

POSTERS

Original American one-sheets, particularly of *The Barefoot Contessa*.

JUDY GARLAND

Born: Grand Rapids, Minnesota, 10 June 1922.
Died: London, 22 June 1969.
Real name: Frances Gumm.
Top box office ranking: 8 in 1945.

MAGAZINE	YEAR	MONTH	REF. No.
ABC Film Review	1951	Jan.	Vol. 1, no. 1
	1955	Feb.	Vol. 5, no. 2
American Film	1983	July/Aug.	Vol. 8, no. 9
Films & Filming	1954	Dec.	Vol. 1, no. 3
	1963	March	Vol. 9, no. 6
Films in Review	1954	Nov.	Vol. 5, no. 9
	1962	Dec.	Vol. 13, no. 10
	1985	March	Vol. 36, no. 3
Life	1944	11 Dec.	Vol. 17, no. 24
	1954	13 Sept.	Vol. 37, no. 11
Look	1940	2 Jan.	Vol. 4, no. 1
		7 May	Vol. 4, no. 10
		8 Oct.	Vol. 4, no. 21
	1955	22 March	Vol. 19, no. 6
Modern Screen	1940	Feb.	Vol. 20, no. 3
	1941	June	Vol. 23, no. 1
	1942	Jan.	Vol. 24, no. 2
	1943	June	Vol. 27, no. 1
Motion Picture	1941	April	Vol. 61, no. 3
Photoplay (American)	1940	Dec.	Vol. 53, no. 12
	1941	Aug.	Vol. 19, no. 3
	1942	July	Vol. 21, no. 2
	1943	July	Vol. 23, no. 2
	1945	Nov.	Vol. 27, no. 6
Picture Show	1940	26 Oct.	Vol. 44, no. 1122
	1941	11 Jan.	Vol. 44, no. 1133
	1943	18 Dec.	Vol. 48, no. 1226
	1945	2 June	Vol. 49, no. 1264
	1946	4 May	Vol. 50, no. 1288
	1947	27 Dec.	Vol. 52, no. 1331
	1949	20 Aug.	Vol. 53, no. 1377
		26 Nov.	Vol. 53, no. 1391
	1955	4 June	Vol. 64, no. 1679
Picturegoer	1943	23 Jan.	Vol. 12, no. 572
	1948	6 Nov.	Vol. 17, no. 722
	1951	31 March	Vol. 21, no. 830
Silver Screen	1946	Feb.	Vol. 16, no. 4
		Aug.	Vol. 18, no. 10
	1952	Sept.	Vol. 22, no. 11

POSTCARDS

Picturegoer series: 1178, a – b, W 644.
Colourgraph: c354.
'Famous Film Partners' series: PC279, *PC298, both w/Mickey Rooney. (*also available in sepia.)

FRONT-OF-HOUSE SETS

Original American sets of *The Wizard Of Oz, For Me And My Gal, Meet Me In St Louis, Easter Parade, A Star Is Born.*

POSTERS

An original American half-sheet of *The Wizard Of Oz* sells for $5000. One-sheets and sizes beyond would cost considerably more.

SIGNED PORTRAITS

Ink-signed photographs from £80.

PROPS AND SOUVENIRS

At an MGM auction in Los Angeles in 1970 Judy's red slippers from *The Wizard Of Oz* were sold along with her costumes from the film. A sequinned jacket, black bolero, and a V-necked cap-sleeved waistcoat, items owned and used by Judy in her stage and television shows, were sold at Christie's on 5 May 1988 for £660. At a later sale, a presentation Gold disc of 'Somewhere Over The Rainbow', mounted above a plaque inscribed 'Judy Garland *Somewhere Over The Rainbow*', awarded in 1939 to commemorate sales of more than a million copies, sold for £350.

BETTY GRABLE

Born: St Louis, Missouri, 18 Dec. 1916.
Died: 2 July 1973.
Real name: Elizabeth Ruth Grable.
Top box office ranking: 1 in 1943.

MAGAZINE	YEAR	MONTH	REF. No.
Cinémonde	1949	31 Jan.	no. 756
Films & Filming	1971	Oct.	Vol. 18, no. 1
Films in	1973	Aug./Sept.	Vol. 24, no. 7
Review	1984	June/July	Vol. 35, no. 6
Illustrated	1944	4 March	Vol. 6, no. 2
	1946	5 Jan.	Vol. 7, no. 46
	1953	8 Aug.	Vol. 15, no. 24
Life	1939	11 Dec.	Vol. 7, no. 24
Look	1949	16 Aug.	Vol. 13, no. 17
	1953	30 June	Vol. 17, no. 13
Modern Screen	1942	Aug.	Vol. 25, no. 3
		Nov.	Vol. 25, no. 6
	1948	March	Vol. 36, no. 4
		Dec.	Vol. 38, no. 1
	1949	Sept.	Vol. 39, no. 4
	1950	July	Vol. 41, no. 2
	1951	Aug.	Vol. 43, no. 3
	1952	April	Vol. 44, no. 5
		Dec.	Vol. 46, no. 1
	1953	Aug.	Vol. 47, no. 3
Motion Picture	1941	July	Vol. 61, no. 6
	1943	Oct.	Vol. 66, no. 3
	1947	Oct.	Vol. 74, no. 3
	1949	June	Vol. 77, no. 5
	1950	Aug.	Vol. 80, no. 1
Photoplay	1942	May	Vol. 20, no. 6
(American)	1943	June	Vol. 23, no. 1
	1946	Nov.	Vol. 29, no. 6
	1948	April	Vol. 32, no. 5
	1949	April	Vol. 34, no. 5
	1951	June	Vol. 39, no. 6
	1952	July	Vol. 42, no. 1.
Picture Post	1942	10 Jan.	Vol. 14, no. 2
	1944	8 Jan.	Vol. 22, no. 2
Picture Show	1938	Summer special	
	1941	22 Feb.	Vol. 44, no. 1139

MAGAZINE	YEAR	MONTH	REF. No.
	1942	3 Jan.	Vol. 46, no. 1175
	1944	29 Jan.	Vol. 48, no. 1229
	1947	14 June	Vol. 51, no. 1317
	1949	13 Aug.	Vol. 53, no. 1376
	1950	29 April	Vol. 54, no. 1413
	1951	8 Dec.	Vol. 57, no. 1497
	1953	27 June	Vol. 60, no. 1578
	1955	3 Dec.	Vol. 65, no. 1705

MAGAZINE	YEAR	MONTH	REF. No.
Picturegoer	1941	13 Dec.	Vol. 11, no. 543
	1943	6 March	Vol. 12, no. 575
	1944	9 Dec.	Vol. 13, no. 621
	1949	9 July	Vol. 18, no. 740
	1951	8 Dec.	Vol. 22, no. 866
	1955	12 March	Vol. 29, no. 1036
Time	1948	23 Aug.	Vol. 52, no. 8

POSTCARDS

Picturegoer series: 1028, a, D 403.

FRONT-OF-HOUSE SETS

Original American sets from *Million Dollar Legs* to *Mother Wore Tights.*

POSTERS

Original American one-sheet of *Moon Over Miami* is particularly collectable as the artwork for the poster was by Alberto Vargas.

PROPS AND SOUVENIRS

Grable dolls, pin-up cards, costumes, and the famous pin-up photo of Betty looking over her right shoulder, which was sent to American GIs during World War II.

JEAN HARLOW

Born: Kansas City, Missouri, 3 March 1911.
Died: 7 June 1937.
Real name: Harlean Carpentier.
Top box office ranking: 6 in 1933.

MAGAZINE	YEAR	MONTH	REF. No.
Film Pictorial	1933	4 Feb.	Vol. 2, no. 50
	1934	10 Feb.	Vol. 4, no. 103
	1935	18 May	Vol. 7, no. 169
Film Weekly	1932	16 Sept.	Vol. 8, no. 205
	1933	9 June	Vol. 9, no. 243
		22 Dec.	Vol. 10, no. 271
	1934	23 Nov.	Vol. 12, no. 319
	1935	28 Dec.	Vol. 14, no. 376
	1936	4 April	Vol. 15, no. 390
		19 Dec.	Vol. 16, no. 427

MAGAZINE	YEAR	MONTH	REF. No.
Films in Review	1978	Dec.	Vol. 29, no. 10
Life	1937	3 May	Vol. 2, no. 18
Modern Screen	1933	July	Vol. 6, no. 2
	1934	Dec.	Vol. 9, no. 1
	1935	Aug.	Vol. 11, no. 3
	1937	May	Vol. 14, no. 6
Motion Picture	1933	April	Vol. 45, no. 3
	1935	July	Vol. 49, no. 6
	1936	May	Vol. 51, no. 4
	1937	Aug.	Vol. 54, no. 1

MAGAZINE	YEAR	MONTH	REF. No.
Photoplay (American)	1931	Dec.	Vol. 41, no. 1
	1932	Aug.	Vol. 42, no. 3
	1935	May	Vol. 47, no. 6
	1937	March	Vol. 51, no. 3
		May	Vol. 51, no. 5
Picture Show	1931	19 Dec.	Vol. 26, no. 659
	1933	4 March	Vol. 28, no. 722
	1936	4 Jan.	Vol. 34, no. 870
		18 April	Vol. 35, no. 885
	1937	16 Jan.	Vol. 36, no. 925
		31 July	Vol. 37, no. 953
		6 Nov.	Vol. 38, no. 967
Picturegoer	1932	26 Nov.	Vol. 2, no. 79
	1934	17 Feb.	Vol. 3, no. 143
	1935	23 Feb.	Vol. 4, no. 196
		Summer annual	
		21 Sept.	Vol. 5, no. 226
	1936	22 Feb.	Vol. 5, no. 248
		3 Oct.	Vol. 6, no. 280
		21 Nov.	Vol. 6, no. 287
	1937	10 April	Vol. 6, no. 307
Screenland	1932	March	
Silver Screen	1934	June	Vol. 4, no. 8
	1936	Feb.	Vol. 6, no. 4
The Picturegoer	1931	Jan.	Vol. 21, no. 121
Time	1935	19 Aug.	Vol. 26, no. 8

POSTCARDS

Picturegoer series: 499, a – c, 712, a – b.
'Famous Film Partners' series: P216, sepia only, w/Robert Taylor.

FRONT-OF-HOUSE SETS

Original American sets of her thirties' films.

POSTERS

Original American one-sheets of films from *Platinum Blonde* to *Saratoga*.

SIGNED PORTRAITS

Ink-signed photographs from £100.

PROPS AND SOUVENIRS

A printed wedding invitation for the marriage of 'Jean Harlow and Mr Paul Bern', in common mount with publicity still of Jean, sold for £88 at a Christie's auction on 5 May 1988. A black lace négligé worn by the star in the film *Libeled Lady* fetched $6,250 at a Sotheby's sale in the United States in 1984.

RITA HAYWORTH

Born: Brooklyn, New York, 17 Oct. 1918.
Died: 15 May 1987.
Real name: Margarita Carmen Cansino.
Never gained the popularity she richly deserved while she was alive.

MAGAZINE	YEAR	MONTH	REF. No.
Cinémonde	1948	25 May	no. 721
	1949	30 May	no. 773
		26 Dec.	no. 803
	1950	4 Dec.	no. 852
	1952	6 June	no. 931
	1953	9 Jan.	no. 962

MAGAZINE	YEAR	MONTH	REF. No.
		14 Aug.	no. 993
Illustrated	1952	6 Sept.	Vol. 14, no. 28
	1958	25 Jan.	Vol. 19, no. 49
Life	1940	15 July	Vol. 9, no. 3
	1941	11 Aug.	Vol. 11, no. 6
	1943	18 Jan.	Vol. 14, no. 3
	1947	10 Nov.	Vol. 23, no. 19
	1971	19 Feb.	Vol. 70, no. 6
Look	1940	27 Feb.	Vol. 4, no. 5
	1945	6 March	Vol. 9, no. 5
Modern Screen	1943	March	Vol. 26, no. 4
	1944	March	Vol. 28, no. 4
	1952	July	Vol. 45, no. 2
	1953	March	Vol. 46, no. 4
Motion Picture	1941	Oct.	Vol. 62, no. 3
	1943	July	Vol. 65, no. 6
	1946	Jan.	Vol. 70, no. 6
	1947	Aug.	Vol. 74, no. 1
	1948	May	Vol. 75, no. 4
Photoplay (American)	1943	Feb.	Vol. 22, no. 3
	1945	Sept.	Vol. 27, no. 4
	1948	Nov.	Vol. 33, no. 6
	1949	Oct.	Vol. 35, no. 5
	1952	Oct.	Vol. 42, no. 4
Picture Post	1943	13 March	Vol. 18, no. 11
	1953	14 March	Vol. 58, no. 11
Picture Show	1942	28 March	Vol. 46, no. 1181
	1943	19 June	Vol. 47, no. 1213
	1944	9 Sept.	Vol. 48, no. 1245
	1952	20 Sept.	Vol. 59, no. 1538
	1953	5 Sept.	Vol. 61, no. 1588
	1954	26 June	Vol. 62, no. 1630
	1957	8 June	Vol. 68, no. 1784
Picturegoer	1941	24 May	Vol. 10, no. 522
	1944	8 July	Vol. 13, no. 610
	1946	16 Feb.	Vol. 15, no. 652
	1948	10 April	Vol. 17, no. 707
	1952	26 April	Vol. 23, no. 886
	1953	11 July	Vol. 26, no. 949
Screen Stories	1953	April	
Time	1941	10 Nov.	Vol. 38, no. 19

POSTCARDS

Picturegoer series: W 173, W 684.

FRONT-OF-HOUSE SETS

Original American sets of *Gilda*.

POSTERS

American one-sheets from *My Gal Sal* to *Miss Sadie Thompson*.

PROPS AND SOUVENIRS

Absolutely any memorabilia relating to *Gilda*.

KATHARINE HEPBURN

Born: Hartford, Connecticut, 9 Nov. 1907.
Top box office ranking: 9 in 1969.

MAGAZINE	YEAR	MONTH	REF. No.
Cahiers du Cinéma	1955	Oct.	Vol. 9, no. 51
Cinegram			no. 36
Film Pictorial	1934	17 March	Vol. 5, no. 108
		12 May	Vol. 5, no. 116
	1935	10 Aug.	Vol. 7, no. 181

MAGAZINE	YEAR	MONTH	REF. No.
	1936	28 March	Vol. 9, no. 214
		18 July	Vol. 9, no. 230
	1938	19 March	Vol. 13, no. 317
	1939	11 Feb.	Vol. 14, no. 364
Film Weekly	1933	27 Oct.	Vol. 10, no. 263
	1934	16 March	Vol. 11, no. 283
		11 May	Vol. 11, no. 291
		26 Oct.	Vol. 12, no. 315
	1936	20 June	Vol. 15, no. 401
	1937	16 Oct.	Vol. 19, no. 470
	1938	19 March	Vol. 20, no. 492
		13 Aug.	Vol. 20, no. 513
Films & Filming	1955	June	Vol. 1, no. 9
	1962	Aug.	Vol. 8, no. 11
	1969	Jan.	Vol. 15, no. 4
Films Illustrated	1975	Nov.	Vol. 5, no. 51
Films in Review	1952	Feb.	Vol. 3, no. 2
	1969	Oct.	Vol. 20, no. 8
	1974	Jan.	Vol. 25, no. 1
	1988	Nov.	Vol. 39, no. 11
Life	1941	6 Jan.	Vol. 10, no. 1
	1968	5 Jan.	Vol. 64, no. 1
Hebdo	1946	22 June	
Modern Screen	1933	May	Vol. 5, no. 6
	1934	May	Vol. 7, no. 6
	1936	Feb.	Vol. 12, no. 3
	1938	Jan.	Vol. 16, no. 2
		Nov.	Vol. 17, no. 6
Motion Picture	1933	March	Vol. 45, no. 2
	1934	April	Vol. 47, no. 3
	1935	Sept.	Vol. 50, no. 2
	1936	Aug.	Vol. 52, no. 1
	1938	Feb.	Vol. 55, no. 1
	1944	Sept.	Vol. 68, no. 2

MAGAZINE	YEAR	MONTH	REF. No.
Photoplay (American)	1934	April	Vol. 45, no. 5
	1936	Sept.	Vol. 50, no. 3
Photoplay (British)	1975	Dec.	Vol. 26, no. 12
Picture Show	1933	22 April	Vol. 29, no. 729
	1933	4 Nov.	Vol. 30, no. 757
	1934	24 March	Vol. 30, no. 777
		19 May	Vol. 31, no. 785
	1935	17 Aug.	Vol. 33, no. 850
		30 Nov.	Vol. 34, no. 865
	1936	27 June	Vol. 35, no. 895
		7 Nov.	Vol. 36, no. 915
	1938	19 March	Vol. 38, no. 986
		13 Aug.	Vol. 39, no. 1007
	1941	31 May	Vol. 45, no. 1153
	1945	30 June	Vol. 49, no. 1266
	1946	28 Dec.	Vol. 51, no. 1305
	1952	8 March	Vol. 58, no. 1510
	1955	12 Nov.	Vol. 65, no. 1702
	1956	18 Aug.	Vol. 67, no. 1742
	1957	9 Feb.	Vol. 68, no. 1767
Picturegoer	1933	21 Jan.	Vol. 2, no. 87
	1934	7 April	Vol. 3, no. 150
	1935	9 March	Vol. 4, no. 198
	1936	29 Feb.	Vol. 5, no. 249
	1937	20 Nov.	Vol. 7, no. 339
	1938	19 March	Vol. 7, no. 356
		27 Aug.	Vol. 8, no. 379
	1941	15 March	Vol. 10, no. 512
	1942	16 May	Vol. 11, no. 554
	1945	9 June	Vol. 14, no. 634
Time	1952	1 Sept.	Vol. 60, no. 9
	1981	16 Nov.	Vol. 118, no. 20
Zie	1970	23 Jan.	

POSTCARDS

Picturegoer series: 734, a, 805, a, 1045, a, W 229.
Colourgraph: c195, c195a.
'Famous Film Partners' series: P183, sepia only, w/Fred McMurray.

FRONT-OF-HOUSE SETS

Original American sets from any of her films with Spencer Tracy, plus *Bringing Up Baby*, *The Philadelphia Story* and *The African Queen*.

POSTERS

Original American one-sheet of *The Philadelphia Story*.

SIGNED PORTRAITS

Collectors can expect to pay from £400 upwards for a signed photograph of Katharine Hepburn, as she rarely signed her photographs.

PROPS AND SOUVENIRS

Absolutely any memorabilia relating to *The Philadelphia Story*.

GRACE KELLY

Born: Philadelphia, 12 Nov. 1928.
Died: 14 Sept. 1982.
Top box office ranking: 2 in 1955.

MAGAZINE	YEAR	MONTH	REF. No.
Cahiers du Cinéma	1954	Oct.	Vol. 7, no. 39
Cinémonde	1956	26 Jan.	no. 1120
		5 April	no. 1130
		23 Aug.	no. 1150.
Epoca	1956	28 June	
Fans' Star Library			no. 32
Films in Review	1954	June/July	Vol. 5, no. 6
	1955	Aug./Sept.	Vol. 6, no. 7
	1956	April	Vol. 7, no. 4
Illustrated	1956	14 April	Vol. 18, no. 8
Life	1954	26 April	Vol. 36, no. 17
	1955	11 April	Vol. 38, no. 15
	1956	9 April	Vol. 40, no. 14
	1961	23 June	Vol. 50, no. 25
Look	1954	15 June	Vol. 18, no. 12
	1955	11 Jan.	Vol. 19, no. 1
	1956	10 Jan.	Vol. 20, no. 1
	1956	11 Dec.	Vol. 20, no. 25
Modern Screen	1954	Dec.	Vol. 49, no. 1
	1955	Sept.	Vol. 49, no. 10

MAGAZINE	YEAR	MONTH	REF. No.
	1956	April	Vol. 50, no. 4
Motion Picture	1955	March	Vol. 89, no. 531
		Nov.	Vol. 90, no. 539
Observer magazine	1982	26 Sept.	
Photoplay (American)	1955	April	Vol. 47, no. 4
	1956	April	Vol. 49, no. 4
Picture Post	1954	4 Sept.	Vol. 64, no. 10
	1955	5 Feb.	Vol. 66, no. 6
		6 Aug.	Vol. 68, no. 6
	1956	28 April	Vol. 71, no. 4
Picture Show	1954	28 Aug.	Vol. 63, no. 1639
	1955	12 Feb.	Vol. 64, no. 1663
		2 April	Vol. 64, no. 1670
		23 April	Vol. 64, no. 1673
	1956	21 April	Vol. 66, no. 1725
		26 May	Vol. 66, no. 1730
		22 Dec.	Vol. 67, no. 1760
Picturegoer	1954	10 July	Vol. 28, no. 1001
Silver Screen	1955	June	Vol. 24, no. 12
Tempo	1956	28 June	
Time	1955	31 Jan.	Vol. 65, no. 5

POSTCARDS

Picturegoer series: D 476

FRONT-OF-HOUSE SETS

Original American sets of all films.

POSTERS

Original American one-sheets of *Dial M For Murder*, *Rear Window*, and *To Catch A Thief.*

SIGNED PORTRAITS

Ink-signed photographs from £100.

PROPS AND SOUVENIRS

Absolutely any memorabilia relating to her films.

STAN LAUREL/OLIVER HARDY

Born: Ulverston, Lancashire, 16 June 1890.	*Born:* Harlem, Georgia, 18 Jan. 1892.
Died: 23 Feb. 1965.	*Died:* 7 Aug. 1957.
Real name: Arthur Jefferson.	

Their popularity increases with each new generation.

MAGAZINE	YEAR	MONTH	REF. No.
Cahiers du Cinéma	1965	Feb.	Vol. 28, no. 163
Film Dope			no. 33
Film Pictorial	1934	8 Dec.	Vol. 6, no. 146
Liberty, Then & Now	1975	summer	Vol. 1, no. 17
Picture Show	1932	25 June	Vol. 27, no. 686

POSTCARDS

Picturegoer series: 491, a, 677, a – b, W 401.

FRONT-OF-HOUSE SETS

Original American sets of any of their films.

POSTERS

Original American one-sheets of all films, particularly those with artwork by Al Hirschfield.

SIGNED PORTRAITS

A three-quarter-length photograph of Stan singing and playing the banjo whilst he unwittingly hits Ollie in the eye with the banjo's tuning pegs, signed and inscribed, sold for £550 at Christie's on 20 December 1989.

PROPS AND SOUVENIRS

A pair of bowler hats, probably used by Laurel and Hardy in the film *Hats Off*, were sold at the same sale at Christie's for £11,000. A collection of letters from Laurel to Mr and Mrs Wray, fans from Tyneside, comprising two handwritten and four typescript letters, signed, various dates, sold for £462 at Christie's on 20 December 1990.

VIVIEN LEIGH

Born: Darjeeling, 5 Nov. 1913.
Died: 8 July 1967.
Real name: Vivian Mary Hartley.

MAGAZINE	YEAR	MONTH	REF. No.
ABC Film Review	1952	April	Vol. 2, no. 4
Cinémonde	1952	14 March	no. 919
Film Pictorial	1937	16 Jan.	Vol. 10, no. 256
Film Weekly	1937	20 Feb.	Vol. 17, no. 436
		28 Aug.	Vol. 19, no. 463
		20 Nov.	Vol. 19, no. 475
Films & Filming	1955	Aug.	Vol. 1, no. 11
Films in Review	1951	Nov.	Vol. 2, no. 9
Illustrated	1940	20 April	Vol. 2, no. 8
	1944	28 Oct.	Vol. 6, no. 36
	1949	12 Feb.	Vol. 10, no. 50
	1953	7 Nov.	Vol. 15, no. 37
Life	1946	29 July	Vol. 21, no. 5
	1988	May	Vol. 11, no. 6
Look	1939	18 July	Vol. 3, no. 15
	1940	17 Dec.	Vol. 4, no. 26
	1952	11 March	Vol. 16, no. 6
Modern Screen	1940	June	Vol. 21, no. 1
	1941	Feb.	Vol. 22, no. 3
Motion Picture	1941	Feb.	Vol. 61, no. 1
New York Sunday News	1940	2 Jan.	
Picture Post	1941	5 April	Vol. 11, no. 1
		20 Sept.	Vol. 12, no. 12
	1945	15 Dec.	Vol. 29, no. 11
	1948	24 Jan.	Vol. 38, no. 4
Picture Show	1937	28 Aug.	Vol. 37, no. 957
		20 Nov.	Vol. 38, no. 969
	1940	7 Dec.	Vol. 44, no. 1128
	1957	29 June	Vol. 68, no. 1787
Picturegoer	1936	5 Dec.	Vol. 6, no. 289
	1938	9 April	Vol. 7, no. 359
		5 Nov.	Vol. 8, no. 389
	1940	27 April	Vol. 9, no. 466
	1941	2 Aug.	Vol. 11, no. 532
	1944	11 Nov.	Vol. 13, no. 619
	1947	16 Aug.	Vol. 16, no. 690
Silver Screen	1940	Feb.	Vol. 10, no. 4
Time	1939	25 Dec.	Vol. 34, no. 26

POSTCARDS

Picturegoer series: 1124, a, D 133.

FRONT-OF-HOUSE SETS

Original American sets from *Gone With The Wind*, *Waterloo Bridge*, *A Streetcar Named Desire*.

POSTERS

Original American one-sheet from *Gone With The Wind*, artwork by Sergio Gargiulo, sells for $3,000.

SIGNED PORTRAITS

Ink-signed photographs from £100 upwards.

PROPS AND SOUVENIRS

Absolutely any memorabilia relating to *Gone With The Wind.*

A signed watercolour heightened with white costume design, Vivien Leigh in *Anna Karenina*, window mounted and framed, fetched £1,045 in an auction at Christie's on 20 December 1990.

GINA LOLLOBRIGIDA

Born: Subiaco, Italy, 14 July 1927.
Real name: Luigina Lollobrigida.

MAGAZINE	YEAR	MONTH	REF. No.
ABC Film Review	1954	Jan.	Vol. 4, no. 1
	1959	Nov.	Vol. 9, no. 9
	1961	July	Vol. 11, no. 7
Cahiers du Cinéma	1954	March	Vol. 6, no. 33
Cinémonde	1952	7 March	no. 918
		22 Aug.	no. 942
	1953	18 Dec.	no. 1011
	1954	21 May	no. 1033
		15 Oct.	no. 1054
	1955	14 July	no. 1093
		24 Nov.	no. 1111
	1956	13 Dec.	no. 1166
	1957	23 May	no. 1189
	1959	20 Oct.	no. 1315
	1960	23 Feb.	no. 1333
		30 Aug.	no. 1360
	1961	5 Sept.	no. 1413
	1963	12 March	no. 1492
Epoca	1954	25 July	
		19 Sept.	
	1957	7 April	
		4 Aug.	
Fans' Star Library			no. 52
Films & Filming	1954	Nov.	Vol. 1, no. 2
	1959	Nov.	Vol. 6, no. 2
Films in Review	1954	Oct.	Vol. 5, no. 8
	1960	Jan	Vol. 11, no. 1
Illustrated	1954	23 Oct.	Vol. 16, no. 35
	1955	4 June	Vol. 17, no. 15
Life	1951	3 Sept.	Vol. 31, no. 10
	1954	15 Nov.	Vol. 37, no. 20
Look	1954	30 Nov.	Vol. 18, no. 24
	1956	15 May	Vol. 20, no. 10
Mon Film	1955	4 May	
		6 July	
Photoplay (British)	1961	April	Vol. 12, no. 4
	1969	April	Vol. 20, no. 4
Picture Post	1952	5 July	Vol. 56, no. 1
	1954	6 Nov.	Vol. 65, no. 6
	1955	26 March	Vol. 66, no. 13
Picture Show	1956	4 Aug.	Vol. 67, no. 1740
	1960	27 Feb.	Vol. 74, no. 1918
Picturegoer	1954	9 Jan.	Vol. 27, no. 975
	1956	21 April	Vol. 31, no. 1094
	1959	14 Nov.	Vol. 38, no. 1273
Tempo	1950	25 Feb.	
	1952	2 Feb.	
		23 Aug.	
	1953	23 July	
	1954	14 Jan.	
		22 April	
		21 Oct.	
	1955	2 June	
	1956	19 Jan.	
	1957	31 Jan.	
		21 March	
	1958	26 Aug.	
	1959	26 May	
	1961	19 Aug.	
	1962	21 July	
Time	1954	16 Aug.	Vol. 64, no. 7

POSTCARDS

Picturegoer series: D 407.

POSTERS

Original Italian and American one-sheets.

FRONT-OF-HOUSE SETS

Original Italian sets of her early films; American set of *Trapeze*.

SHIRLEY MacLAINE

Born: Richmond, Virginia, 24 April 1934.
Real name: Shirley MacLean Beaty.
Top box office ranking: 7 in 1964.

MAGAZINE	YEAR	MONTH	REF. No.
ABC Film Review	1962	March	Vol. 12, no. 3
	1968	Dec.	Vol. 18, no. 12
Film Review	1984	April	Vol. 34, no. 4
Films & Filming	1962	Feb.	Vol. 8, no. 5
	1963	Aug.	Vol. 9, no. 11
	1964	July	Vol. 10, no. 10
	1965	Feb.	Vol. 11, no. 5
	1967	Dec.	Vol. 14, no. 3
Films Illustrated	1978	May	Vol. 7, no. 81
Films in Review	1959	June/July	Vol. 10, no. 6
	1960	April	Vol. 11, no. 4
	1962	June/July	Vol. 13, no. 6
Life	1959	9 Feb.	Vol. 46, no. 6

MAGAZINE	YEAR	MONTH	REF. No.
	1961	17 Feb.	Vol. 50, no. 7
	1962	23 Feb.	Vol. 52, no. 8
	1963	21 June	Vol. 54, no. 25
Look	1959	15 Sept.	Vol. 23, no. 19
New York magazine	1977	April	
Picture Show	1957	13 July	Vol. 69, no. 1789
	1958	21 June	Vol. 70, no. 1838
	1959	23 May	Vol. 72, no. 1886
	1960	16 Jan.	Vol. 74, no. 1912
Time	1959	22 June	Vol. 73, no. 25
	1984	14 May	Vol. 123, no. 20
	1987	7 Dec.	Vol. 130, no 23

FRONT-OF-HOUSE SETS

Original American sets of *The Apartment* and *Sweet Charity*.

POSTERS

Original American one-sheets of above films plus *The Trouble With Harry*.

PROPS AND SOUVENIRS

A simulated pearl and silver necklace, worn by Shirley in *Some Came Running*, was sold at Christie's on 5 May 1988 for £165.

MADONNA

Born: Pontiac, Michigan, 16 Aug. 1958.
Real name: Madonna Louise Veronica Ciconne.

MAGAZINE	YEAR	MONTH	REF. No.
American Film	1987	July/Aug.	Vol. 12, no. 9
Film Review	1987	Oct.	Vol. 37, no. 9
Interview	1989	May	
Life	1986	Dec.	Vol. 9, no. 13

MAGAZINE	YEAR	MONTH	REF. No.
Playboy	1985	Sept.	Vol. 32, no. 9
Rolling Stone	1987	10 Sept.	no. 508
Time	1985	27 May	Vol. 125, no. 21

FRONT-OF-HOUSE SETS

All films, but particularly *Desperately Seeking Susan*.

POSTERS

As above.

PROPS AND SOUVENIRS

Novelties, toys and dolls.

Too early to assess the full impact that this star will have regarding memorabilia sales, but signs seem to suggest that it is appreciating in value already. Her *Time* and *Playboy* magazine covers are worth four times their original cover price.

JAYNE MANSFIELD

Born: Bryn Mawr, Pennsylvania, 13 April 1933.
Died: New Orleans, 29 June 1967.
Real name: Vera Jayne Palmer.

MAGAZINE	YEAR	MONTH	REF. No.
ABC Film Review	1959	Jan.	Vol. 9, no. 1
Cinémonde	1957	7 March	no. 1178
	1958	7 Aug.	no. 1252
	1959	11 Aug.	no. 1305
	1962	3 July	no. 1456
Fans' Star Library			no. 43
Films in Review	1976	June/July	Vol. 27, no. 6
Illustrated	1957	13 July	Vol. 19, no. 21
Life	1956	23 April	Vol. 40, no. 16
Photoplay (American)	1957	March	Vol. 51, no. 3
Photoplay (British)	1957	Feb.	Vol. 8, no. 2
		Aug.	Vol. 8, no. 8
Picture Show	1957	5 Oct.	Vol. 69, no. 1801
	1958	15 Feb.	Vol. 70, no. 1820
		27 Dec.	Vol. 71, no. 1865
Picturegoer	1955	2 July	Vol. 30, no. 1052
	1957	16 March	Vol. 33, no. 1141
		26 Oct.	Vol. 34, no. 1173
	1958	2 Aug.	Vol. 36, no. 1213

FRONT-OF-HOUSE SETS

Original American sets of *The Girl Couldn't Help It*, and *Will Success Spoil Rock Hunter?*

POSTERS

Original American one-sheets of above films.

SIGNED PORTRAITS

Ink-signed photographs from £50.

STEVE McQUEEN

Born: Beech Grove, Indiana, 24 March 1930.
Died: Juarez, 7 Nov. 1980.
Real name: Terrence Steven McQueen.
Top box office ranking: 3 in 1969, 1973.

MAGAZINE	YEAR	MONTH	REF. No.
ABC Film Review	1966	Sept.	Vol. 16, no. 9
	1970	Dec.	Vol. 20, no. 12
	1971	Oct.	Vol. 21, no. 10
Astros E Estrelas			no. 20
Cinémonde	1964	15 Sept.	no. 1571
Film Review	1973	March	Vol. 23, no. 3
	1974	June	Vol. 24, no. 6
	1975	Jan.	Vol. 25, no. 1
	1980	May	Vol. 30, no. 5
Films & Filming	1972	July	Vol. 18, no. 10
Films Illustrated	1972	March	Vol. 1, no. 9
	1973	Feb.	Vol. 2, no. 20
	1975	Feb.	Vol. 4, no. 42
	1980	Nov.	Vol. 10, no. 110
Films in Review	1975	Feb.	Vol. 26, no. 2
Life	1963	12 July	Vol. 55, no. 2
Photoplay (British)	1964	Oct.	Vol. 15, no. 10
	1971	March	Vol. 22, no. 3
	1973	March	Vol. 24, no. 3
	1974	April	Vol. 25, no. 4
	1975	March	Vol. 26, no. 3
Showtime	1964	23 Sept.	

POSTCARDS

Coral-Lee no. 57.

FRONT-OF-HOUSE SETS

Original American sets of *The Magnificent Seven*, *The Great Escape*, *The Cincinnati Kid*, *Nevada Smith*, *The Thomas Crown Affair* and *Bullitt*.

POSTERS

Original American one-sheets of above films.

SIGNED PORTRAITS

Ink-signed photographs from £50.

MARILYN MONROE

Born: Los Angeles, 1 June 1926.
Died: Brentwood, California, 5 Aug. 1962.
Real name: Norma Jean Mortensen.
Top box office ranking: 5 in 1954.

MAGAZINE	YEAR	MONTH	REF. No.
ABC Film Review	1957	Oct.	Vol. 7, no. 10
Cahiers du Cinéma	1953	June	Vol. 4, no. 24
	1955	Christmas	Vol. 9, no. 54
	1956	Nov.	Vol. 11, no. 64
	1987	July/Aug.	no. 398
Cinémonde	1954	16 April	no. 1028
	1960	10 May	no. 1344
	1961	21 Feb.	no. 1385
	1962	14 Aug.	no. 1462
Eros	1962		Vol. 1, no. 3
Fans' Star Library			no. 18
Films & Filming	1957	July	Vol. 3, no. 10
	1959	June	Vol. 5, no. 9
Films in Review	1953	April	Vol. 4, no. 4
	1956	Oct.	Vol. 7, no. 8
	1960	Oct.	Vol. 11, no. 8
	1962	Oct.	Vol. 13, no. 8
	1963	June/July	Vol. 14, no. 6
	1975	June/July	Vol. 26, no. 6
	1979	March	Vol. 30, no. 3
	1983	Aug./Sept.	Vol. 34, no. 7
	1986	May	Vol. 37, no. 5
Illustrated	1953	31 Jan.	Vol. 14, no. 49
		8 Aug.	Vol. 15, no. 24
	1956	14 July	Vol. 18, no. 21
Life	1952	7 April	Vol. 32, no. 14
	1953	25 May	Vol. 34, no. 21
	1959	20 April	Vol. 46, no. 16
		9 Nov.	Vol. 47, no. 19
	1960	15 Aug.	Vol. 49, no. 7
	1962	22 June	Vol. 52, no. 25
		17 Aug.	Vol. 53, no. 7
	1964	7 Aug.	Vol. 57, no. 6
	1972	8 Sept.	Vol. 73, no. 10
	1981	Oct.	Vol. 4, no. 10
	1982	Aug.	Vol. 5, no. 8
Look	1951	23 Oct.	Vol. 15, no. 22
	1952	3 June	Vol. 16, no. 12
		9 Sept.	Vol. 16, no. 19
	1953	30 June	Vol. 17, no. 13
		17 Nov.	Vol. 17, no. 23
	1956	29 May	Vol. 20, no. 11
Modern Screen	1953	Oct.	Vol. 47, no. 5
	1954	March	Vol. 48, no. 4
		Sept.	Vol. 48, no. 10
	1955	June	Vol. 49, no. 7
		Oct.	Vol. 49, no. 11
	1956	Nov.	Vol. 50, no. 11
Motion Picture	1953	Jan	Vol. 84, no. 6
		Nov.	Vol. 86, no. 4
	1954	Jan.	Vol. 86, no. 6
Movie Fan	1952	Dec.	Vol. 7, no. 3
	1954	July	Vol. 9, no. 4
Movie Life	1954	Aug.	
Paris Match	1962	18 Aug.	no. 697
Photo	1974	Nov.	
Photoplay (American)	1953	Feb.	Vol. 43, no. 2
		Dec.	Vol. 44, no. 6
	1954	April	Vol. 45, no. 4
	1956	Oct.	Vol. 50, no. 4
Photoplay (British)	1952	Nov.	Vol. 3, no. 11
	1953	Aug.	Vol. 4, no. 8
	1954	March	Vol. 5, no. 3
		Dec.	Vol. 5, no. 12
	1955	July	Vol. 6, no. 7
	1956	Aug.	Vol. 7, no. 8
Picture Post	1947	13 Dec.	Vol. 37, no. 11
	1949	26 March	Vol. 42, no. 13
		13 Aug.	Vol. 44, no. 7
	1953	15 Aug.	Vol. 60, no. 7
	1954	24 April	Vol. 63, no. 4
	1956	14 July	Vol. 71, no. 15
		22 Oct.	Vol. 73, no. 3
Picture Show	1954	25 Sept.	Vol. 63, no. 1643
	1955	10 Sept.	Vol. 65, no. 1693

MAGAZINE	YEAR	MONTH	REF. No.
	1956	13 Oct.	Vol. 67, no. 1750
	1957	6 July	Vol. 69, no. 1788
	1959	26 Dec.	Vol. 73, no. 1909
	1960	15 Oct.	Vol. 75, no. 1951
Picturegoer	1952	9 Aug.	Vol. 24, no. 901
	1953	9 May	Vol. 25, no. 940
	1954	16 Jan.	Vol. 27, no. 976
		23 Oct.	Vol. 28, no. 1016
	1956	17 Nov.	Vol. 32, no. 1124
Playboy	1953	Dec.	Vol. 1, no. 1

MAGAZINE	YEAR	MONTH	REF. No.
Screen Stars	1953	Feb.	Vol. 11, no. 1
	1954	Nov.	Vol. 12, no. 5
	1955	July	Vol. 13, no. 4
	1956	July	Vol. 14, no. 4
Silver Screen	1952	Feb.	Vol. 22, no. 4
	1953	Oct.	Vol. 23, no. 12
	1954	April	Vol. 24, no. 6
	1962	Dec.	Vol. 28, no. 8
Time	1956	14 May	Vol. 67, no. 20
	1973	16 July	Vol. 102, no. 3

POSTCARDS

Picturegoer series: D 154, D 333, D 383.

FRONT-OF-HOUSE SETS

Original American sets of any of her films.

POSTERS

Original American one-sheets from *Clash By Night* onwards. An original three-sheet poster for *The Prince and the Showgirl*, showing Laurence Olivier kissing Marilyn on her shoulder. Beneath a medal attached to Marilyn's breast, is the caption: 'Some countries have a medal for Everything'. Sold at a Sotheby's auction on 25 April 1990, for £308.

SIGNED PORTRAITS

A half-length portrait photograph of Marilyn by Cecil Beaton, mounted on card, signed and inscribed 'To my dear friend C.H. Crowther whose words have been a constant inspiration. Affectionately Marilyn Monroe (Elsie)', sold at Christie's on 20 December 1989 for £2,420.

A head and shoulders publicity photograph, *c.* 1956, signed and inscribed by Marilyn 'To Charles, Marilyn Monroe'. This item fetched £3,080 at a Christie's auction on 20 December 1990.

PROPS & SOUVENIRS

A skin-tight 'shimmy' dress of black silk satin, designed by Orry Kelly and worn by Marilyn in *Some Like It Hot*, sold at Christie's on 20 December 1989 for £19,800.

Marilyn Monroe's personal script for 'The Sleeping Prince', later to be filmed as *The Prince and the Show Girl*, containing 268 typewritten pages, many crossed through with red crayon or lipstick, and bearing numerous handwritten stage directions. This item was sold at a Sotheby's auction on 25 April 1990, for £2,640.

Absolutely any Monroebilia will appreciate in value. Magazines with Monroe covers will double in value the moment you buy them. The first issue of *Playboy* with a Marilyn centrefold and cover is today valued at £300.

PAUL NEWMAN

Born: Cleveland, Ohio, 26 Jan. 1925.
Top box office ranking: 1 in 1969/70.

MAGAZINE	YEAR	MONTH	REF. No.
ABC Film Review	1962	June	Vol. 12, no. 6
	1966	July	Vol. 16, no. 7
American Film	1982	Dec.	Vol. 8, no. 3
Cahiers du Cinéma	1966	Nov.	Vol. 31, no. 184
	1987	March	no. 393
Cinémonde	1955	8 April	no. 1079
Film Review	1972	June	Vol. 22, no. 6
	1974	March	Vol. 24, no. 3
	1975	Jan.	Vol. 25, no. 1
	1982	Feb.	Vol. 32, no. 2
Films & Filming	1963	May	Vol. 9, no. 8
	1969	Oct.	Vol. 16, no. 1
	1972	April	Vol. 18, no. 7
	1974	Jan.	Vol. 20, no. 4
	1984	May	Vol. 30, no. 356
	1987	March	Vol. 33, no. 390
Films Illustrated	1973	Oct.	Vol. 3, no. 28
Films in Review	1958	March	Vol. 9, no. 3
	1975	Feb.	Vol. 26, no. 2
	1984	Oct.	Vol. 35, no. 8
	1987	Jan.	Vol. 38, no. 1
		April	Vol. 38, no. 4
Life	1968	10 May	Vol. 64, no. 19
	1986	Nov.	Vol. 9, no. 11
	1988	Sept.	Vol. 11, no. 10
Photoplay (British)	1969	Oct.	Vol. 20, no. 10
	1970	April	Vol. 21, no. 4
	1973	Dec.	Vol. 24, no. 12
	1974	Feb.	Vol. 25, no. 2
	1976	Sept.	Vol. 27, no. 9
	1979	Dec.	Vol. 30, no. 12
	1984	June	Vol. 35, no. 6
	1987	April	Vol. 38, no. 4
Picture Show	1956	30 June	Vol. 66, no. 1735
	1958	4 Jan.	Vol. 70, no. 1814
		29 Nov.	Vol. 71, no. 1861
	1959	28 March	Vol. 72, no. 1878
Picturegoer	1960	16 Jan.	Vol. 39, no. 1282
Sunday Times magazine	1984	13 May	
Time	1982	6 Dec.	Vol. 120, no. 23

FRONT-OF-HOUSE SETS

Original American sets of *Cat On A Hot Tin Roof*, *The Hustler*, *Hud*, *Cool Hand Luke*, *Butch Cassidy And The Sundance Kid*, and *Judge Roy Bean*.

POSTERS

Original American one-sheets of above films.

SIGNED PORTRAITS

Ink-signed photographs of this star are rare.

TYRONE POWER

Born: Cincinnati, Ohio, 5 May 1914.
Died: Madrid, 15 Nov. 1958.
Top box office ranking: 2 in 1939.

MAGAZINE	YEAR	MONTH	REF. No.
Cinémonde	1950	16 Oct.	no. 845
Fans' Star Library			no. 37
Film Pictorial	1937	11 Sept.	Vol. 12, no. 290
		Christmas extra	
	1938	23 April	Vol. 13, no. 322
		26 Nov.	Vol. 14, no. 353
	1939	22 April	Vol. 15, no 374
Film Weekly	1937	19 June	Vol. 18, no. 453
		6 Nov.	Vol. 19, no. 473
		4 Dec.	Vol. 19, no. 477
	1938	8 Oct.	Vol. 20, no. 521
	1939	4 Feb.	Vol. 21, no. 538
		3 June	Vol. 21, no. 555
Films & Filming	1957	Feb.	Vol. 3, no. 5
Films in Review	1957	Aug./Sept.	Vol. 8, no. 7
Modern Screen	1937	Aug.	Vol. 15, no. 3
	1938	March	Vol. 16, no. 4
	1947	Dec.	Vol. 36, no. 1
Motion Picture	1937	Oct.	Vol. 54, no. 3
	1939	Jan.	Vol. 56, no. 6
		July	Vol. 57, no. 6
	1946	Oct.	Vol. 72, no. 3
Photoplay (American)	1938	Dec.	Vol. 52, no. 12
	1940	April	Vol. 53, no. 4
	1946	Dec.	Vol. 30, no. 1

MAGAZINE	YEAR	MONTH	REF. No.
Picture Show	1937	11 Sept.	Vol. 37, no. 959
		2 Oct.	Vol. 37, no. 962
	1938	1 Jan.	Vol. 38, no. 975
		23 April	Vol. 39, no. 991
		1 Oct.	Vol. 39, no. 1014
	1939	4 Feb.	Vol. 40, no. 1032
		19 Aug.	Vol. 41, no. 1060
	1940	10 Feb.	Vol. 42, no. 1085
	1941	25 Jan.	Vol. 44, no. 1135
		1 March	Vol. 44, no. 1140
	1942	28 March	Vol. 46, no. 1181
		7 Nov.	Vol. 47, no. 1197
	1943	11 Sept.	Vol. 47, no. 1219
	1949	19 Feb.	Vol. 53, no. 1361
	1950	25 Feb.	Vol. 54, no. 1404
		23 Sept.	Vol. 55, no. 1434
	1955	28 May	Vol. 64, no. 1678
	1956	28 July	Vol. 67, no. 1739
Picturegoer	1938	22 Jan.	Vol. 7, no. 348
		17 Sept.	Vol. 8, no. 382
		19 Nov.	Vol. 8, no. 391
	1939	16 Sept.	Vol. 9, no. 434
	1941	15 Feb.	Vol. 10, no. 508
		13 Dec.	Vol. 11, no. 543
	1942	8 Aug.	Vol. 11, no. 560
	1943	12 June	Vol. 12, no. 582
	1944	22 July	Vol. 13, no. 611
	1947	25 Oct.	Vol. 16, no. 695
	1949	9 April	Vol. 18, no. 733

POSTCARDS

Picturegoer series: 1215, a, 1218, 204, W 755, D 175, 177, w/Annabella, 176, w/Alice Faye, 196, w/Sonja Henie, 201, w/Myrna Loy.

Colourgraph: c306.
'Famous Film Partners' series: P254 (sepia only), w/Norma Shearer.

FRONT-OF-HOUSE SETS

Original American sets of *In Old Chicago, Alexander's Ragtime Band, Rose Of Washington Square, Jesse James, The Mark Of Zorro, The Razor's Edge.*

POSTERS

Original American one-sheet of *The Razor's Edge* is very collectable as the artwork was by Norman Rockwell.

ELVIS PRESLEY

Born: Tupelo, Mississippi, 8 Jan. 1935.
Died: Memphis, Tennessee, 16 Aug. 1977.
Top box office ranking: 4 in 1957.

MAGAZINE	YEAR	MONTH	REF. No.
ABC Film Review	1963	March	Vol. 13, no. 3
		July	Vol. 13, no. 7
	1964	Aug.	Vol. 14, no. 8
	1965	Aug.	Vol. 15, no. 8
A Disco 45 Tribute to Elvis Presley	1977	Poster magazine	
A Tribute to Elvis	1977		
A Tribute to the King: The official Elvis monthly souvenir	1977		
Cinémonde	1957	24 Oct.	no. 1211
	1958	27 Nov.	no. 1268
	1961	7 March	no. 1387
		10 Oct.	no. 1418
	1962	12 June	no. 1453
	1963	8 Jan.	no. 1483
	1964	28 Jan.	no. 1538
		7 July	no. 1561
		27 Oct.	no. 1577
Elvis	1977	Poster magazine	
Elvis and Jimmy	1956	This rare magazine features Elvis Presley and James Dean on the cover and illustrated articles inside.	
Elvis. A tribute to the King of Rock & Roll.		Undated.	
Elvis 50th Birthday Album. Superstar special	1984		no. 14
Elvis. Hero or Heel	1957		no. 1
Elvis. His Loves and his Marriage (U.S.A.)	1957		
Elvis – Long Live The King!	1987		
Elvis Monthly (British)	1962		Vol. 1, no. 1
Elvis Presley, An Appreciation by Mick Farren	1977	Poster magazine	
Elvis Remembered	1979	Ideal's celebrity series no. 5	
Elvis. Remembering You	1977		
Elvis Speaks (U.S.A.)	1956		
Elvis. The Early Years	1989		
Elvis – The Legend Lives On	1988		

MAGAZINE	YEAR	MONTH	REF. No.
Fans' Star Library			no. 2, no. 13
Farewell to Elvis			no. 1
		Poster magazine	
Films & Filming	1966	Aug.	Vol. 12, no. 11
Modern Screen Presents Elvis			Vol. 1, nos 1 –
		(series of special issues devoted to Elvis)	
People Weekly	1975	13 Jan	
Photoplay (American)	1957	July	Vol. 52, no. 1
	1958	Oct.	Vol. 54, no. 4
Photoplay (British)	1959	Feb.	Vol. 10, no. 2
		Nov.	Vol. 10, no. 10
	1961	Nov.	Vol. 12, no. 11
	1962	May	Vol. 13, no. 5

MAGAZINE	YEAR	MONTH	REF. No.
		Nov.	Vol. 13, no. 11
	1963	June	Vol. 14, no. 6
Picture Show	1957	31 Aug.	Vol. 69, no. 1796
	1958	1 March	Vol. 70, no. 1822
		27 Sept.	Vol. 71, no. 1852
		22 Nov.	Vol. 71, no. 1860
Picturegoer	1958	2 Aug.	Vol. 36, no. 1213
Rolling Stone	1969	12 July	
Screen Stars	1959	June	Vol. 17, no. 3
Silver Screen	1960	April	Vol. 27, no. 5
The Great Elvis Presley	1977	Poster magazine	
The King – A Tribute to Elvis Presley	1977	Poster magazine	

FRONT-OF-HOUSE SETS

Original American sets of all films, but particularly those of the fifties: *Love Me Tender*, *Loving You*, *Jailhouse Rock*, *King Creole*.

POSTERS

Original American one-sheets of above films.

SIGNED PORTRAITS

A rare early signed photograph of Elvis Presley, *c.* 1955, the sepia-toned photograph signed and dedicated in blue ballpoint pen, 'To Ron, Elvis Presley', sold at Sotheby's on 21 August 1990, for £1,100.

PROPS AND SOUVENIRS

Absolutely any memorabilia relating to this star.

A custom-made ring modelled as a growling jaguar's head, the mouth and eyes set with navette cut rubies; accompanied by a certificate of authenticity from the Elvis Presley Museum stating that Elvis bought the ring from Schwartz and Ableser fine jewellery store. Sold at an auction at Christie's on 27 April 1990, for £4,620.

At the same sale, a Gibson FJ acoustic guitar in a natural finish, rosewood fingerboard with mother-of-pearl inlays, rosewood bridge, black scratchplate decorated with a floral design, accompanied by a certificate of authenticity from the Elvis Presley Museum confirming that Elvis owned and used the guitar, sold for £6,600.

Elvis Presley's driving license, 1952, the State of Tennessee Operator's License issued on 3 – 24 – 52, with typewritten details of Elvis' name, address and personal details, signed in (faded) ink by Elvis Presley. The license was issued to Elvis when aged 17 and still at high school. This item fetched £3,850 at Sotheby's on 21 August 1990.

A set of five Elvis Presley Sun singles, various dates, comprising 'That's All Right', 'I Don't Care If The Sun Don't Shine', 'Milkcow Blues Boogie', 'I'm Left, You're Right, She's Gone' and 'Mystery Train', all mounted in common, glazed frame. Sold in auction at Sotheby's on 25 April 1990, for £4,840.

GINGER ROGERS

Born: Independence, Missouri, 16 July 1911.
Real name: Virginia Katharine McMath.
Top box office ranking: 3 with partner Fred Astaire in 1936

MAGAZINE	YEAR	MONTH	REF. No.
Cinémonde	1950	1 May	no. 821
Film Pictorial	1932	27 Aug.	Vol. 2, no. 27
	1934	9 June	Vol. 5, no. 120
	1936	11 April	Vol. 9, no. 216
		30 May	Vol. 9, no. 223
		8 Aug.	Vol. 9, no. 233
		26 Dec.	Vol. 10, no. 253
	1938	19 March	Vol. 13, no. 317
	1939	30 Sept.	Vol. 16, no. 397
Film Weekly	1934	16 Nov.	Vol. 12, no. 318
	1935	3 May	Vol. 13, no. 342
	1936	8 Feb.	Vol. 15, no. 382
		11 April	Vol. 15, no. 391
		30 May	Vol. 15, no. 398
		7 Nov.	Vol. 16, no. 421
	1937	15 May	Vol. 18, no. 448
	1938	19 March	Vol. 20, no. 492
		11 June	Vol. 20, no. 504
		6 Aug.	Vol. 20, no. 512
		26 Nov.	Vol. 20, no. 528
	1939	28 Jan.	Vol. 21, no. 537
Life	1938	22 Aug.	Vol. 5, no. 8
	1940	9 Dec.	Vol. 9, no. 24
	1942	2 March	Vol. 12, no. 9
	1951	5 Nov.	Vol. 31, no. 19
Look	1940	9 April	Vol. 4, no. 8
	1941	4 Nov.	Vol. 5, no. 22
	1949	2 Aug.	Vol. 13, no. 16
Modern Screen	1935	Oct.	Vol. 11, no. 5
	1936	Aug.	Vol. 13, no. 3
	1938	April	Vol. 16, no. 5
	1940	May	Vol. 20, no. 6
Motion Picture	1935	Jan.	Vol. 48, no. 6
	1936	Feb.	Vol. 51, no. 1
		Nov.	Vol. 52, no. 4
	1937	Sept.	Vol. 54, no. 2
	1939	March	Vol. 57, no. 2
		Sept.	Vol. 58, no. 2

MAGAZINE	YEAR	MONTH	REF. No.
	1943	June	Vol. 65, no. 5
	1944	March	Vol. 67, no. 2
		Aug.	Vol. 68, no. 1
Photoplay (American)	1936	Feb.	Vol. 49, no. 3
	1937	Jan.	Vol. 51, no. 1
		April	Vol. 51, no. 4
	1938	Feb.	Vol. 52, no. 2
	1939	May	Vol. 53, no. 5
	1940	Sept.	Vol. 53, no. 9
	1941	March	Vol. 18, no. 4
	1942	Nov.	Vol. 21, no. 6
Picture Show	1935	13 April	Vol. 32, no. 832
		20 July	Vol. 33, no. 846
	1936	6 June	Vol. 35, no. 892
		Christmas special	
	1940	10 Aug.	Vol. 43, no. 1111
	1941	14 June	Vol. 45, no. 1155
	1944	20 May	Vol. 48, no. 1237
	1945	11 Aug.	Vol. 49, no. 1269
		6 Oct.	Vol. 49, no. 1273
	1947	3 May	Vol. 51, no. 1314
	1948	21 Aug.	Vol. 52, no. 1348
	1949	29 Oct.	Vol. 53, no. 1387
	1952	23 Aug.	Vol. 59, no. 1534
	1953	18 July	Vol. 61, no. 1581
	1957	19 Jan.	Vol. 68, no. 1764
Picturegoer	1933	23 Sept.	Vol. 3, no. 122
	1935	10 Aug.	Vol. 5, no. 220
	1936	30 May	Vol. 6, no. 262
		Christmas annual	
	1937	15 May	Vol. 7, no. 312
	1938	26 March	Vol. 7, no. 357
		9 July	Vol. 8, no. 372
	1942	26 Dec.	Vol. 11, no. 570
	1944	15 April	Vol. 13, no. 604
	1945	24 Nov.	Vol. 14, no. 646
	1950	29 July	Vol. 20, no. 795
Time	1939	10 April	Vol. 33, no. 15

POSTCARDS

Picturegoer series: 713, a, 939, a – c, 1088, a – b, D 4.
Colourgraph: c295, c335.
'Famous Film Partners' series: *PC231, w/ Adolphe Menjou. *PC248, w/James Stewart. PC292, PC293, *PC294, all w/Fred Astaire. *PC311, w/David Niven. (*also available in sepia.)

FRONT-OF-HOUSE SETS

Original American sets of films with Fred Astaire.

POSTERS

Original American one-sheets as above, but particularly *Top Hat.*

PROPS AND SOUVENIRS

Absolutely anything relating to the Astaire/ Rogers films.

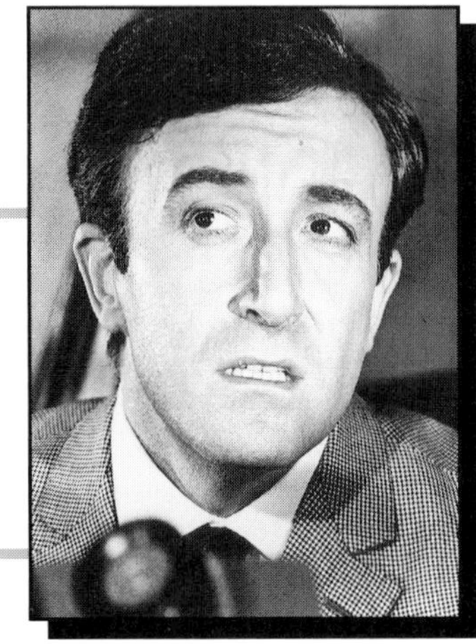

PETER SELLERS

Born: Southsea, Hampshire, 8 Sept. 1925.
Died: London, 24 July 1980.
Top box office ranking: 9 in 1978.

MAGAZINE	YEAR	MONTH	REF. No.
Film	1960	Sept./Oct.	
Film Review	1977	Jan.	Vol. 27, no. 1
	1978	Aug.	Vol. 28, no. 8
Films & Filming	1960	Nov.	Vol. 7, no. 2
Photoplay	1974	March	Vol. 25, no. 3
(British)	1975	Nov.	Vol. 26, no. 11
	1983	Jan.	Vol. 34, no. 1
Showtime	1966	Nov.	
Time	1980	3 March	Vol. 115, no. 9

Note that the star also appears in a small picture on the covers of *Picture Show*, 1 February 1958, and *Picturegoer*, 26 November 1955.

FRONT-OF-HOUSE SETS

Original British sets of *The Ladykillers*, *The Smallest Show On Earth*, *I'm All Right Jack*, *Lolita* and *Dr Strangelove*; American sets of *The Pink Panther*, *A Shot In The Dark*, *The Return Of The Pink Panther*, *The Pink Panther Strikes Again*, *Revenge Of The Pink Panther.*

POSTERS

Original British quad posters of films up to *Dr Strangelove*. Original American one-sheets of all 'Pink Panther' films, plus *Being There*.

PROPS AND SOUVENIRS

A French képi and waistbelt, and a large pin-stripe suit with hat and shoes, items worn by the star in *The Revenge Of The Pink Panther*, were sold at Christie's on 5 May 1988, the former items for £418, the latter for £495.

FRANK SINATRA

Born: Hoboken, New Jersey, 12 Dec. 1915.
Top box office ranking: 5 in 1957.

MAGAZINE	YEAR	MONTH	REF. No.
ABC Film Review	1960	Oct.	Vol. 10, no. 10
	1964	Sept.	Vol. 14, no. 9
Cinémonde	1960	23 Feb.	no. 1333
Fans' Star Library			no. 7
Films & Filming	1959	Nov.	Vol. 6, no. 2
Films in Review	1983	June/July	Vol. 34, no. 6
Illustrated	1946	25 May	Vol. 8, no. 14
Life	1963	23 Aug.	Vol. 55, no. 8
	1965	23 April	Vol. 58, no. 16
	1971	25 June	Vol. 70, no. 24
Look	1955	6 Sept.	Vol. 19, no. 18
	1957	14 May	Vol. 21, no. 10
Modern Screen	1944	Sept.	Vol. 29, no. 4
	1945	Oct.	Vol. 31, no. 5
	1946	Jan.	Vol. 32, no. 2
	1947	Jan.	Vol. 34, no. 2
Photoplay (British)	1950	May	Vol. 1, no. 3
Picture Show	1946	9 March	Vol. 50, no. 1284
	1949	11 June	Vol. 53, no. 1369
	1955	16 April	Vol. 64, no. 1672
	1956	4 Feb.	Vol. 66, no. 1714
		22 Dec.	Vol. 67, no. 1760
	1957	12 Oct.	Vol. 69, no. 1802
		7 Dec.	Vol. 69, no. 1810
	1959	23 May	Vol. 72, no. 1886
Picturegoer	1949	16 July	Vol. 18, no. 741
	1958	1 March	Vol. 35, no. 1191
	1959	11 April	Vol. 37, no. 1249
Time	1955	29 Aug.	Vol. 66, no. 9

POSTCARDS

Picturegoer series: W 372.

FRONT-OF-HOUSE SETS

Original American sets of *On The Town, From Here To Eternity, The Man With The Golden Arm, High Society, The Joker Is Wild, The Manchurian Candidate.*

POSTERS

Original American one-sheets of above films.

SIGNED PORTRAITS

Ink-signed photographs: £50 upwards.

PROPS AND SOUVENIRS

A black felt trilby, worn by the star in *Marriage On The Rocks*, sold with a concert souvenir programme and film still for £715 at a Christie's auction on 5 May 1988.

ELIZABETH TAYLOR

Born: London, 27 Feb. 1932.
Real name: Elizabeth Rosemond Taylor.
Top box office ranking: 1 in 1961.

MAGAZINE	YEAR	MONTH	REF. No.
ABC Film Review	1955	Jan.	Vol. 5, no. 1
	1963	Sept.	Vol. 13, no. 9
	1965	Oct.	Vol. 15, no. 10
	1967	March	Vol. 17, no. 3
	1968	March	Vol. 18, no. 3
Cahiers du Cinéma	1952	March	Vol. 2, no. 10
Cinémonde	1953	15 May	no. 980
	1954	3 Dec.	no. 1061
	1956	25 Oct.	no. 1159
	1957	9 May	no. 1187
	1962	13 Feb.	no. 1436
		17 July	no. 1458
Fans' Star Library			no. 35
Films & Filming	1963	Oct.	Vol. 10, no. 1
	1967	Jan.	Vol. 13, no. 4
	1969	Feb.	Vol. 15, no. 5
	1971	Nov.	Vol. 18, no. 2
Films Illustrated	1972	Oct.	Vol. 2, no. 16
	1973	Aug.	Vol. 3, no. 26
	1980	Oct.	Vol. 10, no. 109
Films in Review	1951	Aug./Sept.	Vol. 2, no. 7
	1963	Aug./Sept.	Vol. 14, no. 7
	1965	Aug./Sept.	Vol. 16, no. 7
	1966	Aug./Sept.	Vol. 17, no. 7
	1967	April	Vol. 18, no. 4

MAGAZINE	YEAR	MONTH	REF. No.
	1968	March	Vol. 19, no. 3
	1970	March	Vol. 21, no. 3
	1973	March	Vol. 24, no. 3
	1988	Jan.	Vol. 39, no. 1
Illustrated	1953	31 Oct.	Vol. 15, no. 36
	1957	21 Dec.	Vol. 19, no. 44
Life	1947	14 July	Vol. 23, no. 2
	1956	15 Oct.	Vol. 41, no. 16
	1957	4 Nov.	Vol. 43, no. 19
	1961	28 April	Vol. 50, no. 17
		6 Oct.	Vol. 51, no. 14
	1962	13 April	Vol. 52, no. 15
	1963	19 April	Vol. 54, no. 16
	1964	18 Dec.	Vol. 57, no. 25
	1966	10 June	Vol. 60, no. 23
	1967	24 Feb.	Vol. 62, no. 8
	1972	25 Feb.	Vol. 72, no. 7
	1982	March	Vol. 5, no. 3
Look	1947	9 Dec.	Vol. 11, no. 25
	1949	5 July	Vol. 13, no. 14
	1951	13 Feb.	Vol. 15, no. 4
	1954	24 Aug.	Vol. 18, no. 17
	1955	28 June	Vol. 19, no. 13
	1956	26 June	Vol. 20, no. 13
	1958	8 July	Vol. 22, no. 14
		11 Oct.	Vol. 22, no. 21
Modern Screen	1949	June	Vol. 39, no. 1

MAGAZINE	YEAR	MONTH	REF. No.
	1950	March	Vol. 40, no. 4
		June	Vol. 41, no. 1
		Nov.	Vol. 41, no. 6
	1951	April	Vol. 42, no. 5
		Sept.	Vol. 43, no. 4
	1952	March	Vol. 44, no. 4
		Oct.	Vol. 45, no. 5
	1953	Feb.	Vol. 46, no. 3
		Sept.	Vol. 47, no. 4
		Dec.	Vol. 48, no. 1
	1954	April	Vol. 48, no. 5
		Oct.	Vol. 48, no. 11
	1955	Nov.	Vol. 49, no. 12
	1956	Dec.	Vol. 50, no. 12
	1958	Feb.	Vol. 52, no. 1
		July	Vol. 52, no. 6
		Oct.	Vol. 52, no. 9
		Dec.	Vol. 52, no. 11
	1959	March	Vol. 53, no. 2
		May	Vol. 53, no. 4
		July	Vol. 53, no. 6
		Sept.	Vol. 53, no. 8
		Nov.	Vol. 53, no. 10
Motion Picture	1949	March	Vol. 77, no. 2
	1950	April	Vol. 79, no. 3
	1951	Feb.	Vol. 81, no. 1
		Aug.	Vol. 82, no. 1
	1952	April	Vol. 83, no. 3
		Oct.	Vol. 84, no. 3
	1953	Feb.	Vol. 85, no. 1
	1954	Jan.	Vol. 86, no. 6
		March	Vol. 87, no. 2
	1955	Jan.	Vol. 88, no. 6
	1956	Feb.	Vol. 45, no. 542
		Nov.	Vol. 45, no. 551
	1957	March	Vol. 46, no. 555
		July	Vol. 47, no. 558
	1958	Feb.	Vol. 48, no. 565
		June	Vol. 48, no. 569
		Sept.	Vol. 48, no. 572
		Dec.	Vol. 48, no. 575
	1959	July	Vol. 49, no. 582

MAGAZINE	YEAR	MONTH	REF. No.
Photoplay (American)	1950	Jan.	Vol. 37, no. 1
		June	Vol. 37, no. 6
		Oct.	Vol. 38, no. 4
	1951	May	Vol. 39, no. 5
		Oct.	Vol. 40, no. 4
	1952	May	Vol. 41, no. 5
		Nov.	Vol. 42, no. 5
	1953	July	Vol. 44, no. 1
	1954	Feb.	Vol. 45, no. 2
		Dec.	Vol. 46, no. 6
	1955	Aug.	Vol. 48, no. 2
	1957	Jan.	Vol. 51, no. 1
		Oct.	Vol. 52, no. 4
	1958	June	Vol. 53, no. 6
Photoplay (British)	1951	May	Vol. 2, no. 5
	1953	Sept.	Vol. 4, no. 9
	1962	April	Vol. 13, no. 4
	1965	June	Vol. 16, no. 6
	1969	Aug.	Vol. 20, no. 8
	1971	May	Vol. 22, no. 5
	1972	Feb.	Vol. 23, no. 2
	1981	March	Vol. 32, no. 3
Picture Post	1948	29 Jan.	Vol. 42, no. 5
	1954	27 March	Vol. 62, no. 13
		20 Nov.	Vol. 65, no. 8
	1957	4 May	Vol. 75, no. 5
Picture Show	1949	24 Sept.	Vol. 53, no. 1382
	1952	26 Jan.	Vol. 58, no. 1504
		9 Feb.	Vol. 58, no. 1506
		6 Sept.	Vol. 59, no. 1536
	1954	4 Sept.	Vol. 63, no. 1640
	1955	1 Jan.	Vol. 64, no. 1657
	1957	12 Jan.	Vol. 68, no. 1763
	1958	20 Sept.	Vol. 71, no. 1851
		29 Nov.	Vol. 71, no. 1861
	1960	21 May	Vol. 74, no. 1930
Picturegoer	1949	1 Jan.	Vol. 18, no. 726
	1950	23 Sept.	Vol. 20, no. 803
	1952	2 Feb.	Vol. 23, no. 874
	1960	26 March	Vol. 39, no. 1292
Time	1949	22 Aug.	Vol. 54, no. 8

POSTCARDS

Picturegoer series: W 761, D 144, D 278, D 477.

FRONT-OF-HOUSE SETS

Original American sets of all of her films up to *Butterfield 8*, then *Who's Afraid Of Virginia Woolf?*

POSTERS

Original American one-sheets of above films.

PROPS AND SOUVENIRS

'Elizabeth Taylor As Lady Patricia', signed watercolour and pencil costume design for the film *Beau Brummell*, window mounted and framed, sold for £160 at Christie's on 27 April 1990.

SHIRLEY TEMPLE

Born: Santa Monica, California, 23 April 1928.
Top box office ranking: 1 in 1935 – 8.

MAGAZINE	YEAR	MONTH	REF. No.
Cinémonde	1948	27 April	no. 717
Film Pictorial	1934	22 Sept.	Vol. 6, no. 135
		29 Dec.	Vol. 6, no. 149
	1935	9 March	Vol. 7, no. 159
		7 Sept.	Vol. 8, no. 185
	1936	25 April	Vol. 9, no. 218
		1 Aug.	Vol. 9, no. 232
	1937	31 July	Vol. 11, no. 284
	1939	5 Aug.	Vol. 15, no. 389
Film Weekly	1935	2 Aug.	Vol. 14, no. 355
	1937	31 July	Vol. 19, no. 459
	1939	12 Aug.	Vol. 22, no. 565
Illustrated	1944	3 June	Vol. 6, no. 15
Life	1938	11 July	Vol. 5, no. 2
	1942	30 March	Vol. 12, no. 13
	1958	3 Feb.	Vol. 44, no. 5
Look	1937	21 Dec.	Vol. 1, no. 22
	1943	16 Nov.	Vol. 7, no. 23
	1949	15 Feb.	Vol. 13, no. 4
Modern Screen	1935	July	Vol. 11, no. 2
	1936	May	Vol. 12, no. 6
	1937	April	Vol. 14, no. 5
	1938	Feb.	Vol. 16, no. 3
	1939	Jan.	Vol. 18, no. 2
	1944	April	Vol. 28, no. 5
		Nov.	Vol. 29, no. 6
	1945	April	Vol. 30, no. 5
	1946	Feb.	Vol. 32, no. 3
	1947	April	Vol. 34, no. 5
	1948	Feb.	Vol. 36, no. 3
		Aug.	Vol. 37, no. 3
	1949	April	Vol. 38, no. 5
		Oct.	Vol. 39, no. 5
	1951	Jan.	Vol. 42, no. 2

MAGAZINE	YEAR	MONTH	REF. No.
Motion Picture	1936	March	Vol. 51, no. 2
	1942	June	Vol. 63, no. 5
	1946	March	Vol. 71, no. 2
	1948	Aug.	Vol. 76, no. 1
	1949	Feb.	Vol. 77, no. 1
		July	Vol. 77, no. 6
	1950	Nov.	Vol. 80, no. 4
Photoplay	1935	Jan.	Vol. 47, no. 2
(American)	1936	March	Vol. 49, no. 4
		Dec.	Vol. 50, no. 6
	1937	June	Vol. 51, no. 6
		Nov.	Vol. 51, no. 11
	1938	May	Vol. 52, no. 5
	1939	Sept.	Vol. 53, no. 9
	1945	March	Vol. 26, no. 4
	1947	June	Vol. 31, no. 1
	1948	Aug.	Vol. 33, no. 3
	1949	Aug.	Vol. 35, no. 3
	1950	Nov.	Vol. 38, no. 5
Picture Show	1935	28 Dec.	Vol. 34, no. 869
	1936	26 Dec.	Vol. 36, no. 922
	1937	3 April	Vol. 36, no. 936
		11 Dec.	Vol. 38, no. 972
	1938	16 April	Vol. 39, no. 990
		30 July	Vol. 39, no. 1005
	1950	10 June	Vol. 54, no. 1419
Picturegoer	1934	30 June	Vol. 4, no. 162
	1936	5 Sept.	Vol. 6, no. 276
Time	1936	27 April	Vol. 27, no. 17
Screen Romances	1937	Nov.	Vol. 17, no. 102
Silver Screen	1935	March	Vol. 5,. no. 5
		Dec.	Vol. 6, no 2
	1936	June	Vol. 6, no. 8
	1939	May	Vol. 9, no. 7

POSTCARDS

Picturegoer series: 30–35, 37–38, 40–43, 46–54, 65–68, 70–75, 77, 81–88, 90, 102–115, 133–152, 158–162, 167–69, 172–74, 181–87, 202, 203, 1345, 841, 942, W 560. The preceding are all film scenes except for the last four.

FRONT-OF-HOUSE SETS

Original American sets of all of her films up to *Susannah Of The Mounties*.

POSTERS

Original American one-sheets of films as above.

PROPS AND SOUVENIRS

Anything pre-1940s on the star, particularly dolls, novelties and picture books.

LANA TURNER

Born: Wallace, Idaho, 8 Feb. 1920.
Real name: Julia Turner.

MAGAZINE	YEAR	MONTH	REF. No.
Cinémonde	1953	21 Aug.	no. 994
	1954	19 Feb.	no. 1020
	1955	17 Nov.	no. 1110
Films in Review	1989	Aug./Sept.	Vol. 40, no. 8/9
Illustrated	1944	7 Oct.	Vol. 6, no. 33
Life	1940	29 Jan.	Vol. 8, no. 5
	1941	13 Oct.	Vol. 11, no. 15
Look	1950	6 June	Vol. 14, no. 12
Modern Screen	1941	Aug.	Vol. 23, no. 3
	1942	Feb.	Vol. 24, no. 3
		Oct.	Vol. 25, no. 5
	1943	May	Vol. 26, no. 6
	1944	Feb.	Vol. 28, no. 3
		Aug.	Vol. 29, no. 3
		Dec.	Vol. 30, no. 1
	1947	Nov.	Vol. 35, no. 6
	1948	Nov.	Vol. 37, no. 6
	1950	Jan.	Vol. 40, no. 2
		Sept.	Vol. 41, no. 4
	1951	Oct.	Vol. 43, no. 5
	1952	Aug.	Vol. 45, no. 3
	1954	June	Vol. 48, no. 7

MAGAZINE	YEAR	MONTH	REF. No.
Motion Picture	1946	May	Vol. 71, no. 4
	1948	June	Vol. 75, no. 5
Photoplay	1941	Dec.	Vol. 20, no. 1
(American)	1943	March	Vol. 22, no. 4
	1946	Oct.	Vol. 29, no. 5
	1947	Aug.	Vol. 31, no. 3
	1948	June	Vol. 33, no. 1
	1949	Feb.	Vol. 34, no. 3
	1951	Jan.	Vol. 39, no. 1
Photoplay (British)	1954	Oct.	Vol. 5, no. 10
Picture Show	1940	9 March	Vol. 42, no. 1089
	1943	16 Jan.	Vol. 47, no. 1202
	1950	2 Dec.	Vol. 55, no. 1444
	1952	15 Nov.	Vol. 59, no. 1546
	1954	2 Jan.	Vol. 62, no. 1605
	1955	27 Aug.	Vol. 65, no. 1691
	1959	16 May	Vol. 72, no. 1885
Picturegoer	1941	9 Aug.	Vol. 11, no. 533
	1942	17 Oct.	Vol. 11, no. 565
	1944	25 Nov.	Vol. 13, no. 620
	1947	27 Sept.	Vol. 16, no. 693
	1953	11 April	Vol. 25, no. 936

POSTCARDS

Picturegoer series: 1228, a, D 366.

FRONT-OF-HOUSE SETS

Original American sets of *The Postman Always Rings Twice* and *The Bad And The Beautiful.*

POSTERS

Original American one-sheets of above films.

PROPS AND SOUVENIRS

Absolutely any memorabilia relating to *The Postman Always Rings Twice.*

RUDOLPH VALENTINO

Born: Castellaneta, Italy, 6 May 1895.
Died: New York, 23 Aug. 1926.
Real name: Rodolfo Guglielmi di Valentina d'Antonguolla.
Unprecedented hysteria and suicides by ardent fans followed the news of his death.

MAGAZINE	YEAR	MONTH	REF. No.
Life	1938	20 June	Vol. 4, no. 25
Motion Picture	1922	Feb.	Vol. 23, no. 1
	1923	Sept.	Vol. 26, no. 8
	1926	Sept.	Vol. 32, no. 2
Picturegoer	1923	Sept.	Vol. 6, no. 33
Monthly	1924	Oct.	Vol. 8, no. 46
Picture Show	1923	3 March	Vol. 8, no. 201
		21 July	Vol. 9, no. 221
		15 Sept.	Vol. 9, no. 229
		22 Sept.	Vol. 9, no. 230
		6 Oct.	Vol. 9, no. 232
		10 Nov.	Vol. 10, no. 237
		24 Nov.	Vol. 10, no. 239
	1924	22 March	Vol. 10, no. 256
		24 May	Vol. 11, no. 265
		5 July	Vol. 11, no. 271
		13 Sept.	Vol. 11, no. 281
		11 Oct.	Vol. 11, no. 285
	1925	3 Jan.	Vol. 12, no. 297
		21 Feb.	Vol. 12, no. 304
		4 April	Vol. 12, no. 310
		30 May	Vol. 13, no. 318
		28 Nov.	Vol. 14, no. 344
	1926	20 Feb.	Vol. 14, no. 356
		17 July	Vol. 15, no. 376
		20 Nov.	Vol. 16, no. 394
	1927	27 Aug.	Vol. 17, no. 434

POSTCARDS

Picturegoer series: 108, 271, a. Beagles Famous Cinema Star Series: 196, 197, 236, a – z.

PROPS AND SOUVENIRS

Rudy's hat, worn by him in *The Eagle*, was the first prize to be given away by *Picture Show* in their free star souvenir competition in 1926.

POSTERS

Original American one-sheets of any of his films.

SIGNED PORTRAITS

Ink-signed photographs from £200 upwards.

FRONT-OF-HOUSE SETS

Original American sets of any of his films.

JOHN WAYNE

Born: Winterset, Iowa, 26 May 1907.
Died: 11 June 1979.
Real name: Marion Michael Morrison.
Top box office ranking: 1 in 1950 – 1, 1954, 1971.

MAGAZINE	YEAR	MONTH	REF. No.
ABC Film Review	1965	Nov.	Vol. 15, no. 11
	1967	Aug.	Vol. 17, no. 8
	1971	Sept.	Vol. 21, no. 9
American Film	1976	June	Vol. 1, no. 8
Cahiers du Cinéma	1952	Sept.	Vol. 3, no. 15
	1962	Oct.	Vol. 23, no. 136
	1963	Oct.	Vol. 25, no. 148
	1967	June	Vol. 32, no. 191
Cinémonde	1951	8 Sept.	no. 892
Film Pictorial	1939	23 Sept.	Vol. 16, no. 396
Films Illustrated	1975	Nov.	Vol. 5, no. 51
Films in Review	1972	Feb.	Vol. 23, no. 2
	1976	Oct.	Vol. 27, no. 8
Life	1965	7 May	Vol. 58, no. 18
	1969	11 July	Vol. 67, no. 2
	1972	28 Jan.	Vol. 72, no. 3
Look	1942	6 Oct.	Vol. 6, no. 20
Motion Picture	1942	April	Vol. 63, no. 3
Photoplay (British)	1970	July	Vol. 21, no. 7
	1975	Dec.	Vol. 26, no. 12
Picture Show	1942	17 Jan.	Vol. 46, no. 1176
		11 April	Vol. 46, no. 1182
	1949	30 April	Vol. 53, no. 1366
	1952	19 July	Vol. 59, no. 1529
	1958	15 Nov.	Vol. 71, no. 1859
Picturegoer	1939	3 June	Vol. 9, no. 419
	1942	18 April	Vol. 11, no. 552
Time	1952	3 March	Vol. 59, no. 9
	1969	8 Aug.	Vol. 94, no. 6

POSTCARDS

Picturegoer series: 797, a – b, W 477, D 118. 'Famous Film Partners' series: *PC289, w/Claire Trevor. (*also available in sepia.)

FRONT-OF-HOUSE SETS

Original American sets of *Stagecoach, The Long Voyage Home, The Spoilers, Fort Apache, Red River, She Wore A Yellow Ribbon, Sands Of Iwo Jima, Rio Grande, The Quiet Man, Hondo, The Searchers, Rio Bravo, The Alamo, The Man Who Shot Liberty Valance.*

POSTERS

Original American one-sheets of above films.

SIGNED PORTRAITS

Ink-signed photographs from £50 upwards.

PROPS AND SOUVENIRS

A biscuit-coloured shirt worn by the star in westerns sold in auction at Christie's on 5 May 1988 for £2,420.

Robert Taylor reading *Picture Show*, on the set of *Valley of the Kings*, February 1954

CHAPTER TWO

A – Z GUIDE TO THE MOST COLLECTABLE MAGAZINES

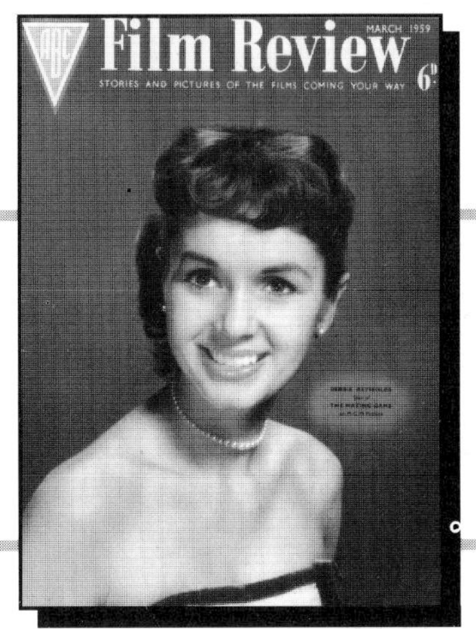

ABC FILM REVIEW 1950 – 72

A British film magazine published by Associated British Cinemas Ltd, this started in 1950 with three trial issues, becoming a monthly in 1951. It was obtainable only at ABC cinemas and was a non-profit making publication, any revenue exceeding costs going to the ABC Staff Benevolent Fund. Edited by W.L. Pember until December 1959, when he was succeeded by N.H. Taylor, its most notable covers were those that featured supporting players rarely chosen for magazine covers. It changed to a larger format in October 1970, becoming *Film Review* in May 1972. Collectors should note that no issues were published in August and September 1959.

The three issues published in 1950 were undated, the most collectable being the first, which featured **Dennis Price** and **Giselle Preville** on the cover.

YEAR	MONTH	REF. No.	COVER STAR
1951	Jan.	Vol. 1, no. 1	**Judy Garland**
	Feb.	Vol. 1, no. 2	**Ruth Roman**
	March	Vol. 1, no. 3	**Audrey Hepburn**
	April	Vol. 1, no. 4	**Richard Todd**
			Glynis Johns
	May	Vol. 1, no. 5	**Jane Powell**
	June	Vol. 1, no. 6	**Gary Cooper**
	July	Vol. 1, no. 7	**Patricia Dainton**
	Aug.	Vol. 1, no. 8	**Ava Gardner**
	Sept.	Vol. 1, no. 9	**Stewart Granger**
	Oct.	Vol. 1, no. 10	**Doris Day**
	Nov.	Vol. 1, no. 11	**Leslie Caron**
	Dec.	Vol. 1, no. 12	**Virginia Mayo**
1952	Jan.	Vol. 2, no. 1	**Robert Donat**
	Feb.	Vol. 2, no. 2	**Robert Taylor**
	March	Vol. 2, no. 3	**Richard Todd**
			Merle Oberon

YEAR	MONTH	REF. No.	COVER STAR
	April	Vol. 2, no. 4	**Vivien Leigh**
	May	Vol. 2, no. 5	**Bobby Henrey**
	June	Vol. 2, no. 6	**Ray Milland**
			Helena Carter
	July	Vol. 2, no. 7	**June Allyson**
	Aug.	Vol. 2, no. 8	**Suzanne Cloutier**
			Peter Graves
			Anna Neagle
			Michael Wilding
	Sept.	Vol. 2, no. 9	**Ray Bolger**
			Allyn McLerie
	Oct.	Vol. 2, no. 10	**Yvonne Furneaux**
	Nov.	Vol. 2, no. 11	**Kathryn Grayson**
			Howard Keel
	Dec.	Vol. 2, no. 12	**Valerie Carton**
			Veronica Hurst
			Susan Stephen
			Yvonne Furneaux
1953	Jan.	Vol. 3, no. 1	**Stewart Granger**
			Deborah Kerr
	Feb.	Vol. 3, no. 2	**Burt Lancaster**
			Nick Cravat
	March	Vol. 3, no. 3	**Spencer Tracy**
	April	Vol. 3, no. 4	**Virginia Mayo**
	May	Vol. 3, no. 5	**Esther Williams**
	June	Vol. 3, no. 6	**Queen Elizabeth II**
	July	Vol. 3, no. 7	**Errol Flynn**
			Beatrice Campbell
	Aug.	Vol. 3, no. 8	**Jean Simmons**
			Stewart Granger
	Sept.	Vol. 3, no. 9	**Doris Day**
	Oct.	Vol. 3, no. 10	**Robert Taylor**
			Deborah Kerr
	Nov.	Vol. 3, no. 11	**Jack Hawkins**
	Dec.	Vol. 3, no. 12	**Kathryn Grayson**
1954	Jan.	Vol. 4, no. 1	**Gina Lollobrigida**
	Feb.	Vol. 4, no. 2	**Ann Blyth**
	March	Vol. 4, no. 3	**Doris Day**
	April	Vol. 4, no. 4	**Glynis Johns**
	May	Vol. 4, no. 5	**Esther Williams**
	June	Vol. 4, no. 6	**Debbie Reynolds**
	July	Vol. 4, no. 7	**Ava Gardner**
	Aug.	Vol. 4, no. 8	**Joan Weldon**
	Sept.	Vol. 4, no. 9	**Jeanne Crain**
	Oct.	Vol. 4, no. 10	**Robert Taylor**
			Ava Gardner
	Nov.	Vol. 4, no. 11	**Jan Sterling**
	Dec.	Vol. 4, no. 12	**Debbie Reynolds**
1955	Jan.	Vol. 5, no. 1	**Elizabeth Taylor**
	Feb.	Vol. 5, no. 2	**Judy Garland**
	March	Vol. 5, no. 3	**Jane Powell**
	April	Vol. 5, no. 4	**Doris Day**
	May	Vol. 5, no. 5	**Elaine Stewart**
	June	Vol. 5, no. 6	**Virginia Mayo**
	July	Vol. 5, no. 7	**Ann Miller**

YEAR	MONTH	REF. No.	COVER STAR
	Aug.	Vol. 5, no. 8	**Anne Francis**
	Sept.	Vol. 5, no. 9	**Taina Elg**
	Oct.	Vol. 5, no. 10	**Anita Ekberg**
	Nov.	Vol. 5, no. 11	**Leslie Caron**
	Dec.	Vol. 5, no. 12	**Diana Dors**
1956	Jan.	Vol. 6, no. 1	**Ludmilla Tcherina**
	Feb.	Vol. 6, no. 2	**Debbie Reynolds**
	March	Vol. 6, no. 3	**Rossana Podesta**
	April	Vol. 6, no. 4	**Janette Scott**
	May	Vol. 6, no. 5	**Elaine Stewart**
	June	Vol. 6, no. 6	**Sarita Montiel**
	July	Vol. 6, no. 7	**Cyd Charisse**
	Aug.	Vol. 6, no. 8	**Diana Dors**
	Sept.	Vol. 6, no. 9	**Lisa Gastoni**
			Baby Baker
	Oct.	Vol. 6, no. 10	**Susan Hayward**
	Nov.	Vol. 6, no. 11	**Ava Gardner**
	Dec.	Vol. 6, no. 12	**Cyd Charisse**
1957	Jan.	Vol. 7, no. 1	**Jean Simmons**
			Marlon Brando
	Feb.	Vol. 7, no. 2	**Vera Miles**
	March	Vol. 7, no. 3	**Barbara Lang**
	April	Vol. 7, no. 4	**Janette Scott**
	May	Vol. 7, no. 5	**Virginia Mayo**
	June	Vol. 7, no. 6	**Maureen O'Hara**
	July	Vol. 7, no. 7	**Sylvia Syms**
	Aug.	Vol. 7, no. 8	**Frankie Vaughan**
	Sept.	Vol. 7, no. 9	**Janis Paige**
	Oct.	Vol. 7, no. 10	**Marilyn Monroe**
	Nov.	Vol. 7, no. 11	**Natalie Wood**
	Dec.	Vol. 7, no. 12	**Janette Scott**
1958	Jan.	Vol. 8, no. 1	**Mitzi Gaynor**
	Feb.	Vol. 8, no. 2	**Myrna Hansen**
	March	Vol. 8, no. 3	**Erin O'Brien**
	April	Vol. 8, no. 4	**Jackie Lane**
	May	Vol. 8, no. 5	**Barbara Lawrence**
	June	Vol. 8, no. 6	**Carole Lesley**
	July	Vol. 8, no. 7	**Danny Kaye**
	Aug.	Vol. 8, no. 8	**Ingrid Bergman**
	Sept.	Vol. 8, no. 9	**Sylvia Syms**
	Oct.	Vol. 8, no. 10	**Barbara Nichols**
	Nov.	Vol. 8, no. 11	**Rhonda Fleming**
	Dec.	Vol. 8, no. 12	**Carole Lesley**
1959	Jan.	Vol. 9, no. 1	**Jayne Mansfield**
	Feb.	Vol. 9, no. 2	**Eva Gabor**
	March	Vol. 9, no. 3	**Debbie Reynolds**
	April	Vol. 9, no. 4	**Brigitte Bardot**
	May	Vol. 9, no. 5	**Donald Sinden with 'Girls in Arms'**
	June	Vol. 9, no. 6	**Martha Hyer**
	July	Vol. 9, no. 7	**Sophia Loren**
	Oct.	Vol. 9, no. 8	**Tina Louise**
	Nov.	Vol. 9, no. 9	**Gina Lollobrigida**
	Dec.	Vol. 9, no. 10	**Tommy Steele**

YEAR	MONTH	REF. No.	COVER STAR
1960	Jan.	Vol. 10, no. 1	**Vanda Hudson**
	Feb.	Vol. 10, no. 2	**Sandra Dee**
			Troy Donahue
	March	Vol. 10, no. 3	**Joan Collins**
	April	Vol. 10, no. 4	**Richard Burton**
			Angie Dickinson
	May	Vol. 10, no. 5	**Audrey Hepburn**
	June	Vol. 10, no. 6	**Karen Steele**
	July	Vol. 10, no. 7	**Terry Moore**
	Aug.	Vol. 10, no. 8	**Sarah Branch**
	Sept.	Vol. 10, no. 9	**Natalie Wood**
	Oct.	Vol. 10, no. 10	**Frank Sinatra**
			Dean Martin
			Peter Lawford
	Nov.	Vol. 10, no. 11	**Elke Sommer**
	Dec.	Vol. 10, no. 12	**Tony Hancock**
1961	Jan.	Vol. 11, no. 1	**Shirley Anne Field**
	Feb.	Vol. 11, no. 2	**Robert Mitchum**
			Deborah Kerr
	March	Vol. 11, no. 3	**Luana Patten**
	April	Vol. 11, no. 4	**Dolores Hart**
	May	Vol. 11, no. 5	**Shirley Eaton**
	June	Vol. 11, no. 6	**Nobu McCarthy**
	July	Vol. 11, no. 7	**Gina Lollobrigida**
	Aug.	Vol. 11, no. 8	**Marlon Brando**
	Sept.	Vol. 11, no. 9	**Connie Stevens**
	Oct.	Vol. 11, no. 10	**Leslie Caron**
			Horst Buchholz
	Nov.	Vol. 11, no. 11	**Audrey Hepburn**
	Dec.	Vol. 11, no. 12	**Anne Heywood**
1962	Jan.	Vol. 12, no. 1	**Sonja Cordeau**
	Feb.	Vol. 12, no. 2	**Natalie Wood**
	March	Vol. 12, no. 3	**Shirley MacLaine**
	April	Vol. 12, no. 4	**Duane Eddy**
	May	Vol. 12, no. 5	**Dilys Laye**
			Liz Fraser
	June	Vol. 12, no. 6	**Paul Newman**
	July	Vol. 12, no. 7	**Ty Hardin**
			Glynis Johns
	Aug.	Vol. 12, no. 8	**Cliff Richard**
	Sept.	Vol. 12, no. 9	**Robert Preston**
			Shirley Jones
	Oct.	Vol. 12, no. 10	**Kirk Douglas**
			Rosanna Schiaffino
	Nov.	Vol. 12, no. 11	**Kenneth More**
			Joan O'Brien
	Dec.	Vol. 12, no. 12	**Denise Warren**
1963	Jan.	Vol. 13, no. 1	**Natalie Wood**
	Feb.	Vol. 13, no. 2	**Cliff Richard**
			Jackie Daryl
			Una Stubbs
	March	Vol. 13, no. 3	**Elvis Presley**
			Uncredited girl
	April	Vol. 13, no. 4	**Doris Day**
	May	Vol. 13, no. 5	**Marlon Brando**
			Tarita

YEAR	MONTH	REF. No.	COVER STAR
	June	Vol. 13, no. 6	**Shirley Anne Field**
	July	Vol. 13, no. 7	**Elvis Presley**
			Joan O'Brien
	Aug.	Vol. 13, no. 8	**Henry Fonda**
			Maureen O'Hara
	Sept.	Vol. 13, no. 9	**Elizabeth Taylor**
	Oct.	Vol. 13, no. 10	**Elsa Martinelli**
	Nov.	Vol. 13, no. 11	**Kathleen Breck**
	Dec.	Vol. 13, no. 12	**Susan Maughan**
1964	Jan.	Vol. 14, no. 1	**Harry H. Corbett**
			Jo Rowbottom
	Feb.	Vol. 14, no. 2	**Elke Sommer**
	March	Vol. 14, no. 3	**Cliff Richard**
	April	Vol. 14, no. 4	**Stanley Baker**
	May	Vol. 14, no. 5	**Sue Lyon**
	June	Vol. 14, no. 6	**Marisa Mell**
			James Booth
	July	Vol. 14, no. 7	**Cliff Richard**
			Susan Hampshire
	Aug.	Vol. 14, no. 8	**Elvis Presley**
			Yvonne Craig
			Pamela Austin
	Sept.	Vol. 14, no. 9	**Frank Sinatra**
			'7 Merry Maids'
	Oct.	Vol. 14, no. 10	**James Stewart**
	Nov.	Vol. 14, no. 11	**Diane Cilento**
	Dec.	Vol. 14, no. 12	**Audrey Hepburn**
1965	Jan.	Vol. 15, no. 1	**Carroll Baker**
	Feb.	Vol. 15, no. 2	**Tony Curtis**
			Natalie Wood
	March	Vol. 15, no. 3	**Ursula Andress**
	April	Vol. 15, no. 4	**Rod Taylor**
	May	Vol. 15, no. 5	**Carroll Baker**
			George Maharis
	June	Vol. 15, no. 6	**George Peppard**
	July	Vol. 15, no. 7	**Sean Connery**
	Aug.	Vol. 15, no. 8	**Elvis Presley**
	Sept.	Vol. 15, no. 9	**Kim Novak**
	Oct.	Vol. 15, no. 10	**Elizabeth Taylor**
			Richard Burton
	Nov.	Vol. 15, no. 11	**John Wayne**
			Martha Hyer
			Dean Martin
			Michael Anderson Jr
	Dec.	Vol. 15, no. 12	**Jim Dale**
			Angela Douglas
1966	Jan.	Vol. 16, no. 1	**Frank Ifield**
			Suzy Kendall
	Feb.	Vol. 16, no. 2	**Sophia Loren**
	March	Vol. 16, no. 3	**David McCallum**
			Dorothy Provine
			Robert Vaughan
	April	Vol. 16, no. 4	**Michael Caine**
	May	Vol. 16, no. 5	**Omar Sharif**
			Julie Christie
	June	Vol. 16, no. 6	**Suzanna Leigh**

YEAR	MONTH	REF. No.	COVER STAR
	July	Vol. 16, no. 7	**Paul Newman**
	Aug.	Vol. 16, no. 8	**Robert Vaughan**
			Leo G. Carroll
			David McCallum
	Sept.	Vol. 16, no. 9	**Steve McQueen**
	Oct.	Vol. 16, no. 10	**Rod Taylor**
			Jill St John
	Nov.	Vol. 16, no. 11	**Robert Vaughan**
			Elke Sommer
	Dec.	Vol. 16, no. 12	**Raquel Welch**
			John Richardson
1967	Jan.	Vol. 17, no. 1	**Audrey Hepburn**
	Feb.	Vol. 17, no. 2	**Hayley Mills**
	March	Vol. 17, no. 3	**Elizabeth Taylor**
			Richard Burton
	April	Vol. 17, no. 4	**Carita**
			Don Murray
	May	Vol. 17, no. 5	**Yul Brynner**
			Britt Ekland
	June	Vol. 17, no. 6	**Susan Denberg**
	July	Vol. 17, no. 7	**Jane Fonda**
	Aug.	Vol. 17, no. 8	**John Wayne**
			Robert Mitchum
	Sept.	Vol. 17, no. 9	**Michael Caine**
			Jane Fonda
	Oct.	Vol. 17, no. 10	**James Garner**
	Nov.	Vol. 17, no. 11	**Lee Marvin**
	Dec.	Vol. 17, no. 12	**Julie Christie**
1968	Jan.	Vol. 18, no. 1	**Tommy Steele**
	Feb.	Vol. 18, no. 2	**Vanessa Redgrave**
	March	Vol. 18, no. 3	**Elizabeth Taylor**
			Richard Burton
	April	Vol. 18, no. 4	**Olinka Berova**
			John Richardson
	May	Vol. 18, no. 5	**Kim Novak**
	June	Vol. 18, no. 6	**Faye Dunaway**
	July	Vol. 18, no. 7	**Audrey Hepburn**
	Aug.	Vol. 18, no. 8	**Brigitte Bardot**
	Sept.	Vol. 18, no. 9	**Richard Harris**
			Franco Nero
			Vanessa Redgrave
	Oct.	Vol. 18, no. 10	**Marianne Faithfull**
			Alain Delon
	Nov.	Vol. 18, no. 11	**Julie Christie**
	Dec.	Vol. 18, no. 12	**Shirley MacLaine**
			James Booth
1969	Jan.	Vol. 19, no. 1	**Warren Mitchell**
			Dandy Nichols
	Feb.	Vol. 19, no. 2	**Sean Connery**
			Brigitte Bardot
	March	Vol. 19, no. 3	**Petula Clark**
			Tommy Steele
	April	Vol. 19, no. 4	**Keir Dullea**
	May/	Vol. 19, no. 5	**Fenella Fielding**
	June		**Ian Bannen**
	July	Vol. 19, no. 6	**Peter Cushing**
			Veronica Carlson

YEAR	MONTH	REF. No.	COVER STAR
	Aug.	Vol. 19, no. 7	**Faye Dunaway**
			Marcello Mastroianni
	Sept.	Vol. 19, no. 8	**James Olson**
			Catherina Von Schell
	Oct.	Vol. 19, no. 9	**Omar Sharif**
			Catherine Deneuve
	Nov.	Vol. 19, no. 10	**Roger Moore**
	Dec.	Vol. 19, no. 11	**Patrick McGoohan**
			Rock Hudson
1970	Jan.	Vol. 20, no. 1	**Richard Burton**
			Ingrid Pitt
	Feb.	Vol. 20, no. 2	**Ingrid Pitt**
	March	Vol. 20, no. 3	**Alan Bates**
			Jennie Linden
	April	Vol. 20, no. 4	**Hannah Gordon**
			Diana Coupland
			James Mason
			Susan George
			Rodney Bewes
			Len Jones
	May	Vol. 20, no. 5	**Marty Feldman**
			Judy Cornwell
	June	Vol. 20, no. 6	**Leigh Taylor-Young**
	July	Vol. 20, no. 7	**Peter McEnery**
	Aug.	Vol. 20, no. 8	**Roger Moore**
	Sept.	Vol. 20, no. 9	**Warren Mitchell**
			Adrienne Posta
			Elaine Taylor
			Valerie Leon
	Oct.	Vol. 20, no. 10	**Ingrid Pitt**
			Pippa Steele
			Kate O'Mara
			Madeleine Smith
			Kirsten Lindholm
	Nov.	Vol. 20, no. 11	**Clint Eastwood**
	Dec.	Vol. 20, no. 12	**Steve McQueen**
1971	Jan.	Vol. 21, no. 1	**Stella Stevens**
	Feb.	Vol. 21, no. 2	**Goldie Hawn**
	March	Vol. 21, no. 3	**Michael Caine**
	April	Vol. 21, no. 4	**Frankie Howerd**
			Julie Ege
	May	Vol. 21, no. 5	**Paloma**
	June	Vol. 21, no. 6	**Dustin Hoffman**
	July	Vol. 21, no. 7	**Barbara Hershey**
	Aug.	Vol. 21, no. 8	**Reg Varney**
	Sept.	Vol. 21, no. 9	**John Wayne**
	Oct.	Vol. 21, no. 10	**Steve McQueen**
	Nov.	Vol. 21, no. 11	**Clint Eastwood**
	Dec.	Vol. 21, no. 12	**Ryan O'Neal**
1972	Jan.	Vol. 22, no. 1	**Frankie Howerd**
			Anne Aston
	Feb.	Vol. 22, no. 2	**Dean Martin**
	March	Vol. 22, no. 3	**Twiggy**
	April	Vol. 22, no. 4	**Harry H. Corbett**
			Carolyn Seymour
			Wilfred Brambell

Last issue as *ABC Film Review*. See *Film Review*.

AMERICAN FILM 1975 –

This is a serious film journal that has produced some excellent photographic covers: Woody Allen, Jack Lemmon, Mia Farrow. Most collectable are the covers by Maureen Lambray: Allen, Carradine and Shields, Adjani, Kinski, Astaire, Capra, Lange, Sarandon, Nicholson, Sutherland, Close, Arquette, Hershey. A regular feature of the magazine is 'Dialogue on Film', an interview between fellows and prominent filmmakers. Since September 1988 *American Film* has been published by Billboard Publications Ltd, but it was originally published by the American Film Institute and edited by Hollis Alpert. Succeeding editors: Peter Biskind, Susan Linfield, Chris Hodenfield.

YEAR	MONTH	REF. No.	COVER STAR
1975	Oct.	Vol. 1, no. 1	**Dustin Hoffman** **Robert Redford**
	Nov.	Vol. 1, no. 2	**Erich Von Stroheim**
	Dec.	Vol. 1, no. 3	**George Grizzard** **Albert Stratton**
1976	Jan./Feb.	Vol. 1, no. 4	**Ingmar Bergman**
	March	Vol. 1, no. 5	**Ingrid Boulting** **Robert De Niro**
	April	Vol. 1, no. 6	**Tribute to William Wyler: 39 film star caricatures**
	May	Vol. 1, no. 7	**Lina Wertmuller's *Seven Beauties***
	June	Vol. 1, no. 8	**James Stewart** **John Wayne**
	July/Aug.	Vol. 1, no. 9	**Billy Dee Williams** **James Earl Jones** **Richard Pryor**
	Sept.	Vol. 1, no. 10	**Donald Sutherland** **Federico Fellini**
	Oct.	Vol. 2, no. 1	**Le Var Burton**
	Nov.	Vol. 2, no. 2	**Dustin Hoffman** **Robert Evans**
	Dec./Jan.	Vol. 2, no. 3	***King Kong***
1977	Feb.	Vol. 2, no. 4	**Sketch for the library sequence in *Gone With The Wind***
	March	Vol. 2, no. 5	**Bette Davis**
	April	Vol. 2, no. 6	**Mark Hamill with See Threepio**
	May	Vol. 2, no. 7	**Woody Allen**
	June	Vol. 2, no. 8	***The Rescuers***
	July/Aug.	Vol. 2, no. 9	**Buster Keaton**
	Sept.	Vol. 2, no. 10	**Nick Nolte**
	Oct.	Vol. 3, no. 1	**Mel Brooks**
	Nov.	Vol. 3, no. 2	**Keith Carradine** **Brooke Shields**
	Dec./Jan.	Vol. 3, no. 3	**Nicola Pagett**
1978	Feb.	Vol. 3, no. 4	**Olivia Newton-John** **John Travolta**
	March	Vol. 3, no. 5	**Clark Gable** **Claudette Colbert**
	April	Vol. 3, no. 6	**Poster for *Le Maître du Mystère***
	May	Vol. 3, no. 7	'Monument Valley'
	June	Vol. 3, no. 8	**Burt Reynolds**
	July/Aug.	Vol. 3, no. 9	**Ricky Schroder** **Jon Voight**
	Sept.	Vol. 3, no. 10	**Bette Midler**
	Oct.	Vol. 4, no. 1	**Isabelle Adjani**
	Nov.	Vol. 4, no. 2	**Billie Holiday**
	Dec./Jan.	Vol. 4, no. 3	**Pamela Hill**
1979	Feb.	Vol. 4, no. 4	**Cast of *Boulevard Nights***

YEAR	MONTH	REF. No.	COVER STAR
	March	Vol. 4, no. 5	**Tom Skerritt**
	April	Vol. 4, no. 6	**Jill Clayburgh**
	May	Vol. 4, no. 7	**Robert Redford**
	June	Vol. 4, no. 8	**Lee Marvin**
	July/Aug.	Vol. 4, no. 9	**Michael Douglas**
	Sept.	Vol. 4, no. 10	**Peter Ellenshaw**
	Oct.	Vol. 5, no. 1	**Richard Gere** **Chick Vennera**
	Nov.	Vol. 5, no. 2	**Bob Fosse**
	Dec.	Vol. 5, no. 3	**Alan Bates**
1980	Jan./Feb.	Vol. 5, no. 4	**Theresa Russell**
	March	Vol. 5, no. 5	**Gary Busey** **Jodie Foster** **Robbie Robertson**
	April	Vol. 5, no. 6	**Richard Chamberlain**
	May	Vol. 5, no. 7	**Klaus Kinski**
	June	Vol. 5, no. 8	**An exhibit at the Cinémathèque Français**
	July/Aug.	Vol. 5, no. 9	**Paul Mazursky**
	Sept.	Vol. 5, no. 10	**John Huston**
	Oct.	Vol. 6, no. 1	**Isabelle Huppert** **Kris Kristofferson**
	Nov.	Vol. 6, no. 2	**Robert De Niro**
	Dec.	Vol. 6, no. 3	**Robin Williams** **Shelley Duvall**
1981	Jan./Feb.	Vol. 6, no. 4	**Joel Schumacher** **Jeremy Joe Kronsberg** **Taylor Hackford**
	March	Vol. 6, no. 5	**Nigel Terry** **Cherie Lunghi**
	April	Vol. 6, no. 6	**Fred Astaire**
	May	Vol. 6, no. 7	**A movie theatre cashier**
	June	Vol. 6, no. 8	**Jon Alpert** **Keiko Tsuno**
	July/Aug.	Vol. 6, no. 9	**Blake Edwards**
	Sept.	Vol. 6, no. 10	**Robert Duvall**
	Oct.	Vol. 7, no. 1	**Francis Coppola**
	Nov.	Vol. 7, no. 2	**Jane Fonda**
	Dec.	Vol. 7, no. 3	**James Cagney**
1982	Jan./Feb.	Vol. 7, no. 4	**Rod Steiger**
	March	Vol. 7, no. 5	**Frank Capra**
	April	Vol. 7, no. 6	**Nastassja Kinski**
	May	Vol. 7, no. 7	**Arnold Schwarzenegger**
	June	Vol. 7, no. 8	**Klaus Kinski**
	July/Aug.	Vol. 7, no. 9	**Mickey Mouse** **Tron** **Matt Dillon**
	Sept.	Vol. 7, no. 10	**Jack Lemmon**
	Oct.	Vol. 8, no. 1	**John Sayles**
	Nov.	Vol. 8, no. 2	**Jackie Gleason**
	Dec.	Vol. 8, no. 3	**Paul Newman**
1983	Jan./Feb.	Vol. 8, no. 4	**Jessica Lange**
	March	Vol. 8, no. 5	**Gene Hackman**
	April	Vol. 8, no. 6	**Dustin Hoffman**
	May	Vol. 8, no. 7	**Susan Sarandon**
	June	Vol. 8, no. 8	**George Lucas**
	July/Aug.	Vol. 8, no. 9	**Judy Garland**
	Sept.	Vol. 8, no. 10	**David Bowie**
	Oct.	Vol. 9, no. 1	**Gérard Depardieu**
	Nov.	Vol. 9, no. 2	**Lance Henrikson** **Scott Paulin** **Philip Kaufman** **Ed Harris** **Charles Frank** **Scott Glenn** **Fred Ward** **Dennis Quaid**
	Dec.	Vol. 9, no. 3	**Meryl Streep**
1984	Jan./Feb.	Vol. 9, no. 4	**Jack Nicholson**
	March	Vol. 9, no. 5	**Lillian Gish**
	April	Vol. 9, no. 6	**Donald Sutherland**
	May	Vol. 9, no. 7	**Glenn Close**
	June	Vol. 9, no. 8	**Robert De Niro**
	July/Aug.	Vol. 9, no. 9	**Albert Finney**
	Sept.	Vol. 9, no. 10	**Charlie Chaplin**
	Oct.	Vol. 10, no. 1	**Sam Shepard**
	Nov.	Vol. 10, no. 2	**Kathleen Turner**
	Dec.	Vol. 10, no. 3	**Gregory Hines**
1985	Jan./Feb.	Vol. 10, no. 4	**Gillian Armstrong**
	March	Vol. 10, no. 5	**Gene Kelly**
	April	Vol. 10, no. 6	**Rebecca De Mornay**
	May	Vol. 10, no. 7	**Rip Torn**
	June	Vol. 10, no. 8	**Art cover designed by Andy Warhol**
	July/Aug.	Vol. 10, no. 9	**Rosanna Arquette**
	Sept.	Vol. 10, no. 10	**Griffin Dunne** **Amy Robinson**
	Oct.	Vol. 11, no. 1	**John Malkovich**
	Nov.	Vol. 11, no. 2	**Ally Sheedy**
	Dec.	Vol. 11, no. 3	**Whoopi Goldberg**
1986	Jan./Feb.	Vol. 11, no. 4	**Julie Christie**
	March	Vol. 11, no. 5	**Billy Wilder**
	April	Vol. 11, no. 6	**Sean Penn**
	May	Vol. 11, no. 7	**Barbara Hershey**
	June	Vol. 11, no. 8	**William Desmond Taylor**
	July/Aug.	Vol. 11, no. 9	**William Hurt**
	Sept.	Vol. 11, no. 10	**Sean Connery**
	Oct.	Vol. 12, no. 1	**Kirk Douglas** **Burt Lancaster**
	Nov.	Vol. 12, no. 2	**Robert De Niro**
	Dec.	Vol. 12, no. 3	**Harrison Ford**
1987	Jan./Feb.	Vol. 12, no. 4	**Diane Keaton** **Jessica Lange** **Sissy Spacek**

YEAR	MONTH	REF. No.	COVER STAR
	March	Vol. 12, no. 5	**Mia Farrow**
	April	Vol. 12, no. 6	**Barbara Stanwyck**
	May	Vol. 12, no. 7	**Dustin Hoffman**
			Warren Beatty
			Isabelle Adjani
	June	Vol. 12, no. 8	**Kevin Costner**
			David Mamet
	July/Aug.	Vol. 12, no. 9	**Madonna**
	Sept.	Vol. 12, no. 10	**Anjelica Huston**
	Oct.	Vol. 13, no. 1	**Matthew Modine**
	Nov.	Vol. 13, no. 2	**Mickey Rourke**
	Dec.	Vol. 13, no. 3	**Oliver Stone**
1988	Jan./Feb.	Vol. 13, no. 4	**Meryl Streep**
	March	Vol. 13, no. 5	**Jack Lemmon**
	April	Vol. 13, no. 6	**Gary Oldman**
	May	Vol. 13, no. 7	**Lily Tomlin**
	June	Vol. 13, no. 8	**Francis Ford Coppola**
	July/Aug.	Vol. 13, no. 9	**Debra Winger**
	Sept.	Vol. 13, no. 10	**Clint Eastwood**
	Oct.	Vol. 14, no. 1	**Jodie Foster**
	Nov.	Vol. 14, no. 2	**Steve Martin**
	Dec.	Vol. 14, no. 3	**Dustin Hoffman**
1989	Jan./Feb.	Vol. 14, no. 4	**Ted Turner**
	March	Vol. 14, no. 5	**Martin Scorsese**
	April	Vol. 14, no. 6	**Theresa Russell**
	May	Vol. 14, no. 7	**Sean Connery**
	June	Vol. 14, no. 8	**Dennis Quaid**
	July/Aug.	Vol. 14, no. 9	**Spike Lee**
	Sept.	Vol. 14, no. 10	**Danny De Vito**
	Oct.	Vol. 15, no. 1	**Robert De Niro**
	Nov.	Vol. 15, no 2	**Lena Olin**
	Dec.	Vol. 15, no. 3	**Holly Hunter**

CAHIERS DU CINEMA 1951 –

The French magazine that is fondly remembered for employing François Truffaut, Claude Chabrol and Eric Rohmer as critics. Although the magazine is directed at an art-cinema going audience, there is much to offer the collector of film star covers, including film stills depicting rare cover subjects: Laurel and Hardy, Buster Keaton, Jack Palance, Ben Gazzara, etc. During the seventies, the quality of the magazine fell dramatically and the illustrated covers disappeared until the end of the decade. Originally edited by André Bazin and Jacques Doniol-Valcroze, it was published by Les Editions de L'Etoile.

Selected covers only:

YEAR	MONTH	REF. No.	COVER STAR
1951	April	no. 1	**Gloria Swanson**
	May	no. 2	**Bette Davis**
			Gary Merrill
			Anne Baxter
	Sept.	no. 5	**Hedy Lamarr**
	Oct./Nov.	no. 6	**Fernandel**
			Françoise Rosay
1952	March	no. 10	**Elizabeth Taylor**
			Montgomery Clift
	April	no. 11	**Kirk Douglas**
			Jan Sterling
	May	no. 12	**Audie Murphy**
	July/Aug.	no. 14	**Gene Kelly**
	Sept.	no. 15	**John Wayne**
			Maureen O'Hara
	Nov.	no. 17	**Charlie Chaplin**
			Claire Bloom
1953	Jan.	no. 19	**Jean Peters**
			Marlon Brando
	Feb.	no. 20	**Anna Magnani**
	March	no. 21	**Fredric March**
	April	no. 22	**Jacques Tati**
	May	no. 23	**Jack Hawkins**
	June	no. 24	**Marilyn Monroe**
	July	no. 25	**Ingrid Bergman**
	Aug./Sept.	no. 26	**Dawn Addams**
	Oct.	no. 27	**Danielle Darrieux**
	Nov.	no. 28	**Michele Morgan**
			Gérard Philipe
	Dec.	no. 29	**Jean Simmons**
1954	March	no. 33	**Gina Lollobrigida**
	April	no. 34	**Audrey Hepburn**
	May	no. 35	**Gérard Philipe**
			Joan Greenwood
	July	no. 37	**Ingrid Bergman**
	Aug./Sept.	no. 38	**Dan O'Herlihy**
	Oct.	no. 39	**Robert Cummings**
			Grace Kelly
	Nov.	no. 40	**Danielle Darrieux**
			Gérard Philipe
	Dec.	no. 41	**Susan Shentall**
			Laurence Harvey
	Special issue	no. 42	**Audrey Hepburn**
1955	Feb.	no. 44	**Groucho Marx**
			Thelma Todd
	June	no. 48	**Sophia Loren**
	Aug./Sept.	no. 50	**Betsy Blair**
			Ernest Borgnine
	Oct.	no. 51	**Katharine Hepburn**
	Dec.	no. 53	**Jack Palance**
			Shelley Winters
	Special issue	no. 54	**Marilyn Monroe**

YEAR	MONTH	REF. No.	COVER STAR
1956	March	no. 57	**Giulietta Masina**
			Broderick Crawford
	April	no. 58	**Anna Magnani**
	June	no. 60	**Kim Novak**
	July	no. 61	**Harriet Andersson**
			Ulla Jacobsson
	Aug./Sept.	no. 62	**Alfred Hitchcock**
	Nov.	no. 64	**Marilyn Monroe**
	Dec.	no. 65	**Audrey Hepburn**
1957	March	no. 69	**Audrey Hepburn**
	June	no. 72	**Erich Von Stroheim**
			Zasu Pitts
	July	no. 73	**Orson Welles**
	Nov.	no. 76	**Audrey Hepburn**
1958	Jan.	no. 79	**Jeanne Moreau**
	Feb.	no. 80	**Jean Seberg**
	March	no. 81	**Dorothy Malone**
			Rock Hudson
	April	no. 82	**Jacques Tati**
	June	no. 84	**Orson Welles**
	July	no. 85	**Harriet Andersson**
	Aug.	no. 86	**Buster Keaton**
	Sept.	no. 87	**Orson Welles**
	Oct.	no. 88	**Ava Gardner**
1959	Feb.	no. 92	**James Stewart**
			Kim Novak
1960	Jan.	no. 103	**Jean Seberg**
	May	no. 107	**Cyd Charisse**
	Nov.	no. 113	**Janet Leigh**
			John Gavin
1961	Aug.	no. 122	**Anna Karina**
			Jean-Paul Belmondo
	Sept.	no. 123	**Delphine Seyrig**
	Oct.	no. 124	**Jean-Paul Belmondo**
			Emmanuelle Riva
1962	Jan.	no. 127	**Jeffrey Hunter**
	Feb.	no. 128	**Ingrid Thulin**
			Glenn Ford
	March	no. 129	**Louis Jourdan**
	June	no. 132	**Jerry Lewis**
	July	no. 133	**Anna Karina**
	Oct.	no. 136	**John Wayne**
			James Stewart
1963	May	no. 143	**Tippi Hedren**
	Sept.	no. 147	**Delphine Seyrig**
	Oct.	no. 148	**John Wayne**
			Lee Marvin
	Nov.	no. 149	**Rod Steiger**
1964	March	no. 153	**Catherine Deneuve**
			Nino Castelnuovo

YEAR	MONTH	REF. No.	COVER STAR
	May	no. 155	**Anna Karina**
	July	no. 157	**Randolph Scott**
			Karen Steele
	Nov.	no. 160	**Monica Vitti**
1965	Feb.	no. 163	**Laurel and Hardy**
	April	no. 165	**Orson Welles**
			Jeanne Moreau
	May/June	nos. 166 – 7	**Eddie Constantine**
			Anna Karina
	July	no. 168	**Marlene Dietrich**
	Oct.	no. 171	**Anna Karina**
			Jean-Paul Belmondo
	Nov.	no. 172	**Monica Vitti**
	Dec.	no. 173	**Michael Craig**
			Claudia Cardinale
1966	Feb.	no. 175	**Catherine Deneuve**
	March	no. 176	**Julie Christie**
	May	no. 178	**Edie Adams**
	June	no. 179	**Orson Welles**
			Jeanne Moreau
	Sept.	no. 182	**Anna Karina**
	Nov.	no. 184	**Paul Newman**
1967	Jan.	no. 186	**Sophia Loren**
	March	no. 188	**Bibi Andersson**
			Liv Ullmann
	June	no. 191	**James Caan**
			Robert Mitchum
			John Wayne
	Sept.	no. 193	**Jerry Lewis**
	Oct.	no. 194	**Albert Finney**
			Audrey Hepburn
	Dec.	no. 196	**Warren Beatty**
			Faye Dunaway
	Special issue	no. 197	**Jerry Lewis**
			Mary Ann Mobley
1968	Feb.	no. 198	**Jeanette MacDonald**
			Maurice Chevalier
1969	May	no. 212	**Catherine Deneuve**
			Jean-Paul Belmondo
1970	July	no. 222	**Catherine Deneuve**
1978	Feb.	no. 285	**Charlie Chaplin**
			Martha Raye
	Oct.	no. 293	**Ben Gazzara**
			Gena Rowlands
			John Cassavetes
1979	July/Aug.	no. 302	**Martin Sheen**
1980	May	no. 311	**Mark Hamill**
	Sept.	no. 315	**Gérard Depardieu**
			Catherine Deneuve
	Nov.	no. 317	**Shelley Duvall**
			Danny Lloyd
			Jack Nicholson
1981	March	no. 321	**Cathy Moriarty**
			Robert De Niro
1982	Feb.	no. 332	**Ben Gazzara**
			Ornella Muti
	March	no. 333	**Jacqueline Bisset**
			Candice Bergen
	Sept.	no. 339	**Kirsty McNichol**
	Oct.	no. 340	**Julie Andrews**
1983	Jan.	no. 343	**Jeremy Irons**
	May	no. 347	**Robert De Niro**
1984	May	no. 359	**Robert De Niro**
			James Wood
	Special Cannes issue	nos 360 – 1	**Harry Dean Stanton**
			Hunter Carson
	Nov.	no. 365	**Tom Hulce**
1985	Jan.	no. 367	**Gena Rowlands**
			John Cassavetes
	March	no. 369	**Lena Olin**
			Erland Josephson
	Sept.	no. 375	**Gérard Depardieu**
			Sophie Marceau
	Nov.	no. 377	**Ariane**
			Mickey Rourke
1986	Feb.	no. 380	**Marcello Mastroianni**
			Giulietta Masina
	May	nos 383 – 4	**Catherine Deneuve**
	Oct.	no. 388	**Tom Cruise**
1987	March	no. 393	**Tom Cruise**
			Paul Newman
	July/Aug.	no. 398	**Marilyn Monroe**
1988	March	no. 405	**Juliette Binoche**
			Lena Olin
	April	no. 406	**Harrison Ford**
			Emmanuelle Seigner
	June	no. 409	**Forest Whitaker**
	Sept.	no. 411	**Isabelle Huppert**
	Oct.	no. 412	**Willem Dafoe**
	Dec.	no. 414	**Yves Montand**
1989	Jan.	no. 415	**Jeff Bridges**
	March	no. 417	**John Cassavetes**
	Sept.	no. 423	**Michael Keaton**
	Oct.	no. 424	**Meg Ryan**
			Billy Crystal
	Dec.	no. 426	**Veronica Lake**
			Joel McCrea

CINÉMONDE 1928 – 66

A French weekly that offers the collector some excellent photographic covers, this was originally edited by Gaston Thierry and Nath Imbert. The first cover, 26 October 1928, featured Falconetti.

Its original sepia covers gave way to colour in February 1947, and many of these have now become covetable collectables. One only has to look at the vibrancy of the Gene Kelly and Debbie Reynolds cover from *Singin' In The Rain*, issue no. 997, or appreciate the beautiful portrait of Elizabeth Taylor, issue no. 1187, to realize that this magazine was several degrees above its competitors in quality. By November 1966, however, the magazine had become *Le Nouveau Cinémonde*, and a shadow of its former self.

Selected covers only:

YEAR	MONTH	REF. No.	COVER STAR
1947	14 Jan.	no. 650	**Alan Ladd**
			Veronica Lake
	28 Jan.	no. 652	**Jennifer Jones**
	11 Feb.	no. 654	**Danielle Darrieux**
	20 May	no. 668	**Veronica Lake**
	27 May	no. 669	**Michele Morgan**
	1 July	no. 674	**Errol Flynn**
	8 July	no. 675	**Greta Garbo**
	22 July	no. 677	**Bette Davis**
	29 July	no. 678	**Jean Gabin**
	5 Aug.	no. 679	**Ingrid Bergman**
	26 Aug.	no. 682	**Hedy Lamarr**
	16 Sept.	no. 685	**Dorothy Lamour**
	23 Sept.	no. 686	**Charles Boyer**
	21 Oct.	no. 690	**Joan Crawford**
	28 Oct.	no. 691	**Gary Cooper**
	25 Nov.	no. 695	**Linda Darnell**
	2 Dec.	no. 696	**Maureen O'Hara**
	23 Dec.	no. 699	**Dolores Del Rio**
1948	13 Jan	no. 702	**Ann Sheridan**
	10 Feb.	no. 706	**Marlene Dietrich**
	17 Feb.	no. 707	**Ingrid Bergman**
	2 March	no. 709	**Martha Vickers**
	9 March	no. 710	**Dany Robin**
	23 March	no. 712	**Lauren Bacall**
	6 April	no. 714	**Joan Fontaine**

YEAR	MONTH	REF. No.	COVER STAR
	13 April	no. 715	**Ingrid Bergman**
	27 April	no. 717	**Shirley Temple**
	4 May	no. 718	**Simone Signoret**
	11 May	no. 719	**Jane Russell**
	25 May	no. 721	**Rita Hayworth**
	22 June	no. 725	**Loretta Young**
	29 June	no. 726	**Jean Marais**
	6 July	no. 727	**Maureen O'Hara**
	10 Aug.	no. 732	**Yvonne De Carlo**
	17 Aug.	no. 733	**Gérard Philipe**
	24 Aug.	no. 734	**Lauren Bacall**
	31 Aug.	no. 735	**Cecile Aubry**
	7 Sept.	no. 736	**Ellen Drew**
	21 Sept.	no. 738	**Ava Gardner**
	28 Sept.	no. 739	**Ingrid Bergman**
	19 Oct.	no. 741	**Maureen O'Hara**
	9 Nov.	no. 744	**Janis Paige**
	23 Nov.	no. 746	**Jennifer Jones**
	6 Dec.	no. 748	**Ann Sheridan**
	13 Dec.	no. 749	**Corinne Calvet**
	20 Dec.	no. 750	**Joan Fontaine**
1949	3 Jan.	no. 752	**Marlene Dietrich**
	17 Jan.	no. 754	**Irene Dunne**
	24 Jan.	no. 755	**Yves Montand**
	31 Jan.	no. 756	**Betty Grable**
	14 Feb.	no. 758	**Myrna Loy**

YEAR	MONTH	REF. No.	COVER STAR
	7 March	no. 761	**Ingrid Bergman**
	21 March	no. 763	**Martine Carol**
	4 April	no. 765	**Deanna Durbin**
	9 May	no. 770	**Marlene Dietrich**
	30 May	no. 773	**Rita Hayworth**
	6 June	no. 774	**Michele Morgan**
	27 June	no. 777	**Virginia Mayo**
	18 July	no. 780	**Viveca Lindfors**
	1 Aug.	no. 782	**Betty Hutton**
	8 Aug.	no. 783	**Danielle Darrieux**
	22 Aug.	no. 785	**Jean Marais**
	10 Oct.	no. 792	**Errol Flynn**
			Greer Garson
	17 Oct	no. 793	**Fernandel**
	24 Oct	no. 794	**Michele Morgan**
	12 Dec.	no. 801	**Errol Flynn**
			Viveca Lindfors
	26 Dec.	no. 803	**Rita Hayworth**
1950	9 Jan.	no. 805	**Roddy McDowall**
			Jane Powell
	10 April	no. 818	**Michele Morgan**
	1 May	no. 821	**Ginger Rogers**
	15 May	no. 823	**Joan Crawford**
	29 May	no. 825	**John Wayne**
			Gail Russell
	19 June	no. 828	**Viveca Lindfors**
	3 July	no. 830	**Gene Tierney**
	31 July	no. 834	**Alexis Smith**
			Clark Gable
	28 Aug.	no. 838	**Esther Williams**
	25 Sept.	no. 842	**Rod Cameron**
			Ilona Massey
	9 Oct.	no. 844	**Ingrid Bergman**
	16 Oct.	no. 845	**Tyrone Power**
	30 Oct.	no. 847	**Barbara Bates**
			Danny Kaye
	4 Dec.	no. 852	**Rita Hayworth**
	11 Dec.	no. 853	**Martine Carol**
1951	6 Jan.	no. 857	**Micheline Presle**
			Errol Flynn
	13 Jan.	no. 858	**Robert Newton**
			Bobby Driscoll
	17 Feb.	no. 863	**Danielle Darrieux**
	10 March	no. 866	**Debra Paget**
	2 June	no. 878	**Jean Gabin**
	9 June	no. 879	**Ingrid Bergman**
	16 June	no. 880	**Jean Marais**
	14 July	no. 884	**Nadia Gray**
	28 July	no. 886	**Lex Barker**
			Vanessa Brown
	11 Aug.	no. 888	**Esther Williams**
	18 Aug.	no. 889	**Jean Gabin**
			Danielle Darrieux
	25 Aug.	no. 890	**Anthony Dexter**
			Eleanor Parker
	1 Sept.	no. 891	**Ava Gardner**

YEAR	MONTH	REF. No.	COVER STAR
	8 Sept.	no. 892	**John Wayne**
			Maureen O'Hara
	29 Sept.	no. 895	**Corinne Calvet**
	6 Oct.	no. 896	**Faith Domergue**
	13 Oct.	no. 897	**Farley Granger**
			Shelley Winters
	20 Oct.	no. 898	**Martine Carol**
	1 Dec.	no. 904	**Orson Welles**
			Suzanne Cloutier
	22 Dec.	no. 907	**Gregory Peck**
	29 Dec.	no. 908	**Esther Williams**
1952	11 Jan.	no. 910	**Errol Flynn**
			Laurette Luez
	18 Jan.	no. 911	**Danny Kaye**
			Gene Tierney
	7 March	no. 918	**Gérard Philipe**
			Gina Lollobrigida
	14 March	no. 919	**Vivien Leigh**
	21 March	no. 920	**Marge and Gower Champion**
			Joe E. Brown
			Ava Gardner
	18 April	no. 924	**Gregory Peck**
			Susan Hayward
	9 May	no. 927	**Jane Russell**
	6 June	no. 931	**Rita Hayworth**
	20 June	no. 933	**Michele Morgan**
	11 July	no. 936	**Gene Tierney**
	18 July	no. 937	**Gérard Philipe**
	25 July	no. 938	**Debra Paget**
	8 Aug.	no. 940	**Ingrid Bergman**
	15 Aug.	no. 941	**Esther Williams**
	22 Aug.	no. 942	**Gina Lollobrigida**
	19 Sept.	no. 946	**Martine Carol**
	26 Sept.	no. 947	**Richard Todd**
			Joan Rice
	17 Oct.	no. 950	**Jean Gabin**
			Michele Morgan
	7 Nov.	no. 953	**John Wayne**
			Maureen O'Hara
	19 Dec.	no. 959	**Michele Morgan**
1953	9 Jan.	no. 962	**Rita Hayworth**
	20 Feb.	no. 968	**Susan Hayward**
	6 March	no. 970	**Esther Williams**
	3 April	no. 974	**Piper Laurie**
	10 April	no. 975	**Yves Montand**
			Vera Clouzot
			Charles Vanel
	24 April	no. 977	**Ava Gardner**
	15 May	no. 980	**Elizabeth Taylor**
	5 June	no. 983	**Ruth Roman**
			Gary Cooper
	19 June	no. 985	**Danielle Darrieux**
			Charles Boyer
	3 July	no. 987	**Michele Morgan**
	10 July	no. 988	**Esther Williams**

YEAR	MONTH	REF. No.	COVER STAR
	17 July	no. 989	**Jean Marais**
	24 July	no. 990	**Farley Granger**
			Zizi Jeanmaire
	14 Aug.	no. 993	**Rita Hayworth**
	21 Aug.	no. 994	**Fernando Lamas**
			Lana Turner
	28 Aug.	no. 995	**Martine Carol**
			Raf Vallone
	4 Sept.	no. 996	**Françoise Arnoul**
	11 Sept.	no. 997	**Gene Kelly**
			Debbie Reynolds
	18 Sept.	no. 998	**Robert Taylor**
			Deborah Kerr
	16 Oct.	no. 1002	**Yvonne De Carlo**
	23 Oct.	no. 1003	**Yves Montand**
	27 Nov.	no. 1008	**Richard Burton**
			Jean Simmons
	18 Dec.	no. 1011	**Gina Lollobrigida**
	25 Dec.	no. 1012	**Leslie Caron**
1954	15 Jan.	no. 1015	**Hildegarde Neff**
	5 Feb.	no. 1018	**Ava Gardner**
			Robert Taylor
	19 Feb.	no. 1020	**Lana Turner**
			Carlos Thompson
	5 March	no. 1022	**Pier Angeli**
			Fernandel
	26 March	no. 1025	**Deborah Kerr**
			Burt Lancaster
	2 April	no. 1026	**Jean Marais**
	9 April	no. 1027	**Martine Carol**
	16 April	no. 1028	**Marilyn Monroe**
	30 April	no. 1030	**Jane Russell**
	7 May	no. 1031	**Françoise Arnoul**
	14 May	no. 1032	**Ava Gardner**
	21 May	no. 1033	**Gina Lollobrigida**
	4 June	no. 1035	**Danielle Darrieux**
			Gérard Philipe
	25 June	no. 1038	**Ingrid Bergman**
	6 Aug.	no. 1044	**Martine Carol**
	20 Aug.	no. 1046	**Marlene Dietrich**
	3 Sept.	no. 1048	**Ava Gardner**
	24 Sept.	no. 1051	**Yves Montand**
			Simone Signoret
	15 Oct.	no. 1054	**Gina Lollobrigida**
	22 Oct.	no. 1055	**Michele Morgan**
	29 Oct.	no. 1056	**Richard Todd**
			Glynis Johns
	12 Nov.	no. 1058	**Martine Carol**
	19 Nov.	no. 1059	**Eleanor Parker**
	26 Nov.	no. 1060	**Jean Gabin**
			Françoise Arnoul
	3 Dec.	no. 1061	**Elizabeth Taylor**
	10 Dec.	no. 1062	**Gérard Philipe**
	24 Dec.	no. 1064	**Dany Robin**
1955	28 Jan.	no. 1069	**Sophia Loren**
	18 Feb.	no. 1072	**Dawn Addams**
	11 March	no. 1075	**Dany Robin**
	25 March	no. 1077	**Martine Carol**
	8 April	no. 1079	**Paul Newman**
			Pier Angeli
	15 April	no. 1080	**Jeanne Moreau**
	29 April	no. 1082	**Diana Dors**
	5 May	no. 1083	**Jean Gabin**
			Françoise Arnoul
	12 May	no. 1084	**Esther Williams**
	19 May	no. 1085	**Julie Harris**
			James Dean
	30 June	no. 1091	**Sophia Loren**
	7 July	no. 1092	**Ann Miller**
	14 July	no. 1093	**Gina Lollobrigida**
	4 Aug.	no. 1096	**Mara Corday**
	11 Aug.	no. 1097	**Anne Baxter**
			Rock Hudson
	18 Aug.	no. 1098	**Mala Powers**
	25 Aug.	no. 1099	**Martine Carol**
	1 Sept.	no. 1100	**Eddie Constantine**
			Françoise Arnoul
	8 Sept.	no. 1101	**Marlon Brando**
	15 Sept.	no. 1102	**Pier Angeli**
	22 Sept.	no. 1103	**Kerima**
			Marcello Mastroianni
	13 Oct.	no. 1105	**Gérard Philipe**
	20 Oct.	no. 1106	**Brigitte Bardot**
	27 Oct.	no. 1107	**Sophia Loren**
	10 Nov.	no. 1109	**Danielle Darrieux**
	17 Nov.	no. 1110	**Lana Turner**
			Edmund Purdom
	24 Nov.	no. 1111	**Gina Lollobrigida**
	1 Dec.	no. 1112	**Leslie Caron**
	8 Dec.	no. 1113	**Jeanne Crain**
	29 Dec.	no. 1116	**Ingrid Bergman**
1956	12 Jan.	no. 1118	**Rossana Podesta**
	19 Jan.	no. 1119	**Marlon Brando**
			Jean Simmons
	26 Jan.	no. 1120	**Grace Kelly**
	2 Feb.	no. 1121	**Susan Hayward**
	9 Feb.	no. 1122	**Burt Lancaster**
	8 March	no. 1126	**Jeff Chandler**
			Jane Russell
	22 March	no. 1128	**Sophia Loren**
	5 April	no. 1130	**Grace Kelly**
	12 April	no. 1131	**Michele Morgan**
	19 April	no. 1132	**Sophia Loren**
			Brigitte Bardot
			Michele Morgan
	3 May	no. 1134	**Eddie Constantine**
	10 May	no. 1135	**Fernandel**
			Carmen Sevilla
	17 May	no. 1136	**Diana Dors**
	24 May	no. 1137	**Ingrid Bergman**
	21 June	no. 1141	**Brigitte Bardot**
	12 July	no. 1144	**Marlon Brando**
	2 Aug.	no. 1147	**Ava Gardner**
	23 Aug.	no. 1150	**Grace Kelly**

YEAR	MONTH	REF. No.	COVER STAR
	6 Sept.	no. 1152	**Maria Schell**
	27 Sept.	no. 1155	**James Dean**
	4 Oct.	no. 1156	**Françoise Arnoul**
	11 Oct.	no. 1157	**Pier Angeli**
	18 Oct.	no. 1158	**Martine Carol**
	25 Oct.	no. 1159	**Elizabeth Taylor**
	15 Nov.	no. 1162	**Gordon MacRae**
			Shirley Jones
	13 Dec.	no. 1166	**Gina Lollobrigida**
	20 Dec.	no. 1167	**Danielle Darrieux**
	27 Dec.	no. 1168	**Cyd Charisse**
1957	3 Jan.	no. 1169	**Anita Ekberg**
	10 Jan.	no. 1170	**Eddie Constantine**
			Zizi Jeanmaire
	24 Jan.	no. 1172	**Ava Gardner**
			Stewart Granger
			David Niven
	31 Jan.	no. 1173	**Nicole Maurey**
	7 Feb.	no. 1174	**Audrey Hepburn**
	14 Feb.	no. 1175	**James Dean**
	7 March	no. 1178	**Jayne Mansfield**
	21 March	no. 1180	**Kim Novak**
	28 March	no. 1181	**Gregory Peck**
			Lauren Bacall
	4 April	no. 1182	**Brigitte Bardot**
	11 April	no. 1183	**Marlon Brando**
			Machiko Kyo
	2 May	no. 1186	**Martine Carol**
	9 May	no. 1187	**Elizabeth Taylor**
	23 May	no. 1189	**Milko**
			Gina Lollobrigida
	20 June	no. 1193	**Anita Ekberg**
	11 July	no. 1196	**Diana Dors**
	18 July	no. 1197	**Pier Angeli**
	25 July	no. 1198	**Cyd Charisse**
	8 Aug.	no. 1200	**Leslie Caron**
	5 Sept.	no. 1204	**Marina Vlady**
	26 Sept.	no. 1207	**Michele Morgan**
	24 Oct.	no. 1211	**Elvis Presley**
	14 Nov.	no. 1214	**Vera Miles**
	21 Nov.	no. 1215	**Romy Schneider**
			Curt Jurgens
	12 Dec.	no. 1218	**Zizi Jeanmaire**
	19 Dec.	no. 1219	**Sophia Loren**
1958	27 Feb.	no. 1229	**Pier Angeli**
	6 March	no. 1230	**Charles Aznavour**
	27 March	no. 1233	**Dorothy Malone**
	17 April	no. 1236	**Mylene Demongeot**
	1 May	no. 1238	**Maria Schell**
	15 May	no. 1240	**Brigitte Bardot**
	12 June	no. 1244	**Kim Novak**
	19 June	no. 1245	**Sophia Loren**
	31 July	no. 1251	**Hildegarde Neff**
	7 Aug.	no. 1252	**Jayne Mansfield**
	21 Aug.	no. 1254	**Rita Moreno**
	28 Aug.	no. 1255	**Mylene Demongeot**

YEAR	MONTH	REF. No.	COVER STAR
	11 Sept.	no. 1257	**Yves Montand**
	23 Oct.	no. 1263	**Michele Morgan**
	13 Nov.	no. 1266	**Leslie Caron**
	20 Nov.	no. 1267	**Marina Vlady**
	27 Nov.	no. 1268	**Elvis Presley**
1959	22 Jan.	no. 1276	**Sophia Loren**
	26 Feb.	no. 1281	**Audrey Hepburn**
	19 March	no. 1284	**Maria Schell**
			Gary Cooper
	26 March	no. 1285	**Brigitte Bardot**
	16 April	no. 1288	**Michele Morgan**
	13 May	no. 1292	**Kim Novak**
	20 May	no. 1293	**Millie Perkins**
	9 June	no. 1296	**Tina Louise**
	14 July	no. 1301	**Mamie Van Doren**
	11 Aug.	no. 1305	**Jayne Mansfield**
	1 Sept.	no. 1308	**Claudia Cardinale**
	8 Sept.	no. 1309	**Cary Grant**
			Eva Marie Saint
	15 Sept.	no. 1310	**Anita Ekberg**
	13 Oct.	no. 1314	**Brigitte Bardot**
	20 Oct.	no. 1315	**Gina Lollobrigida**
	1 Dec.	no. 1321	**Mamie Van Doren**
1960	19 Jan.	no. 1328	**Brigitte Bardot**
	2 Feb.	no. 1330	**Gérard Philipe**
	23 Feb.	no. 1333	**Gina Lollobrigida**
			Frank Sinatra
	1 March	no. 1334	**Charlton Heston**
	8 March	no. 1335	**Danielle Darrieux**
	22 March	no. 1337	**Claudia Cardinale**
	12 April	no. 1340	**Brigitte Bardot**
	19 April	no. 1341	**Jean-Paul Belmondo**
	26 April	no. 1342	**Anita Ekberg**
	10 May	no. 1344	**Marilyn Monroe**
	24 May	no. 1346	**Sophia Loren**
	31 May	no. 1347	**Mylene Demongeot**
	7 June	no. 1348	**Tina Louise**
	14 June	no. 1349	**Janet Leigh**
	5 July	no. 1352	**Elke Sommer**
	12 July	no. 1353	**Brigitte Bardot**
	23 Aug.	no. 1359	**Sandra Dee**
	30 Aug.	no. 1360	**Gina Lollobrigida**
	21 Sept.	no. 1363	**Sophia Loren**
	8 Nov.	no. 1370	**Rita Gam**
	15 Nov.	no. 1371	**Gérard Philipe**
	6 Dec.	no. 1374	**Anita Ekberg**
	13 Dec.	no. 1375	**Sophia Loren**
	27 Dec.	no. 1377	**Jeanne Moreau**
1961	3 Jan.	no. 1378	**Jean Marais**
	10 Jan.	no. 1379	**Barbara Nichols**
	17 Jan.	no. 1380	**Horst Buchholz**
	7 Feb.	no. 1383	**Claudia Cardinale**
	21 Feb.	no. 1385	**Marilyn Monroe**
	7 March	no. 1387	**Elvis Presley**
	14 March	no. 1388	**Richard Burton**
			Angie Dickinson

YEAR	MONTH	REF. No.	COVER STAR
	28 March	no. 1390	**Brigitte Bardot**
	25 April	no. 1394	**Tina Louise**
	13 May	no. 1397	**Anthony Perkins**
	23 May	no. 1398	**Anita Ekberg**
	30 May	no. 1399	**Elke Sommer**
	6 June	no. 1400	**Brigitte Bardot**
	1 Aug.	no. 1408	**Natalie Wood**
			Robert Wagner
	5 Sept.	no. 1413	**Rock Hudson**
			Gina Lollobrigida
	12 Sept.	no. 1414	**Audrey Hepburn**
	19 Sept.	no. 1415	**Marlon Brando**
			Tarita
	26 Sept.	no. 1416	**Tina Louise**
	3 Oct.	no. 1417	**Brigitte Bardot**
	10 Oct.	no. 1418	**Elvis Presley**
	31 Oct.	no. 1421	**Claudia Cardinale**
	7 Nov.	no. 1422	**Jean Marais**
			Jeanne Crain
1962	9 Jan.	no. 1431	**Ava Gardner**
	30 Jan.	no. 1434	**Pat Boone**
	13 Feb.	no. 1436	**Elizabeth Taylor**
	20 Feb.	no. 1437	**Jane Fonda**
	13 March	no. 1440	**Kim Novak**
	20 March	no. 1441	**Anthony Perkins**
	3 April	no. 1443	**Claudia Cardinale**
	10 April	no. 1444	**Shirley Knight**
	17 April	no. 1445	**Anna Karina**
	1 May	no. 1447	**Anita Ekberg**
	22 May	no. 1450	**Elke Sommer**
	12 June	no. 1453	**Elvis Presley**
	26 June	no. 1455	**Anthony Perkins**
	3 July	no. 1456	**Jayne Mansfield**
	17 July	no. 1458	**Elizabeth Taylor**
	24 July	no. 1459	**Senta Berger**
	14 Aug.	no. 1462	**Marilyn Monroe**
	18 Sept.	no. 1467	**Brigitte Bardot**
	2 Oct.	no. 1469	**Sue Lyon**
	9 Oct.	no. 1470	**Marlon Brando**
			Tarita
	16 Oct.	no. 1471	**Sophia Loren**
	23 Oct.	no. 1472	**Anthony Perkins**
	6 Nov.	no. 1474	**Jane Fonda**
			Efrem Zimbalist Jr
	13 Nov.	no. 1475	**Julie Christie**
	25 Dec.	no. 1481	**Senta Berger**
1963	8 Jan.	no. 1483	**Elvis Presley**
			Stella Stevens
			Laurel Goodwin
			Beverley Englander

YEAR	MONTH	REF. No.	COVER STAR
	22 Jan.	no. 1485	**Roger Moore**
			Sherry Jackson
	26 Feb.	no. 1490	**Catherine Deneuve**
	5 March	no. 1491	**Brigitte Bardot**
	12 March	no. 1492	**Gina Lollobrigida**
			Stephen Boyd
	19 March	no. 1493	**Ann-Margret**
	26 March	no. 1494	**Anna Karina**
	23 April	no. 1498	**Stella Stevens**
	30 April	no. 1499	**Claudia Cardinale**
	7 May	no. 1500	**Brigitte Bardot**
	14 May	no. 1501	**Sophia Loren**
	18 June	no. 1506	**Natalie Wood**
1964	7 Jan.	no. 1535	**Romy Schneider**
	21 Jan.	no. 1537	**Senta Berger**
	28 Jan.	no. 1538	**Elvis Presley**
	17 March	no. 1545	**Brigitte Bardot**
	21 April	no. 1550	**Jean-Paul Belmondo**
	9 June	no. 1557	**Cliff Richard**
	30 June	no. 1560	**Sean Connery**
			Shirley Eaton
	7 July	no. 1561	**Elvis Presley**
	14 July	no. 1562	**Jeanne Moreau**
	11 Aug.	no. 1566	**Cliff Richard**
			Susan Hampshire
	15 Sept.	no. 1571	**Steve McQueen**
	22 Sept.	no. 1572	**Brigitte Bardot**
	13 Oct.	no. 1575	**Jean-Paul Belmondo**
	20 Oct.	no. 1576	**Jane Fonda**
	27 Oct.	no. 1577	**Elvis Presley**
			Ann-Margret
	10 Nov.	no. 1579	**Ursula Andress**
	24 Nov.	no. 1581	**Mylene Demongeot**
	29 Dec.	no. 1586	**Audrey Hepburn**
1965	12 Jan.	no. 1588	**Geraldine Chaplin**
	26 Jan.	no. 1590	**Jane Fonda**
	16 Feb.	no. 1593	**Shirley Eaton**
			Sean Connery
	23 Feb.	no. 1594	**Carroll Baker**
	2 March	no. 1595	**Pamela Tiffin**
	13 April	no. 1601	**Brigitte Bardot**
	20 April	no. 1602	**Petula Clark**
	11 May	no. 1605	**Ursula Andress**
	18 May	no. 1606	**Elsa Martinelli**
	25 May	no. 1607	**Ann-Margret**
	22 June	no. 1611	**Virna Lisi**

FANS' STAR LIBRARY 1958 – 60

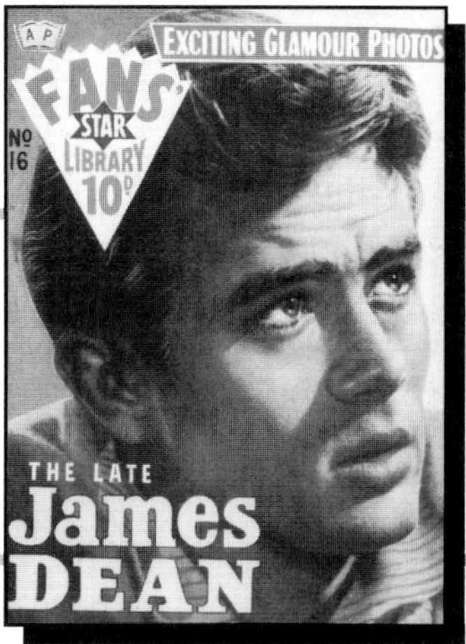

This British pocketsize magazine was printed and published on the third Monday in each month by Amalgamated Press Ltd. Each issue was devoted entirely to one star and was illustrated throughout. Although it ran for only 54 issues, it is today a very collectable magazine: Presley, Monroe, Dean numbers will fetch anything from £15 upwards per copy.

NO.	COVER STAR
1	Frankie Vaughan
2	Elvis Presley
3	Pat Boone
4	Dirk Bogarde
5	Perry Como
6	Rock Hudson
7	Frank Sinatra
8	Richard Todd
9	Harry Belafonte
10	Dale Robertson
11	Marlon Brando
12	Lonnie Donegan
13	Elvis in the army
14	Jeff Chandler
15	Doris Day
16	James Dean
17	Clint Walker

NO.	COVER STAR
18	Marilyn Monroe
19	Tony Curtis
20	Jeremy Spenser
21	Brigitte Bardot
22	Hugh O'Brian
23	Dennis Lotis
24	Debbie Reynolds
25	Tommy Steele
26	Mario Lanza
27	Ava Gardner
28	Cliff Richard
29	Sophia Loren
30	Robert Horton
31	John Saxon
32	Grace Kelly
33	Marty Wilde
34	David Whitfield
35	Elizabeth Taylor
36	Yul Brynner

NO.	COVER STAR
37	Tyrone Power
38	Janette Scott
39	Max Bygraves
40	Kim Novak
41	Dickie Valentine
42	Hardy Kruger
43	Jayne Mansfield
44	Kenneth More
45	Ricky Nelson
46	Alma Cogan
47	James Garner
48	Paul Anka
49	Connie Francis
50	Ronnie Hilton
51	Ty Hardin
52	Gina Lollobrigida
53	Audie Murphy
54	Everly Brothers

FILM FAVOURITE 1931 – 2

Although this British weekly film magazine ran for only 16 issues it is a significant collectable as it was the forerunner to *Film Pictorial*. Its early covers were devoted to artists' drawings illustrating a serialized story and a small picture inset of a film star. It was published by Amalgamated Press Ltd.

YEAR	MONTH	REF. No.	COVER STAR
1931	14 Nov.	Vol. 1, no. 1	**'From Factory Girl to Film Star'**
	21 Nov.	Vol. 1, no. 2	**'The Talkies Took Her From Him!'**
	28 Nov.	Vol. 1, no. 3	**'This Was Her Own Lost Child!'**
	5 Dec.	Vol. 1, no. 4	**'A Hundred Hearts At His Feet'**
	12 Dec.	Vol. 1, no. 5	**'Dead In His Dressing Room!'**
	19 Dec.	Vol. 1, no. 6	**'From Star To Starvation'**
	26 Dec.	Vol. 1, no. 7	**Adolphe Menjou Irene Dunne**

YEAR	MONTH	REF. No.	COVER STAR
1932	2 Jan	Vol. 1, no. 8	**Edmund Lowe Lois Moran**
	9 Jan.	Vol. 1, no. 9	**Ramon Novarro Carmel Myers**
	16 Jan.	Vol. 1, no. 10	**Barbara Stanwyck**
	23 Jan.	Vol. 1, no. 11	**Norma Shearer Clark Gable**
	30 Jan.	Vol. 1, no. 12	**Lawrence Tibbett Lupe Velez**
	6 Feb.	Vol. 1, no. 13	**James Cagney Joan Blondell Noel Francis**
	13 Feb.	Vol. 1, no. 14	**Rosalie Roy**
	20 Feb.	Vol. 1, no. 15	**Kay Francis Ricardo Cortez**
	27 Feb.	Vol. 1, no. 16	**Gary Cooper**

FILM PICTORIAL 1932 – 9

Printed entirely in photogravure, *Film Pictorial* was lavishly illustrated and offered the reader gossip pages, news of current and forthcoming films and titbits about the stars. It was a definite improvement on *Film Favourite*, with star back covers as well as front. With issue no. 99 came the first of many free supplements, 'The Private Life of Greta Garbo'. Special summer and Christmas issues contained superb black and white portraits of the most popular stars; regrettably the covers of these 'specials' were substandard. Sepia covers began to appear in 1937, issue no. 291. Until then the covers were black and white with a coloured background. In its last issues, nos 391 – 7, excellent sepia portraits with brief biographies appeared of Joan Blondell, Laurence Olivier, James Stewart, Norma Shearer, Mickey Rooney, Jeanette MacDonald, Fred Astaire. Rare cover subjects were Laurel and Hardy, no. 146, and George Formby, no. 366. *Film Pictorial* was edited by Clarence Winchester and published by Amalgamated Press Ltd. In October 1939 the title was incorporated with *Picture Show*.

YEAR	MONTH	REF. No.	COVER STAR
1932	27 Feb.	Vol. 1, no. 1	**Dorothy Lee**
	5 March	Vol. 1, no. 2	**Joan Marsh**
	12 March	Vol. 1, no. 3	**Anita Louise**
	19 March	Vol. 1, no. 4	**Nedra Norris**
	26 March	Vol. 1, no. 5	**Lupe Velez**
	2 April	Vol. 1, no. 6	**Astrid Allwyn**
	9 April	Vol. 1, no. 7	**Ronald Colman**
	16 April	Vol. 1, no. 8	**Joan Blondell**
	23 April	Vol. 1, no. 9	**Renée Gadd**
	30 April	Vol. 1, no. 10	**Mitzi Green**
	7 May	Vol. 1, no. 11	**Mary Brian**
	14 May	Vol. 1, no. 12	**Constance Bennett**
	21 May	Vol. 1, no. 13	**Nancy Carroll**
	28 May	Vol. 1, no. 14	**Marian Marsh**
	4 June	Vol. 1, no. 15	**Peggy Shannon**
	11 June	Vol. 1, no. 16	**Karen Morley**
	18 June	Vol. 1, no. 17	**Heather Angel**
	25 June	Vol. 1, no. 18	**Sally Eilers**
	2 July	Vol. 1, no. 19	**Frances Dee**
	9 July	Vol. 1, no. 20	**June Collyer**
	16 July	Vol. 1, no. 21	**Ann Dvorak**
	23 July	Vol. 1, no. 22	**Dorothy Bartlam**
	30 July	Vol. 1, no. 23	**Barbara Stanwyck**
	6 Aug.	Vol. 1, no. 24	**Norma Shearer**
	13 Aug.	Vol. 1, no. 25	**Belle Chrystall**
	20 Aug.	Vol. 1, no. 26	**June Clyde**
	27 Aug.	Vol. 2, no. 27	**Ginger Rogers**
	3 Sept.	Vol. 2, no. 28	**Kay Francis**
	10 Sept.	Vol. 2, no. 29	**Ruth Chatterton**
	17 Sept.	Vol. 2, no. 30	**Loretta Young**
	24 Sept.	Vol. 2, no. 31	**Greta Garbo**
	1 Oct	Vol. 2, no. 32	**Sidney Fox**
	8 Oct.	Vol. 2, no. 33	**Bette Davis**
	15 Oct	Vol. 2, no. 34	**Gwili André**
	22 Oct	Vol. 2, no. 35	**Ramon Novarro**
	29 Oct.	Vol. 2, no. 36	**Claudette Colbert**
	5 Nov.	Vol. 2, no. 37	**Jeanette MacDonald**
	12 Nov.	Vol. 2, no. 38	**Molly Lamont**
	19 Nov.	Vol. 2, no. 39	**Jack Hulbert**
	26 Nov.	Vol. 2, no. 40	**Miriam Hopkins**
	3 Dec.	Vol. 2, no. 41	**Sari Maritza**
	10 Dec.	Vol. 2, no. 42	**Uncredited starlet**
	17 Dec.	Vol. 2, no. 43	**Gary Cooper**
	24 Dec.	Vol. 2, no. 44	**Joan Crawford**
	31 Dec.	Vol. 2, no. 45	**Adrienne Ames**

YEAR	MONTH	REF. No.	COVER STAR
1933	7 Jan.	Vol. 2, no. 46	**Elizabeth Allan**
	14 Jan.	Vol. 2, no. 47	**Dorothy Jordan**
	21 Jan.	Vol. 2, no. 48	**Helen Twelvetrees**
	28 Jan.	Vol. 2, no. 49	**Maureen O'Sullivan**
	4 Feb.	Vol. 2 no. 50	**Jean Harlow**
	11 Feb.	Vol. 2, no. 51	**Lilian Harvey**
	18 Feb.	Vol. 2, no. 52	**Gloria Stuart**
	25 Feb.	Vol. 3, no. 53	**Janet Gaynor**
	4 March	Vol. 3, no 54	**Norma Shearer**
	11 March	Vol. 3, no. 55	**Evalyn Knapp**
	18 March	Vol. 3, no. 56	**Benita Hume**
	25 March	Vol. 3, no. 57	**Irene Dunne**
	1 April	Vol. 3, no. 58	**Binnie Barnes**
	8 April	Vol. 3, no. 59	**Marie Dressler**
	15 April	Vol. 3, no. 60	**Jean Parker**
	22 April	Vol. 3, no. 61	**Sally Blane**
	29 April	Vol. 3, no. 62	**Madge Evans**
	6 May	Vol. 3, no. 63	**Wendy Barrie**
	13 May	Vol. 3, no. 64	**Zasu Pitts**
	20 May	Vol. 3, no. 65	**Marian Nixon**
	27 May	Vol. 3, no. 66	**Ann Harding**
	3 June	Vol. 3, no. 67	**Carole Lombard**
	10 June	Vol. 3, no. 68	**Nancy Carroll**
	17 June	Vol. 3, no. 69	**Jessie Matthews**
	24 June	Vol. 3, no. 70	**Bebe Daniels**
	1 July	Vol. 3, no. 71	**Mae Clarke**
	8 July	Vol. 3, no. 72	**Carol Goodner**
	15 July	Vol. 3, no. 73	**Greta Garbo**
	22 July	Vol. 3, no. 74	**Ida Lupino**
	29 July	Vol. 3, no. 75	**Myrna Loy**
	5 Aug.	Vol. 3, no. 76	**Constance Bennett**
	12 Aug.	Vol. 3, no. 77	**Betty Stockfield**
	19 Aug.	Vol. 3, no. 78	**Wynne Gibson**
	26 Aug.	Vol. 4, no. 79	**Clark Gable**
	2 Sept.	Vol. 4, no. 80	**Evelyn Laye**
	9 Sept.	Vol. 4, no. 81	**Fay Wray**
	16 Sept.	Vol. 4, no. 82	**Robert Montgomery**
	23 Sept.	Vol. 4, no. 83	**Elissa Landi**
	30 Sept.	Vol. 4, no. 84	**Leslie Howard**
	7 Oct.	Vol. 4, no. 85	**Diana Wynyard**
	14 Oct.	Vol. 4, no. 86	**Gracie Fields**
	21 Oct.	Vol. 4, no. 87	**Helen Hayes**
	28 Oct.	Vol. 4. no. 88	**Madeleine Carroll**
	4 Nov.	Vol. 4, no. 89	**Karen Morley**
	11 Nov.	Vol. 4, no. 90	**Frances Dee**
	18 Nov.	Vol. 4, no. 91	**Anna Neagle**
	25 Nov.	Vol. 4, no. 92	**Marion Davies**
	2 Dec.	Vol. 4, no. 93	**Sylvia Sidney**
	9 Dec.	Vol. 4, no. 94	**Uncredited child**
	16 Dec.	Vol. 4, no. 95	**Gwenllian Gill**
	23 Dec.	Vol. 4, no. 96	**Charlotte Henry**
	30 Dec.	Vol. 4, no. 97	**Florine McKinney**
1934	6 Jan.	Vol. 4, no. 98	**Miriam Hopkins**
	13 Jan.	Vol. 4, no. 99	**Greta Garbo**
	20 Jan.	Vol. 4, no. 100	**Robert Montgomery** **Helen Hayes**
	27 Jan.	Vol. 4, no. 101	**Benita Hume**
	3 Feb.	Vol. 4, no. 102	**Ronald Colman** **Elissa Landi**
	10 Feb.	Vol. 4, no. 103	**Jean Harlow**
	17 Feb.	Vol. 4, no. 104	**Heather Angel**
	24 Feb.	Vol. 5, no. 105	**Ben Lyon** **Claudette Colbert**
	3 March	Vol. 5, no. 106	**Gary Cooper** **Frances Fuller**
	10 March	Vol. 5, no. 107	**Maurice Chevalier** **Ann Dvorak**
	17 March	Vol. 5, no. 108	**Katharine Hepburn** **Douglas Fairbanks Jr**
	24 March	Vol. 5, no. 109	**Constance Bennett**
	31 March	Vol. 5, no. 110	**Una Merkel**
	7 April	Vol. 5, no. 111	**Judith Allen** **Bing Crosby**
	14 April	Vol. 5, no. 112	**Mae West**
	21 April	Vol. 5, no. 113	**Sally Blane**
	28 April	Vol. 5, no. 114	**Jessie Matthews**
	5 May	Vol. 5, no. 115	**Dorothea Wieck**
	12 May	Vol. 5, no. 116	**Katharine Hepburn**
	19 May	Vol. 5, no. 117	**Ramon Novarro** **Jeanette MacDonald**
	26 May	Vol. 5, no. 118	**Marion Davies**
	2 June	Vol. 5, no. 119	**Elizabeth Allan**
	9 June	Vol. 5, no. 120	**Ginger Rogers**
	16 June	Vol. 5, no. 121	**Miriam Hopkins**
	23 June	Vol. 5, no. 122	**Pat Paterson**
	30 June	Vol. 5, no. 123	**Genevieve Tobin**
	7 July	Vol. 5, no. 124	**Bette Davis**
	14 July	Vol. 5, no. 125	**Frances Dee**
	21 July	Vol. 5, no. 126	**Helen Twelvetrees**
	28 July	Vol. 5, no. 127	**Leila Hyams**
	Special summer extra		**Dorothy Jordan**
	4 Aug.	Vol. 5, no. 128	**Lola André**
	11 Aug.	Vol. 5, no. 129	**Jean Parker** **Robert Young**
	18 Aug.	Vol. 5, no. 130	**June Knight**
	25 Aug.	Vol. 6, no. 131	**Marian Marsh**
	1 Sept.	Vol. 6, no. 132	**Charles Farrell** **Janet Gaynor**
	8 Sept.	Vol. 6, no. 133	**Greta Garbo**
	15 Sept.	Vol. 6, no. 134	**Anna Sten**
	22 Sept.	Vol. 6, no. 135	**Shirley Temple**
	29 Sept.	Vol. 6, no. 136	**Sylvia Sidney**
	6 Oct.	Vol. 6, no. 137	**Clark Gable** **Claudette Colbert**
	13 Oct.	Vol. 6, no. 138	**Jean Muir**

YEAR	MONTH	REF. No.	COVER STAR
	20 Oct.	Vol. 6, no. 139	**Greta Garbo**
	27 Oct.	Vol. 6, no. 140	**Ramon Novarro**
	3 Nov.	Vol. 6, no. 141	**Elissa Landi**
	10 Nov.	Vol. 6, no. 142	**Betty Stockfield**
	17 Nov.	Vol. 6, no. 143,	**Jeanette MacDonald**
	24 Nov.	Vol. 6, no. 144	**Evelyn Laye**
	1 Dec.	Vol. 6, no. 145	**Loretta Young**
	8 Dec.	Vol. 6, no. 146	**Laurel and Hardy**
	15 Dec.	Vol. 6, no. 147	**Winifred Shotter**
	22 Dec.	Vol. 6, no. 148	**Janet Gaynor**
	29 Dec.	Vol. 6, no. 149	**Shirley Temple**
	Christmas extra		**Joan Blondell**
1935	5 Jan.	Vol. 6, no. 150	**Maureen O'Sullivan**
	12 Jan.	Vol. 6, no. 151	**Joan Crawford**
	19 Jan.	Vol. 6, no. 152	**Pert Kelton**
	26 Jan.	Vol. 6, no. 153	**Harold Lloyd**
	2 Feb.	Vol. 6, no. 154	**Jeanette MacDonald** **Maurice Chevalier**
	9 Feb.	Vol. 6, no. 155	**Madeleine Carroll**
	16 Feb.	Vol. 6, no. 156	**Dick Powell** **Ruby Keeler**
	23 Feb.	Vol. 7, no. 157	**Joan Blondell**
	2 March	Vol. 7, no. 158	**Jean Parker**
	9 March	Vol. 7, no. 159	**Shirley Temple** **Janet Gaynor**
	16 March	Vol. 7, no. 160	**Pat Paterson**
	23 March	Vol. 7, no. 161	**William Powell** **Myrna Loy**
	30 March	Vol. 7, no. 162	**Barbara Stanwyck**
	6 April	Vol. 7, no. 163	**Victoria Hopper**
	13 April	Vol. 7, no. 164	**Greta Garbo**
	20 April	Vol. 7, no. 165	**Norma Shearer**
	27 April	Vol. 7, no. 166	**Jessie Matthews**
	4 May	Vol. 7, no. 167	**Madeleine Carroll**
	11 May	Vol. 7, no. 168	**Elissa Landi**
	18 May	Vol. 7, no. 169	**Jean Harlow**
	25 May	Vol. 7, no. 170	**Joan Crawford**
	1 June	Vol. 7, no. 171	**Jeanette MacDonald**
	8 June	Vol. 7, no. 172	**Gary Cooper**
	15 June	Vol. 7, no. 173	**Myrna Loy**
	22 June	Vol. 7, no. 174	**Kay Francis**
	29 June	Vol. 7, no. 175	**Madge Evans**
	6 July	Vol. 7, no. 176	**Bette Davis**
	13 July	Vol. 7, no. 177	**Anna Lee**
	20 July	Vol. 7, no. 178	**Grace Moore**
	27 July	Vol. 7, no. 179	**Maureen O'Sullivan**
	Summer extra		**Wendy Barrie**
	3 Aug.	Vol. 7, no. 180	**Gracie Fields**
	10 Aug.	Vol. 7, no. 181	**Katharine Hepburn**
	17 Aug.	Vol. 7, no. 182	**Ruby Keeler**
	24 Aug.	Vol. 8, no. 183	**Virginia Bruce**
	31 Aug.	Vol. 8, no. 184	**Janet Gaynor**
	7 Sept.	Vol. 8, no. 185	**Shirley Temple**
	14 Sept.	Vol. 8, no. 186	**Barbara Stanwyck**
	21 Sept.	Vol. 8, no. 187	**Leslie Howard** **Merle Oberon**
	28 Sept.	Vol. 8, no. 188	**Adrienne Ames**
	5 Oct.	Vol. 8, no. 189	**Greta Garbo**
	12 Oct.	Vol. 8, no. 190	**Marlene Dietrich**
	19 Oct.	Vol. 8, no. 191	**Carole Lombard**
	26 Oct.	Vol. 8, no. 192	**Anna Neagle**
	2 Nov.	Vol. 8, no. 193	**Loretta Young**
	9 Nov.	Vol. 8, no. 194	**Ann Harding**
	16 Nov.	Vol. 8, no. 195	**Claudette Colbert**
	23 Nov.	Vol. 8, no. 196	**Fay Wray**
	30 Nov.	Vol. 8, no. 197	**Madge Evans**
	7 Dec.	Vol. 8, no. 198	**Joan Crawford**
	14 Dec.	Vol. 8, no. 199	**Heather Angel**
	21 Dec.	Vol. 8, no. 200	**Elizabeth Allan**
	28 Dec.	Vol. 8, no. 201	**Jessie Matthews**
	Christmas extra		**Iris Adrian**
1936	4 Jan.	Vol. 8, no. 202	**Lilian Harvey**
	11 Jan.	Vol. 8, no. 203	**Grace Moore** **Michael Bartlett**
	18 Jan.	Vol. 8, no. 204	**Robert Young**
	25 Jan.	Vol. 8, no. 205	**'Buddy' Rogers** **Mary Brian**
	1 Feb.	Vol. 8, no. 206	**Gary Cooper** **Ann Harding**
	8 Feb.	Vol. 8, no. 207	**Binnie Barnes**
	15 Feb.	Vol. 8, no. 208	**Marion Davies**
	22 Feb.	Vol. 9, no. 209	**Maureen O'Sullivan** **Norman Foster**
	29 Feb.	Vol. 9, no. 210	**Myrna Loy**
	7 March	Vol. 9, no. 211	**Multiple stars**
	14 March	Vol. 9, no. 212	**Charlie Chaplin**
	21 March	Vol. 9, no. 213	**Wendy Barrie**
	28 March	Vol. 9, no. 214	**Katharine Hepburn**
	4 April	Vol. 9, no. 215	**Claudette Colbert**
	11 April	Vol. 9, no. 216	**Ginger Rogers**
	18 April	Vol. 9, no. 217	**Margaret Sullavan**
	25 April	Vol. 9, no. 218	**Shirley Temple**
	2 May	Vol. 9, no. 219	**Eric Linden** **Cecilia Parker**
	9 May	Vol. 9, no. 220,	**Clark Gable** **Myrna Loy**
	16 May	Vol. 9, no. 221	**Mary Carlisle**
	23 May	Vol. 9, no. 222	**Robert Taylor**
	30 May	Vol. 9, no. 223	**Fred Astaire** **Ginger Rogers**
	6 June	Vol. 9, no. 224	**Franchot Tone** **Joan Crawford**
	13 June	Vol. 9, no. 225	**Claudette Colbert**
	20 June	Vol. 9, no. 226	**Cary Grant** **Joan Bennett**
	27 June	Vol. 9, no. 227	**Carole Lombard**

YEAR	MONTH	REF. No.	COVER STAR
	4 July	Vol. 9, no. 228	**Marlene Dietrich**
	11 July	Vol. 9, no. 229	**Ida Lupino**
			Francis Lederer
	18 July	Vol. 9, no. 230	**Katharine Hepburn**
	25 July	Vol. 9, no. 231	**Fred MacMurray**
	1 Aug.	Vol. 9, no. 232	**Shirley Temple**
	8 Aug.	Vol. 9, no. 233	**Ginger Rogers**
	15 Aug.	Vol. 9, no. 234	**Gary Cooper**
	22 Aug.	Vol. 10, no. 235	**Constance Cummings**
	29 Aug.	Vol. 10, no. 236	**Kay Francis**
	5 Sept.	Vol. 10, no. 237	**William Powell**
			Myrna Loy
	12 Sept.	Vol. 10, no. 238	**Fay Wray**
	19 Sept.	Vol. 10, no. 239	**Charles Laughton**
			Clark Gable
			Franchot Tone
	26 Sept.	Vol. 10, no. 240	**Sylvia Sidney**
	3 Oct.	Vol. 10, no. 241	**Nova Pilbeam**
	10 Oct.	Vol. 10, no. 242	**Gary Cooper**
			Madeleine Carroll
	17 Oct.	Vol. 10, no. 243	**Paulette Goddard**
	24 Oct.	Vol. 10, no. 244	**Merle Oberon**
	31 Oct.	Vol. 10, no. 245	**Ronald Colman**
			Claudette Colbert
	7 Nov.	Vol. 10, no. 246	**Dolores Costello**
			Freddie Bartholomew
	14 Nov.	Vol. 10, no. 247	**Robert Taylor**
			Loretta Young
	21 Nov.	Vol. 10, no. 248,	**Grace Moore**
			Franchot Tone
	28 Nov.	Vol. 10, no. 249	**Clark Gable**
			Joan Crawford
	5 Dec.	Vol. 10, no. 250	**Diana Napier**
			Richard Tauber
	12 Dec.	Vol. 10, no. 251	**Ann Harding**
	19 Dec.	Vol. 10, no. 252	**Marlene Dietrich**
	26 Dec.	Vol. 10, no. 253	**Fred Astaire**
			Ginger Rogers
1937	2 Jan.	Vol. 10, no. 254	**Olivia De Havilland**
			Errol Flynn
	9 Jan.	Vol. 10, no. 255	**Cicely Courtneidge**
			Jack Hulbert
	16 Jan.	Vol. 10, no. 256	**Vivien Leigh**
	23 Jan.	Vol. 10, no. 257	**Fred MacMurray**
			Gladys Swarthout
	30 Jan.	Vol. 10, no. 258	**Greta Garbo**
	6 Feb.	Vol. 10, no. 259	**Robert Montgomery**
			Madge Evans
	13 Feb.	Vol. 10, no. 260	**Robert Taylor**

YEAR	MONTH	REF. No.	COVER STAR
	20 Feb.	Vol. 11, no. 261	**Nelson Eddy**
			Jeanette MacDonald
	27 Feb.	Vol. 11, no. 262	**William Powell**
	6 March	Vol. 11, no. 263	**Bing Crosby**
	13 March	Vol. 11, no. 264	**Brian Aherne**
			Merle Oberon
	20 March	Vol. 11, no. 265	**Deanna Durbin**
	27 March	Vol. 11, no. 266	**Jessie Matthews**
	3 April	Vol. 11, no. 267	**Robert Taylor**
	10 April	Vol. 11, no. 268	**Jack Oakie**
	17 April	Vol. 11, no. 269	**Madeleine Carroll**
	24 April	Vol. 11, no. 270	**Margo**
	1 May	Vol. 11, no. 271	**Anna Neagle**
	8 May	Vol. 11, no. 272	**Robert Douglas**
	15 May	Vol. 11, no. 273	**Eleanor Whitney**
	22 May	Vol. 11, no. 274	**Nan Grey**
			Barbara Read
			Deanna Durbin
	29 May	Vol. 11, no. 275	**Anne Shirley**
	5 June	Vol. 11, no. 276	**Simone Simon**
			James Stewart
	12 June	Vol. 11, no. 277	**Gracie Fields**
	19 June	Vol. 11, no. 278	**Jeanette MacDonald**
	26 June	Vol. 11, no. 279	**Gary Cooper**
			Jean Arthur
	3 July	Vol. 11, no. 280	**Loretta Young**
	10 July	Vol. 11, no. 281	**Jessie Matthews**
	17 July	Vol. 11, no. 282	**Jean Parker**
	24 July	Vol. 11, no. 283	**Dick Powell**
			Joan Blondell
	31 July	Vol. 11, no. 284	**Shirley Temple**
	Special summer extra		**Madge Evans**
	7 Aug.	Vol. 11, no. 285	**Chester Morris**
			Helen Mack
	14 Aug.	Vol. 11, no. 286	**Henry Fonda**
			Annabella
	21 Aug.	Vol. 12, no. 287	**Arthur Tracy**
			Lilli Palmer
	28 Aug.	Vol. 12, no. 288	**Conrad Veidt**
	4 Sept.	Vol. 12, no. 289	**Errol Flynn**
			Olivia De Havilland
	11 Sept.	Vol. 12, no. 290	**Tyrone Power**
			Madeleine Carroll
	18 Sept.	Vol. 12, no. 291	**Anna Neagle**
	25 Sept.	Vol. 12, no. 292	**William Powell**
			Myrna Loy
	2 Oct.	Vol. 12, no. 293	**Cary Grant**
			Grace Moore
	9 Oct.	Vol. 12, no. 294	**Martha Raye**
			Bing Crosby
			Shirley Ross
	16 Oct.	Vol. 12, no. 295	**Ronald Colman**
			Jane Wyatt
	23 Oct.	Vol. 12, no. 296	**Elizabeth Allan**
			Warner Baxter

YEAR	MONTH	REF. No.	COVER STAR
	30 Oct.	Vol. 12, no. 297	**Nan Grey**
	6 Nov.	Vol. 12, no. 298	**Conrad Veidt**
			Annabella
	13 Nov.	Vol. 12, no. 299	**Joan Blondell**
	20 Nov.	Vol. 12, no. 300	**Maureen O'Sullivan**
	27 Nov.	Vol. 12, no. 301	**Greta Garbo**
	4 Dec.	Vol. 12, no. 302	**Jane Withers**
	11 Dec.	Vol. 12, no. 303	**Robert Young**
			Joan Crawford
			Franchot Tone
	18 Dec.	Vol. 12, no. 304	**Bing Crosby**
	25 Dec.	Vol. 12, no. 305	**Ann Rutherford**
			Priscilla Lawson
	Christmas extra		**Tyrone Power**
			Sonja Henie
1938	1 Jan.	Vol. 12, no. 306,	**Luise Rainer**
			Paul Muni
	8 Jan.	Vol. 12, no. 307	**Anna Neagle**
	15 Jan.	Vol. 12, no. 308	**Fredric March**
			Janet Gaynor
	22 Jan.	Vol. 12, no. 309	**Ann Todd**
			Clive Brook
	29 Jan.	Vol. 12, no. 310	**Nova Pilbeam**
	5 Feb.	Vol. 12, no. 311	**Allan Jones**
			Jeanette MacDonald
	12 Feb.	Vol. 12, no. 312	**Norma Shearer**
	19 Feb.	Vol. 13, no. 313	**Deanna Durbin**
	26 Feb.	Vol. 12, no. 314	**Frances Dee**
			Joel McCrea
	5 March	Vol. 13, no. 315	**Greta Garbo**
	12 March	Vol. 13, no. 316	**Ronald Colman**
			Madeleine Carroll
	19 March	Vol. 13, no. 317	**Adolphe Menjou**
			Ginger Rogers
			Katharine Hepburn
	26 March	Vol. 13, no. 318	**Cary Grant**
			Irene Dunne
	2 April	Vol. 13, no. 319	**David Niven**
			Annabella
	9 April	Vol. 13, no. 320	**Sabu**
	16 April	Vol. 13, no. 321	**Virginia Dale**
	23 April	Vol. 13, no. 322	**Tyrone Power**
			Norma Shearer
	30 April	Vol. 13, no. 323	**Tommy Kelly**
	7 May	Vol. 13, no. 324	**John Trent**
			Shirley Ross
			Edward Arnold
	14 May	Vol. 13, no. 325	**Kent Taylor**
	21 May	Vol. 13, no. 326	**Jean Parker**
	28 May	Vol. 13, no. 327	**Joan Fontaine**
			Nino Martini
	4 June	Vol. 13, no. 328	**Margaret Lockwood**

YEAR	MONTH	REF. No.	COVER STAR
	11 June	Vol. 13, no. 329	**Preston Foster**
			Kay Francis
	18 June	Vol. 13, no. 330	**Allan Jones**
	25 June	Vol. 13, no. 331	**Alice Faye**
	2 July	Vol. 13, no. 332	**Jean Gillie**
	9 July	Vol. 13, no. 333	**Dorothy Lamour**
	16 July	Vol. 13, no. 334	**Tim Holt**
			Louise Platt
	23 July	Vol. 13, no. 335	**Jane Withers**
	30 July	Vol. 13, no. 336	**Diana Churchill**
	Special summer extra		**Rochelle Hudson**
	6 Aug.	Vol. 13, no. 337	**Ann Miller**
	13 Aug.	Vol. 13, no. 338	**Clark Gable**
	20 Aug.	Vol. 14, no. 339	**Joan Blondell**
			Dick Powell
	27 Aug.	Vol. 14, no. 340	**Jessie Matthews**
	3 Sept.	Vol. 14, no. 341	**Robert Taylor**
	10 Sept.	Vol. 14, no. 342	**Richard Greene**
			Sonja Henie
	17 Sept.	Vol. 14, no. 343	***Snow White and the Seven Dwarfs***
	24 Sept.	Vol. 14, no. 344	**Corinne Luchaire**
	1 Oct.	Vol. 14, no. 345	**Cecilia Parker**
			Mickey Rooney
			Lewis Stone
			Fay Holden
	8 Oct.	Vol. 14, no. 346	**Fredric March**
			Virginia Bruce
	15 Oct.	Vol. 14, no. 347	**Anna Neagle**
			Anton Walbrook
	22 Oct.	Vol. 14, no. 348	**Valerie Hobson**
			Roger Livesey
	29 Oct.	Vol. 14, no. 349	**Gracie Fields**
	5 Nov.	Vol. 14, no. 350	**Virginia Bruce**
	12 Nov.	Vol. 14, no. 351	**Greta Garbo**
	19 Nov.	Vol. 14, no. 352	**Gary Cooper**
			Sigrid Gurie
	26 Nov.	Vol. 14, no. 353	**Loretta Young**
			Tyrone Power
	3 Dec.	Vol. 14, no. 354	**Jackie Cooper**
			Deanna Durbin
	10 Dec.	Vol. 14, no. 355	**Margaret Lockwood**
	17 Dec.	Vol. 14, no. 356	**Fred MacMurray**
			Ellen Drew
	24 Dec.	Vol. 14, no. 357	**Paulette Goddard**
			Janet Gaynor
			Douglas Fairbanks Jr.
	31 Dec.	Vol. 14, no. 358	**Errol Flynn**
	Christmas extra		**Irene Dare**
1939	7 Jan.	Vol. 14, no. 359	**Dick Powell**
			Priscilla Lane
	14 Jan.	Vol. 14, no. 360	**Joan Bennett**
	21 Jan.	Vol. 14, no. 361	**Danielle Darrieux**

YEAR	MONTH	REF. No.	COVER STAR
1939 *(cont.)*	28 Jan.	Vol. 14, no. 362	**Richard Greene**
			Nancy Kelly
	4 Feb.	Vol. 14, no. 363	**Spencer Tracy**
			Hedy Lamarr
	11 Feb.	Vol. 14, no. 364	**Katharine Hepburn**
			Cary Grant
	18 Feb.	Vol. 15, no. 365	**Sonja Henie**
	25 Feb.	Vol. 15, no. 366	**George Formby**
	4 March	Vol. 15, no. 367	**Victor McLaglen**
			Joan Fontaine
			Cary Grant
	11 March	Vol. 15, no. 368	**Fred MacMurray**
	18 March	Vol. 15, no. 369	**Adolphe Menjou**
	25 March	Vol. 15, no. 370	**Greer Garson**
			Robert Donat
	1 April	Vol. 15, no. 371	**Madge Evans**
			Preston Foster
	8 April	Vol. 15, no. 372	**Susan Hayward**
	15 April	Vol. 15, no. 373	**John Clements**
			June Duprez
	22 April	Vol. 15, no. 374	**Tyrone Power**
			Nancy Kelly
	29 April	Vol. 15, no. 375	**Nelson Eddy**
			Virginia Bruce
	6 May	Vol. 15, no. 376	**Joan Fontaine**
			Louis Hayward
	13 May	Vol. 15, no. 377	**Robert Taylor**
			Barbara Stanwyck
	20 May	Vol. 15, no. 378	**Paulette Goddard**

YEAR	MONTH	REF. No.	COVER STAR
	27 May	Vol. 15, no. 379	**Ellen Drew**
	3 June	Vol. 15, no. 380	**Ann Sheridan**
	10 June	Vol. 15, no. 381	**'Sandy' Henville**
	17 June	Vol. 15, no. 382	**Una Merkel**
	24 June	Vol. 15, no. 383	**Geraldine Fitzgerald**
	1 July	Vol. 15, no. 384	**Greer Garson**
	8 July	Vol. 15, no. 385	**Brian Aherne**
			June Lang
	15 July	Vol. 15, no. 386	**Claudette Colbert**
			Don Ameche
	22 July	Vol. 15, no. 387	**Susan Hayward**
	29 July	Vol. 15, no. 388	**Jane Wyman**
	5 Aug.	Vol. 15, no. 389	**Shirley Temple**
	12 Aug.	Vol. 15, no. 390	**Isa Miranda**
			Ray Milland
	19 Aug.	Vol. 16, no. 391	**Gracie Fields**
	26 Aug.	Vol. 16, no. 392	**Charles Boyer**
			Irene Dunne
	2 Sept.	Vol. 16, no. 393	**Joan Crawford**
			James Stewart
	9 Sept.	Vol. 16, no. 394	**Richard Greene**
			Wendy Barrie
	16 Sept.	Vol. 16, no. 395	**Douglas Fairbanks Jr**
			Joan Fontaine
	23 Sept.	Vol. 16, no. 396	**Claire Trevor**
			John Wayne
	30 Sept.	Vol. 16, no. 397	**Fred Astaire**
			Ginger Rogers

FILM REVIEW 1972 –

Originally published by Thorn EMI Screen Entertainment and edited by Norman H. Taylor, *Film Review* was a continuation of *ABC Film Review*. A larger format and multiple picture covers during the late seventies reflected the growing conversion of single screens into multiples. Covers crowded with teasers and smaller pictures appeared until January 1985, when, coinciding with British Film Year, in which the industry was pledged to a programme of renewal on an unprecedented scale, *Film Review* was relaunched and was available for the first time on bookstalls as well as in cinemas. Covers improved and the magazine was filled with displayable pictures: Cruise, Dillon, Basinger, Hauer, Schwarzenegger, Turner. The middle to late eighties has been the magazine's best period. When the Cannon Group took over EMI Cinemas in 1986 they inherited the magazine. Subsequent publishers have been Spotlight Publications Ltd and Orpheus. Editors: Peter Haigh, March 1975 to January 1986, and September 1987; John George, February 1986 to August 1987. From October 1987 it has been edited by David Aldridge. Erroneous volume numbers that appeared on issues December 1972 to February 1973 have been corrected.

YEAR	MONTH	REF. No.	COVER STAR
1972	May	Vol. 22, no. 5	**Malcolm McDowell**
	June	Vol. 22, no. 6	**Paul Newman**
	July	Vol. 22, no. 7	**Oliver Reed**
	Aug.	Vol. 22, no. 8	**Reg Varney**
			Janet Mahoney
	Sept.	Vol. 22, no. 9	**Marlon Brando**
	Oct.	Vol. 22, no. 10	**Clint Eastwood**
	Nov.	Vol. 22, no. 11	**Sophia Loren**
	Dec.	Vol. 22, no. 12	**Sarah Miles**
1973	Jan.	Vol. 23, no. 1	**Danny La Rue**
	Feb.	Vol. 23, no. 2	**Madeline Smith**
	March	Vol. 23, no. 3	**Steve McQueen**
	April	Vol. 23, no. 4	**Charles Bronson**
	May	Vol. 23, no. 5	**Michael J. York**
	June	Vol. 23, no. 6	**Peter Finch**
	July	Vol. 23, no. 7	**Victor Garber**
	Aug.	Vol. 23, no. 8	**Edward Fox**
	Sept.	Vol. 23, no. 9	**Roger Moore**
	Oct.	Vol. 23, no. 10	**James Coburn**
	Nov.	Vol. 23, no. 11	**Richard Beckinsale**
			Paula Wilcox
	Dec.	Vol. 23, no. 12	**Valerie Leon**

YEAR	MONTH	REF. No.	COVER STAR
1974	Jan.	Vol. 24, no. 1	**Cliff Richard**
			Debbie Watling
	Feb.	Vol. 24, no. 2	**Sid James**
			Margaret Nolan
			Valerie Leon
			Barbara Windsor
	March	Vol. 24, no. 3	**Robert Redford**
			Paul Newman
	April	Vol. 24, no. 4	**Oliver Reed**
			Frank Finlay
			Michael J. York
			Richard Chamberlain
	May	Vol. 24, no. 5	**Mia Farrow**
			Robert Redford
	June	Vol. 24, no. 6	**Steve McQueen**
	July	Vol. 24, no. 7	**Bruce Lee**
	Aug.	Vol. 24, no. 8	**Joseph Bottoms**
			Deborah Raffin
	Sept.	Vol. 24, no. 9	**Bruce Lee**
	Oct.	Vol. 24, no. 10	**Roger Moore**
			Susannah York
	Nov.	Vol. 24, no. 11	**David Essex**

YEAR	MONTH	REF. No.	COVER STAR
	Dec.	Vol. 24, no. 12	**Agneta Eckemyr**
1975	Jan.	Vol. 25, no. 1	**Paul Newman**
			Steve McQueen
	Feb.	Vol. 25, no. 2	**Roger Moore**
			Christopher Lee
	March	Vol. 25, no. 3	**Slade**
	April	Vol. 25, no. 4	**Charlton Heston**
	May	Vol. 25, no. 5	**Roger Daltrey**
	June	Vol. 25, no. 6	**Barbra Streisand**
	July	Vol. 25, no. 7	**Robert Redford**
	Aug.	Vol. 25, no. 8	**Clint Eastwood**
	Sept.	Vol. 25, no. 9	**Michael Caine**
	Oct.	Vol. 25, no. 10	**James Caan**
	Nov.	Vol. 25, no. 11	**Telly Savalas**
	Dec.	Vol. 25, no. 12	**Britt Ekland**
1976	Jan.	Vol. 26, no. 1	**Ryan O'Neal**
	Feb.	Vol. 26, no. 2	***Jaws***
	March	Vol. 26, no. 3	**Charles Bronson**
	April	Vol. 26, no. 4	**Burt Reynolds**
	May	Vol. 26, no. 5	**Robert Shaw**
	June	Vol. 26, no. 6	**Lee Marvin**
			Barbara Parkins
	July	Vol. 26, no. 7	**Robert Redford**
	Aug.	Vol. 26, no. 8	**Sean Connery**
			Audrey Hepburn
	Sept.	Vol. 26, no. 9	**Clint Eastwood**
	Oct.	Vol. 26, no. 10	**Robin Askwith**
	Nov.	Vol. 26, no. 11	**Michael York**
			Jenny Agutter
	Dec.	Vol. 26, no. 12	**Raquel Welch**
1977	Jan.	Vol. 27, no. 1	**Peter Sellers**
	Feb.	Vol. 27, no. 2	***King Kong***
	March	Vol. 27, no. 3	**Charlton Heston**
	April	Vol. 27, no. 4	**Gene Wilder**
			Jill Clayburgh
			Richard Pryor
			Scatman Crothers
	May	Vol. 27, no. 5	**Michael Caine**
	June	Vol. 27, no. 6	**Sylvester Stallone**
	July	Vol. 27, no. 7	**Kris Kristofferson**
	Aug.	Vol. 27, no. 8	**Roger Moore**
	Sept.	Vol. 27, no. 9	***Are You Being Served?***
	Oct.	Vol. 27, no. 10	**Liza Minnelli**
			Robert De Niro
	Nov.	Vol. 27, no. 11	**Peter Fonda**
	Dec.	Vol. 27, no. 12	**Nick Nolte**
1978	Jan.	Vol. 28, no. 1	**Clint Eastwood**
	Feb.	Vol. 28, no. 2	**See Threepio and Artoo Detoo**
	March	Vol. 28, no. 3	***The Choirboys***
	April	Vol. 28, no. 4	***Close Encounters of the Third Kind***
	May	Vol. 28, no. 5	***Sweeney 2***
	June	Vol. 28, no. 6	**Burt Reynolds**
			Kris Kristofferson
	July	Vol. 28, no. 7	**Bruce Lee**
	Aug.	Vol. 28, no. 8	**Peter Sellers**
	Sept.	Vol. 28, no. 9	**Kris Kristofferson**
	Oct.	Vol. 28, no. 10	**John Travolta**
			Olivia Newton-John
	Nov.	Vol. 28, no. 11	**Peter Ustinov**
	Dec.	Vol. 28, no. 12	**Robert Shaw**
			Harrison Ford
1979	Jan.	Vol. 29, no. 1	**Christopher Reeve**
	Feb.	Vol. 29, no. 2	**Christopher Reeve**
	March	Vol. 29, no. 3	**Robert De Niro**
	April	Vol. 29, no. 4	**Michael Caine**
			Maggie Smith
	May	Vol. 29, no. 5	**Richard Hatch**
			Dirk Benedict
	June	Vol. 29, no. 6	***The Warriors***
	July	Vol. 29, no. 7	**Lois Chiles**
			Roger Moore
	Aug.	Vol. 29, no. 8	***Arabian Adventure***
	Sept.	Vol. 29, no. 9	**Ryan O'Neal**
			Barbra Streisand
	Oct.	Vol. 29, no. 10	**Frank Langella**
	Nov.	Vol. 29, no. 11	***Airport 80 – The Concorde***
	Dec.	Vol. 29, no. 12	**Clint Eastwood**
1980	Jan.	Vol. 30, no. 1	***Star Trek – The Motion Picture***
	Feb.	Vol. 30, no. 2	**Clint Eastwood**
	March	Vol. 30, no. 3	**Dudley Moore**
			Bo Derek
	April	Vol. 30, no. 4	**Robert Redford**
	May	Vol. 30, no. 5	**Steve McQueen**
	June	Vol. 30, no. 6	**Harrison Ford**
			Carrie Fisher
	July	Vol. 30, no. 7	**Clint Eastwood**
	Aug.	Vol. 30, no. 8	***Can't Stop The Music***
	Sept.	Vol. 30, no. 9	**John Travolta**
	Oct.	Vol. 30, no. 10	**Robert Redford**
	Nov.	Vol. 30, no. 11	**Michael Beck**
			Olivia Newton-John
	Dec.	Vol. 30, no. 12	**Christopher Atkins**
			Brooke Shields
1981	Jan.	Vol. 31, no. 1	**Sam Jones**
			Melody Anderson
	Feb.	Vol. 31, no. 2	**Goldie Hawn**
	March	Vol. 31, no. 3	**Neil Diamond**
			Lucie Arnaz
	April	Vol. 31, no. 4	**Christopher Reeve**
	May	Vol. 31, no. 5	**Lily Tomlin**

YEAR	MONTH	REF. No.	COVER STAR
	June	Vol. 31, no. 6	**Roger Moore**
	July	Vol. 31, no. 7	**Harry Hamlin**
	Aug.	Vol. 31, no. 8	**Burt Reynolds**
			Farrah Fawcett
	Sept.	Vol. 31, no. 9	**Harrison Ford**
			Karen Allen
	Oct.	Vol. 31, no. 10	**Bo Derek**
			Miles O'Keefe
	Nov.	Vol. 31, no. 11	**Sylvester Stallone**
			Michael Caine
	Dec.	Vol. 31, no. 12	**John Travolta**
			Nancy Allen
1982	Jan.	Vol. 32, no. 1	**Ryan O'Neal**
	Feb.	Vol. 32, no. 2	**Paul Newman**
	March	Vol. 32, no. 3	**Peter Ustinov**
	April	Vol. 32, no. 4	**Jane Fonda**
	May	Vol. 32, no. 5	**Burt Reynolds**
			Rachel Ward
	June	Vol. 32, no. 6	**Sylvester Stallone**
	July	Vol. 32, no. 7	**De Forrest Kelley**
			Leonard Nimoy
			William Shatner
	Aug.	Vol. 32, no. 8	**Clint Eastwood**
	Sept.	Vol. 32, no. 9	**Lewis Collins**
	Oct.	Vol. 32, no. 10	**Sting**
	Nov.	Vol. 32, no. 11	**Michael Caine**
			Christopher Reeve
	Dec.	Vol. 32, no. 12	**Dolly Parton**
1983	Jan.	Vol. 33, no. 1	***E.T.***
	Feb.	Vol. 33, no. 2	**Sylvester Stallone**
	March	Vol. 33, no. 3	**Richard Gere**
			Debra Winger
	April	Vol. 33, no. 4	**Cannon and Ball**
	May	Vol. 33, no. 5	**Dustin Hoffman**
	June	Vol. 33, no. 6	**Mel Gibson**
	July	Vol. 33, no. 7	**Carrie Fisher**
			Mark Hamill
	Aug.	Vol. 33, no. 8	**Christopher Reeve**
	Sept.	Vol. 33, no. 9	**David Bowie**
	Oct.	Vol. 33, no. 10	**John Travolta**
	Nov.	Vol. 33, no. 11	**Richard Gere**
			Valerie Kaprisky
	Dec.	Vol. 33, no. 12	**Pia Zadora**
1984	Jan.	Vol. 34, no. 1	**Sean Connery**
			Barbara Carrera
	Feb.	Vol. 34, no. 2	**Clint Eastwood**
	March	Vol. 34, no. 3	**Al Pacino**
	April	Vol. 34, no. 4	**Debra Winger**
			Shirley MacLaine
	May	Vol. 34, no. 5	**Kevin Bacon**
			Lori Singer
	June	Vol. 34, no. 6	**Jacqueline Bisset**
	July	Vol. 34, no. 7	**Harrison Ford**
	Aug.	Vol. 34, no. 8	**Helen Slater**
	Sept.	Vol. 34, no. 9	**Michael Douglas**
			Kathleen Turner

YEAR	MONTH	REF. No.	COVER STAR
	Oct.	Vol. 34, no. 10	**Mel Gibson**
	Nov.	Vol. 34, no. 11	**Clint Eastwood**
	Dec.	Vol. 34, no. 12	**Paul McCartney**
1985	Jan.	Vol. 35, no. 1	**Sting**
	Feb.	Vol. 35, no. 2	**Arnold Schwarzenegger**
	March	Vol. 35, no. 3	**Burt Reynolds**
			Clint Eastwood
	April	Vol. 35, no. 4	***A Passage to India***
	May	Vol. 35, no. 5	**Richard Gere**
	June	Vol. 35, no. 6	**Tom Selleck**
			Cynthia Rhodes
	July	Vol. 35, no. 7	**Matthew Modine**
	Aug.	Vol. 35, no. 8	**Vanity**
	Sept.	Vol. 35, no. 9	**Sylvester Stallone**
	Oct.	Vol. 35, no. 10	**Mel Gibson**
	Nov.	Vol. 35, no. 11	**Meryl Streep**
	Dec.	Vol. 35, no. 12	**Michael J. Fox**
1986	Jan.	Vol. 36, no. 1	**Arnold Schwarzenegger**
	Feb.	Vol. 36, no. 2	**Sylvester Stallone**
	March	Vol. 36, no. 3	**Christopher Lambert**
	April	Vol. 36, no. 4	**David Bowie**
	May	Vol. 36, no. 5	**Rutger Hauer**
	June	Vol. 36, no. 6	**Matt Dillon**
	July	Vol. 36, no. 7	**Rob Lowe**
	Aug.	Vol. 36, no. 8	**Sylvester Stallone**
	Sept.	Vol. 36, no. 9	**Christopher Lambert**
	Oct.	Vol. 36, no. 10	**Tom Cruise**
	Nov.	Vol. 36, no. 11	**Rob Lowe**
	Dec.	Vol. 36, no. 12	**David Bowie**
1987	Jan.	Vol. 37, no. 1	**Arnold Schwarzenegger**
			Kathryn Harrold
	Feb.	Vol. 37, no. 2	**Matthew Broderick**
	March	Vol. 37, no. 3	**Tom Cruise**
	April	Vol. 37, no. 4	**Sylvester Stallone**
			Brigitte Nielsen
	May	Vol. 37, no. 5	**Kim Basinger**
	June	Vol. 37, no. 6	**Michael J. Fox**
	July/Aug.	Vol. 37, no. 7	**Mel Gibson**
	Sept.	Vol. 37, no. 8	**Matt Dillon**
	Oct.	Vol. 37, no. 9	**Madonna**
	Nov.	Vol. 37, no. 10	**Steve Martin**
	Dec.	Vol. 37, no. 11	**Sean Penn**
1988	Jan.	Vol. 38, no. 1	**Hollywood bargain tour offer**
	Feb.	Vol. 38, no. 2	**Joan Chen**
	March	Vol. 38, no. 3	**Michael J. Fox**
	April	Vol. 38, no. 4	**Tom Selleck**
			Ted Danson
			Steve Guttenberg

YEAR	MONTH	REF. No.	COVER STAR
	May	Vol. 38, no. 5	**Mickey Rourke**
	June	Vol. 38, no. 6	**Molly Ringwald**
	July	Vol. 38, no. 7	**Jon Cryer**
	Aug.	Vol. 38, no. 8	**Timothy Dalton**
	Sept.	Vol. 38, no. 9	**Humphrey Bogart**
	Oct.	Vol. 38, no. 10	**Steven Nico**
	Nov.	Vol. 38, no. 11	**Ricki Lake**
	Dec.	Vol. 38, no. 12	**Bob Hoskins and Roger Rabbit**
1989	Jan.	Vol. 39, no. 1	**Emilio Estevez**
	Feb.	Vol. 39, no. 2	**Jodie Foster**
			Kelly McGillis
	March	Vol. 39, no. 3	**Dennis Quaid**
			Glenn Close
			Mel Gibson
	April	Vol. 39, no. 4	**Sigourney Weaver**
	May	Vol. 39, no. 5	**Richard Gere**
	June	Vol. 39, no. 6	**Timothy Dalton**
	July	Vol. 39, no. 7	**Harrison Ford**
			Sean Connery
	Aug.	Vol. 39, no. 8	**Michael Keaton**
	Sept.	Vol. 39, no. 9	**Mel Gibson**
	Oct.	Vol. 39, no. 10	**Yahoo Serious**
	Nov.	Vol. 39, no. 11	**Dennis Quaid**
	Dec.	Vol. 39, no. 12	**Sigourney Weaver**
			Bill Murray
			Dan Aykroyd
			Harold Ramis
			Rick Moranis

FILM WEEKLY 1928 – 39

The first seven issues, 3 September – 15 October 1928, bore little resemblance to the well-known film newspaper that was officially launched on Monday 22 October 1928 and these unillustrated four-paged bulletins offer little if any interest to today's collector.

In its official launching editorial, however, *Film Weekly* promised to 'supply the need of immediate information about films. It will be the first paper in the world to do so. It will be a newspaper for all those interested in films, in the improvement of films, in the better exhibition of films, in the personalities of the films'. At this time over 25 million people in Britain were paying over a million pounds a week to see films such as *The Jazz Singer*, starring Al Jolson, *Gosta Berling*, with Greta Garbo and *The Fleet's In*, with Clara Bow.

Film Weekly's cover consisted of a framed heading, with a sepia on white logo, beneath which appeared a sepia art photogravure of a popular film star. Full page art portraits appeared inside, as well as gossip pages, informative articles and film reviews. Souvenir supplements began to appear by 1930.

Nine covers, issues nos 307 – 15, were drawn by Canadian artist Grant MacDonald. The most collectable covers are those of the first eleven illustrated issues, which include a rare one of Louise Brooks, 17 December 1928. Another rarity is the cover of Al Jolson, 6 May 1929.

Film Weekly was published by English Newspapers Ltd until 1 November 1935, after which it was published by Odhams. Throughout its long run it was edited by Herbert Thompson. There were numerous errors in the numbering of volumes and issues, but these have been corrected in the following entries. From 23 September 1939 *Film Weekly* was incorporated with *Picturegoer*.

YEAR	MONTH	REF. No.	COVER STAR
1928	22 Oct.	Vol. 1, no. 1	**Clara Bow**
	29 Oct.	Vol. 1, no. 2	**Joan Crawford**
	5 Nov.	Vol. 1, no. 3	**Ronald Colman**
	12 Nov.	Vol. 1, no. 4	**Renée Adorée**
	19 Nov.	Vol. 1, no. 5	**Ramon Novarro**
	26 Nov.	Vol. 1, no. 6	**Colleen Moore**
	3 Dec.	Vol. 1, no. 7	**Leila Hyams**
	10 Dec.	Vol. 1, no. 8	**Lupe Velez**
	17 Dec.	Vol. 1, no. 9	**Louise Brooks**
	24 Dec.	Vol. 1, no. 10	**Norma Shearer**
	31 Dec.	Vol. 1, no. 11	**Billie Dove**
1929	7 Jan.	Vol. 1, no. 12	**Vilma Banky**
	14 Jan.	Vol. 1, no. 13	**Richard Dix**
	21 Jan.	Vol. 1, no. 14	**Chili Bouchier**
	28 Jan.	Vol. 1, no. 15	**Lois Moran**
	4 Feb.	Vol. 1, no. 16	**John Gilbert**
	11 Feb.	Vol. 1, no. 17	**Anna May Wong**
	18 Feb.	Vol. 1, no. 18	**Sue Carol**
	25 Feb.	Vol. 1, no. 19	**Raquel Torres**
	4 March	Vol. 1, no. 20	**Charles Farrell**
	11 March	Vol. 1, no. 21	**Estelle Brody**
	18 March	Vol. 1, no. 22	**Rod La Rocque**
	25 March	Vol. 1, no. 23	**Gertrude Olmstead**
	1 April	Vol. 1, no. 24	**Dolores Costello**
	8 April	Vol. 1, no. 25	**Ivor Novello**
	15 April	Vol. 1, no. 26	**Dorothy Sebastian**
	22 April	Vol. 1, no. 27	**'Sonny Boy' David Lee**
	29 April	Vol. 1, no. 28	**Emil Jannings**
	6 May	Vol. 1, no. 29	**Al Jolson**
	13 May	Vol. 1, no. 30	**Marion Davies**
	20 May	Vol. 1, no. 31	**Carl Brisson**
	27 May	Vol. 1, no. 32	**Clive Brook**
	3 June	Vol. 1, no. 33	**Joseph Schildkraut**
	10 June	Vol. 1, no. 34	**John Stuart**
	17 June	Vol. 1, no. 35	**Esther Ralston**
	24 June	Vol. 1, no. 36	**Janet Gaynor**
	1 July	Vol. 1, no. 37	**Douglas Fairbanks Sr**
	8 July	Vol. 1, no. 38	**Olive Borden**
	15 July	Vol. 1, no. 39	**Charlie Chaplin**
	22 July	Vol. 1, no. 40	**Madeleine Carroll**
	29 July	Vol. 2, no. 41	**Laura La Plante**
	5 Aug.	Vol. 2, no. 42	**Ronald Colman**
	12 Aug.	Vol. 2, no. 43	**Betty Balfour**
	19 Aug.	Vol. 2, no. 44	**Warwick Ward**
	26 Aug.	Vol. 2, no. 45	**Evelyn Brent**
	2 Sept.	Vol. 2, no. 46	**Bessie Love**
	9 Sept.	Vol. 2, no. 47	**Marguerite Allen**
	16 Sept.	Vol. 2, no. 48	**Fay Wray**
	23 Sept.	Vol. 2, no. 49	**William Powell**
	30 Sept.	Vol. 2, no. 50	**Greta Garbo**
	7 Oct.	Vol. 2, no. 51	**Victor McLaglen**
	14 Oct.	Vol. 2, no. 52	**Maurice Chevalier**

YEAR	MONTH	REF. No.	COVER STAR
	21 Oct.	Vol. 2, no. 53	**Nancy Carroll**
	28 Oct.	Vol. 2, no. 54	**Betty Compson**
	4 Nov.	Vol. 2, no. 55	**Joan Crawford**
	11 Nov.	Vol. 2, no. 56	**Charles Farrell**
	18 Nov.	Vol. 2, no. 57	**Norma Shearer**
	25 Nov.	Vol. 2, no. 58	**Dolores Costello**
	2 Dec.	Vol. 2, no. 59	**Merna Kennedy**
	9 Dec.	Vol. 2, no. 60	**Bebe Daniels**
	16 Dec.	Vol. 2, no. 61	**Mary Brian**
	23 Dec.	Vol. 2, no. 62	**Marian Nixon**
	30 Dec.	Vol. 2, no. 63	**Francis Lee Jerry McGrath**
1930	4 Jan.	Vol. 3, no. 64	**Barbara Kent**
	11 Jan.	Vol. 3, no. 65	**Jameson Thomas**
	18 Jan.	Vol. 3, no. 66	**Ronald Colman**
	25 Jan.	Vol. 3, no. 67	**Sue Carol**
	1 Feb.	Vol. 3, no. 68	**Charles 'Buddy' Rogers**
	8 Feb.	Vol. 3, no. 69	**Marion Davies**
	15 Feb.	Vol. 3, no. 70	**Dorothy Mackaill**
	22 Feb.	Vol. 3, no. 71	**Georges Carpentier**
	1 March	Vol. 3, no. 72	**Joan Bennett**
	8 March	Vol. 3, no. 73	**Ramon Novarro**
	15 March	Vol. 3, no. 74	**Alice White**
	22 March	Vol. 3, no. 75	**Warner Baxter**
	29 March	Vol. 3, no. 76	**Gary Cooper**
	5 April	Vol. 3, no. 77	**Norma Talmadge**
	12 April	Vol. 3, no. 78	**John Longden**
	19 April	Vol. 3, no. 79	**Norma Shearer**
	26 April	Vol. 3, no. 80	**Greta Garbo**
	3 May	Vol. 3, no. 81	**Carl Brisson**
	10 May	Vol. 3, no. 82	**Mary Brian**
	17 May	Vol. 3, no. 83	**Dennis King**
	24 May	Vol. 3, no. 84	**Lawrence Tibbett**
	31 May	Vol. 3, no. 85	**Jeanette MacDonald**
	7 June	Vol. 3, no. 86	**Lupe Velez**
	14 June	Vol. 3, no. 87	**Richard Dix**
	21 June	Vol. 3, no. 88	**Lila Lee**
	28 June	Vol. 3, no. 89	**Gary Cooper**
	5 July	Vol. 4, no. 90	**Billie Dove**
	12 July	Vol. 4, no. 91	**Greta Garbo**
	19 July	Vol. 4, no. 92	**Nancy Carroll**
	26 July	Vol. 4, no. 93	**Jeanette MacDonald**
	2 Aug.	Vol. 4, no. 94	**Ronald Colman**
	9 Aug.	Vol. 4, no. 95	**Norma Shearer**
	16 Aug.	Vol. 4, no. 96	**Merna Kennedy**
	23 Aug.	Vol. 4, no. 97	**Maurice Chevalier**
	30 Aug.	Vol. 4, no. 98	**Stewart Rome**
	6 Sept.	Vol. 4, no. 99	**Janet Gaynor**
	13 Sept.	Vol. 4, no. 100	**Helen Twelvetrees**
	20 Sept.	Vol. 4, no. 101	**Madeleine Carroll**
	27 Sept.	Vol. 4, no. 102	**Loretta Young**
	4 Oct.	Vol. 4, no. 103	**Sue Carol**
	11 Oct.	Vol. 4, no. 104	**Maurice Chevalier**

YEAR	MONTH	REF. No.	COVER STAR
	18 Oct.	Vol. 4, no. 105	**Richard Arlen**
	25 Oct.	Vol. 4, no. 106	**Billie Dove**
	1 Nov.	Vol. 4, no. 107	**Anita Page**
	8 Nov.	Vol. 4, no. 108	**Dorothy Mackaill**
	15 Nov.	Vol. 4, no. 109	**Alice White**
	22 Nov.	Vol. 4, no. 110	**Clara Bow**
	29 Nov.	Vol. 4, no. 111	**Lupe Velez**
	6 Dec.	Vol. 4, no. 112	**Benita Hume**
	13 Dec.	Vol. 4, no. 113	**Sue Carol**
	20 Dec.	Vol. 4, no. 114	**Mitzi Green**
	27 Dec.	Vol. 4, no. 115	**Janet Gaynor**
1931	3 Jan.	Vol. 5, no. 116	**Mary Brian**
	10 Jan.	Vol. 5, no. 117	**Esther Ralston**
	17 Jan.	Vol. 5, no. 118	**Raquel Torres**
	24 Jan.	Vol. 5, no. 119	**Ann Harding**
	31 Jan.	Vol. 5, no. 120	**'Buddy' Rogers**
	7 Feb.	Vol. 5, no. 121	**Leila Hyams**
	14 Feb.	Vol. 5, no. 122	**Marlene Dietrich**
	21 Feb.	Vol. 5, no. 123	**Dorothy Sebastian**
	28 Feb.	Vol. 5, no. 124	**Nancy Carroll**
	7 March	Vol. 5, no. 125	**Gary Cooper**
	14 March	Vol. 5, no. 126	**Maurice Chevalier**
	21 March	Vol. 5, no. 127	**Greta Garbo**
	28 March	Vol. 5, no. 128	**Mary Brian**
	4 April	Vol. 5, no. 129	**Madeleine Carroll**
	11 April	Vol. 5, no. 130	**Ramon Novarro**
	18 April	Vol. 5, no. 131	**Jack Mulhall**
	25 April	Vol. 5, no. 132	**Helen Twelvetrees**
	2 May	Vol. 5, no. 133	**Kay Francis**
	9 May	Vol. 5, no. 134	**Norma Shearer**
	16 May	Vol. 5, no. 135	**Janet Gaynor**
	23 May	Vol. 5, no. 136	**Leila Hyams**
	30 May	Vol. 5, no. 137	**Juliette Compton**
	6 June	Vol. 5, no. 138	**Nancy Carroll**
	13 June	Vol. 5, no. 139	**Carole Lombard**
	20 June	Vol. 5, no. 140	**Lois Wilson**
	27 June	Vol. 5, no. 141	**Anita Page**
	4 July	Vol. 5, no. 142	**Edna Best**
	11 July	Vol. 5, no. 143	**Constance Bennett**
	18 July	Vol. 6, no. 144	**Eleanor Boardman**
	25 July	Vol. 6, no. 145	**Marion Davies**
	1 Aug.	Vol. 6, no. 146	**Loretta Young**
	8 Aug.	Vol. 6, no. 147	**Lupe Velez**
	15 Aug.	Vol. 6, no. 148	**Ruth Chatterton**
	22 Aug.	Vol. 6, no. 149	**Joan Crawford**
	29 Aug.	Vol. 6, no. 150	**Dorothy Mackaill**
	5 Sept.	Vol. 6, no. 151	**Jack Buchanan**
	12 Sept.	Vol. 6, no. 152	**Leila Hyams**
	19 Sept.	Vol. 6, no. 153	**Evelyn Brent**
	26 Sept.	Vol. 6, no. 154	**Dorothy Jordan**
	3 Oct.	Vol. 6, no. 155	**Mary Brian**
	10 Oct.	Vol. 6, no. 156	**Charles Farrell** **Janet Gaynor**

YEAR	MONTH	REF. No.	COVER STAR
	17 Oct.	Vol. 6, no. 157	**Edwina Booth**
	24 Oct.	Vol. 6, no. 158	**Frances Dee**
	31 Oct.	Vol. 6, no. 159	**Lupe Velez**
	7 Nov.	Vol. 6, no. 160	**Dorothy Bouchier** **Joseph Schildkraut**
	14 Nov.	Vol. 6, no. 161	**Richard Arlen** **Peggy Shannon**
	21 Nov.	Vol. 6, no. 162	**Greta Garbo** **Ramon Novarro**
	28 Nov.	Vol. 6, no. 163	**Paul Lukas** **Dorothy Jordan**
	5 Dec.	Vol. 6, no. 164	**Lew Ayres** **Anita Louise**
	12 Dec.	Vol. 6, no. 165	**Charles Rogers**
	19 Dec.	Vol. 6, no. 166	**Anita Page**
	26 Dec.	Vol. 6, no. 167	**Janet Gaynor**
1932	2 Jan.	Vol. 7, no. 168	**Anna May Wong**
	9 Jan.	Vol. 7, no. 169	**Lawrence Tibbett** **Lupe Velez**
	16 Jan.	Vol. 7, no. 170	**Dorothy Jordan**
	23 Jan.	Vol. 7, no. 171	**Loretta Young**
	30 Jan.	Vol. 7, no. 172	**Joan Crawford**
	6 Feb.	Vol. 7, no. 173	**Kay Francis**
	13 Feb.	Vol. 7, no. 174	**Robert Montgomery** **Madge Evans**
	20 Feb.	Vol. 7, no. 175	**Charles Farrell** **Janet Gaynor**
	27 Feb.	Vol. 7, no. 176	**Sari Maritza**
	5 March	Vol. 7, no. 177	**Madge Evans**
	12 March	Vol. 7, no. 178	**Sylvia Sidney**
	18 March	Vol. 7, no. 179	**Norma Shearer**
	25 March	Vol. 7, no. 180	**Ronald Colman** **Helen Hayes**
	1 April	Vol. 7, no. 181	**Maurice Chevalier**
	8 April	Vol. 7, no. 182	**Leila Hyams**
	15 April	Vol. 7, no. 183	**Fay Wray**
	22 April	Vol. 7, no. 184	**Sidney Fox**
	29 April	Vol. 7, no. 185	**Jack Buchanan**
	6 May	Vol. 7, no. 186	**Maurice Chevalier**
	13 May	Vol. 7, no. 187	**Dolores Del Rio**
	20 May	Vol. 7, no. 188	**Joan Marsh**
	27 May	Vol. 7, no. 189	**Miriam Hopkins**
	3 June	Vol. 7, no. 190	**Lillian Bond**
	10 June	Vol. 7, no. 191	**Karen Morley**
	17 June	Vol. 7, no. 192	**Frances Dee**
	24 June	Vol. 7, no. 193	**Molly Lamont** **Gene Gerrard**
	1 July	Vol. 8, no. 194	**Clive Brook**
	8 July	Vol. 8, no. 195	**Leila Hyams**
	15 July	Vol. 8, no. 196	**Miriam Hopkins**
	22 July	Vol. 8, no. 197	**Wynne Gibson**
	29 July	Vol. 8, no. 198	**Charles Farrell** **Janet Gaynor**
	5 Aug.	Vol. 8, no. 199	**Carole Lombard**
	12 Aug.	Vol. 8, no. 200	**Anna Neagle**

YEAR	MONTH	REF. No.	COVER STAR
	19 Aug.	Vol. 8, no. 201	**Joel McCrea Dolores Del Rio**
	26 Aug.	Vol. 8, no. 202	**Anita Page**
	2 Sept.	Vol. 8, no. 203	**Kay Francis**
	9 Sept.	Vol. 8, no. 204	**Tallulah Bankhead**
	16 Sept.	Vol. 8, no. 205	**Jean Harlow**
	23 Sept.	Vol. 8, no. 206	**Marian Marsh**
	30 Sept.	Vol. 8, no. 207	**Esther Ralston**
	7 Oct.	Vol. 8, no. 208	**Karen Morley**
	14 Oct.	Vol. 8, no. 209	**Dorothy Jordan**
	21 Oct.	Vol. 8, no. 210	**Ann Harding**
	28 Oct.	Vol. 8, no. 211	**Wendy Barrie**
	4 Nov.	Vol. 8, no. 212	**Frances Dee**
	11 Nov.	Vol. 8, no. 213	**Sari Maritza**
	18 Nov.	Vol. 8, no. 214	**Constance Bennett**
	25 Nov.	Vol. 8, no. 215	**Janet Gaynor**
	2 Dec.	Vol. 8, no. 216	**Joan Barry**
	9 Dec.	Vol. 8, no. 217	**Kay Francis**
	16 Dec.	Vol. 8, no. 218	**Frances Dee**
	23 Dec.	Vol. 8, no. 219	**Madge Evans**
	30 Dec.	Vol. 8, no. 220	**Douglas Fairbanks Sr**
1933	6 Jan.	Vol. 9, no. 221	**Dorothy Jordan**
	13 Jan.	Vol. 9, no. 222	**Kathleen Burke**
	20 Jan.	Vol. 9, no. 223	**Binnie Barnes**
	27 Jan.	Vol. 9, no. 224	**Janet Gaynor**
	3 Feb.	Vol. 9, no. 225	**Sari Maritza**
	10 Feb.	Vol. 9, no. 226	**Joel McCrea Constance Bennett**
	17 Feb.	Vol. 9, no. 227	**Lupe Velez**
	24 Feb.	Vol. 9, no. 228	**Ramon Novarro**
	3 March	Vol. 9, no. 229	**Kay Francis**
	10 March	Vol. 9, no. 230	**Wynne Gibson**
	17 March	Vol. 9, no. 231	**Joan Crawford**
	24 March	Vol. 9, no. 232	**Claudette Colbert**
	31 March	Vol. 9, no. 233	**Margot Grahame**
	7 April	Vol. 9, no. 234	**Clara Bow**
	14 April	Vol. 9, no. 235	**Norma Shearer**
	21 April	Vol. 9, no. 236	**Douglas Fairbanks Jr**
	28 April	Vol. 9, no. 237	**Kay Francis Herbert Marshall**
	5 May	Vol. 9, no. 238	**Greta Nissen**
	12 May	Vol. 9, no. 239	**Constance Cummings**
	19 May	Vol. 9, no. 240	**Carl Brisson**
	26 May	Vol. 9, no. 241	**Madeleine Carroll**
	2 June	Vol. 9, no. 242	**Benita Hume**
	9 June	Vol. 9, no. 243	**Jean Harlow**
	16 June	Vol. 9, no. 244	**Tala Birell**
	23 June	Vol. 9, no. 245	**Bebe Daniels**
	30 June	Vol. 9, no. 246	**Joan Blondell**
	7 July	Vol. 10, no. 247	**Lilian Harvey**
	14 July	Vol. 10, no. 248	**Thelma Todd**

YEAR	MONTH	REF. No.	COVER STAR
	21 July	Vol. 10, no. 249	**Maureen O'Sullivan**
	28 July	Vol. 10, no. 250	**Heather Angel**
	4 Aug.	Vol. 10, no. 251	**Frances Dee**
	11 Aug.	Vol. 10, no. 252	**Nancy Carroll**
	18 Aug.	Vol. 10, no. 253	**Elissa Landi**
	25 Aug.	Vol. 10, no. 254	**Anna Neagle**
	1 Sept.	Vol. 10, no. 255	**Ruby Keeler**
	8 Sept.	Vol. 10, no. 256	**Myrna Loy**
	15 Sept.	Vol. 10, no. 257	**Carole Lombard**
	22 Sept.	Vol. 10, no. 258	**Jessie Matthews**
	29 Sept.	Vol. 10, no. 259	**Kay Francis**
	6 Oct.	Vol. 10, no. 260	**Diana Wynyard**
	13 Oct.	Vol. 10, no. 261	**Sylvia Sidney**
	20 Oct.	Vol. 10, no. 262	**Janet Gaynor**
	27 Oct.	Vol. 10, no. 263	**Katharine Hepburn**
	3 Nov.	Vol. 10, no. 264	**Nancy Carroll**
	10 Nov.	Vol. 10, no. 265	**Ann Harding**
	17 Nov.	Vol. 10, no. 266	**Madeleine Carroll**
	24 Nov.	Vol. 10, no. 267	**Marion Davies**
	1 Dec.	Vol. 10, no. 268	**Greta Garbo**
	8 Dec.	Vol. 10, no. 269	**Irene Dunne**
	15 Dec.	Vol. 10, no. 270	**Bebe Daniels**
	22 Dec.	Vol. 10, no. 271	**Jean Harlow**
	29 Dec.	Vol. 10, no. 272	**Joan Blondell**
1934	5 Jan.	Vol. 11, no. 273	**Myrna Loy**
	12 Jan.	Vol. 11, no. 274	**Miriam Hopkins**
	19 Jan.	Vol. 11, no. 275	**Gloria Stuart**
	26 Jan.	Vol. 11, no. 276	**Maureen O'Sullivan**
	2 Feb.	Vol. 11, no. 277	**Jessie Matthews**
	9 Feb.	Vol. 11, no. 278	**Jack Buchanan**
	16 Feb.	Vol. 11, no. 279	**Merle Oberon**
	23 Feb.	Vol. 11, no. 280	**Claudette Colbert**
	2 March	Vol. 11, no. 281	**Robert Montgomery**
	9 March	Vol. 11, no. 282	**Barbara Stanwyck**
	16 March	Vol. 11, no. 283	**Katharine Hepburn**
	23 March	Vol. 11, no. 284	**Claire Trevor**
	30 March	Vol. 11, no. 285	**Jack Hulbert**
	6 April	Vol. 11, no. 286	**Heather Angel**
	13 April	Vol. 11, no. 287	**Mae West**
	20 April	Vol. 11, no. 288	**Sally Blane**
	27 April	Vol. 11, no. 289	**Jean Muir**
	4 May	Vol. 11, no. 290	**British film number: Ten small pictures**
	11 May	Vol. 11, no. 291	**Katharine Hepburn**
	18 May	Vol. 11, no. 292	**Margaret Sullavan**
	25 May	Vol. 11, no. 293	**Lilian Harvey**
	1 June	Vol. 11, no. 294	**Ruth Chatterton**
	8 June	Vol. 11, no. 295	**Joan Blondell**
	15 June	Vol. 11, no. 296	**Sari Maritza**
	22 June	Vol. 11, no. 297	**Paul Lukas**

YEAR	MONTH	REF. No.	COVER STAR
	29 June	Vol. 11, no. 298	**Genevieve Tobin**
	6 July	Vol. 12, no. 299	**Jean Parker**
	13 July	Vol. 12, no. 300	**Madge Evans**
	20 July	Vol. 12, no. 301	**Maureen O'Sullivan**
	27 July	Vol. 12, no. 302	**Robert Montgomery** **Elizabeth Allan**
	3 Aug.	Vol. 12, no. 303	**Ida Lupino**
	10 Aug.	Vol. 12, no. 304	**Adrienne Ames**
	17 Aug.	Vol. 12, no. 305	**Raquel Torres**
	24 Aug.	Vol. 12, no. 306	**Elizabeth Bergner**
	31 Aug.	Vol. 12, no. 307	**Greta Garbo**
	7 Sept.	Vol. 12, no. 308	**Marlene Dietrich**
	14 Sept.	Vol. 12, no. 309	**Anna Sten**
	21 Sept.	Vol. 12, no. 310	**Anna Neagle**
	28 Sept.	Vol. 12, no. 311	**Claudette Colbert**
	5 Oct.	Vol. 12, no. 312	**Anna May Wong**
	12 Oct.	Vol. 12, no. 313	**Irene Dunne**
	19 Oct.	Vol. 12, no. 314	**Loretta Young**
	26 Oct.	Vol. 12, no. 315	**Katharine Hepburn**
	2 Nov.	Vol. 12, no. 316	**Claudette Colbert**
	9 Nov.	Vol. 12, no. 317	**Elissa Landi**
	16 Nov.	Vol. 12, no. 318	**Ginger Rogers**
	23 Nov.	Vol. 12, no. 319	**Jean Harlow**
	30 Nov.	Vol. 12, no. 320	**Carole Lombard**
	7 Dec.	Vol. 12, no. 321	**Ten pictures of stars**
	14 Dec.	Vol. 12, no. 322	**Madge Evans**
	21 Dec.	Vol. 12, no. 323	**Jane Baxter**
	28 Dec.	Vol. 12, no. 324	**Norma Shearer**
1935	4 Jan.	Vol. 13, no. 325	**Maureen O'Sullivan**
	11 Jan.	Vol. 13, no. 326	**Dolores Del Rio**
	18 Jan.	Vol. 13, no. 327	**Anna Neagle**
	25 Jan.	Vol. 13, no. 328	**Jeanette MacDonald**
	1 Feb.	Vol. 13, no. 329	**Dolly Haas**
	8 Feb.	Vol. 13, no. 330	**Margaret Sullavan**
	15 Feb.	Vol. 13, no. 331	**Loretta Young**
	22 Feb.	Vol. 13, no. 332	**Wendy Barrie**
	1 March	Vol. 13, no. 333	**Merle Oberon**
	8 March	Vol. 13, no. 334	**Greta Garbo**
	15 March	Vol. 13, no. 335	**Pat Paterson**
	22 March	Vol. 13, no. 336	**Myrna Loy**
	29 March	Vol. 13, no. 337	**Barbara Stanwyck**
	5 April	Vol. 13, no. 338	**Collage of stars**
	12 April	Vol. 13, no. 339	**Miriam Hopkins**
	19 April	Vol. 13, no. 340	**Helen Chandler**
	26 April	Vol. 13, no. 341	**Warner Baxter** **Myrna Loy**
	3 May	Vol. 13, no. 342	**Ginger Rogers**
	10 May	Vol. 13, no. 343	**Binnie Barnes**
	17 May	Vol. 13, no. 344	**Sally Blane**
	24 May	Vol. 13, no. 345	**Helen Hayes**
	31 May	Vol. 13, no. 346	**Helen Vinson**
	7 June	Vol. 13, no. 347	**Gary Cooper** **Kathleen Burke**
	14 June	Vol. 13, no. 348	**Claudette Colbert**
	21 June	Vol. 13, no. 349	**Madge Evans**
	28 June	Vol. 13, no. 350	**Anne Shirley**
	5 July	Vol. 14, no. 351	**Bette Davis**
	12 July	Vol. 14, no. 352	**Carole Lombard**
	19 July	Vol. 14, no. 353	**Leila Hyams**
	26 July	Vol. 14, no. 354	**Arline Judge**
	2 Aug.	Vol. 14, no. 355	**Shirley Temple**
	9 Aug.	Vol. 14, no. 356	**Gertrude Lawrence** **Douglas Fairbanks Jr**
	16 Aug.	Vol. 14, no. 357	**Kay Francis** **Leslie Howard**
	23 Aug.	Vol. 14, no. 358	**Josephine Hutchinson**
	30 Aug.	Vol. 14, no. 359	**Janet Gaynor**
	6 Sept.	Vol. 14, no. 360	**Marlene Dietrich**
	13 Sept.	Vol. 14, no. 361	**Maureen O'Sullivan** **Frank Lawton**
	20 Sept.	Vol. 14, no. 362	**Merle Oberon**
	27 Sept.	Vol. 14, no. 363	**Jean Muir**
	4 Oct.	Vol. 14, no. 364	**Jeanette MacDonald** **Nelson Eddy**
	11 Oct.	Vol. 14, no. 365	**Gloria Stuart**
	18 Oct.	Vol. 14, no. 366	**Margaret Sullavan**
	25 Oct.	Vol. 14, no. 367	**Miriam Hopkins**
	1 Nov.	Vol. 14, no. 368	**Loretta Young**
	9 Nov.	Vol. 14, no. 369	**Jean Parker**
	16 Nov.	Vol. 14, no. 370	**Robert Montgomery** **Joan Crawford**
	23 Nov.	Vol. 14, no. 371	**Multitude of star pictures**
	30 Nov.	Vol. 14, no. 372	**Joan Bennett**
	7 Dec.	Vol. 14, no. 373	**Margot Grahame**
	14 Dec.	Vol. 14, no. 374	**Ida Lupino**
	21 Dec.	Vol. 14, no. 375	**Bette Davis**
	28 Dec.	Vol. 14, no. 376	**Jean Harlow**
1936	4 Jan.	Vol. 15, no. 377	**Greta Garbo**
	11 Jan.	Vol. 15, no. 378	**Luise Rainer**
	18 Jan.	Vol. 15, no. 379	**Virginia Bruce**
	25 Jan.	Vol. 15, no. 380	**George Brent**
	1 Feb.	Vol. 15, no. 381	**Jessie Matthews**
	8 Feb.	Vol. 15, no. 382	**Fred Astaire** **Ginger Rogers**
	15 Feb.	Vol. 15, no. 383	**Claudette Colbert**
	22 Feb.	Vol. 15, no. 384	**Maureen O'Sullivan**
	29 Feb.	Vol. 15, no. 385	**Sylvia Sidney**
	7 March	Vol. 15, no. 386	**Robert Donat** **Jean Parker**
	14 March	Vol. 15, no. 387	**Frances Dee**

YEAR	MONTH	REF. No.	COVER STAR
	21 March	Vol. 15, no. 388	**Eleanor Powell**
	28 March	Vol. 15, no. 389	**Joan Crawford**
	4 April	Vol. 15, no. 390	**Jean Harlow**
	11 April	Vol. 15, no. 391	**Ginger Rogers**
			George Brent
	18 April	Vol. 15, no. 392	**Walter Abel**
			Heather Angel
	25 April	Vol. 15, no. 393	**Claudette Colbert**
			Fred MacMurray
	2 May	Vol. 15, no. 394	**Anna Neagle**
	9 May	Vol. 15, no. 395	**Molly Lamont**
	16 May	Vol. 15, no. 396	**Jean Arthur**
			Herbert Marshall
	23 May	Vol. 15, no. 397	**Joan Blondell**
	30 May	Vol. 15, no. 398	**Ginger Rogers**
	6 June	Vol. 15, no. 399	**Virginia Bruce**
	13 June	Vol. 15, no. 400	**Maureen O'Sullivan**
			Eric Linden
	20 June	Vol. 15, no. 401	**Katharine Hepburn**
			Brian Aherne
	27 June	Vol. 15, no. 402	**James Stewart**
			Margaret Sullavan
	4 July	Vol. 16, no. 403	**Joan Bennett**
	11 July	Vol. 16, no. 404	**Rosalind Russell**
	18 July	Vol. 16, no. 405	**Jean Muir**
	25 July	Vol. 16, no. 406	**Madge Evans**
	1 Aug.	Vol. 16, no. 407	**Marlene Dietrich**
			Gary Cooper
	8 Aug.	Vol. 16, no. 408	**Loretta Young**
	15 Aug.	Vol. 16, no. 409	**Elissa Landi**
			Douglas Fairbanks Jr
	22 Aug.	Vol. 16, no. 410	**Nova Pilbeam**
			John Mills
	27 Aug.	Vol. 16, no. 411	**Wendy Barrie**
			James Stewart
	5 Sept.	Vol. 16, no. 412	**Anna Neagle**
	12 Sept.	Vol. 16, no. 413	**Clark Gable**
			Myrna Loy
	19 Sept.	Vol. 16, no. 414	**Franchot Tone**
			Movita
	26 Sept.	Vol. 16, no. 415	**Sylvia Sidney**
			Henry Fonda
	3 Oct.	Vol. 16, no. 416	**Ronald Colman**
	10 Oct.	Vol. 16, no. 417	**Janet Gaynor**
			Robert Taylor
	17 Oct.	Vol. 16, no. 418	**Merle Oberon**
	24 Oct.	Vol. 16, no. 419	**Robert Montgomery**
			Rosalind Russell
	31 Oct.	Vol. 16, no. 420	**William Powell**
			Jean Arthur
	7 Nov.	Vol. 16, no. 421	**Fred Astaire**
			Ginger Rogers
	14 Nov.	Vol. 16, no. 422	**Sylvia Sidney**
			Spencer Tracy

YEAR	MONTH	REF. No.	COVER STAR
	21 Nov.	Vol. 16, no. 423	**Kay Francis**
	28 Nov.	Vol. 16, no. 424	**Constance Cummings**
			Edmund Lowe
	Christmas extra		**Eleanor Powell**
	5 Dec.	Vol. 16, no. 425	**Joan Crawford**
	12 Dec.	Vol. 16, no. 426	**Olivia De Havilland**
	19 Dec.	Vol. 16, no. 427	**Jean Harlow**
	26 Dec.	Vol. 16, no. 428	**Myrna Loy**
			Warner Baxter
1937	2 Jan.	Vol. 17, no. 429	**Errol Flynn**
			Olivia De Havilland
	9 Jan.	Vol. 17, no. 430	**Clark Gable**
			Jeanette MacDonald
	16 Jan.	Vol. 17, no. 431	**Frances Farmer**
	23 Jan.	Vol. 17, no. 432	**Irene Dunne**
	30 Jan.	Vol. 17, no. 433	**Joan Crawford**
	6 Feb.	Vol. 17, no. 434	**Sylvia Sidney**
			John Loder
	13 Feb.	Vol. 17, no. 435	**Carole Lombard**
			William Powell
	20 Feb.	Vol. 17, no. 436	**Vivien Leigh**
	27 Feb.	Vol. 17, no. 437	**Luise Rainer**
	6 March	Vol. 17, no. 438	**Rosalind Russell**
			John Boles
	13 March	Vol. 17, no. 439	**Errol Flynn**
	20 March	Vol. 18, no. 440	**William Powell**
			Myrna Loy
	27 March	Vol. 18, no. 441	**Loretta Young**
	3 April	Vol. 18, no. 442	**Irene Dunne**
	10 April	Vol. 18, no. 443	**Merle Oberon**
			Brian Aherne
	17 April	Vol. 18, no. 444	**Miriam Hopkins**
	24 April	Vol. 18, no. 445	**Joan Crawford**
			Clark Gable
	1 May	Vol. 18, no. 446	**Sylvia Sidney**
	8 May	Vol. 18, no. 447	**Anna Neagle**
	15 May	Vol. 18, no. 448	**Ginger Rogers**
	22 May	Vol. 18, no. 449	**Barbara Stanwyck**
			Joel McCrea
	29 May	Vol. 18, no. 450	**James Stewart**
			Simone Simon
	5 June	Vol. 18, no. 451	**Sylvia Sidney**
			Henry Fonda
	12 June	Vol. 18, no. 452	**Lily Pons**
			Gene Raymond
	19 June	Vol. 18, no. 453	**Tyrone Power**
			Loretta Young
	26 June	Vol. 18, no. 454	**Jean Arthur**
			Gary Cooper
	3 July	Vol. 19, no. 455	**Merle Oberon**
	Summer extra		**Luise Rainer**
	10 July	Vol. 19, no. 456	**Edmund Lowe**
			Madge Evans

YEAR	MONTH	REF. No.	COVER STAR
	17 July	Vol. 19, no. 457	**Fred MacMurray** **Claudette Colbert**
	24 July	Vol. 19, no. 458	**Joan Blondell**
	31 July	Vol. 19, no. 459	**Shirley Temple**
	7 Aug	Vol. 19, no. 460	**Barbara Stanwyck**
	14 Aug.	Vol. 19, no. 461	**Claudette Colbert**
	21 Aug.	Vol. 19, no. 462	**Myrna Loy**
	28 Aug.	Vol. 19, no. 463	**Conrad Veidt** **Vivien Leigh**
	4 Sept.	Vol. 19, no. 464	**Greta Garbo** **Robert Taylor**
	11 Sept.	Vol. 19, no. 465	**Fredric March** **Janet Gaynor**
	18 Sept.	Vol. 19, no. 466	**John Loder** **Anna Lee**
	25 Sept.	Vol. 19, no. 467	**Carole Lombard** **Fred MacMurray**
	2 Oct.	Vol. 19, no. 468	**Sylvia Sidney** **Henry Fonda**
	9 Oct.	Vol. 19, no. 469	**William Powell** **Joan Crawford**
	16 Oct.	Vol. 19, no. 470	**Katharine Hepburn** **Franchot Tone**
	23 Oct.	Vol. 19, no. 471	**Warner Baxter** **Elizabeth Allan**
	30 Oct.	Vol. 19, no. 472	**Ronald Colman** **Madeleine Carroll**
	6 Nov.	Vol. 19, no. 473	**Sonja Henie** **Tyrone Power**
	13 Nov.	Vol. 19, no. 474	**Clark Gable** **Myrna Loy**
	20 Nov.	Vol. 19, no. 475	**Rex Harrison** **Vivien Leigh**
	27 Nov.	Vol. 19, no. 476	**Miriam Hopkins** **Joel McCrea**
	4 Dec.	Vol. 19, no. 477	**Tyrone Power** **Loretta Young**
	11 Dec.	Vol. 19, no. 478	**Sally Eilers** **James Dunn**
	18 Dec.	Vol. 19, no. 479	**Sophie Stewart** **Barry K. Barnes**
	Christmas extra		**Greta Garbo**
	25 Dec.	Vol. 19, no. 480	**Anna Neagle**
1938	1 Jan.	Vol. 20, no. 481	**Grace Moore** **Melvyn Douglas**
	8 Jan.	Vol. 20, no. 482	**Robert Donat**
	15 Jan.	Vol. 20, no. 483	**Ray Milland** **Jean Arthur**
	22 Jan.	Vol. 20, no. 484	**Irene Dunne** **Randolph Scott**
	29 Jan.	Vol. 20, no. 485	**Annabella**
	5 Feb.	Vol. 20, no. 486	**Sonja Henie**
	12 Feb.	Vol. 20, no. 487	**Gary Cooper**
	19 Feb.	Vol. 20, no. 488	**Olivia De Havilland**
	26 Feb.	Vol. 20, no. 489	**Warner Baxter** **Loretta Young**
	5 March	Vol. 20, no. 490	**Franchot Tone** **Joan Crawford**
	12 March	Vol. 20, no. 491	**Ronald Colman**
	19 March	Vol. 20, no. 492	**Ginger Rogers** **Katharine Hepburn**
	26 March	Vol. 20, no. 493	**Kay Francis**
	2 April	Vol. 20, no. 494	**Sylvia Sidney** **Joel McCrea**
	9 April	Vol. 20, no. 495	**Greta Garbo** **Charles Boyer**
	16 April	Vol. 20, no. 496	**Norma Shearer**
	23 April	Vol. 20, no. 497	**Nelson Eddy** **Eleanor Powell**
	30 April	Vol. 20, no. 498	**Gary Cooper** **Claudette Colbert**
	7 May	Vol. 20, no. 499	**Margaret Sullavan**
	14 May	Vol. 20, no. 500	**Ray Milland** **Frances Farmer**
	21 May	Vol. 20, no. 501	**Myrna Loy** **Spencer Tracy**
	28 May	Vol. 20, no. 502	**Frances Dee**
	4 June	Vol. 20, no. 503	**Joan Bennett**
	11 June	Vol. 20, no. 504	**Ginger Rogers**
	18 June	Vol. 20, no. 505	**Fred MacMurray** **Carole Lombard**
	25 June	Vol. 20, no. 506	**Robert Taylor** **Margaret Sullavan**
	2 July	Vol. 20, no. 507	**Barbara Stanwyck**
	9 July	Vol. 20, no. 508	**Loretta Young**
	Summer extra		**Norma Shearer**
	16 July	Vol. 20, no. 509	**Gary Cooper** **Merle Oberon**
	23 July	Vol. 20, no. 510	**Simone Simon**
	30 July	Vol. 20, no. 511	**Joel McCrea** **Andrea Leeds**
	6 Aug.	Vol. 20, no. 512	**Ginger Rogers** **Fred Astaire**
	13 Aug.	Vol. 20, no. 513	**Cary Grant** **Katharine Hepburn**
	20 Aug.	Vol. 20, no. 514	**John Beal** **Maureen O'Sullivan**
	27 Aug.	Vol. 20, no. 515	**Joan Crawford**
	3 Sept.	Vol. 20, no. 516	**Janet Gaynor**
	10 Sept.	Vol. 20, no. 517	**Jeanette MacDonald**
	17 Sept.	Vol. 20, no. 518	**Clark Gable** **Myrna Loy**
	24 Sept.	Vol. 20, no. 519	**Merle Oberon**
	1 Oct.	Vol. 20, no. 520	**Irene Dunne** **Douglas Fairbanks Jr**
	8 Oct.	Vol. 20, no. 521	**Tyrone Power** **Nancy Kelly**

YEAR	MONTH	REF. No.	COVER STAR
	15 Oct.	Vol. 20, no. 522	**Anna Neagle**
	22 Oct.	Vol. 20, no. 523	**Hedy Lamarr**
	29 Oct.	Vol. 20, no. 524	**Melvyn Douglas** **Joan Blondell**
	5 Nov.	Vol. 20, no. 525	**Andrea Leeds**
	12 Nov.	Vol. 20, no. 526	**Robert Taylor** **Florence Rice**
	19 Nov.	Vol. 20, no. 527	**Claire Trevor** **Edward G. Robinson**
	26 Nov.	Vol. 20, no. 528	**Ginger Rogers**
	3 Dec.	Vol. 20, no. 529	**Margaret Sullavan**
	Christmas extra		**Myrna Loy**
	10 Dec.	Vol. 20, no. 530	**Deanna Durbin**
	17 Dec.	Vol. 20, no. 531	**Barry K. Barnes** **Valerie Hobson**
	24 Dec.	Vol. 20, no. 532	**Merle Oberon** **Gary Cooper**
	31 Dec.	Vol. 20, no. 533	**Eleanor Powell**
1939	7 Jan.	Vol. 21, no. 534	**Franchot Tone** **Janet Gaynor**
	14 Jan.	Vol. 21, no. 535	**Joan Bennett** **Randolph Scott**
	21 Jan.	Vol. 21, no. 536	**Hedy Lamarr**
	28 Jan.	Vol. 21, no. 537	**Ginger Rogers** **Fred Astaire**
	4 Feb.	Vol. 21, no. 538	**Norma Shearer** **Tyrone Power**
	11 Feb.	Vol. 21, no. 539	**Priscilla Lane** **Wayne Morris**
	18 Feb.	Vol. 21, no. 540	**Ann Sheridan**
	25 Feb.	Vol. 21, no. 541	**Joan Crawford**
	4 March	Vol. 21, no. 542	**Rosalind Russell** **Robert Donat**
	11 March	Vol. 21, no. 543	**Claudette Colbert**
	18 March	Vol. 21, no. 544	**Olivia De Havilland**

YEAR	MONTH	REF. No.	COVER STAR
	25 March	Vol. 21, no. 545	**Madeleine Carroll**
	1 April	Vol. 21, no. 546	**Robert Taylor**
	8 April	Vol. 21, no. 547	**Norma Shearer** **Clark Gable**
	15 April	Vol. 21, no. 548	**Andrea Leeds**
	22 April	Vol. 21, no. 549	**Bette Davis**
	29 April	Vol. 21, no. 550	**Constance Bennett**
	6 May	Vol. 21, no. 551	**Irene Dunne**
	13 May	Vol. 21, no. 552	**Margaret Sullavan**
	20 May	Vol. 21, no. 553	**Hedy Lamarr**
	27 May	Vol. 21, no. 554	**Anne Shirley**
	3 June	Vol. 21, no. 555	**Tyrone Power** **Alice Faye**
	10 June	Vol. 21, no. 556	**Joan Blondell**
	17 June	Vol. 21, no. 557	**Joan Bennett**
	24 June	Vol. 21, no. 558	**Robert Young** **Eleanor Powell**
	1 July	Vol. 22, no. 559	**Sonja Henie**
	Summer extra		**Virginia Bruce**
	8 July	Vol. 22, no. 560	**Robert Montgomery** **Rosalind Russell**
	15 July	Vol. 22, no. 561	**Norma Shearer**
	22 July	Vol. 22, no. 562	**Alice Faye**
	29 July	Vol. 22, no. 563	**Margaret Lockwood**
	5 Aug.	Vol. 22, no. 564	**Patricia Ellis**
	12 Aug.	Vol. 22, no. 565	**Shirley Temple**
	19 Aug.	Vol. 22, no. 566	**Barbara Stanwyck**
	26 Aug.	Vol. 22, no. 567	**Olivia De Havilland** **Errol Flynn**
	2 Sept.	Vol. 22, no. 568	**Geraldine Fitzgerald**
	9 Sept.	Vol. 22, no. 569	**Norma Shearer**
	16 Sept.	Vol. 22, no. 570	**Priscilla Lane**

FILMS AND FILMING 1954 – 90

A British film monthly originally published by Hansom Books and edited by Peter Brinson, *Films and Filming* was designed for the more discerning middle-of-the-road filmgoer, and was at its best during its early days and up to the time of the last of its bordered covers (the Belmondo and Riva cover of March 1962). It is these first 90 issues, easily distinguishable by their coloured borders or logo banner, that are the most collectable, their covers always enticing the browser to buy and read the contents. Inside there was a still, personality, and film of the month, plenty of picture-spreads, reviews, articles on international films. Later it became bulkier, less readable, with sensation-seeking covers.

Collectors should note that *Films and Filming* ceased publication from July 1980 to September 1981. It restarted with issue no. 325, and used this numbering from then on. Peter G. Baker edited the magazine from November 1955 to September 1968. Succeeding editors were: Robin Bean, October 1968 to June 1980; Allan Eyles, October 1981 to January 1983; John Russell Taylor, February 1983 to September 1989; Richard James, October 1989 onwards. It was published by Brevet Publishing Ltd from October 1981 and by Orpheus Publications Ltd from June 1989. *Films and Filming* was incorporated with *Film Review* in April 1990.

YEAR	MONTH	REF. No.	COVER STAR
1954	Oct.	Vol. 1, no. 1	**Marlon Brando** **Eva Marie Saint**
	Nov.	Vol. 1, no. 2	**Gina Lollobrigida**
	Dec.	Vol. 1, no. 3	**Judy Garland**
1955	Jan.	Vol. 1, no. 4	**Robert Newton**
	Feb.	Vol. 1, no. 5	**Gregory Peck**
	March	Vol. 1, no. 6	**Jonathan Ashmore**
	April	Vol. 1, no. 7	**Laurence Olivier**
	May	Vol. 1, no. 8	**Richard Burton**
	June	Vol. 1, no. 9	**Katharine Hepburn**
	July	Vol. 1, no. 10	**Laurence Harvey** **Julie Harris**
	Aug.	Vol. 1, no. 11	**Vivien Leigh**
	Sept.	Vol. 1, no. 12	**Bette Davis**
	Oct.	Vol. 2, no. 1	**Gérard Philipe** **Danielle Darrieux**
	Nov.	Vol. 2, no. 2	**Anna Magnani** **Burt Lancaster**
	Dec.	Vol. 2, no. 3	**Danny Kaye**
1956	Jan.	Vol. 2, no. 4	**Jean Simmons** **Marlon Brando**
	Feb.	Vol. 2, no. 5	**Danielle Darrieux** **Richard Burton**
	March	Vol. 2, no. 6	**Robert Taylor** **Kay Kendall**
	April	Vol. 2, no. 7	**Anthony Steel** **Anna Maria Sandri**
	May	Vol. 2, no. 8	**Bette Davis**
	June	Vol. 2, no. 9	**Gregory Peck** **Jennifer Jones**
	July	Vol. 2, no. 10	**James Stewart**
	Aug.	Vol. 2, no. 11	**Yves Montand**
	Sept.	Vol. 2, no. 12	**Ava Gardner**
	Oct.	Vol. 3, no. 1	**Cecil B. De Mille**
	Nov.	Vol. 3, no. 2	**Audrey Hepburn** **Mel Ferrer**
	Dec.	Vol. 3, no. 3	**Carroll Baker**
1957	Jan.	Vol. 3, no. 4	**Dirk Bogarde** **Jon Whiteley**

YEAR	MONTH	REF. No.	COVER STAR
	Feb.	Vol. 3, no. 5	**Tyrone Power**
			Mai Zetterling
	March	Vol. 3, no. 6	**Marlon Brando**
			Machiko Kyo
	April	Vol. 3, no. 7	**Cary Grant**
			Sophia Loren
	May	Vol. 3, no. 8	**Harry Belafonte**
			Joan Fontaine
	June	Vol. 3, no. 9	**Deborah Kerr**
			John Kerr
	July	Vol. 3, no. 10	**Laurence Olivier**
			Marilyn Monroe
	Aug.	Vol. 3, no. 11	**Charlie Chaplin**
	Sept.	Vol. 3, no. 12	**Marla Landi**
	Oct.	Vol. 4, no. 1	**Don Murray**
			Eva Marie Saint
	Nov.	Vol. 4, no. 2	**Mitzi Gaynor**
			Gene Kelly
	Dec.	Vol. 4, no. 3	**Anthony Perkins**
			Silvano Mangano
1958	Jan.	Vol. 4, no. 4	**Jennifer Jones**
			Rock Hudson
	Feb.	Vol. 4, no. 5	**Dirk Bogarde**
	March	Vol. 4, no. 6	**Marlon Brando**
	April	Vol. 4, no. 7	**Yul Brynner**
			Maria Schell
	May	Vol. 4, no. 8	**Sophia Loren**
			Trevor Howard
	June	Vol. 4, no. 9	**Curt Jurgens**
			Danny Kaye
	July	Vol. 4, no. 10	**Shirley Booth**
	Aug.	Vol. 4, no. 11	**Gregory Peck**
			Charlton Heston
	Sept.	Vol. 4, no. 12	**Peter Finch**
			Audrey Hepburn
	Oct.	Vol. 5, no. 1	**Alf Kjellin**
			Mai Zetterling
	Nov.	Vol. 5, no. 2	**Rex Harrison**
			Kay Kendall
	Dec.	Vol. 5, no. 3	**Robert Donat**
			Ingrid Bergman
1959	Jan.	Vol. 5, no. 4	**Rosalind Russell**
	Feb.	Vol. 5, no. 5	**Bette Davis**
			Alec Guinness
	March	Vol. 5, no. 6	**James Cagney**
	April	Vol. 5, no. 7	**Anna Magnani**
			Giulietta Masina
	May	Vol. 5, no. 8	**Joanne Woodward**
			Yul Brynner
	June	Vol. 5, no. 9	**Marilyn Monroe**
			Jack Lemmon
			Tony Curtis
	July	Vol. 5, no. 10	**Fredric March**
			Kim Novak
	Aug.	Vol. 5, no. 11	**Leslie Caron**
			Henry Fonda
	Sept.	Vol. 5, no. 12	**Johnny Nash**
			Ellen Holly
	Oct.	Vol. 6 no. 1	**Noel Coward**
			Alec Guinness
	Nov.	Vol. 6, no. 2	**Gina Lollobrigida**
			Frank Sinatra
	Dec.	Vol. 6, no. 3	**Ava Gardner**
			Fred Astaire
1960	Jan.	Vol. 6, no. 4	**Albert Dekker**
			Montgomery Clift
	Feb.	Vol. 6, no. 5	**Eleanor Parker**
			George Hamilton
	March	Vol. 6, no. 6	**Bradford Dillman**
			Juliette Greco
			Orson Welles
	April	Vol. 6, no. 7	**Horst Buchholz**
	May	Vol. 6, no. 8	**Dean Stockwell**
			Trevor Howard
	June	Vol. 6, no. 9	**Spencer Tracy**
			Fredric March
	July	Vol. 6, no. 10	**Peter Finch**
	Aug.	Vol. 6, no. 11	**Anna Magnani**
			Marlon Brando
	Sept.	Vol. 6, no. 12	**Dirk Bogarde**
			Ava Gardner
	Oct.	Vol. 7, no. 1	**Alain Delon**
	Nov.	Vol. 7, no. 2	**Sophia Loren**
			Peter Sellers
	Dec.	Vol. 7, no. 3	**Laurence Harvey**
1961	Jan.	Vol. 7, no. 4	**Marcello Mastroianni**
			Anita Ekberg
	Feb.	Vol. 7, no. 5	**Troy Donahue**
			Claudette Colbert
	March	Vol. 7, no. 6	**Tatiana Samoilova**
	April	Vol. 7, no. 7	**Warren Beatty**
			Natalie Wood
	May	Vol. 7, no. 8	**Jill Haworth**
			Sal Mineo
	June	Vol. 7, no. 9	**Richard Widmark**
			Senta Berger
	July	Vol. 7, no. 10	**Horst Buchholz**
			Leslie Caron
	Aug.	Vol. 7, no. 11	**James Stewart**
	Sept.	Vol. 7, no. 12	**Hayley Mills**
			Alan Bates
	Oct.	Vol. 8, no. 1	**Audrey Hepburn**
			George Peppard
	Nov.	Vol. 8, no. 2	**Lucyna Winnicka**
	Dec.	Vol. 8, no. 3	**Richard Beymer**
			Terry-Thomas
1962	Jan.	Vol. 8, no. 4	**Spencer Tracy**
			Marlene Dietrich
	Feb.	Vol. 8, no. 5	**Shirley MacLaine**
			Edward G. Robinson
	March	Vol. 8, no. 6	**Jean-Paul Belmondo**
			Emmanuelle Riva

YEAR	MONTH	REF. No.	COVER STAR
	April	Vol. 8, no. 7	**Dirk Bogarde**
			Alec Guinness
	May	Vol. 8, no. 8	**Brigitte Bardot**
	June	Vol. 8, no. 9	**Richard Beymer**
			Michael J. Pollard
	July	Vol. 8, no. 10	**Melina Mercouri**
			Raf Vallone
	Aug.	Vol. 8, no. 11	**Dean Stockwell**
			Katharine Hepburn
	Sept.	Vol. 8, no. 12	**Patty Duke**
			Anne Bancroft
	Oct.	Vol. 9, no. 1	**Inga Swenson**
			Don Murray
			Walter Pidgeon
			Charles Laughton
	Nov.	Vol. 9, no. 2	**Horst Buchholz**
			J.S. Casshyap
	Dec.	Vol. 9, no. 3	**Marlon Brando**
			Trevor Howard
1963	Jan.	Vol. 9, no. 4	**Peter O'Toole**
	Feb.	Vol. 9, no. 5	**Joanne Woodward**
	March	Vol. 9, no. 6	**Judy Garland**
	April	Vol. 9, no. 7	**Bette Davis**
			Joan Crawford
	May	Vol. 9, no. 8	**Paul Newman**
			Melvyn Douglas
	June	Vol. 9, no. 9	**Burt Lancaster**
			Claudia Cardinale
			Alain Delon
	July	Vol. 9, no. 10	**Albert Finney**
	Aug.	Vol. 9, no. 11	**Shirley MacLaine**
	Sept.	Vol. 9, no. 12	**George Hamilton**
	Oct.	Vol. 10, no. 1	**Elizabeth Taylor**
			Richard Burton
	Nov.	Vol. 10, no. 2	**Jesse Pearson**
			Ann-Margret
	Dec.	Vol. 10, no. 3	**Anthony Perkins**
1964	Jan.	Vol. 10, no. 4	**Colin Campbell**
			Dudley Sutton
	Feb.	Vol. 10, no. 5	**Alain Delon**
	March	Vol. 10, no. 6	**Stephen Boyd**
			Christopher Plummer
	April	Vol. 10, no. 7	**Peter O'Toole**
			Richard Burton
	May	Vol. 10, no. 8	**John Marley**
			Stathis Giallelis
	June	Vol. 10, no. 9	**Burt Lancaster**
			Fredric March
	July	Vol. 10, no. 10	**Robert Mitchum**
			Shirley MacLaine
	Aug.	Vol. 10 no. 11	***Lord of the Flies***
	Sept.	Vol. 10, no. 12	**Anthony Quinn**
	Oct.	Vol. 11, no. 1	**Sophia Loren**
	Nov.	Vol. 11, no. 2	**George Peppard**
			Carroll Baker
	Dec.	Vol. 11, no. 3	**Burt Lancaster**
1965	Jan.	Vol. 11, no. 4	**Julie Andrews**
			Dick Van Dyke
	Feb.	Vol. 11, no. 5	**Alain Delon**
			Shirley MacLaine
	March	Vol. 11, no. 6	**Peter O'Toole**
	April	Vol. 11, no. 7	**Anthony Perkins**
	May	Vol. 11, no. 8	***The Party's Over***
	June	Vol. 11, no. 9	***The Hill***
	July	Vol. 11, no. 10	**Gert Frobe**
	Aug.	Vol. 11, no. 11	**Elvis Presley**
			Dave Clark
			Paul McCartney
			Ringo Starr
	Sept.	Vol. 11, no. 12	**Tony Curtis**
			Natalie Wood
			Jack Lemmon
	Oct.	Vol. 12, no. 1	**Sean Connery**
	Nov.	Vol. 12, no. 2	**Robert Redford**
	Dec.	Vol. 12, no. 3	**Stanley Baker**
			Susannah York
1966	Jan.	Vol. 12, no. 4	**Sacha Pitoeff**
	Feb.	Vol. 12, no. 5	**Tom Courtenay**
			Julie Christie
	March	Vol. 12, no. 6	**Brigitte Bardot**
			Jeanne Moreau
	April	Vol. 12, no. 7	**Monica Vitti**
	May	Vol. 12, no. 8	**Brandon De Wilde**
	June	Vol. 12, no. 9	**Horst Buchholz**
			Perette Pradier
	July	Vol. 12, no. 10	**Marcello Mastroianni**
			Pamela Tiffin
	Aug.	Vol. 12, no. 11	**Elvis Presley**
			Donna Butterworth
	Sept.	Vol. 12, no. 12	**Sophia Loren**
	Oct.	Vol. 13, no. 1	**Adam West**
			Burt Ward
	Nov.	Vol. 13, no. 2	**Michael Parks**
			Ulla Bergryd
	Dec.	Vol. 13, no. 3	**George Zelnik**
			Barbara Bryl
1967	Jan.	Vol. 13, no. 4	**Elizabeth Taylor**
			Richard Burton
			Peter O'Toole
			Tom Courtenay
	Feb.	Vol. 13, no. 5	**Alain Delon**
	March	Vol. 13, no. 6	**Vanessa Redgrave**
			David Hemmings
	April	Vol. 13, no. 7	**Small pictures of seven films**
	May	Vol. 13, no. 8	**Terence Cooper**
			Joanna Pettet
	June	Vol. 13, no. 9	**Paul Jones**
			Jean Shrimpton

YEAR	MONTH	REF. No.	COVER STAR
	July	Vol. 13, no. 10	**Albert Finney**
	Aug.	Vol. 13, no. 11	**Françoise Dorléac**
			Jacques Perrin
	Sept.	Vol. 13, no. 12	**Dean Stockwell**
	Oct.	Vol. 14, no. 1	**Faye Dunaway**
			Denver Pyle
			Warren Beatty
	Nov.	Vol. 14, no. 2	**Richard Burton**
	Dec.	Vol. 14, no. 3	**Shirley MacLaine**
			Christopher Jones
1968	Jan.	Vol. 14, no. 4	**Bette Davis**
	Feb.	Vol. 14, no. 5	**Carol White**
	March	Vol. 14, no. 6	**Leonard Whiting**
	April	Vol. 14, no. 7	**Michael Sarrazin**
			Jacqueline Bisset
	May	Vol. 14, no. 8	**David McBride**
			Marilyn Rickard
			Kathy Simmonds
			Judy Huxtable
			Esther Anderson
	June	Vol. 14, no. 9	**Udo Kier**
	July	Vol. 14, no. 10	**Alain Delon**
			Marianne Faithfull
	Aug.	Vol. 14, no. 11	**Marcello Mastroianni**
			Anna Karina
	Sept.	Vol. 14, no. 12	**Robin Phillips**
			Hal Frederick
	Oct.	Vol. 15, no. 1	**Patricia Gozzi**
			Julie Dassin
	Nov.	Vol. 15, no. 2	**Christopher Jones**
	Dec.	Vol. 15, no. 3	**Terence Stamp**
1969	Jan.	Vol. 15, no. 4	**Katharine Hepburn**
	Feb.	Vol. 15, no. 5	**Elizabeth Taylor**
			Mia Farrow
	March	Vol. 15, no. 6	**James Fox**
	April	Vol. 15, no. 7	**Michael J. Pollard**
			Oliver Reed
	May	Vol. 15, no. 8	**Linda Hayden**
			Derek Lamden
	June	Vol. 15, no. 9	**Victoria Vetri**
			Robin Hawdon
	July	Vol. 15, no. 10	**Susanne Von Sass**
			Udo Kier
	Aug.	Vol. 15, no. 11	**Jon Voight**
			Dustin Hoffman
	Sept.	Vol. 15, no. 12	**Rosemary Dexter**
			Giuliano Gemma
	Oct.	Vol. 16, no. 1	**Robert Redford**
			Paul Newman
	Nov.	Vol. 16, no. 2	**Hiram Keller**
			Hylette Adolphe
			Martin Potter
	Dec.	Vol. 16, no. 3	**Alan Bates**
			Oliver Reed
1970	Jan.	Vol. 16, no. 4	**Nathalie Delon**
			Susan Strasberg
	Feb.	Vol. 16, no. 5	**Christopher Jones**
	March	Vol. 16, no. 6	**Mark Frechette**
			Daria Halprin
	April	Vol. 16, no. 7	**Michael Sarrazin**
	May	Vol. 16, no. 8	**Peter McEnery**
			Beryl Reid
	June	Vol. 16, no. 9	**Alain Delon**
	July	Vol. 16, no. 10	**Roy Holder**
			Hywel Bennett
	Aug.	Vol. 16, no. 11	**Don Johnson**
			Richard Johnson
	Sept.	Vol. 16, no. 12	**Mark Frechette**
	Oct.	Vol. 17, no. 1	**Raquel Welch**
			Robert Herrien
	Nov.	Vol. 17, no. 2	***There Was A Crooked Man***
	Dec.	Vol. 17, no. 3	**Udo Kier**
1971	Jan.	Vol. 17, no. 4	**Multitude of stars**
	Feb.	Vol. 17, no. 5	**Stanley Glick**
	March	Vol. 17, no. 6	**Hywel Bennett**
			Christian Roberts
	April	Vol. 17, no. 7	**Joe Dallesandro**
	May	Vol. 17, no. 8	**Ryan O'Neal**
			William Holden
	June	Vol. 17, no. 9	**Jurgen Draegger**
			Terry Scott
			Kenneth Williams
	July	Vol. 17, no. 10	**Oliver Reed**
	Aug.	Vol. 17, no. 11	**Mick Jagger**
	Sept.	Vol. 17, no. 12	**Marianne Blomquist**
			Hartmut Becker
	Oct.	Vol. 18, no. 1	**Betty Grable**
	Nov.	Vol. 18, no. 2	**Elizabeth Taylor**
			Peter O'Toole
	Dec.	Vol. 18, no. 3	**Helmut Berger**
1972	Jan.	Vol. 18, no. 4	**Multitude of stars**
	Feb.	Vol. 18, no. 5	**Michael Bates**
			Malcolm McDowell
	March	Vol. 18, no. 6	**Zooey Hall**
	April	Vol. 18, no. 7	**Paul Newman**
	May	Vol. 18, no. 8	**Stephanie Beacham**
	June	Vol. 18, no. 9	**Susanna East**
			Ryan O'Neal
	July	Vol. 18, no. 10	**Steve McQueen**
	Aug.	Vol. 18, no. 11	**Joe Dallesandro**
			Sylvia Miles
	Sept.	Vol. 18, no. 12	**Talia Shire**
			Marlon Brando
	Oct.	Vol. 19, no. 1	**Scott Antony**
	Nov.	Vol. 19, no. 2	**Richard Chamberlain**
			Sarah Miles
	Dec.	Vol. 19, no. 3	**Ryan O'Neal**
1973	Jan.	Vol. 19, no. 4	**Michael Maien**
	Feb.	Vol. 19, no. 5	***Pink Narcissus***

YEAR	MONTH	REF. No.	COVER STAR
	March	Vol. 19, no. 6	**Maggie Smith**
	April	Vol. 19, no. 7	**Graham Faulkner**
	May	Vol. 19, no. 8	**Anthony Nicholls**
			Mona Washbourne
	June	Vol. 19, no. 9	**Alec Guinness**
	July	Vol. 19, no. 10	**Udo Kier**
	August	Vol. 19, no. 11	**Helmut Berger**
			John Moulder-Brown
	Sept.	Vol. 19, no. 12	**Charlotte Rampling**
	Oct.	Vol. 20, no. 1	**Bruce Lee**
	Nov.	Vol. 20, no. 2	***A Thousand and One Nights***
	Dec.	Vol. 20, no. 3	***The Tenderness of Wolves***
1974	Jan.	Vol. 20, no. 4	**Paul Newman**
			Robert Redford
	Feb.	Vol. 20, no. 5	**Warhol's *Dracula***
	March	Vol. 20, no. 6	**Sean Connery**
	April	Vol. 20, no. 7	**Various pictures**
	May	Vol. 20, no. 8	**Joseph Bottoms**
	June	Vol. 20, no. 9	**Maria A. Beluzzi**
	July	Vol. 20, no. 10	**Paul Nicholas**
	Aug.	Vol. 20, no. 11	**Nathalie Delon**
			Leigh Lawson
	Sept.	Vol. 20, no. 12	**James Dean**
			Martin Sheen
	Oct.	Vol. 21, no. 1	**Warren Beatty**
	Nov.	Vol. 21, no. 2	**Sean Bury**
			Anicée Alvina
	Dec.	Vol. 21, no. 3	**Roger Moore**
1975	Jan.	Vol. 21, no. 4	**Alan Price**
			Joan Collins
	Feb.	Vol. 21, no. 5	**Pierre Clementi**
			Britt Ekland
	March	Vol. 21, no. 6	**Roger Daltrey**
	April	Vol. 21, no. 7	**Peter Hinwood**
	May	Vol. 21, no. 8	**Britt Ekland**
			Malcolm McDowell
	June	Vol. 21, no. 9	***And Now My Love***
	July	Vol. 21, no. 10	**Maria Schneider**
			Jack Nicholson
	Aug.	Vol. 21, no. 11	**Liza Minnelli**
			Burt Reynolds
	Sept.	Vol. 21, no. 12	**Pasolini's *Salo***
	Oct.	Vol. 22, no. 1	**David Bowie**
	Nov.	Vol. 22, no. 2	**Paul Nicholas**
			Roger Daltrey
	Dec.	Vol. 22, no. 3	**Ryan O'Neal**
			Marisa Berenson
1976	Jan.	Vol. 22, no. 4	**Raquel Welch**
	Feb.	Vol. 22, no. 5	**Candy Clark**
			David Bowie
	March	Vol. 22, no. 6	**Jane Birkin**
			Patrick Dewaere
	April	Vol. 22, no. 7	**Alessio Orano**
			Ornella Muti
	May	Vol. 22, no. 8	**Donald Sutherland**
	June	Vol. 22, no. 9	**Marianne Morris**
			Anulka
			Karl Lanchbury
	July	Vol. 22, no. 10	***The First Nudie Musical***
	Aug.	Vol. 22, no. 11	**Robert De Niro and Gus (Won Ton Ton dog)**
	Sept.	Vol. 22, no. 12	***Per Le Antiche Scale***
	Oct.	Vol. 23, no. 1	**Michael York**
	Nov.	Vol. 23, no. 2	**Ken Hicks**
			Janusz Romanov
	Dec.	Vol. 23, no. 3	**Françoise Fabian**
1977	Jan.	Vol. 23, no. 4	**Renaud Verley**
	Feb.	Vol. 23, no. 5	**Peter Firth**
	March	Vol. 23, no. 6	**Beverly D'Angelo**
			Sylvia Miles
			Cristina Raines
	April	Vol. 23, no. 7	**Michael Berger**
			Laura Betti
	May	Vol. 23, no. 8	**Therese Ann Savoy**
			Lajos Balazsovits
	June	Vol. 23, no. 9	**Jackie Gleason**
	July	Vol. 23, no. 10	**Byron Stewart**
			Alan Arkin
	Aug.	Vol. 23, no. 11	**Artoo Detoo and See Threepio**
	Sept.	Vol. 23, no. 12	**Helmut Berger**
	Oct.	Vol. 24, no. 1	**Arnold Schwarze-negger**
	Nov.	Vol. 24, no. 2	**Rudolf Nureyev**
			Michelle Phillips
	Dec.	Vol. 24, no. 3	**Tommy Lewis**
1978	Jan.	Vol. 24, no. 4	**John Travolta**
	Feb.	Vol. 24, no. 5	**Mark Hamill**
			Andrew Manson
			Pat Astley
	March	Vol. 24, no. 6	**Adam Ant**
	April	Vol. 24, no. 7	**Oliver Tobias**
			Tania Rogers
	May	Vol. 24, no. 8	**Marin Denis**
			Christian De Wolf
	June	Vol. 24, no. 9	**Bud Cort**
	July	Vol. 24, no. 10	**John Travolta**
	Aug.	Vol. 24, no. 11	**Henry Winkler**
	Sept.	Vol. 24, no. 12	***Lemon Popsicle***
	Oct.	Vol. 25, no. 1	**Burt Reynolds**
			Jan-Michael Vincent
	Nov.	Vol. 25, no. 2	**Eric Roberts**
	Dec.	Vol. 25, no. 3	**Richard Gere**
1979	Jan.	Vol. 25 no. 4	**Bette Midler**
			Frederic Forrest
	Feb.	Vol. 25, no. 5	**Tom Berenger**

YEAR	MONTH	REF. No.	COVER STAR
	March	Vol. 25, no. 6	**William Katt**
			Tom Berenger
	April	Vol. 25, no. 7	**Michael Beck**
			Terry Michos
	May	Vol. 25, no. 8	**Ken Wahl**
	June	Vol. 25, no. 9	**Dean-Paul Martin**
	July	Vol. 25, no. 10	***Scum***
	Aug.	Vol. 25, no. 11	**Barbra Streisand**
			Ryan O'Neal
	Sept.	Vol. 25, no. 12	**Peter Falk**
	Oct.	Vol. 26, no. 1	**Village People**
	Nov.	Vol. 26, no. 2	**Dayton Ka'ne**
			Mia Farrow
	Dec.	Vol. 26, no. 3	**Davil Marshall Grant**
			Valerie Quennessen
			Miles Chapin
1980	Jan.	Vol. 26, no. 4	**Leland Palmer**
	Feb.	Vol. 26, no. 5	**Hazel O'Connor**
	March	Vol. 26, no. 6	**Eddie Kidd**
	April	Vol. 26, no. 7	**George De La Pena**
			Alan Bates
	May	Vol. 26, no. 8	**Gene Ray**
	June	Vol. 26, no. 9	**Georgina Hale**
			Roger Daltrey
1981	Oct.	Vol. 28, no. 325	**Meryl Streep**
	Nov.	Vol. 28, no. 326	**John Travolta**
	Dec.	Vol. 28, no. 327	**Kate Nelligan**
1982	Jan.	Vol. 28, no. 328	**William Hurt**
	Feb.	Vol. 28, no. 329	**Elizabeth McGovern**
	March	Vol. 28, no. 330	**Warren Beatty**
	April	Vol. 28, no. 331	***Sharky's Machine***
	May	Vol. 28, no. 332	**Jack Lemmon**
			Sissy Spacek
	June	Vol. 28, no. 333	**Graham Crowden**
	July	Vol. 28, no. 334	**Susan Clark**
	Aug.	Vol. 28, no. 335	**Rialto Cinema, Coventry Street**
	Sept.	Vol. 28, no. 336	**Bugs Bunny**
	Oct.	Vol. 29, no. 337	***Tron***
	Nov.	Vol. 29, no. 338	**Janet Suzman**
	Dec.	Vol. 29, no. 339	**Ben Kingsley**
1983	Jan.	Vol. 29, no. 340	**Greta Scacchi**
	Feb.	Vol. 29, no. 341	**E.T. and Henry Thomas**
	March	Vol. 29, no. 342	**Miss Piggy**
	April	Vol. 29, no. 343	**Jessica Lange**
	May	Vol. 29, no. 344	**Anthony Andrews**
	June	Vol. 29, no. 345	**Various stills**
	July	Vol. 29, no. 346	***Return of the Jedi***
	Aug.	Vol. 29, no. 347	**Christopher Reeve**
	Sept.	Vol. 29, no. 348	**John Travolta**
			Fiona Hughes
	Oct.	Vol. 30, no. 349	***Something Wicked This Way Comes***
	Nov.	Vol. 30, no. 350	**Richard Charles**
	Dec.	Vol. 30, no. 351	**Sean Connery**
1984	Jan.	Vol. 30, no. 352	**Ben Cross**
	Feb.	Vol. 30, no. 353	**Clint Eastwood**
	March	Vol. 30, no. 354	**Helmut Berger**
			Linda Evans
	April	Vol. 30, no. 355	**Tom Selleck**
			Bess Armstrong
	May	Vol. 30, no. 356	**Paul Newman**
	June	Vol. 30, no. 357	**Nastassja Kinski**
	July	Vol. 30, no. 358	**Harrison Ford**
	Aug.	Vol. 30, no. 359	**C.P. Grogan**
	Sept.	Vol. 30, no. 360	**Arnold Schwarzenegger**
	Oct.	Vol. 31, no. 361	**Robert Redford**
	Nov.	Vol. 31, no. 362	**Richard Farnsworth**
	Dec.	Vol. 31, no. 363	**Paul McCartney**
1985	Jan.	Vol. 31, no. 364	**Michael Caine**
			Valerie Perrine
	Feb.	Vol. 31, no. 365	**Jessica Lange**
	March	Vol. 31, no. 366	**David Lean**
	April	Vol. 31, no. 367	**Robert De Niro**
			Meryl Streep
	May	Vol. 31, no. 368	**Harrison Ford**
	June	Vol. 31, no. 369	**Richard Gere**
	July	Vol. 31, no. 370	**Theresa Russell**
	Aug.	Vol. 31, no. 371	**Christopher Lambert**
	Sept.	Vol. 31, no. 372	**James Dean**
	Oct.	Vol. 32, no. 373	**Jack Nicholson**
			Kathleen Turner
	Nov.	Vol. 32, no. 374	**Daniel Day-Lewis**
			Gordon Warnecke
	Dec.	Vol. 32, no. 375	**Christopher Lloyd**
1986	Jan.	Vol. 32, no. 376	**Mickey Rourke**
	Feb.	Vol. 32, no. 377	**Arnold Schwarzenegger**
	March	Vol. 32, no. 378	**Robert Redford**
	April	Vol. 32, no. 379	**Kathleen Turner**
	May	Vol. 32, no. 380	**Nick Nolte**
	June	Vol. 32, no. 381	***The Color Purple***
	July	Vol. 32, no. 382	**Bob Hoskins**
	Aug.	Vol. 32, no. 383	**Christopher Lambert**
	Sept.	Vol. 32, no. 384	**Walter Matthau**
	Oct.	Vol. 33, no. 385	**Robert De Niro**
	Nov.	Vol. 33, no. 386	**Debra Winger**
	Dec.	Vol. 33, no. 387	**Paul Hogan**
1987	Jan.	Vol. 33, no. 388	**James Woods**
	Feb.	Vol. 33, no. 389	**Harrison Ford**
	March	Vol. 33, no. 390	**Paul Newman**
	April	Vol. 33, no. 391	**Sigourney Weaver**
	May	Vol. 33, no. 392	**Jacqueline Bisset**
	June	Vol. 33, no. 393	**Rupert Everett**

YEAR	MONTH	REF. No.	COVER STAR
	July	Vol. 33, no. 394	**Christopher Reeve**
	Aug.	Vol. 33, no. 395	**Mel Gibson**
	Sept.	Vol. 33, no. 396	**Nick Nolte**
			Maria Conchita Alonso
	Oct.	Vol. 34, no. 397	**Brian Dennehy**
	Nov.	Vol. 34, no. 398	**James Wilby**
	Dec.	Vol. 34, no. 399	**Arnold Schwarzenegger**
1988	Jan.	Vol. 34, no. 400	**Isabella Rossellini**
	Feb.	Vol. 34, no. 401	**Peter O'Toole**
	March	Vol. 34, no. 402	**Bette Davis**
			Lillian Gish
	April	Vol. 34, no. 403	**Holly Hunter**
			William Hurt
			Albert Brooks
	May	Vol. 34, no. 404	**Jack Nicholson**
	June	Vol. 34, no. 405	**Alec Guinness**
	July	Vol. 34, no. 406	**Glenda Jackson**
			Stratford Johns
	Aug.	Vol. 34, no. 407	**Marcello Mastroianni**
	Sept.	Vol. 34, no. 408	**Robin Williams**

YEAR	MONTH	REF. No.	COVER STAR
	Oct.	Vol. 35, no. 409	**Robert De Niro**
	Nov./	Vol. 35, no. 410	**Maggie Smith**
	Dec.		**Bob Hoskins**
1989	Jan.	Vol. 35, no. 411	**Kiefer Sutherland**
	Feb.	Vol. 35, no. 412	**Sigourney Weaver**
	March	Vol. 35, no. 413	**Glenn Close**
	April	Vol. 35, no. 414	**Tom Hanks**
	May	Vol. 35, no. 415	**Peter O'Toole**
	June	Vol. 35, no. 416	**Richard Dreyfuss**
	July	Vol. 35, no. 417	**Michelle Pfeiffer**
			Dean Stockwell
	Aug.	Vol. 35, no. 418	**River Phoenix**
	Sept.	Vol. 35, no. 419	**Mel Gibson**
	Oct.	Vol. 36, no. 420	**Michael Chiklis**
	Nov.	Vol. 36, no. 421	***The Abyss***
	Dec.	Vol. 36, no. 422	**Michael Douglas**
1990	Jan.	Vol. 36, no. 423	**Clint Eastwood**
	Feb.	Vol. 36, no. 424,	**Al Pacino**
	March	Vol. 36, no. 425	**Kevin Costner**

FILMS ILLUSTRATED 1971 – 82

Informative and intelligent articles with fine photographic covers made this British monthly a must for filmgoers. Stars not often chosen for covers were sometimes selected: George C. Scott, Peter Cushing, George Segal, George Chakiris, Theresa Russell, Roy Scheider. Due to a three-day strike and a world paper shortage, there were no issues published for February and March 1974. Published by Films in London Publications until April 1974 when Independent Magazines took over as publishers, it was edited by David Castell.

YEAR	MONTH	REF. No.	COVER STAR
1971	July	Vol. 1, no. 1	**Joan Collins**
	Aug.	Vol. 1, no. 2	**Uncredited girl biker**
	Sept.	Vol. 1, no. 3	**Robert Walker Jr Mimsy Farmer**
	Oct.	Vol. 1, no. 4	**Ann-Margret**
	Nov.	Vol. 1, no. 5	**Raquel Welch**
	Dec.	Vol. 1, no. 6	**James Taylor**
1972	Jan.	Vol. 1, no. 7	**Mickey Mouse**
	Feb.	Vol. 1, no. 8	**Robert Redford**
	March	Vol. 1, no. 9	**Steve McQueen**
	April	Vol. 1, no. 10	**Liza Minnelli Michael Douglas Jane Fonda**
	May	Vol. 1, no. 11	**Susannah York**
	June	Vol. 1, no. 12	**Oliver Reed**
	July	Vol. 2, no. 13	**Simon Ward**
	Aug.	Vol. 2, no. 14	**Alain Delon**
	Sept.	Vol. 2, no. 15	**Scott Antony Dorothy Tutin**
	Oct.	Vol. 2, no. 16	**Elizabeth Taylor**
	Nov.	Vol. 2, no. 17	**Sarah Miles**
	Dec.	Vol. 2, no. 18	**Charles Bronson**
1973	Jan.	Vol. 2, no. 19	**Sophia Loren**
	Feb.	Vol. 2, no. 20	**Steve McQueen**
	March	Vol. 2, no. 21	**Paula Prentiss**
	April	Vol. 2, no. 22	**Liv Ullmann**
	May	Vol. 2, no. 23	**Peter Finch Glenda Jackson**
	June	Vol. 2, no. 24	***Godspell***
	July	Vol. 3, no. 25	**Jan-Michael Vincent**
	Aug.	Vol. 3, no. 26	**Elizabeth Taylor**
	Sept.	Vol. 3, no. 27	**Alain Delon**
	Oct.	Vol. 3, no. 28	**Paul Newman**
	Nov.	Vol. 3, no. 29	**Barbra Streisand**
	Dec.	Vol. 3, no. 30	**Disney's *Robin Hood***
1974	Jan.	Vol. 3, no. 31	**George C. Scott**
	April	Vol. 3, no. 32	**Robert Redford**
	May	Vol. 3, no. 33	**Peter Cushing**
	June	Vol. 3, no. 34	**Candice Bergen**
	July	Vol. 3, no. 35	**Barbra Streisand**
	Aug.	Vol. 3, no. 36	**Jean Seberg**
	Sept.	Vol. 4, no. 37	**James Coburn**
	Oct.	Vol. 4, no. 38	**David Essex**
	Nov.	Vol. 4, no. 39	**Jon Voight**
	Dec.	Vol. 4, no. 40	**Burt Reynolds**
1975	Jan.	Vol. 4, no. 41	**Susan George**
	Feb.	Vol. 4, no. 42	**Steve McQueen**
	March	Vol. 4, no. 43	**Barbra Streisand**
	April	Vol. 4, no. 44	**Robert Redford**
	May	Vol. 4, no. 45	**Warren Beatty**
	June	Vol. 4, no. 46	**Sophia Loren**
	July	Vol. 4, no. 47	**Valerie Perrine**

YEAR	MONTH	REF. No.	COVER STAR
	Aug.	Vol. 4, no. 48	**Malcolm McDowell**
	Sept.	Vol. 5, no. 49	**James Caan**
	Oct.	Vol. 5, no. 50	**Robert Redford**
	Nov.	Vol. 5, no. 51	**John Wayne Katharine Hepburn**
	Dec.	Vol. 5, no. 52	**Sean Connery Michael Caine**
1976	Jan.	Vol. 5, no. 53	**Liza Minnelli**
	Feb.	Vol. 5, no. 54	**Michael York Jenny Agutter**
	March	Vol. 5, no. 55	**James Caan**
	April	Vol. 5, no. 56	**Richard Chamberlain**
	May	Vol. 5, no. 57	**George Segal**
	June	Vol. 5, no. 58	**Audrey Hepburn**
	July	Vol. 5, no. 59	**Jodie Foster**
	Aug.	Vol. 5, no. 60	**Sarah Miles**
	Sept.	Vol. 6, no. 61	**Robert De Niro**
	Oct.	Vol. 6, no. 62	**Michael York**
	Nov.	Vol. 6, no. 63	**Rita Moreno**
	Dec.	Vol. 6, no. 64	**Glenda Jackson**
1977	Jan.	Vol. 6, no. 65	**Dustin Hoffman**
	Feb.	Vol. 6, no. 66	**Charlton Heston**
	March	Vol. 6, no. 67	**Peter Finch**
	April	Vol. 6, no. 68	**Kris Kristofferson Barbra Streisand**
	May	Vol. 6, no. 69	**Talia Shire Sylvester Stallone**
	June	Vol. 6, no. 70	**Raquel Welch**
	July	Vol. 6, no. 71	**Robert Redford**
	Aug.	Vol. 6, no. 72	**Mia Farrow**
	Sept.	Vol. 7, no. 73	**Richard Burton**
	Oct	Vol. 7, no. 74	**Robert De Niro**
	Nov.	Vol. 7, no. 75	**Al Pacino**
	Dec.	Vol. 7, no. 76	**Jacqueline Bisset**
1978	Jan.	Vol. 7. no. 77	**Christopher Plummer**
	Feb.	Vol. 7, no. 78	**Glenda Jackson Walter Matthau**
	March	Vol. 7, no. 79	**Stéphane Audran**
	April	Vol. 7, no. 80	**Richard Dreyfuss**
	May	Vol. 7, no. 81	**Anne Bancroft Shirley MacLaine**
	June	Vol. 7, no. 82	**Gregory Peck**
	July	Vol. 7, no. 83	**Michael Caine**
	Aug.	Vol. 7, no. 84	**Nanette Newman**
	Sept.	Vol. 8. no. 85	**John Travolta**
	Oct.	Vol. 8, no. 86	**Warren Beatty**
	Nov.	Vol. 8, no. 87	**Jacqueline Bisset**
	Dec.	Vol. 8, no. 88	**Christopher Reeve**
1979	Jan.	Vol. 8, no. 89	**Clint Eastwood**
	Feb.	Vol. 8, no. 90	**Anthony Hopkins**
	March	Vol. 8, no. 91	**George Peppard**
	April	Vol. 8, no. 92	**Donald Sutherland**

YEAR	MONTH	REF. No.	COVER STAR
	May	Vol. 8, no. 93	**Sophia Loren**
	June	Vol. 8, no. 94	**Jan-Michael Vincent**
	July	Vol. 8, no. 95	**Jane Fonda**
			Jack Lemmon
			Michael Douglas
	Aug.	Vol. 8, no. 96	**Ryan O'Neal**
			Barbra Streisand
	Sept.	Vol. 9, no. 97	**Sigourney Weaver**
	Oct.	Vol. 9, no. 98	**George Chakiris**
	Nov.	Vol. 9, no. 99	**Marlon Brando**
	Dec.	Vol. 9, no. 100	**Meryl Streep**
1980	Jan.	Vol. 9, no. 101	**William Shatner**
			Leonard Nimoy
	Feb.	Vol. 9, no. 102	**John Savage**
	March	Vol. 9, no. 103	**Dustin Hoffman**
			Meryl Streep
			Justin Henry
	April	Vol. 9, no. 104	**Robert Redford**
	May/ June	Vol. 9, no. 105	**Theresa Russell**
	July	Vol. 9, no. 106	**Clint Eastwood**
	Aug.	Vol. 9, no. 107	**Roy Scheider**
	Sept.	Vol. 9, no. 108	**John Travolta**
	Oct.	Vol. 10, no. 109	**Elizabeth Taylor**
	Nov.	Vol. 10, no. 110	**Steve McQueen**
	Dec.	Vol. 10, no. 111	**Sam Jones**
1981	Jan.	Vol. 10, no. 112	**Clint Eastwood**
	Feb.	Vol. 10, no. 113	**Robert De Niro**
	March	Vol. 10, no. 114	**Jane Fonda**
			Lily Tomlin
			Dolly Parton
	April	Vol. 10, no. 115	**Christopher Reeve**
	May	Vol. 10, no. 116	**Peter Firth**
			Nastassja Kinski
	June	Vol. 10, no. 117	**Jodie Foster**
	July	Vol. 10, no. 118	**Roger Moore**
	Aug.	Vol. 10, no. 119	**Harrison Ford**
	Sept.	Vol. 10, no. 120	**Sylvester Stallone**
	Oct.	Vol. 11, no. 121	**Frank Doubleday**
	Nov.	Vol. 11, no. 122	**John Travolta**
	Dec.	Vol. 11, no. 123	**Faye Dunaway**
1982	Jan.	Vol. 11, no. 124	**Candice Bergen**

FILMS IN REVIEW 1950 –

This pocketsize American film magazine, published by the National Board of Review of Motion Pictures, Inc., New York, has included excellent career articles on Garbo, Valentino, Chaney, Dietrich, Davis, Crawford, Bogart, and many more. All have been fully illustrated and have had complete filmographies. Each year the magazine gives its own awards for exceptional films and performances; these awards were renamed the David Wark Griffith Awards in 1980, honouring the great director of the silent screen.

The covers of the magazine are generally stills from current or classic films. Rare cover stars have been Broderick Crawford, Richard Widmark, Diane Varsi and Gena Rowlands. The first seven issues were edited by John B. Turner. Succeeding editors were Henry Hart, November 1950 – February 1972; Charles Phillips Reilly, March 1972 – June/July 1983; Robin Little, August/September 1972 to date. *Films In Review* is published ten times a year.

YEAR	MONTH	REF. No.	COVER STAR
1950	Feb.	Vol. 1, no. 1	**Broderick Crawford**
	March	Vol. 1, no. 2	**Howard Keel**
	April	Vol. 1, no. 3	**Richard Todd**
	May/June	Vol. 1, no. 4	**Barbara Stanwyck** **Thomas Gomez**
	July/Aug.	Vol. 1, no. 5	**Cantinflas**
	Sept.	Vol. 1, no. 6	**Charlie Chaplin**
	Oct.	Vol. 1, no. 7	**Edinburgh film festival venue**
	Nov.	Vol. 1, no. 8	**Dore Schary** **William Wellman**
	Dec.	Vol. 1, no. 9	**Anne Baxter**
1951	Jan.	Vol. 2, no. 1	**Andrew Ray**
	Feb.	Vol. 2, no. 2	**Orson Welles**
	March	Vol. 2, no. 3	**Richard Widmark**
	April	Vol. 2, no. 4	**Ludmilla Tcherina**
	May	Vol. 2, no. 5	**Richard Basehart**
	June/July	Vol. 2, no. 6	**Adrienne Corri**
	Aug./Sept.	Vol. 2, no. 7	**Elizabeth Taylor**
	Oct.	Vol. 2, no. 8	**Leslie Caron** **Gene Kelly**
	Nov.	Vol. 2, no. 9	**Vivien Leigh**
	Dec.	Vol. 2, no. 10	**Robert Taylor** **Deborah Kerr**
1952	Jan.	Vol. 3, no. 1	**Fredric March**
	Feb.	Vol. 3, no. 2	**Katharine Hepburn**
	March	Vol. 3, no. 3	**Marlon Brando** **Jean Peters**
	April	Vol. 3, no. 4	**Gene Kelly** **Cyd Charisse**
	May	Vol. 3, no. 5	**Kerima**
	June/July	Vol. 3, no. 6	**Eleanor Parker** **Stewart Granger**
	Aug./Sept.	Vol. 3, no. 7	**Maureen O'Hara**
	Oct.	Vol. 3, no. 8	**Ava Gardner** **Gregory Peck**
	Nov.	Vol. 3, no. 9	**Charlie Chaplin** **Claire Bloom**
	Dec.	Vol. 3, no. 10	**Emmer's *Leonardo Da Vinci***
1953	Jan.	Vol. 4, no. 1	**Richard Burton**
	Feb.	Vol. 4, no. 2	**Marjorie Steele**
	March	Vol. 4, no. 3	**Anne Baxter** **Montgomery Clift**
	April	Vol. 4, no. 4	**Marilyn Monroe**
	May	Vol. 4, no. 5	**Marlon Brando**
	June/July	Vol. 4, no. 6	**Jean Simmons** **Stewart Granger**
	Aug./Sept.	Vol. 4, no. 7	**Tony Monaco** **Tallulah Bankhead**
	Oct.	Vol. 4, no. 8	**Henry Koster** **Jean Simmons**
	Nov.	Vol. 4, no. 9	**John Ford**
	Dec.	Vol. 4, no. 10	**Robert Morley**
1954	Jan.	Vol. 5, no. 1	**Marge and Gower Champion**
	Feb.	Vol. 5, no. 2	**Ava Gardner** **Robert Taylor**
	March	Vol. 5, no. 3	**Anna Magnani**
	April	Vol. 5, no. 4	**Jennifer Jones**
	May	Vol. 5, no. 5	**Gregory Peck** **Rita Gam**
	June/July	Vol. 5, no. 6	**Grace Kelly** **Anthony Dawson**
	Aug./Sept.	Vol. 5, no. 7	**Audrey Hepburn** **William Holden**
	Oct.	Vol. 5, no. 8	**Daniel Gelin** **Gina Lollobrigida**
	Nov.	Vol. 5, no. 9	**Judy Garland**
	Dec.	Vol. 5, no. 10	**Susan Shentall**
1955	Jan.	Vol. 6, no. 1	**Carl Dreyer**
	Feb.	Vol. 6, no. 2	***Dames***
	March	Vol. 6, no. 3	**Leslie Caron**
	April	Vol. 6, no. 4	**Glenn Ford** **Eleanor Parker**
	May	Vol. 6, no. 5	**Olivia De Havilland** **Stanley Kramer**
	June/July	Vol. 6, no. 6	**Orson Welles** **Suzanne Cloutier**
	Aug./Sept.	Vol. 6, no. 7	**Cary Grant** **Grace Kelly**
	Oct.	Vol. 6, no. 8	**Cyd Charisse**
	Nov.	Vol. 6, no. 9	**Shirley Jones** **Gordon MacRae**
	Dec.	Vol. 6, no. 10	**Adrienne Corri**
1956	Jan.	Vol. 7, no. 1	**Laurence Olivier**
	Feb.	Vol. 7, no. 2	**Jacques Sernas** **Rossana Podesta**
	March	Vol. 7, no. 3	**Claire Bloom** **Laurence Olivier**
	April	Vol. 7, no. 4	**Alec Guinness** **Grace Kelly**
	May	Vol. 7, no. 5	**Ava Gardner**
	June/July	Vol. 7, no. 6	**Claire Sombert** **Igor Youskevitch**
	Aug./Sept.	Vol. 7, no. 7	**Audrey Hepburn**

YEAR	MONTH	REF. No.	COVER STAR
	Oct.	Vol. 7, no. 8	**Marilyn Monroe**
	Nov.	Vol. 7, no. 9	**Joan Collins**
			Dolores Gray
	Dec.	Vol. 7, no. 10	**Joan Crawford**
1957	Jan.	Vol. 8, no. 1	**Marina Vlady**
	Feb.	Vol. 8, no. 2	**Fred Astaire**
	March	Vol. 8, no. 3	**Barbara Laage**
	April	Vol. 8, no. 4	**Ava Gardner**
	May	Vol. 8, no. 5	**Humphrey Bogart**
	June/July	Vol. 8, no. 6	**Joan Collins**
	Aug./Sept.	Vol. 8, no. 7	**Juliette Greco**
			Tyrone Power
	Oct.	Vol. 8, no. 8	**Joanne Woodward**
	Nov.	Vol. 8, no. 9	**Jennifer Jones**
			Rock Hudson
	Dec.	Vol. 8, no. 10	**Diane Varsi**
1958	Jan.	Vol. 9, no. 1	**Marlene Dietrich**
	Feb.	Vol. 9, no. 2	**Yul Brynner**
			Maria Schell
	March	Vol. 9 no. 3	**Joanne Woodward**
			Paul Newman
	April	Vol. 9, no. 4	**Mitzi Gaynor**
			Buddy Adler
	May	Vol. 9, no. 5	**Suzy Parker**
	June/July	Vol. 9, no. 6	**Kirk Douglas**
	Aug./Sept.	Vol. 9, no. 7	**May Britt**
	Oct.	Vol. 9, no. 8	**Juliette Greco**
	Nov.	Vol. 9, no. 9	**Deborah Kerr**
			David Niven
	Dec.	Vol. 9, no. 10	**Ingrid Bergman**
1959	Jan.	Vol. 10, no. 1	**Joan Collins**
	Feb.	Vol. 10, no. 2	**Deborah Kerr**
			Yul Brynner
	March	Vol. 10, no. 3	**Joanne Woodward**
			Stuart Whitman
	April	Vol. 10, no. 4	**Audrey Hepburn**
	May	Vol. 10, no. 5	**Gregory Peck**
	June/July	Vol. 10, no. 6	**Shirley MacLaine**
	Aug./Sept.	Vol. 10, no. 7	**Leslie Caron**
	Oct.	Vol. 10, no. 8	**May Britt**
	Nov.	Vol. 10, no. 9	**Nadja Tiller**
	Dec.	Vol. 10, no. 10	**José Greci**
1960	Jan.	Vol. 11, no. 1	**Gina Lollobrigida**
	Feb.	Vol. 11, no. 2	**Joan Collins**
	March	Vol. 11, no. 3	**Sophia Loren**
	April	Vol. 11, no. 4	**Marc Wilder**
			Shirley MacLaine
	May	Vol. 11, no. 5	**Jane Fonda**
	June/July	Vol. 11, no. 6	**Lee Remick**
	Aug./Sept.	Vol. 11, no. 7	**Heather Sears**
			Dean Stockwell
	Oct.	Vol. 11, no. 8	**Marilyn Monroe**
	Nov.	Vol. 11, no. 9	**Linda Cristal**
	Dec.	Vol. 11, no. 10	**Clark Gable**
			Claudette Colbert
1961	Jan.	Vol. 12, no. 1	**Dina Merrill**
	Feb.	Vol. 12, no. 2	**Clark Gable**
			Marilyn Monroe
	March	Vol. 12, no. 3	**Marlon Brando**
	April	Vol. 12, no. 4	**Keir Dullea**
	May	Vol. 12, no. 5	**Sophia Loren**
	June/July	Vol. 12, no. 6	**Salome Jens**
	Aug./Sept.	Vol. 12, no. 7	**Horst Buchholz**
			Leslie Caron
	Oct.	Vol. 12, no. 8	**Mary Peach**
			Peter Finch
	Nov.	Vol. 12, no. 9	**Jeffrey Hunter**
	Dec.	Vol. 12, no. 10	**Charlton Heston**
			Sophia Loren
1962	Jan.	Vol. 13, no. 1	**Deborah Kerr**
	Feb.	Vol. 13, no. 2	**Yvette Mimieux**
	March	Vol. 13, no. 3	**Ingrid Thulin**
	April	Vol. 13, no. 4	**Mariette Hartley**
	May	Vol. 13, no. 5	**Lee Remick**
	June/July	Vol. 13, no. 6	**Shirley MacLaine**
	Aug./Sept.	Vol. 13, no. 7	**Yvette Mimieux**
	Oct.	Vol. 13, no. 8	**Marilyn Monroe**
	Nov.	Vol. 13, no. 9	**Terence Stamp**
	Dec.	Vol. 13, no. 10	**Judy Garland**
1963	Jan.	Vol. 14, no. 1	**Janet Margolin**
			Keir Dullea
	Feb.	Vol. 14, no. 2	**Sophia Loren**
	March	Vol. 14, no. 3	**George Peppard**
	April	Vol. 14, no. 4	**Alfred Hitchcock**
			Tippi Hedren
	May	Vol. 14, no. 5	**Gunnar Bjornstrand**
			Ingrid Thulin
	June/July	Vol. 14, no. 6	**Marilyn Monroe**
	Aug./Sept.	Vol. 14, no. 7	**Elizabeth Taylor**
			Rex Harrison
	Oct.	Vol. 14, no. 8	**Jean Seberg**
	Nov.	Vol. 14, no. 9	**Jean Simmons**
	Dec.	Vol. 14, no. 10	**Cary Grant**
1964	Jan.	Vol. 15, no. 1	**Tom Tryon**
			Romy Schneider
	Feb.	Vol. 15, no. 2	**Angie Dickinson**
	March	Vol. 15, no. 3	**Catharine Spaak**
	April	Vol. 15, no. 4	**Audrey Hepburn**
			William Holden
	May	Vol. 15, no. 5	**Daniela Bianchi**
	June/July	Vol. 15, no. 6	**Martha Hyer**

YEAR	MONTH	REF. No.	COVER STAR
	Aug./Sept.	Vol. 15, no. 7	**Elke Sommer**
	Oct.	Vol. 15, no. 8	**Siobhan McKenna**
			Laurence Harvey
	Nov.	Vol. 15, no. 9	**Julie Andrews**
			James Coburn
			James Garner
			Melvyn Douglas
	Dec.	Vol. 15, no. 10	**Honor Blackman**
1965	Jan.	Vol. 16, no. 1	**Leslie Caron**
	Feb.	Vol. 16, no. 2	**Virna Lisi**
	March	Vol. 16, no. 3	**Max Von Sydow**
	April	Vol. 16, no. 4	**Rod Taylor**
			Julie Christie
	May	Vol. 16, no. 5	**Marisa Mell**
	June/July	Vol. 16, no. 6	**Diane Baker**
	Aug./Sept.	Vol. 16, no. 7	**Elizabeth Taylor**
	Oct.	Vol. 16, no. 8	**Charlton Heston**
	Nov.	Vol. 16, no. 9	**Carol Lynley**
	Dec.	Vol. 16, no. 10	**Caterina Boratto**
1966	Jan.	Vol. 17, no. 1	**Julie Christie**
	Feb.	Vol. 17, no. 2	**Irina Demick**
	March	Vol. 17, no. 3	**Natalie Wood**
	April	Vol. 17, no. 4	**Candice Bergen**
	May	Vol. 17, no. 5	**Sophia Loren**
	June/July	Vol. 17, no. 6	**Sean Connery**
	Aug./Sept.	Vol. 17, no. 7	**Elizabeth Taylor**
	Oct.	Vol. 17, no. 8	**Ava Gardner**
	Nov.	Vol. 17, no. 9	**Julie Andrews**
	Dec.	Vol. 17, no. 10	**Oskar Werner**
			Julie Christie
1967	Jan.	Vol. 18, no. 1	**Paul Scofield**
	Feb.	Vol. 18, no. 2	**Peter O'Toole**
	March	Vol. 18, no. 3	**Virna Lisi**
			Anthony Quinn
	April	Vol. 18, no. 4	**Elizabeth Taylor**
	May	Vol. 18, no. 5	**Jacqueline Bisset**
	June/July	Vol. 18, no. 6	**Ursula Andress**
	Aug./Sept.	Vol. 18, no. 7	**Sean Connery**
	Oct.	Vol. 18, no. 8	**Jean Shrimpton**
	Nov.	Vol. 18, no. 9	**Prunella Ransome**
	Dec.	Vol. 18, no. 10	**Audrey Hepburn**
1968	Jan.	Vol. 19, no. 1	**Rex Harrison**
	Feb.	Vol. 19, no. 2	**Dean Martin**
			Stella Stevens
	March	Vol. 19, no. 3	**Richard Burton**
			Elizabeth Taylor
	April	Vol. 19, no. 4	**Barry Evans**
	May	Vol. 19, no. 5	**Judy Geeson**
			David Dundas
	June/July	Vol. 19, no. 6	**Vyacheslav Tihonov**
			Vladislav Strzhelchik

YEAR	MONTH	REF. No.	COVER STAR
	Aug./Sept.	Vol. 19, no. 7	**Oskar Werner**
	Oct.	Vol. 19, no. 8	**Olivia Hussey**
			Leonard Whiting
	Nov.	Vol. 19, no. 9	**Fred Astaire**
	Dec.	Vol. 19, no. 10	**Anthony Quinn**
1969	Jan.	Vol. 20, no. 1	**Liv Ullmann**
	Feb.	Vol. 20, no. 2	**Catherine Deneuve**
	March	Vol. 20, no. 3	**Gregory Peck**
			Eva Marie Saint
	April	Vol. 20, no. 4	**Pamela Franklin**
	May	Vol. 20, no. 5	**Ali MacGraw**
	June/July	Vol. 20, no. 6	**Vanessa Redgrave**
	Aug./Sept.	Vol. 20, no. 7	**Catherine Deneuve**
	Oct.	Vol. 20, no. 8	**Katharine Hepburn**
	Nov.	Vol. 20, no. 9	**Jean Seberg**
	Dec.	Vol. 20, no. 10	**Peter O'Toole**
1970	Jan.	Vol. 21, no. 1	**George Lazenby**
	Feb.	Vol. 21, no. 2	**Richard Burton**
	March	Vol. 21, no. 3	**Elizabeth Taylor**
	April	Vol. 21, no. 4	**Jacqueline Bisset**
	May	Vol. 21, no. 5	**Catherine Deneuve**
			Jean-Paul Belmondo
	June/July	Vol. 21, no. 6	**Jack Lemmon**
	Aug./Sept.	Vol. 21, no. 7	**Stefanie Powers**
	Oct.	Vol. 21, no. 8	**Robert Forster**
			Lauren Hutton
	Nov.	Vol. 21, no. 9	**François Truffaut**
	Dec.	Vol. 21, no. 10	**Sarah Miles**
1971	Jan.	Vol. 22, no. 1	**Yves Montand**
	Feb.	Vol. 22, no. 2	**Timothy Dalton**
	March	Vol. 22, no. 3	**Marian McCargo**
	April	Vol. 22, no. 4	**Sophia Loren**
	May	Vol. 22, no. 5	**Jennifer O'Neill**
	June/July	Vol. 22, no. 6	**Lucille Ball**
	Aug./Sept.	Vol. 22, no. 7	**Sal Mineo**
			Kim Hunter
			Roddy McDowall in monkey masks
	Oct.	Vol. 22, no. 8	**Julie Christie**
	Nov.	Vol. 22, no. 9	**Irene Papas**
	Dec.	Vol. 22, no. 10	**Janet Suzman**
			Michael Jayston
1972	Jan.	Vol. 23, no. 1	**Sean Connery**
			Jill St John
	Feb.	Vol. 23, no. 2	**John Wayne**
			Norman Howell Jr

YEAR	MONTH	REF. No.	COVER STAR
	March	Vol. 23, no. 3	**Liza Minnelli**
	April	Vol. 23, no. 4	**Marlon Brando**
			Talia Shire
	May	Vol. 23, no. 5	**Barbra Streisand**
			Ryan O'Neal
	June/July	Vol. 23, no. 6	**Orson Welles**
	Aug./Sept.	Vol. 23, no. 7	**Alfred Hitchcock**
	Oct.	Vol. 23, no. 8	**Kevin Hooks**
			Paul Winfield
	Nov.	Vol. 23, no. 9	**Federico Fellini**
	Dec.	Vol. 23, no. 10	**Virginia Vestoff**
			William Daniels
1973	Jan.	Vol. 24, no. 1	**Sophia Loren**
	Feb.	Vol. 24, no. 2	**Cybill Shepherd**
	March	Vol. 24, no. 3	**Peter O'Toole**
			Elizabeth Taylor
			Richard Burton
	April	Vol. 24, no. 4	**Sarah Miles**
			Richard Chamberlain
	May	Vol. 24, no. 5	**Peter Finch**
			Liv Ullmann
	June/July	Vol. 24, no. 6	**Ryan O'Neal**
			Tatum O'Neal
	Aug./Sept.	Vol. 24, no. 7	**Betty Grable**
	Oct.	Vol. 24, no. 8	**Busby Berkeley and chorus girls**
	Nov.	Vol. 24, no. 9	**Robert Redford**
			Barbra Streisand
	Dec.	Vol. 24, no. 10	**Clarence Brown**
			Greta Garbo
			John Gilbert
1974	Jan.	Vol. 25, no. 1	**Katharine Hepburn**
			Lee Remick
	Feb.	Vol. 25, no. 2	**Carol Kane**
			Jack Nicholson
	March	Vol. 25, no. 3	**Shelley Duvall**
			Keith Carradine
	April	Vol. 25, no. 4	**Lucille Ball**
	May	Vol. 25, no. 5	**Mia Farrow**
			Robert Redford
	June/July	Vol. 25, no. 6	**Cybill Shepherd**
			Barry Brown
	Aug./Sept.	Vol. 25, no. 7	**Mabel Normand**
	Oct.	Vol. 25, no. 8	**Liv Ullmann**
			Erland Josephson
	Nov.	Vol. 25, no. 9	**Bruno Zanin**
			Magali Noel
	Dec.	Vol. 25, no. 10	**Albert Finney**
			Anthony Perkins
			Sean Connery
			Vanessa Redgrave
			Ingrid Bergman

YEAR	MONTH	REF. No.	COVER STAR
	Dec. (*cont.*)		**George Coulouris**
			Rachel Roberts
			Wendy Hiller
			Dennis Quilley
			Michael York
			Jacqueline Bisset
			Lauren Bacall
1975	Jan.	Vol. 26, no. 1	**Valerie Perrine**
	Feb.	Vol. 26, no. 2	**Steve McQueen**
			Faye Dunaway
			Paul Newman
	March	Vol. 26, no. 3	**Jean-Paul Belmondo**
			Charles Boyer
	April	Vol. 26, no. 4	**Burt Reynolds**
			Cybill Shepherd
	May	Vol. 26, no. 5	**Ann-Margret**
			Jack Nicholson
	June/July	Vol. 26, no. 6	**Marilyn Monroe**
	Aug./Sept.	Vol. 26, no. 7	**Woody Allen**
	Oct.	Vol. 26, no. 8	**David Wark Griffith (US stamp)**
	Nov.	Vol. 26, no. 9	**Ingmar Bergman**
	Dec.	Vol. 26, no. 10	**Mae Murray**
1976	Jan.	Vol. 27, no. 1	**Jack Nicholson**
	Feb.	Vol. 27, no. 2	**Murray Melvin**
			Marisa Berenson
	March	Vol. 27, no. 3	**Lina Wertmuller**
	April	Vol. 27, no. 4	**Audrey Hepburn**
			Sean Connery
	May	Vol. 27, no. 5	**Robert Redford**
	June/July	Vol. 27, no. 6	**Jayne Mansfield**
	Aug./Sept.	Vol. 27, no. 7	**Elsa Lanchester**
	Oct.	Vol. 27, no. 8	**John Wayne**
			James Stewart
	Nov.	Vol. 27, no. 9	**Liza Minnelli**
			Ingrid Bergman
	Dec.	Vol. 27, no. 10	**Richard Chamberlain**
			Gemma Craven
1977	Jan.	Vol. 28, no. 1	**Oskar Werner**
			Faye Dunaway
	Feb.	Vol. 28, no. 2	**Jessica Lange and 'King Kong'**
	March	Vol. 28, no. 3	**Ellen Burstyn**
			John Gielgud
	April	Vol. 28, no. 4	**Leatrice Joy**
	May	Vol. 28, no. 5	**Sissy Spacek**
			Shelley Duvall
	June/July	Vol. 28, no. 6	**Woody Allen**
	Aug./Sept.	Vol. 28, no. 7	**See Threepio and Artoo Detoo**

YEAR	MONTH	REF. No.	COVER STAR
	Oct.	Vol. 28, no. 8	**Liza Minnelli** **Robert De Niro**
	Nov.	Vol. 28, no. 9	**Vanessa Redgrave** **Jane Fonda**
	Dec.	Vol. 28, no. 10	**Richard Burton**
1978	Jan.	Vol. 29, no. 1	**Liv Ullmann** **David Carradine**
	Feb.	Vol. 29, no. 2	**Kim Novak**
	March	Vol. 29, no. 3	**Candice Bergen**
	April	Vol. 29, no. 4	**Jane Fonda** **Jon Voight**
	May	Vol. 29, no. 5	**Janet Gaynor** **Diane Keaton**
	June/July	Vol. 29, no. 6	**Sylvester Stallone** **Melinda Dillon**
	Aug./Sept.	Vol. 29, no. 7	**John Travolta**
	Oct.	Vol. 29, no. 8	**Faye Dunaway**
	Nov.	Vol. 29, no. 9	**Bette Davis** **Angela Lansbury** **Maggie Smith**
	Dec.	Vol. 29, no. 10	**Jean Harlow**
1979	Jan.	Vol. 30, no. 1	**Margot Kidder** **Christopher Reeve**
	Feb.	Vol. 30, no. 2	**Liv Ullmann** **Ingrid Bergman**
	March	Vol. 30, no. 3	**Marilyn Monroe**
	April	Vol. 30, no. 4	**Sean Connery** **Lesley-Anne Down**
	May	Vol. 30, no. 5	**Michael Douglas** **Jack Lemmon** **Jane Fonda**
	June/July	Vol. 30, no. 6	**Woody Allen**
	Aug./Sept.	Vol. 30, no. 7	**Joan Crawford** **Nils Asther**
	Oct.	Vol. 30 no. 8	**Lisa Eichhorn** **Richard Gere**
	Nov.	Vol. 30, no. 9	**Greta Garbo**
	Dec.	Vol. 30, no. 10	**Robert Redford** **Jane Fonda**
1980	Jan.	Vol. 31, no. 1	***Star Trek: The Motion Picture***
	Feb.	Vol. 31, no. 2	**Angela Lansbury**
	March	Vol. 31, no. 3	**Richard Gere** **Lauren Hutton**
	April	Vol. 31, no. 4	**Sissy Spacek** **Tommy Lee Jones**
	May	Vol. 31, no. 5	**George De La Pena** **Alan Bates**
	June/July	Vol. 31, no. 6	**Shelley Winters**
	Aug./Sept.	Vol. 31, no. 7	**John Travolta**
	Oct.	Vol. 31, no. 8	**Gena Rowlands**
	Nov.	Vol. 31, no. 9	**Robert Redford** **MaryTylerMoore** **Donald Sutherland** **Timothy Hutton**
	Dec.	Vol. 31, no. 10	**Robert De Niro**
1981	Jan.	Vol. 32, no. 1	**Jane Fonda** **Lily Tomlin** **Dolly Parton**
	Feb.	Vol. 32, no. 2	**Gloria Swanson**
	March	Vol. 32, no. 3	**Myrna Loy** **Lillian Gish** **Gloria Swanson**
	April	Vol. 32, no. 4	**Sigourney Weaver** **William Hurt**
	May	Vol. 32, no. 5	**Sally Field** **Tommy Lee Jones**
	June/July	Vol. 32, no. 6	**Sissy Spacek** **Robert De Niro** **Ronald L. Schwary** **Robert Redford**
	Aug./Sept.	Vol. 32, no. 7	**Cecil B. De Mille** **Yul Brynner**
	Oct.	Vol. 32, no. 8	**Greta Garbo** **Melvyn Douglas** **Ina Claire**
	Nov.	Vol. 32, no. 9	**Frank Perry** **Faye Dunaway**
	Dec.	Vol. 32, no. 10	**Pat O'Brien** **Betty Compson**
1982	Jan.	Vol. 33, no. 1	**Judy Davis** **Sam Neill**
	Feb.	Vol. 33, no. 2	**Josef Von Sternberg** **Merle Oberon** **Charles Laughton**
	March	Vol. 33, no. 3	**James Cagney**
	April	Vol. 33, no. 4	**Dolores Del Rio** **Charles Farrell** **Raoul Walsh**
	May	Vol. 33, no. 5	**William Wellman**
	June/July	Vol. 33, no. 6	**Mickey Rooney**
	Aug./Sept.	Vol. 33, no. 7	**Robert Preston**
	Oct.	Vol. 33, no. 8	**Myrna Loy** **William Powell**
	Nov.	Vol. 33, no. 9	**Alice Faye**
	Dec.	Vol. 33, no. 10	**King Vidor**
1983	Jan.	Vol. 34, no. 1	**Ben Kingsley**

YEAR	MONTH	REF. No.	COVER STAR
	Feb.	Vol. 34, no. 2	**Glenn Close**
	March	Vol. 34, no. 3	**Victor Fleming**
			Henry Fonda
			Janet Gaynor
	April	Vol. 34, no. 4	**Patricia Neal**
	May	Vol. 34, no. 5	**Robert Duvall**
	June/July	Vol. 34, no. 6	**Frank Sinatra**
			Gene Kelly
			Kathryn Grayson
	Aug./Sept.	Vol. 34, no. 7	**Marilyn Monroe**
			Eli Wallach
			Clark Gable
	Oct.	Vol. 34, no. 8	**Loretta Young**
			David Niven
	Nov.	Vol. 34, no. 9	**Martin Sheen**
			Blair Brown
	Dec.	Vol. 34, no. 10	**Carole Lombard**
			William Powell
			Gail Patrick
1984	Jan.	Vol. 35, no. 1	**Johnny Weissmuller**
			Maureen O'Sullivan
	Feb.	Vol. 35, no. 2	**James Stewart**
			Joan Fontaine
			Eddie Albert
	March	Vol. 35, no. 3	**Ann Harding**
			Gary Cooper
	April	Vol. 35, no. 4	**Gregory Peck**
	May	Vol. 35, no. 5	**Robert Taylor**
			Eleanor Powell
	June/July	Vol. 35, no. 6	**Jackie Coogan**
			Betty Grable
	Aug./Sept.	Vol. 35, no. 7	**Boris Karloff and wife**
	Oct.	Vol. 35, no. 8	**Paul Newman**
			Sidney Lumet
	Nov.	Vol. 35, no. 9	**Monty Woolley**
			Bette Davis
			Ann Sheridan
	Dec.	Vol. 35, no. 10	**Jack Lemmon**
1985	Jan.	Vol. 36, no. 1	**Dean Stockwell**
			Sting
	Feb.	Vol. 36, no. 2	**James Stewart**
			Marlene Dietrich
	March	Vol. 36, no. 3	**Burt Lancaster**
			Judy Garland
	April	Vol. 36, no. 4	**John Huston**
	May	Vol. 36, no. 5	**Leslie Howard**
			Myrna Loy
	June/July	Vol. 36, nos 6/7	**Nazimova**
	Aug./Sept.	Vol. 36, nos 8/9	**Jamie Lee Curtis**
			John Travolta
	Oct.	Vol. 36, no. 10	**May Robson**
			Anna Neagle
			Edna May Oliver
	Nov.	Vol. 36, no. 11	**Louise Brooks**
	Dec.	Vol. 36, no. 12	**Spencer Tracy**
			Robert Wagner
1986	Jan.	Vol. 37, no. 1	**Richard Attenborough**
	Feb.	Vol. 37, no. 2	**Tuesday Weld**
	March	Vol. 37, no. 3	**Ronald Colman**
			Blanche Sweet
	April	Vol. 37, no. 4	**Michael Douglas**
			Maureen Stapleton
	May	Vol. 37, no. 5	**Richard Widmark**
			Marilyn Monroe
	June/July	Vol. 37, nos 6/7	**Karen Black**
			William Atherton
	Aug./Sept	Vol. 37, nos 8/9	**Deanna Durbin**
	Oct.	Vol. 37, no. 10	**Kim Hunter**
			Marlon Brando
	Nov.	Vol. 37, no. 11	**Geena Davis**
			Jeff Goldblum
	Dec.	Vol. 37, no. 12	**Marlee Matlin**
			William Hurt
1987	Jan.	Vol. 38, no. 1	**Paul Newman**
			Tom Cruise
	Feb.	Vol. 38, no. 2	**José Ferrer**
			Gene Tierney
	March	Vol. 38, no. 3	**Marlene Dietrich**
			Clive Brook
			Lawrence Grant
			Anna May Wong
	April	Vol. 38, no. 4	**Jack Lemmon**
			Kathleen Turner
			Paul Newman and editor, Robin Little
	May	Vol. 38, no. 5	**Mel Gibson**
	June/July	Vol. 38, nos 6/7	**Peter Lawford**
			Jane Powell
			Fred Astaire
	Aug./Sept.	Vol. 38, nos 8/9	**Orson Welles**
	Oct.	Vol. 38, no. 10	**Maryam D'Abo**
			Timothy Dalton
	Nov.	Vol. 38, no. 11	**Loretta Young**
			Constance Bennett
			Janet Gaynor
	Dec.	Vol. 38, no. 12	**Kevin Kline**
			Denzil Washington
1988	Jan.	Vol. 39, no. 1	**Elizabeth Taylor**
			Joseph Mankiewicz
	Feb.	Vol. 39, no. 2	**Christian Bale**
			Steven Spielberg
			John Malkovich

YEAR	MONTH	REF. No.	COVER STAR
	March	Vol. 39, no. 3	**Linda Darnell** **Ann Sothern** **Jeanne Crain**
	April	Vol. 39, no 4	**Norman Jewison** **Cher**
	May	Vol. 39, no. 5	**Donald Trump** **Steven Spielberg**
	June/July	Vol. 39, nos 6/7	**Peter Lorre** **Vincent Price**
	Aug./Sept.	Vol. 39, nos 8/9	**Angela Lansbury** **Roddy McDowall**
	Oct.	Vol. 39, no. 10	**Robert Loggia** **Tom Hanks**
	Nov.	Vol. 39, no. 11	**Katharine Hepburn** **Lee Remick**
	Dec.	Vol. 39, no. 12	**Joe Mantegna** **Don Ameche**
1989	Jan.	Vol. 40, no. 1	**Johnny Weissmuller**
	Feb.	Vol. 40, no. 2	**Gene Hackman** **Frances McDormand**

YEAR	MONTH	REF. No.	COVER STAR
	March	Vol. 40, no. 3	**Myrna Loy** **William Powell** **Donald MacBride** **Gloria De Haven**
	April	Vol. 40, no. 4	**Kurt Russell** **Michelle Pfeiffer** **Mel Gibson**
	May	Vol. 40, no. 5	**Jodie Foster** **Kirk Douglas**
	June/July	Vol. 40, nos 6/7	**Boris Karloff** **Mae Clarke**
	Aug./Sept.	Vol. 40, nos 8/9	**Kirk Douglas** **Lana Turner**
	Oct.	Vol. 40, no. 10	**Andie MacDowell** **James Spader**
	Nov.	Vol. 40, no. 11	**Lee Bowman** **Susan Hayward** **Marsha Hunt**
	Dec.	Vol. 40, no. 12	**Jack Palance** **Joan Crawford** **Gloria Grahame** **Touch (Mike) Connors** **Bruce Bennett**

FLICKS 1985 –

A British monthly that is distributed free in cinemas throughout Britain, or by subscription, this magazine started life as a bimonthly colour tabloid newspaper in October 1985. The magazine format appeared in October 1988 and has been published monthly since then. Lavishly illustrated film reviews, lively gossip pages, quick reference guide to current and future films, and attractive film star covers make this essential reading for the regular filmgoer. Free posters of *Flicks*' covers are available to readers. January issues include an excellent illustrated preview of the year's films. *Flicks* is edited by Quentin Falk and published by Flicks Publications Ltd.

YEAR	MONTH	REF. No.	COVER STAR
1988	Oct.	Vol. 2, no. 1	**John Cleese**
			Jamie Lee Curtis
	Nov.	Vol. 2, no. 2	**Bill Murray**
	Dec.	Vol. 2, no. 3	**Bob Hoskins and Roger Rabbit**
1989	Jan.	Vol. 2, no. 4	**Tom Cruise**
	Feb.	Vol. 2, no. 5	**Priscilla Presley**
	March	Vol. 2, no. 6	**Arnold Schwarzenegger**
			Danny De Vito
	April	Vol. 2, no. 7	**Kim Basinger**
	May	Vol. 2, no. 8	**Meryl Streep**
	June	Vol. 2, no. 9	**Timothy Dalton**
	July	Vol. 2, no. 10	**Harrison Ford**
	Aug.	Vol. 2, no. 11	**Michael Keaton**
	Sept.	Vol. 2, no. 12	**Mel Gibson**
			Danny Glover
	Oct.	Vol. 2, no. 13	**Yahoo Serious**
	Nov.	Vol. 2, no. 14	***Ghostbusters***
	Dec.	Vol. 2, no. 15	**Michael J. Fox**

LIFE 1936 –

The world's most respected photojournal was born on 23 November 1936. Its founder was Henry Robinson Luce, editor of *Time* magazine, and its first cover a black and white picture of a dam at Fort Peck, Montana, under a red rectangle logo with four white letters spelling its name: LIFE. It was a weekly from 1936 to 1972 and a monthly from October 1978 onwards. During the period in between these dates *Life*'s existence was threatened by television news coverage but the magazine still managed to produce two special issues a year. While other magazines have crumpled and died, *Life* has survived.

On 3 May 1937 *Life* devoted its front page to Jean Harlow; this was its first film star cover. It was the start of a long love affair with the cinema, producing to date over 300 film orientated covers. Many of these were of stars not generally allotted the front page of a magazine: Raymond Massey, Roy Rogers, Celeste Holm, Audie Murphy, Peggy Ann Garner, Ricardo Montalban, Ed Wynn, Judy Holliday, Ernie Kovacs, Boris Karloff. Then there were the 11 Monroe covers, the first appearing on 7 April 1952, a treasure each one. *Life* was originally edited by Henry R. Luce, John Shaw Billings, and Daniel Longwell. It is published by Time Inc.

YEAR	MONTH	REF. No.	COVER STAR
1937	3 May	Vol. 2, no. 18	**Jean Harlow**
	6 Sept.	Vol. 3, no. 10	**Harpo Marx**
	27 Sept.	Vol. 3, no. 13	**Nelson Eddy**
	8 Nov.	Vol. 3, no. 19	**Greta Garbo**
1938	7 Feb.	Vol. 4, no. 6	**Gary Cooper**
	18 April	Vol. 4, no. 16	**Paulette Goddard**
	23 May	Vol. 4, no. 21	**Errol Flynn**
	13 June	Vol. 4, no. 24	**Gertrude Lawrence**

YEAR	MONTH	REF. No.	COVER STAR
	20 June	Vol. 4, no. 25	**Rudolph Valentino**
	11 July	Vol. 5, no. 2	**Shirley Temple**
	22 Aug.	Vol. 5, no. 8	**Ginger Rogers Fred Astaire**
	17 Oct.	Vol. 5, no. 16	**Carole Lombard**
	31 Oct.	Vol. 5, no. 18	**Raymond Massey**
	19 Dec.	Vol. 5, no. 25	**Mary Martin**
1939	23 Jan.	Vol. 6, no. 4	**Bette Davis**
	13 Feb.	Vol. 6, no. 7	**Norma Shearer**
	6 March	Vol. 6, no. 10	**Tallulah Bankhead**
	24 July	Vol. 7, no. 4	**Ann Sheridan**
	31 July	Vol. 7, no. 5	**Diana Barrymore**
	14 Aug.	Vol. 7, no. 7	**Sandra Lee Henville**
	4 Sept.	Vol. 7, no. 10	**Rosalind Russell**
	13 Nov.	Vol. 7, no. 20	**Claudette Colbert**
	11 Dec.	Vol. 7, no. 24	**Betty Grable**
1940	29 Jan.	Vol. 8, no. 5	**Lana Turner**
	8 April	Vol. 8, no. 15	**Anna Neagle**
	15 July	Vol. 9, no. 3	**Rita Hayworth**
	7 Oct.	Vol. 9, no. 15	**Gary Cooper**
	9 Dec.	Vol. 9, no. 24	**Ginger Rogers**
1941	6 Jan.	Vol. 10, no. 1	**Katharine Hepburn**
	11 Aug.	Vol. 11, no. 6	**Rita Hayworth**
	25 Aug.	Vol. 11, no. 8	**Fred Astaire and son**
	13 Oct.	Vol. 11, no. 15	**Lana Turner Clark Gable**
	11 Nov.	Vol. 11, no. 19	**Gene Tierney**
1942	2 March	Vol. 12, no. 9	**Ginger Rogers**
	30 March	Vol. 12, no. 13	**Shirley Temple**
	11 May	Vol. 12, no. 19	**Joan Caulfield**
	1 June	Vol. 12, no. 22	**Hedy Lamarr**
	26 Oct.	Vol. 13, no. 17	**Joan Leslie**
1943	18 Jan.	Vol. 14, no. 3	**Rita Hayworth**
	24 May	Vol. 14, no. 21	**Peggy Lloyd**
	12 July	Vol. 15, no. 2	**Roy Rogers and Trigger**
	25 Oct.	Vol. 15, no. 17	**Mary Martin**
1944	10 Jan.	Vol. 16, no. 2	**Bob Hope**
	24 Jan.	Vol. 16, no. 4	**Margaret Sullavan**
	21 Feb.	Vol. 16, no. 8	**Patrice Munsel**
	28 Feb.	Vol. 16, no. 9	**Ella Raines**
	17 April	Vol. 16, no. 16	**Esther Williams**
	24 July	Vol. 17, no. 4	**Jennifer Jones**
	7 Aug.	Vol. 17, no. 6	**Geraldine Fitzgerald**
	16 Oct.	Vol. 17, no. 16	**Lauren Bacall**
	6 Nov.	Vol. 17, no. 19	**Celeste Holm**
	27 Nov.	Vol. 17, no. 22	**Gertrude Lawrence**
	11 Dec.	Vol. 17, no. 24	**Judy Garland**
	18 Dec.	Vol. 17, no. 25	**Fredric March**
1945	28 May	Vol. 18, no. 22	**Barbara Bates**
	16 July	Vol. 19, no. 3	**Audie Murphy**
	23 July	Vol. 19, no. 4	**Peggy Ann Garner**
	24 Sept.	Vol. 19, no. 13	**James Stewart**
	1 Oct.	Vol. 19, no. 14	**June Allyson**
	12 Nov.	Vol. 19, no. 20	**Ingrid Bergman**
	3 Dec.	Vol. 19, no. 23	**Spencer Tracy**
	17 Dec.	Vol. 19, no. 25	**Paulette Goddard**
1946	4 Feb.	Vol. 20, no. 5	**Bob Hope Bing Crosby**
	18 Feb.	Vol. 20, no. 7	**Dorothy McGuire**
	25 March	Vol. 20, no. 12	**Lucille Bremer**
	6 May	Vol. 20, no. 18	**Margaret Leighton**
	10 June	Vol. 20, no. 23	**Donna Reed**
	29 July	Vol. 21, no. 5	**Vivien Leigh**
	12 Aug.	Vol. 21, no. 7	**Loretta Young**
	9 Sept.	Vol. 21, no. 11	**Jane Powell**
	30 Sept.	Vol. 21, no. 14	**Jeanne Crain**
	7 Oct.	Vol. 21, no. 15	**Bing Crosby Joan Crawford**
	21 Oct	Vol. 21, no. 17	**Gloria Grahame**
	2 Dec.	Vol. 21, no. 23	**Ingrid Bergman**
	16 Dec.	Vol. 21, no. 25	**Teresa Wright**
1947	2 June	Vol. 22, no. 22	**Jane Greer**
	14 July	Vol. 23, no. 2	**Elizabeth Taylor**
	11 Aug.	Vol. 23, no. 6	**Ella Raines**
	10 Nov.	Vol. 23, no. 19	**Rita Hayworth**
	1 Dec.	Vol. 23, no. 22	**Gregory Peck**
1948	16 Feb.	Vol. 24, no. 7	**Joan Tetzel**
	15 March	Vol. 24, no. 11	**Laurence Olivier**
	12 April	Vol. 24, no. 15	**Barbara Bel Geddes**
	14 June	Vol. 24, no. 24	**Phyllis Calvert**
	9 Aug.	Vol. 25, no. 6	**Marlene Dietrich**
	8 Nov.	Vol. 25, no. 19	**Helena Carter**
	15 Nov.	Vol. 25, no. 20	**Ingrid Bergman**
	6 Dec.	Vol. 25, no. 23	**Montgomery Clift**
1949	14 Feb.	Vol. 26, no. 7	**Viveca Lindfors**
	7 March	Vol. 26, no. 10	**Marge and Gower Champion**
	28 March	Vol. 26, no. 13	**Joi Lansing**
	18 April	Vol. 26, no. 16	**Mary Martin**
	23 May	Vol. 26, no. 21	**Sarah Churchill**
	13 June	Vol. 26, no. 24	**Marta Toren**
	5 Sept.	Vol. 27, no. 10	**Ben Turpin**
	19 Sept.	Vol. 27, no. 12	**Arlene Dahl**
	17 Oct.	Vol. 27, no. 16	**Jeanne Crain**
	21 Nov.	Vol. 27, no. 21	**Ricardo Montalban**
1950	6 Feb.	Vol. 28, no. 6	**Eva Gabor**
	20 Feb.	Vol. 28, no. 8	**Gregory Peck**

YEAR	MONTH	REF. No.	COVER STAR
	6 March	Vol. 28, no. 10	**Marsha Hunt**
	1 May	Vol. 28, no. 18	**Ruth Roman**
	12 June	Vol. 28, no. 24	**William Boyd**
	26 June	Vol. 28, no. 26	**Cecile Aubry**
	7 Aug.	Vol. 29, no. 6	**Peggy Dow**
	18 Sept.	Vol. 29, no. 12	**Ezio Pinza**
	9 Oct	Vol. 29, no. 15	**Jean Simmons**
	23 Oct.	Vol. 29, no. 17	**Ed Wynn**
	30 Oct.	Vol. 29, no. 18	**Faye Emerson**
	11 Dec.	Vol. 29, no. 24	**Lilli Palmer Rex Harrison**
1951	8 Jan.	Vol. 30, no. 2	**Janice Rule**
	26 Feb.	Vol. 30, no. 9	**Debbie Reynolds**
	12 March	Vol. 30, no. 11	**Paul Douglas**
	16 April	Vol. 30, no. 16	**Esther Williams**
	7 May	Vol. 30, no. 19	**Phyllis Kirk**
	4 June	Vol. 30, no. 23	**Ursula Thiess**
	11 June	Vol. 30, no. 24	**Vivian Blaine**
	25 June	Vol. 30, no. 26	**Janet Leigh**
	13 Aug.	Vol. 31, no. 7	**Martin and Lewis**
	3 Sept.	Vol. 31, no. 10	**Gina Lollobrigida**
	24 Sept.	Vol. 31, no. 13	**Gene Tierney**
	15 Oct.	Vol. 31, no. 16	**Zsa Zsa Gabor**
	5 Nov.	Vol. 31, no. 19	**Ginger Rogers**
	17 Dec.	Vol. 31, no. 25	**Vivien Leigh Laurence Olivier**
1952	3 March	Vol. 32, no. 9	**Patrice Munsel**
	10 March	Vol. 32, no. 10	**Brandon De Wilde**
	7 April	Vol. 32, no. 14	**Marilyn Monroe**
	5 May	Vol. 32, no. 18	**Diana Lynn**
	19 May	Vol. 32, no. 20	**Kerima**
	26 May	Vol. 32, no. 21	**Stewart Granger**
	7 July	Vol. 33, no. 1	**Arlene Dahl**
	28 July	Vol. 33, no. 4	**Audrey Dalton Joan Elan Dorothy Bromiley**
	11 Aug.	Vol. 33, no. 6	**Joan Rice**
	18 Aug.	Vol. 33, no. 7	**Marlene Dietrich and daughter**
	15 Sept.	Vol. 33, no. 11	**Rita Gam**
	20 Oct.	Vol. 33, no. 16	**Lucia Bose**
	1 Dec.	Vol. 33, no. 22	**Suzanne Cloutier**
1953	9 March	Vol. 34, no. 10	**Vanessa Brown**
	23 March	Vol. 34, no. 12	**Elaine Stewart**
	6 April	Vol. 34, no. 14	**Lucille Ball, Desi Arnaz and kids**
	20 April	Vol. 34, no. 16	**Marlon Brando**
	25 May	Vol. 34, no. 21	**Marilyn Monroe Jane Russell**
	29 June	Vol. 34, no. 36	**Cyd Charisse**
	6 July	Vol. 35, no. 1	**Terry Moore**
	3 Aug.	Vol. 35, no. 5	**Nicole Maurey**
	31 Aug.	Vol. 35, no. 9	**Donna Reed**
	7 Dec.	Vol. 35, no. 23	**Audrey Hepburn**

YEAR	MONTH	REF. No.	COVER STAR
1954	1 March	Vol. 36, no. 9	**Rita Moreno**
	29 March	Vol. 36, no. 13	**Pat Crowley**
	26 April	Vol. 36, no. 17	**Grace Kelly**
	17 May	Vol. 36, no. 20	**Dawn Addams**
	24 May	Vol. 36, no. 21	**Kaye Ballard**
	31 May	Vol. 36, no. 22	**William Holden**
	12 July	Vol. 37, no. 2	**Pier Angeli**
	19 July	Vol. 37, no. 3	**Eva Marie Saint**
	30 Aug.	Vol. 37, no. 9	**Anna Maria Alberghetti**
	13 Sept.	Vol. 37, no. 11	**Judy Garland**
	1 Nov.	Vol. 37, no. 18	**Dorothy Dandridge**
	15 Nov.	Vol. 37, no. 20	**Gina Lollobrigida**
	22 Nov.	Vol. 37, no. 21	**Judy Holliday**
1955	10 Jan.	Vol. 38, no. 2	**Greta Garbo**
	31 Jan.	Vol. 38, no. 5	**Spencer Tracy**
	28 Feb.	Vol. 38, no. 9	**Shelley Winters**
	21 March	Vol. 38, no. 12	**Sheree North**
	11 April	Vol. 38, no. 15	**Grace Kelly**
	2 May	Vol. 38, no. 18	***Oklahoma!***
	23 May	Vol. 38, no. 21	**Leslie Caron**
	6 June	Vol. 38, no. 23	**Henry Fonda**
	11 July	Vol. 39, no. 2	**Susan Strasberg**
	18 July	Vol. 39, no. 3	**Audrey Hepburn**
	22 Aug.	Vol. 39, no. 8	**Sophia Loren**
	12 Sept.	Vol. 39, no. 11	**Joan Collins**
	19 Sept.	Vol. 39 no. 12	***Guys and Dolls***
	3 Oct.	Vol. 39, no. 14	**Rock Hudson**
	24 Oct.	Vol. 39, no. 17	***The Ten Command-ments***
	28 Nov.	Vol. 39, no. 22	**Carol Channing**
1956	16 Jan.	Vol. 40, no. 2	**Anita Ekberg**
	16 Feb.	Vol. 40, no. 5	**Shirley Jones**
	20 Feb.	Vol. 40, no. 7	**Claire Bloom**
	5 March	Vol. 40, no. 9	**Kim Novak**
	26 March	Vol. 40, no. 12	**Julie Andrews**
	9 April	Vol. 40, no. 14	**Grace Kelly**
	22 April	Vol. 40, no. 16	**Jayne Mansfield**
	28 May	Vol. 40, no. 21	**Deborah Kerr Yul Brynner**
	11 June	Vol. 40, no. 23	**Carroll Baker**
	16 July	Vol. 41, no. 3	**Gary Cooper Anthony Perkins**
	30 July	Vol. 41, no. 5	**Pier Angeli**
	20 Aug.	Vol. 41, no. 8	**Audrey Hepburn**
	10 Sept.	Vol. 41, no. 11	**Siobhan McKenna**
	24 Sept.	Vol. 41, no. 13	**Janet Blair**
	15 Oct.	Vol. 41, no. 16	**Elizabeth Taylor**
	12 Nov.	Vol. 41, no. 20	**Rosalind Russell**
	26 Nov.	Vol. 41, no. 22	**Ingrid Bergman**
1957	4 Feb.	Vol. 42, no. 5	**Mel Ferrer Audrey Hepburn**
	18 Feb.	Vol. 42, no. 7	**Julie London**
	18 March	Vol. 42, no. 11	**Beatrice Lillie**

YEAR	MONTH	REF. No.	COVER STAR
	15 April	Vol. 42, no. 15	**Ernie Kovacs**
	22 April	Vol. 42, no. 16	**Carol Lynley**
	6 May	Vol. 42, no. 18	**Sophia Loren**
	13 May	Vol. 42, no. 19	**Bert Lahr**
	15 July	Vol. 43, no. 3	**Maria Schell**
	12 Aug.	Vol. 43, no. 7	**May Britt**
	23 Sept.	Vol. 43, no. 13	**Suzy Parker**
	30 Sept.	Vol. 43, no. 14	**Kay Kendall Rex Harrison**
	4 Nov.	Vol. 43, no. 19	**Elizabeth Taylor and daughter**
	25 Nov.	Vol. 43, no. 22	**Elsa Martinelli**
1958	3 Feb.	Vol. 44, no. 5	**Shirley Temple and daughter**
	10 Feb.	Vol. 44, no. 6	**Ralph Bellamy**
	3 March	Vol. 44, no. 9	**Sally Ann Howes**
	10 March	Vol. 44, no. 10	**Yul Brynner**
	14 April	Vol. 44, no. 15	**Gwen Verdon**
	19 May	Vol. 44, no. 20	**Margaret O'Brien**
	22 Sept.	Vol. 45, no. 12	**Burns and Allen**
	29 Sept.	Vol. 45, no. 13	***The Big Country***
	6 Oct.	Vol. 45, no. 14	**France Nuyen**
	24 Nov.	Vol. 45, no. 21	**Kim Novak**
	1 Dec.	Vol. 45, no. 22	**Ricky Nelson**
1959	2 Feb.	Vol. 46, no. 5	**Pat Boone**
	9 Feb.	Vol. 46, no. 6	**Shirley MacLaine and daughter**
	23 Feb.	Vol. 46, no. 8	**Gwen Verdon**
	30 March	Vol. 46, no. 13	**Debbie Reynolds**
	20 April	Vol. 46, no. 16	**Marilyn Monroe**
	8 June	Vol. 46, no. 23	**Audrey Hepburn**
	29 June	Vol. 46, no. 26	**Zsa Zsa Gabor**
	17 Aug.	Vol. 47, no. 7	**May Britt**
	2 Nov.	Vol. 47, no. 18	**Jackie Gleason**
	9 Nov.	Vol. 47, no. 19	**Marilyn Monroe**
1960	11 Jan.	Vol. 48, no. 1	**Dina Merrill**
	1 Feb.	Vol. 48, no. 4	**Dinah Shore**
	22 Feb.	Vol. 48, no. 7	**Jane and Henry Fonda**
	4 April	Vol. 48, no. 13	**Marlon Brando**
	11 April	Vol. 48, no. 14	**Silvano Mangano**
	9 May	Vol. 48, no. 18	**Yvette Mimieux**
	6 June	Vol. 48, no. 22	**Lee Remick**
	13 June	Vol. 48, no. 23	**Hayley Mills**
	18 July	Vol. 49, no. 3	**Ina Balin**
	15 Aug.	Vol. 49, no. 7	**Yves Montand Marilyn Monroe**
	10 Oct.	Vol. 49, no. 15	**Doris Day**
	24 Oct.	Vol. 49, no. 17	**Nancy Kwan**
	14 Nov.	Vol. 49, no. 20	**Sophia Loren**
	28 Nov.	Vol. 49, no. 22	**Carroll Baker**
	12 Dec.	Vol. 49, no. 24	**Sal Mineo Jill Haworth**
1961	13 Jan.	Vol. 50, no. 2	**Clark Gable**

YEAR	MONTH	REF. No.	COVER STAR
	17 Feb.	Vol. 50, no. 7	**Shirley MacLaine**
	10 March	Vol. 50, no. 10	**Maurice Chevalier Bing Crosby**
	28 April	Vol. 50, no. 17	**Elizabeth Taylor**
	5 May	Vol. 50, no. 18	**Anna Maria Alberghetti**
	23 June	Vol. 50, no. 25	**Princess Grace**
	30 June	Vol. 50, no. 26	**Leslie Caron**
	28 July	Vol. 51, no. 4	**Brigitte Bardot**
	11 Aug.	Vol. 51, no. 6	**Sophia Loren**
	6 Oct.	Vol. 51, no. 14	**Elizabeth Taylor**
1962	5 Jan.	Vol. 52, no. 1	**Lucille Ball**
	16 Feb.	Vol. 52, no. 7	**Rock Hudson**
	23 Feb.	Vol. 52, no. 8	**Shirley MacLaine**
	13 April	Vol. 52, no. 15	**Richard Burton Elizabeth Taylor**
	20 April	Vol. 52, no. 16	**Audrey Hepburn**
	11 May	Vol. 52, no. 19	**Bob Hope**
	15 June	Vol. 52, no. 24	**Natalie Wood**
	22 June	Vol. 52, no. 25	**Marilyn Monroe**
	27 July	Vol. 53, no. 4	**Elsa Martinelli**
	10 Aug.	Vol. 53, no. 6	**Janet Leigh**
	17 Aug.	Vol. 53, no. 7	**Marilyn Monroe**
	5 Oct.	Vol. 53, no. 14	**Jackie Gleason**
	30 Nov.	Vol. 53, no. 22	**Sid Caesar**
	14 Dec.	Vol. 53, no. 24	**Marlon Brando**
1963	11 Jan.	Vol. 54, no. 2	**Ann-Margret**
	1 Feb.	Vol. 54, no. 5	**Alfred Hitchcock**
	8 March	Vol. 54, no. 10	**Jean Seberg**
	19 April	Vol. 54, no. 16	**Richard Burton Elizabeth Taylor**
	21 June	Vol. 54, no. 25	**Shirley MacLaine**
	12 July	Vol. 55, no. 2	**Steve McQueen Neile Adams**
	26 July	Vol. 55, no. 4	**Tuesday Weld**
	23 Aug.	Vol. 55, no. 6	**Frank Sinatra and son**
	25 Oct.	Vol. 55, no. 17	**Yvette Mimieux**
	22 Nov.	Vol. 55, no. 21	**Elizabeth Ashley**
	22 Dec.	Vol. 55, no. 26	**Hollywood magic**
1964	31 Jan.	Vol. 56, no. 5	**Geraldine Chaplin**
	3 April	Vol. 56, no. 14	**Carol Channing**
	24 April	Vol. 56, no. 17	**Richard Burton**
	22 May	Vol. 56, no. 21	**Barbra Streisand**
	17 July	Vol. 57, no. 3	**Carroll Baker**
	7 Aug.	Vol. 57, no. 6	**Marilyn Monroe**
	28 Aug.	Vol. 57, no. 9	**The Beatles**
	18 Sept.	Vol. 57, no. 12	**Sophia Loren**
	6 Nov.	Vol. 57, no. 19	**Shirley Eaton**
	18 Dec.	Vol. 57, no. 25	**Elizabeth Taylor**
1965	22 Jan.	Vol. 58, no. 3	**Peter O'Toole**
	12 March	Vol, 58, no. 10	**Julie Andrews**
	23 April	Vol. 58, no. 16	**Frank Sinatra**
	7 May	Vol. 58, no. 18	**John Wayne**
	22 Oct.	Vol. 59, no. 17	**Mary Martin**

YEAR	MONTH	REF. No.	COVER STAR
1966	7 Jan.	Vol. 60, no. 1	**Sean Connery**
	28 Jan.	Vol. 60, no. 4	**Catherine Spaak**
	4 Feb.	Vol. 60, no. 5	**Sammy Davis Jr**
			Sidney Poitier
			Harry Belafonte
	11 March	Vol. 60, no. 10	***Batman***
	18 March	Vol. 60, no. 11	**Barbra Streisand**
	1 April	Vol. 60, no. 13	**Sophia Loren**
			Charlie Chaplin
	15 April	Vol. 60, no. 15	**Louis Armstrong**
	29 April	Vol. 60, no. 17	**Julie Christie**
	10 June	Vol. 60, no. 23	**Elizabeth Taylor**
	17 June	Vol. 60, no. 24	**Angela Lansbury**
	8 July	Vol. 61, no. 2	**Claudia Cardinale**
	16 Sept.	Vol. 61, no. 12	**Sophia Loren**
	30 Sept.	Vol. 61, no. 14	**Rex Harrison**
	11 Nov.	Vol. 61, no. 20	**Jean-Paul Belmondo**
	2 Dec.	Vol. 61, no. 23	**Melina Mercouri**
1967	24 Feb.	Vol. 62, no. 8	**Elizabeth Taylor**
	5 May	Vol. 62, no. 18	**Mia Farrow**
	20 May	Vol. 62, no. 19	**Scott Wilson**
			Truman Capote
			Robert Blake
	13 Oct.	Vol. 63, no. 16	**Ingrid Bergman**
1968	5 Jan.	Vol. 64, no. 1	**Katharine Hepburn**
	12 Jan.	Vol. 64, no. 2	**Faye Dunaway**
	15 March	Vol. 64, no. 11	**Boris Karloff**
	29 March	Vol. 64, no. 13	**Jane Fonda**
	10 May	Vol. 64, no. 19	**Paul Newman**
	13 Sept.	Vol. 65, no. 11	**The Beatles**
	18 Oct.	Vol. 65, no. 16	**Paul Newman**
			Joanne Woodward
1969	24 Jan.	Vol. 66, no. 3	**Catherine Deneuve**
	14 Feb.	Vol. 66, no. 6	**Barbra Streisand**
	21 March	Vol. 66, no. 11	**Woody Allen**
			Humphrey Bogart
	9 May	Vol. 66, no. 18	**Peter Falk**
			Ben Gazzara
			John Cassavetes
	11 July	Vol. 67, no. 2	**John Wayne**
			Dustin Hoffman
	7 Nov.	Vol. 67, no. 21	**Paul McCartney and family**
	21 Nov.	Vol. 67, no. 23	**Johnny Cash**
1970	6 Feb.	Vol. 68, no. 4	**Robert Redford**
	27 Feb.	Vol. 68, no. 7	**Hollywood tightens belt**
	3 April	Vol. 68, no. 12	**Lauren Bacall**
	29 May	Vol. 68, no. 20	**Brenda Vaccaro**
	19 June	Vol. 68, no. 23	**Dennis Hopper**
	24 July	Vol. 69, no. 4	**Candice Bergen**
1971	29 Jan.	Vol. 70, no. 3	**Bob Hope**
	19 Feb.	Vol. 70, no. 6	**Rita Hayworth**
			Ruby Keeler
			Paulette Goddard
			Myrna Loy
			Joan Blondell
			Betty Hutton
	16 April	Vol. 70, no. 14	**Paul and Linda McCartney**
	23 April	Vol. 70, no. 15	**Jane Fonda**
	14 May	Vol. 70, no. 18	**Carol Burnett**
	25 June	Vol. 70, no. 24	**Frank Sinatra**
	23 July	Vol. 71, no. 4	**Clint Eastwood**
	6 Aug.	Vol. 71, no. 6	**Ann-Margret**
	10 Dec.	Vol. 71, no. 24	**Cybill Shepherd**
1972	28 Jan.	Vol. 72, no. 3	**John Wayne**
	25 Feb.	Vol. 72, no. 7	**Elizabeth Taylor**
	10 March	Vol. 72, no. 9	**Marlon Brando**
	7 April	Vol. 72, no. 13	**Oscar time**
	21 April	Vol. 72, no. 15	**Charlie and Oona Chaplin**
	2 June	Vol. 72, no. 21	**Raquel Welch**
	14 July	Vol. 73, no. 2	**Mick Jagger**
	8 Sept.	Vol. 73, no. 10	**Marilyn Monroe**
	8 Dec.	Vol. 73, no. 23	**Diana Ross**
1978	Nov.	Vol. 1, no. 2	**Mickey Mouse**
1979	March	Vol. 2, no. 3	**Lesley-Anne Down**
	June	Vol. 2, no. 6	**Marlon Brando**
	Oct.	Vol. 2, no. 10	**Dolly Parton**
1980	Feb.	Vol. 3, no. 2	**Mary Astor**
	March	Vol. 3, no. 3	**Mickey Rooney**
1981	April	Vol. 4, no. 4	**Meryl Streep**
	Oct.	Vol. 4, no. 10	**Marilyn Monroe**
	Dec.	Vol. 4, no. 12	**Brooke Shields**
1982	March	Vol. 5, no. 3	**Elizabeth Taylor**
	July	Vol. 5, no. 7	**Raquel Welch**
	Aug.	Vol. 5, no. 8	**Marilyn Monroe**
	Oct.	Vol. 5, no. 10	**Sandahl Bergman**
			Arnold Schwarzenegger
1983	Feb.	Vol. 6, no. 2	**Brooke Shields**
	May	Vol. 6, no. 5	**Debra Winger**
	June	Vol. 6, no. 6	**Lucas's empire**
	Dec.	Vol. 6, no. 12	**Barbra Streisand**
1984	Feb.	Vol. 7, no. 2	**The Beatles**
	March	Vol. 7, no. 3	**Daryl Hannah**
	June	Vol. 7, no. 6	**Harrison Ford**
			Kate Capshaw
	Sept.	Vol. 7, no. 10	**Michael Jackson**

YEAR	MONTH	REF. No.	COVER STAR
1985	Feb.	Vol. 8, no. 2	**Brooke Shields**
	Oct.	Vol. 8, no. 11	**Joan Collins**
1986	March	Vol. 9, no. 3	**Molly Ringwald**
	May	Vol. 9, no. 5	**Jessica Lange**
			Sally Field
			Barbra Streisand
			Goldie Hawn
			Jane Fonda
	Nov.	Vol. 9, no. 11	**Tom Cruise**
			Paul Newman
	Dec.	Vol. 9, no. 13	**Madonna**
1987	April	Vol. 10, no. 4	**Hollywood is 100**
	May	Vol. 10, no. 5	**Warren Beatty**
			Dustin Hoffman
	Dec.	Vol. 10, no. 13	**Meryl Streep**
1988	May	Vol. 11, no. 6	**Clark Gable**
			Vivien Leigh
	Sept.	Vol. 11, no. 10	**Paul Newman**
	Oct.	Vol. 11, no. 11	**Sigourney Weaver**
1989	April	Vol. 12, no. 4	**Melanie Griffith**
			Don Johnson

MODERN SCREEN 1930 –

Born at the beginning of Hollywood's 'Golden Age', *Modern Screen* was the epitome of a fan magazine with gossipy pages, fashion and beauty hints, and enticing covers. Although the covers were generally reserved for actresses, *Modern Screen* has allowed actors on its front pages more than one would expect: Robert Taylor, Sterling Hayden, Clark Gable, John Payne, Errol Flynn, Van Johnson, Frank Sinatra, Ronald Reagan, Alan Ladd, Dana Andrews and many more. One of the most popular cover girls was Debbie Reynolds, who appeared 17 times on the cover between June 1953 and November 1959. Many of *Modern Screen*'s early covers were portraits drawn by Earl Christy and are now very collectable. Originally published by Syndicate Publishing Company Inc., later by Dell Publishing Company Inc., *Modern Screen* had the largest circulation of any film magazine. Editors have been Ernest Heyn, Mary Burgum, Regina Cannon, Pearl Finley, Albert Delacorte, Henry Malmgreen, Wade Nichols, William Hartley, Charles Saxon, and David Myers. Once a monthly, it now appears at irregular intervals*. The following entry is incomplete and ends at 1959.

*Collectors should note that there was no volume 10. From 1954 there were 12, sometimes 13, issues per volume and they were numbered accordingly. Further discrepancies in numbering appear from 1958 onwards.

YEAR	MONTH	REF. No.	COVER STAR
1930	Dec.	Vol. 1, no. 1	**Kay Francis**
1931	Feb.	Vol. 1, no. 3	**Constance Bennett**
	May	Vol. 1, no. 6	**Marlene Dietrich**
	June	Vol. 2, no. 1	**Dorothy Jordan**
	July	Vol. 2, no. 2	**Helen Twelvetrees**
	Aug.	Vol. 2, no. 3	**Norma Shearer**
	Sept.	Vol. 2, no. 4	**Nancy Carroll**
	Oct.	Vol. 2, no. 5	**Dorothy Mackaill**
	Nov.	Vol. 2, no. 6	**Elissa Landi**
	31 Dec.	Vol. 3, no. 1	**Greta Garbo** **Clark Gable**
1932	Jan.	Vol. 3, no. 2	**Carole Lombard**
	Feb.	Vol. 3, no. 3	**Joan Crawford**
	March	Vol. 3, no. 4	**Janet Gaynor**
	April	Vol. 3, no. 5	**Marian Marsh**
	May	Vol. 3, no. 6	**Irene Dunne**
	June	Vol. 4, no. 1	**Sylvia Sidney**
	July	Vol. 4, no. 2	**Marie Dressler**
	Aug.	Vol. 4, no. 3	**Barbara Stanwyck**
	Sept.	Vol. 4, no. 4	**Marian Nixon**
	Oct.	Vol. 4, no. 5	**Constance Bennett**
	Nov.	Vol. 4, no. 6	**Marlene Dietrich**
	Dec.	Vol. 5, no. 1	**Norma Shearer**
1933	Jan.	Vol. 5, no. 2	**Sidney Fox**
	Feb.	Vol. 5, no. 3	**Bette Davis**
	March	Vol. 5, no. 4	**Helen Hayes**
	April	Vol. 5, no. 5	**Claudette Colbert**
	May	Vol. 5, no. 6	**Katharine Hepburn**
	June	Vol. 6, no. 1	**Sally Eilers**
	July	Vol. 6, no. 2	**Jean Harlow**
	Aug.	Vol. 6, no. 3	**Ruby Keeler**
	Sept.	Vol. 6, no. 4	**Clark Gable** **Mae West**
	Oct.	Vol. 6, no. 5	**Joan Crawford**
	Nov.	Vol. 6, no. 6	**Janet Gaynor**
	Dec.	Vol. 7, no. 1	**Kay Francis**
1934	Jan	Vol. 7, no. 2	**Ann Harding**
	Feb.	Vol. 7, no. 3	**Max Baer** **Myrna Loy**
	March	Vol. 7, no. 4	**Miriam Hopkins**
	April	Vol. 7, no. 5	**Greta Garbo**
	May	Vol. 7, no. 6	**Katharine Hepburn**
	June	Vol. 8, no. 1	**Norma Shearer**
	July	Vol. 8, no. 2	**Baby Leroy**
	Aug.	Vol. 8, no. 3	**Kay Francis**
	Sept.	Vol. 8, no. 4	**Dolores Del Rio**
	Oct.	Vol. 8, no. 5	**Janet Gaynor**
	Nov.	Vol. 8, no. 6	**Claudette Colbert**
	Dec.	Vol. 9, no. 1	**Jean Harlow**
1935	Jan.	Vol. 9, no. 2	**Anna Sten**
	Feb.	Vol. 9, no. 3	**Margaret Sullavan**
	March	Vol. 9, no. 4	**Joan Crawford**
	April	Vol. 9, no. 5	**Miriam Hopkins**
	May	Vol. 9, no. 6	**Kay Francis**
	June	Vol. 11,* no. 1	**Mae West**
	July	Vol. 11, no. 2	**Shirley Temple**
	Aug.	Vol. 11, no. 3	**Jean Harlow**
	Sept.	Vol. 11, no. 4	**Grace Moore**
	Oct.	Vol. 11, no. 5	**Ginger Rogers** **Fred Astaire**
	Nov.	Vol. 11, no. 6	**Jeanette MacDonald** **Nelson Eddy**
	Dec.	Vol. 12, no. 1	**Claudette Colbert**
1936	Jan.	Vol. 12, no. 2	**Dolores Del Rio**
	Feb.	Vol. 12, no. 3	**Katharine Hepburn**
	March	Vol. 12, no. 4	**Marlene Dietrich**
	April	Vol. 12, no. 5	**The Quints**
	May	Vol. 12, no. 6	**Shirley Temple**
	June	Vol. 13, no. 1	**Myrna Loy**
	July	Vol. 13, no. 2	**The Quints**
	Aug.	Vol. 13, no. 3	**Ginger Rogers**
	Sept.	Vol. 13, no. 4	**Carole Lombard**
	Oct.	Vol. 13, no. 5	**Jeanette MacDonald**
	Nov.	Vol. 13, no. 6	**Jean Arthur**
	Dec.	Vol. 14, no. 1	**Merle Oberon**
1937	Jan.	Vol. 14, no. 2	**Robert Taylor**
	Feb.	Vol. 14, no. 3	**Loretta Young**
	March	Vol. 14, no. 4	**Carole Lombard** **Clark Gable**
	April	Vol. 14, no. 5	**Shirley Temple and The Quints**
	May	Vol. 14, no. 6	**Jean Harlow** **Robert Taylor**
	June	Vol. 15, no. 1	**Luise Rainer**
	July	Vol. 15, no. 2	**Madeleine Carroll**
	Aug.	Vol. 15, no. 3	**Tyrone Power** **Loretta Young**
	Sept.	Vol. 15, no. 4	**Olivia De Havilland**
	Oct.	Vol. 15, no. 5	**Myrna Loy** **William Powell**
	Nov.	Vol. 15, no. 6	**Marlene Dietrich**
	Dec.	Vol. 16, no. 1	**Deanna Durbin**
1938	Jan.	Vol. 16, no. 2	**Katharine Hepburn**
	Feb.	Vol. 16, no. 3	**Shirley Temple**
	March	Vol. 16, no. 4	**Tyrone Power** **Sonja Henie**
	April	Vol. 16, no. 5	**Ginger Rogers**
	May	Vol. 16, no. 6	**Carole Lombard**
	June	Vol. 17, no. 1	**Greta Garbo** **Leopold Stokowski**
	July	Vol. 17, no. 2	**Simone Simon**
	Aug.	Vol. 17, no. 3	**Bette Davis**
	Sept.	Vol. 17, no. 4	**Jeanette MacDonald**
	Oct.	Vol. 17, no. 5	**Irene Dunne**
	Nov.	Vol. 17, no. 6	**Katharine Hepburn** **Howard Hughes**
1939	Jan.	Vol. 18, no. 2	**Shirley Temple**

YEAR	MONTH	REF. No.	COVER STAR
	June	Vol. 19, no. 1	**Olivia De Havilland**
	July	Vol. 19, no. 2	**Madeleine Carroll**
	Aug.	Vol. 19, no. 3	**Priscilla Lane**
	Sept.	Vol. 19, no. 4	**Myrna Loy**
			Asta
	Oct.	Vol. 19, no. 5	**Ann Sheridan**
	Nov.	Vol. 19, no. 6	**Joan Blondell**
	Dec.	Vol. 20, no. 1	**Baby Sandy**
1940	Jan.	Vol. 20, no. 2	**Jeanette MacDonald**
	Feb.	Vol. 20, no. 3	**Mickey Rooney**
			Judy Garland
	March	Vol. 20, no. 4	**Deanna Durbin**
	April	Vol. 20, no. 5	**Alice Faye**
	May	Vol. 20, no. 6	**Ginger Rogers**
	June	Vol. 21, no. 1	**Vivien Leigh**
	July	Vol. 21, no. 2	**Ann Rutherford**
	Aug.	Vol. 21, no. 3	**Deanna Durbin**
	Sept.	Vol. 21, no. 4	**Claudette Colbert**
	Oct.	Vol. 21, no. 5	**Bette Davis**
	Nov.	Vol. 21, no. 6	**Marlene Dietrich**
	Dec.	Vol. 22, no. 1	**Norma Shearer**
1941	Feb.	Vol. 22, no. 3	**Vivien Leigh**
	March	Vol. 22, no. 4	**Linda Darnell**
	April	Vol. 22, no. 5	**Olivia De Havilland**
	May	Vol. 22, no. 6	**Barbara Stanwyck**
	June	Vol. 23, no. 1	**Judy Garland**
	July	Vol. 23, no. 2	**Paulette Goddard**
	Aug.	Vol. 23, no. 3	**Lana Turner**
	Sept.	Vol. 23, no. 4	**Merle Oberon**
	Oct.	Vol. 23, no. 5	**Gene Tierney**
	Nov.	Vol. 23, no. 6	**Sterling Hayden**
	Dec.	Vol. 24, no. 1	**Linda Darnell**
1942	Jan.	Vol. 24, no. 2	**Judy Garland**
	Feb.	Vol. 24, no. 3	**Lana Turner**
	March	Vol. 24, no. 4	**Sonja Henie**
	April	Vol. 24, no. 5	**Maureen O'Hara**
	May	Vol. 24, no. 6	**Ann Sheridan**
	June	Vol. 25, no. 1	**Carole Lombard**
	July	Vol. 25, no. 2	**Deanna Durbin**
	Aug.	Vol. 25, no. 3	**Betty Grable**
	Sept.	Vol. 25, no. 4	**Olivia De Havilland**
	Oct.	Vol. 25, no. 5	**Lana Turner**
	Nov.	Vol. 25, no. 6	**Clark Gable**
	Dec.	Vol. 26, no. 1	**Betty Grable**
			John Payne
1943	Jan.	Vol. 26, no. 2	**Jane Wyman**
			Ronald Reagan
	Feb.	Vol. 26, no. 3	**Deanna Durbin**
	March,	Vol. 26, no. 4	**Rita Hayworth**
	April	Vol. 26, no. 5	**John Payne**
	May	Vol. 26, no. 6	**Lana Turner**
	June	Vol. 27, no. 1	**Judy Garland**
	July	Vol. 27, no. 2	**Clark Gable**
	Aug.	Vol. 27, no. 3	**Ingrid Bergman**

YEAR	MONTH	REF. No.	COVER STAR
	Sept.	Vol. 27, no. 4	**Deanna Durbin**
	Nov.	Vol. 27, no. 6	**Errol Flynn**
	Dec.	Vol. 28, no. 1	**Alan Ladd**
1944	Jan.	Vol. 28, no. 2	**Betty Hutton**
	Feb.	Vol. 28, no. 3	**Lana Turner**
	March	Vol. 28, no. 4	**Rita Hayworth**
	April	Vol. 28, no. 5	**Shirley Temple**
	May	Vol. 28, no. 6	**Deanna Durbin**
	June	Vol. 29, no. 1	**Hedy Lamarr**
	July	Vol. 29, no. 2	**Van Johnson**
	Aug.	Vol. 29, no. 3	**Lana Turner**
	Sept.	Vol. 29, no. 4	**Frank Sinatra**
	Oct.	Vol. 29, no. 5	**Ronald Reagan**
	Nov.	Vol. 29, no. 6	**Shirley Temple**
	Dec.	Vol. 30, no. 1	**Lana Turner**
1945	Jan.	Vol. 30, no. 2	**Joan Leslie**
	Feb.	Vol. 30, no. 3	**Jeanne Crain**
	March	Vol. 30, no. 4	**Alan Ladd**
	April	Vol. 30, no. 5	**Shirley Temple**
	May	Vol. 30, no. 6	**Van Johnson**
	June	Vol. 31, no. 1	**June Allyson**
	July	Vol. 31, no. 2	**June Haver**
	Aug.	Vol. 31, no. 3	**Dana Andrews**
	Oct.	Vol. 31, no. 5	**Frank Sinatra**
	Nov.	Vol. 31, no. 6	**Ingrid Bergman**
1946	Jan.	Vol. 32, no. 2	**Van Johnson**
			June Allyson
			Frank Sinatra
	Feb.	Vol. 32, no. 3	**Shirley Temple**
	March	Vol. 32, no. 4	**Dennis Morgan**
	April	Vol. 32, no. 5	**Alan Ladd**
	May	Vol. 32, no. 6	**Ether Williams**
	June	Vol. 33, no. 1	**Gene Kelly**
	July	Vol. 33, no. 2	**June Allyson**
	Aug.	Vol. 33, no. 3	**Gregory Peck**
	Nov.	Vol. 33, no. 6	**Cornel Wilde**
	Dec.	Vol. 34, no. 1	**Jeanne Crain**
1947	Jan.	Vol. 34, no. 2	**Frank Sinatra**
	Feb.	Vol. 34, no. 3	**June Allyson**
	March	Vol. 34, no. 4	**Clark Gable**
	April	Vol. 34, no. 5	**Shirley Temple**
	May	Vol. 34, no. 6	**Ingrid Bergman**
	June	Vol. 35, no. 1	**June Haver**
	July	Vol. 35, no. 2	**Esther Williams**
	Aug.	Vol. 35, no. 3	**Cornel Wilde**
	Sept.	Vol. 35, no. 4	**Gene Tierney**
	Oct.	Vol. 35, no. 5	**Lizabeth Scott**
	Nov.	Vol. 35, no. 6	**Lana Turner**
	Dec.	Vol. 36, no. 1	**Tyrone Power**
1948	Jan.	Vol. 36, no. 2	**June Allyson**
	Feb.	Vol. 36, no. 3	**Shirley Temple**
	March	Vol. 36, no. 4	**Betty Grable**
	April	Vol. 36, no. 5	**Esther Williams**

YEAR	MONTH	REF. No.	COVER STAR
	May	Vol. 36, no. 6	**Ingrid Bergman**
	June	Vol. 37, no. 1	**Jeanne Crain**
	July	Vol. 37, no. 2	**June Haver**
	Aug.	Vol. 37, no. 3	**Shirley Temple**
	Sept.	Vol. 37, no. 4	**Bing Crosby**
	Oct.	Vol. 37, no. 5	**Judy Garland**
	Nov.	Vol. 37, no. 6	**Lana Turner**
	Dec.	Vol. 38, no. 1	**Betty Grable**
1949	Jan.	Vol. 38, no. 2	**June Allyson**
	Feb.	Vol. 38, no. 3	**Esther Williams**
	March	Vol. 38, no. 4	**Ava Gardner**
	April	Vol. 38, no. 5	**Shirley Temple**
	May	Vol. 38, no. 6	**Alan Ladd**
	June	Vol. 39, no. 1	**Elizabeth Taylor**
	July	Vol. 39, no. 2	**Jeanne Crain**
	Sept.	Vol. 39, no. 4	**Betty Grable**
	Oct.	Vol. 39, no. 5	**Shirley Temple**
	Nov.	Vol. 39, no. 6	**Ava Gardner**
	Dec.	Vol. 40, no. 1	**Jane Powell**
1950	Jan.	Vol. 40, no. 2	**Lana Turner**
	Feb.	Vol. 40, no. 3	**Esther Williams**
	March	Vol. 40, no. 4	**Elizabeth Taylor**
	April	Vol. 40, no. 5	**Jeanne Crain**
	May	Vol. 40, no. 6	**June Allyson**
	June	Vol. 41, no. 1	**Elizabeth Taylor**
	July	Vol. 41, no. 2	**Betty Grable**
	Aug.	Vol. 41, no. 3	**Jane Powell**
	Sept.	Vol. 41, no. 4	**Lana Turner**
	Oct.	Vol. 41, no. 5	**Ava Gardner**
	Nov.	Vol. 41, no. 6	**Elizabeth Taylor**
	Dec.	Vol. 42, no. 1	**Janet Leigh**
1951	Jan.	Vol. 42, no. 2	**Shirley Temple**
	Feb.	Vol. 42, no. 3	**Jane Powell**
	March	Vol. 42, no. 4	**Esther Williams**
	April	Vol. 42, no. 5	**Elizabeth Taylor**
	May	Vol. 42, no. 6	**Jeanne Crain**
	June	Vol. 43, no. 1	**Jane Wyman**
	July	Vol. 43, no. 2	**June Allyson**
	Aug.	Vol. 43, no. 3	**Betty Grable**
	Sept.	Vol. 43, no. 4	**Elizabeth Taylor**
	Oct.	Vol. 43, no. 5	**Lana Turner**
	Nov.	Vol. 43, no. 6	**June Allyson and baby**
	Dec.	Vol. 44, no. 1	**Esther Williams**
1952	Jan.	Vol. 44, no. 2	**Ava Gardner**
	Feb.	Vol. 44, no. 3	**Jane Powell**
	March	Vol. 44, no. 4	**Elizabeth Taylor**
	April	Vol. 44, no. 5	**Betty Grable**
	May	Vol. 44, no. 6	**Doris Day**
	June	Vol. 45, no. 1	**June Allyson**
	July	Vol. 45, no. 2	**Rita Hayworth**
	Aug.	Vol. 45, no. 3	**Lana Turner**
	Sept.	Vol. 45, no. 4	**Ava Gardner**
	Oct.	Vol. 45, no. 5	**Elizabeth Taylor**
	Nov.	Vol. 45, no. 6	**Jane Powell**
	Dec.	Vol. 46, no. 1	**Betty Grable**
1953	Jan.	Vol. 46, no. 2	**Ava Gardner**
	Feb.	Vol. 46, no. 3	**Elizabeth Taylor**
	March	Vol. 46, no. 4	**Rita Hayworth**
	April	Vol. 46, no. 5	**Doris Day**
	June	Vol. 47, no. 1	**Debbie Reynolds**
	July	Vol. 47, no. 2	**Ann Blyth**
	Aug.	Vol. 47, no. 3	**Betty Grable**
	Sept.	Vol. 47, no. 4	**Elizabeth Taylor**
	Oct.	Vol. 47, no. 5	**Marilyn Monroe**
	Nov.	Vol. 47, no. 6	**Ava Gardner**
	Dec.	Vol. 48, no. 1	**Elizabeth Taylor and baby**
1954	Jan.	Vol. 48, no. 2	**Janet Leigh**
	Feb.	Vol. 48, no. 3	**Susan Hayward**
	March	Vol. 48, no. 4	**Marilyn Monroe**
	April	Vol. 48, no. 5	**Elizabeth Taylor**
	May	Vol. 48, no. 6	**Esther Williams**
	June	Vol. 48, no. 7	**Lana Turner**
	July	Vol. 48, no. 8	**Doris Day**
	Aug.	Vol. 48, no. 9	**Ann Blyth**
	Sept.	Vol. 48, no. 10	**Marilyn Monroe**
	Oct.	Vol. 48, no. 11	**Elizabeth Taylor**
	Nov.	Vol. 48, no. 12	**Debbie Reynolds**
	Dec.	Vol. 49, no. 1	**Grace Kelly**
1955	Jan.	Vol. 49, no. 2	**Janet Leigh Tony Curtis**
	March	Vol. 49, no. 4	**Doris Day**
	April	Vol. 49, no. 5	**Ann Blyth**
	June	Vol. 49, no. 7	**Marilyn Monroe**
	July	Vol. 49, no. 8	**Eddie Fisher Debbie Reynolds**
	Aug.	Vol. 49, no. 9	**Pier Angeli**
	Sept.	Vol. 49, no. 10	**Grace Kelly**
	Oct.	Vol. 49, no. 11	**Marilyn Monroe**
	Nov.	Vol. 49, no. 12	**Elizabeth Taylor**
	Dec.	Vol. 49, no. 13	**Janet Leigh**
1956	Jan.	Vol. 50, no. 1	**Debbie Reynolds**
	April	Vol. 50, no. 4	**Grace kelly**
	May	Vol. 50, no. 5	**Eddie Fisher Debbie Reynolds**
	June	Vol. 50, no. 6	**Jane Powell**
	July	Vol. 50, no. 7	**Kim Novak**
	Aug.	Vol. 50, no. 8	**Debbie Reynolds**
	Sept.	Vol. 50, no. 9	**Jane Russell**
	Nov.	Vol. 50, no. 11	**Marilyn Monroe**
	Dec.	Vol. 50, no. 12	**Elizabeth Taylor**
1957	Jan.	Vol. 51, no. 1	**Debbie Reynolds**
	Feb.	Vol. 51, no. 2	**Natalie Wood**
	March	Vol. 51, no. 3	**Kim Novak**
	April	Vol. 51, no. 4	**Doris Day**
	May	Vol. 51, no. 5	**Eddie Fisher Debbie Reynolds**

YEAR	MONTH	REF. No.	COVER STAR
	June	Vol. 51, no. 6	**Janet Leigh Tony Curtis**
	July	Vol. 51, no. 7	**Doris Day**
	Oct.	Vol. 51, no. 10	**Debbie Reynolds**
	Nov.	Vol. 51, no. 11	**Doris Day**
	Dec.	Vol. 51, no. 12	**Debbie Reynolds Eddie Fisher**
1958	Feb.	Vol. 52, no. 1	**Elizabeth Taylor and baby**
	April	Vol. 52, no. 3	**Robert Wagner Natalie Wood**
	May	Vol. 52, no. 4	**Janet Leigh Tony Curtis**
	June	Vol. 52, no. 5	**Debbie Reynolds and baby**
	July	Vol. 52, no. 6	**Mike Todd Elizabeth Taylor**
	Aug.	Vol. 52, no. 7	**Natalie Wood Robert Wagner**
	Sept.	Vol. 52, no. 8	**Debbie Reynolds, Eddie Fisher and children**
	Oct.	Vol. 52, no. 9	**Elizabeth Taylor and twins**

YEAR	MONTH	REF. No.	COVER STAR
	Nov.	Vol. 52, no. 10	**Ricky Nelson Marianne Gaba**
	Dec.	Vol. 52, no. 11	**Eddie Fisher Elizabeth Taylor Debbie Reynolds**
1959	Feb.	Vol. 53, no. 1	**Debbie Reynolds and baby**
	March	Vol. 53, no. 2	**Elizabeth Taylor**
	April	Vol. 53, no. 3	**Debbie Reynolds**
	May	Vol. 53, no. 4	**Elizabeth Taylor, Eddie Fisher and twins**
	June	Vol. 53, no. 5	**Rock Hudson**
	July	Vol. 53, no. 6	**Elizabeth Taylor Eddie Fisher**
	Aug.	Vol. 53, no. 7	**Debbie Reynolds**
	Sept.	Vol. 53, no. 8	**Eddie Fisher Elizabeth Taylor**
	Oct.	Vol. 53, no. 9	**Edd Byrnes Asa Maynor**
	Nov.	Vol. 53, no. 10	**Elizabeth Taylor Debbie Reynolds**
	Dec.	Vol. 53, no. 11	**Fabian**

MOTION PICTURE 1911 – 77

The most collectable of all film fan magazines was founded by Stuart Blackton and Eugene Brewster in February 1911, and published by the Motion Picture Story Publishing Company of New York. *Motion Picture Story Magazine*, as it was first called, was designed for the film fanatic who wanted to know more about the films and the stars they were creating. Illustrated picture plays were soon vying with studio portraits of popular stars and informative articles on the lives they led. Early covers of film scenes soon gave way to beautiful full-colour portraits by artists. Today many of these signed covers are treasurable items. Leo Sielke painted over 50 covers for *Motion Picture* from 1916 to 1921; finely executed portraits of such luminaries as Theda Bara, William S. Hart, Pearl White, Douglas Fairbanks. Florhi and Alberto Vargas were other celebrated artists who followed, but it was Marland Stone who became *Motion Picture*'s favourite cover illustrator with over 100 covers to his name, including a Greta Garbo portrait, December issue 1927. By the forties, soft colour photographs had appeared on covers and soon names like Mead-Maddick and Carlyle Blackwell set the standard for top quality portraits. From March 1914 to February 1925, the title was *Motion Picture Magazine*, *Motion Picture* thereafter. The magazine was published by Brewster Publications, July 1920 to July 1938; Fawcett Publications up to September 1963, and Macfadden-Bartell from then on. Major editors have been Adele Whitely Fletcher, Laurence Reid, Roscoe Fawcett, Joan Curtis, Maxwell Hamilton, Sam Schneider and Jack Podell. Teaser captions began to appear in 1943. Collectors should note that the August 1950 cover is erroneously credited as Jeanne Crain and has been corrected by the author. Covers began to deteriorate from the late fifties, when television began to influence the magazine. The following entries are complete to 1959, except for three issues: June 1914, November 1915, August 1921. *Discrepancy in numbering.

YEAR	MONTH	REF. No.	COVER STAR
1911	Feb.	Vol. 1, no. 1	**Thomas Edison (window cover)**
	March	Vol. 1, no. 2	**Thomas Edison**
	April	Vol. 1, no. 3	***Tale of Two Cities***
	May	Vol. 1, no. 4	***Cupid's Conquest***
	June	Vol. 1, no. 5	***The Steel Alarm***
	July	Vol. 1, no. 6	**Uncredited film**
	Aug.	Vol. 2, no. 7	***The Two-Gun Man***
	Sept.	Vol. 2, no. 8	***Billy's Marriage***
	Oct.	Vol. 2, no. 9	***The Battle of Trafalgar***
	Nov.	Vol. 2, no. 10	***Daniel Boone's Bravery***
	Dec.	Vol. 2, no. 11	***The Battle***
1912	Jan.	Vol. 2, no. 12	***After Waterloo***
	Feb.	Vol. 3, no. 1	***Martin Chuzzlewit***
	March	Vol. 3, no. 2	***The Bell of Penance***
	April	Vol. 3, no. 3	***The Stolen Invention***
	May	Vol. 3, no. 4	***The Anonymous Letter***
	June	Vol. 3, no. 5	***Darby and Joan***
	July	Vol. 3, no. 6	***The Cowboy Kid***
	Aug.	Vol. 4, no. 7	***The Barrier that was Burned***
	Sept.	Vol. 4, no. 8	***The Fall of Montezuma***
	Oct.	Vol. 4, no. 9	***The Prisoner's Story***
	Nov.	Vol. 4, no. 10	***The Mills Of The Gods***
	Dec.	Vol. 4, no. 11	***The Informer***
1913	Jan.	Vol. 4, no. 12	**Uncredited film**
	Feb.	Vol. 5, no. 1	**Valentine design**
	March	Vol. 5, no. 2	***His Children***
	April	Vol. 5, no. 3	***The Gauntlets Of Washington***
	May	Vol. 5, no. 4	***In the Days of War***
	June	Vol. 5, no. 5	***Brightened Sunsets***
	July	Vol. 5, no. 6	***Shenandoah***
	Aug.	Vol. 6, no. 7	**Augustus Carney**
	Sept.	Vol. 6, no. 8	**Alice Joyce**
	Oct.	Vol. 6, no. 9	**Romaine Fielding**
	Nov.	Vol. 6, no. 10	**Mary Pickford**
	Dec.	Vol. 6, no. 11	**Anna Nilsson**
1914	Jan.	Vol. 6, no. 12	**Thomas Edison**
	Feb.	Vol. 7, no. 1	**Carlyle Blackwell Crane Wilbur Arthur Johnson Lottie Briscoe Clara K. Young**
	March	Vol. 7, no. 2	**Lillian Walker**
	April	Vol. 7, no. 3	**Mary Fuller Ben Wilson**
	May	Vol. 7, no. 4	**Norma Talmadge Leo Delaney**
	July	Vol. 7, no. 6	**Painting of ship at sea**
	Aug.	Vol. 8, no. 7	**Painting by Louis L'Eschamps**
	Sept.	Vol. 8, no. 8	**Artist's cover**
	Oct.	Vol. 8, no. 9	**Artist's cover**
	Nov.	Vol. 8, no. 10	**Alice Joyce**
	Dec.	Vol. 8, no. 11	**Mary Fuller**
1915	Jan.	Vol. 8, no. 12	**Anita Stewart**
	Feb.	Vol. 9, no. 1	**Ethel Clayton**
	March	Vol. 9, no. 2	**Mabel Trunnelle**
	April	Vol. 9, no. 3	**Ruth Stonehouse**
	May	Vol. 9, no. 4	**Norma Talmadge Antonio Moreno**

YEAR	MONTH	REF. No.	COVER STAR
	June	Vol. 9, no. 5	**Mary Pickford**
	July	Vol. 9, no. 6	**Charlie Chaplin**
	Aug.	Vol. 10, no. 7	**Viola Dana**
	Sept.	Vol. 10, no. 8	**Marguerite Courtot**
	Oct.	Vol. 10, no. 9	***The Battle Cry Of Peace***
	Dec.	Vol. 10, no. 11	**Ormi Hawley**
1916	Jan.	Vol. 10, no. 12	**Mabel Normand**
	Feb.	Vol. 11, no. 1	**Fay Tincher**
	March	Vol. 11, no. 2	**May Martin**
	April	Vol. 11, no. 3	**Marguerite Snow**
	May	Vol. 11, no. 4	**Rose Melville**
	June	Vol. 11, no. 5	**Ruth Roland**
	July	Vol. 11, no. 6	**Carlyle Blackwell**
	Aug.	Vol. 12, no. 7	**Mary Pickford**
	Sept.	Vol. 12, no. 8	**Francis X. Bushman**
	Oct.	Vol. 12, no. 9	**Theda Bara**
	Nov.	Vol. 12, no. 10	**Kathlyn Williams**
	Dec.	Vol. 12, no. 11	**Cleo Madison**
1917	Jan.	Vol. 12, no. 12	**June Caprice**
	Feb.	Vol. 13, no. 1	**Wallace Reid**
	March	Vol. 13, no. 2	**Violet Mersereau**
	April	Vol. 13, no. 3	**Fay Tincher**
	May	Vol. 13, no. 4	**Anita Stewart**
	June	Vol. 13, no. 5	**William S. Hart**
	July	Vol. 13, no. 6	**Pauline Frederick**
	Aug.	Vol. 14, no. 7	**Myrtle Stedman**
	Sept.	Vol. 14, no. 8	**Harold Lockwood**
	Oct.	Vol. 14, no. 9	**Clara Kimball Young**
	Nov.	Vol. 14, no. 10	**Marguerite Clark**
	Dec.	Vol. 14, no. 11	**Mae Marsh**
1918	Jan.	Vol. 14, no. 12	**Pearl White**
	Feb.	Vol. 15, no. 1	**Mary McAlister**
	March	Vol. 15, no. 2	**Norma Talmadge**
	April	Vol. 15, no. 3	**May Allison**
	May	Vol. 15, no. 4	**Dorothy Bernard**
	June	Vol. 15, no. 5	**Corinne Griffith**
	July	Vol. 15, no. 6	**Alla Nazimova**
	Aug.	Vol. 16, no. 7	**Douglas Fairbanks**
	Sept.	Vol. 16, no. 8	**Lillian Gish**
	Oct.	Vol. 16, no. 9	**Ruth Roland**
	Nov.	Vol. 16, no. 10	**William S. Hart**
	Dec.	Vol. 16, no. 11	**Shirley Mason**
1919	Jan.	Vol. 16, no. 12	**Dorothy Gish**
	Feb.	Vol. 17, no. 1	**Mary Miles Minter**
	March	Vol. 17, no. 2	**Ann Little**
	April	Vol. 17, no. 3	**Anita Stewart**
	May	Vol. 17, no. 4	**Gladys Lesley**

YEAR	MONTH	REF. No.	COVER STAR
	June	Vol. 17, no. 5	**Olive Thomas**
	July	Vol. 17, no. 6	**Dorothy Phillips**
	Aug.	Vol. 18, no. 7	**Mary Pickford**
	Sept.	Vol. 18, no. 8	**Dorothy Dalton**
	Oct.	Vol. 18, no. 9	**Marion Davies**
	Nov.	Vol. 18, no. 10	**Billie Burke**
	Dec.	Vol. 18, no. 11	**Douglas Fairbanks**
1920	Jan.	Vol. 18, no. 12	**Mae Murray**
	Feb.	Vol. 19, no. 1	**Antonio Moreno**
	March	Vol. 19, no. 2	**Anetha Getwell**
	April/May	Vol. 19, nos 3/4	**Lillian Gish**
	June	Vol. 19, no. 5	**Florence Evelyn Martin**
	July	Vol. 19, no. 6	**Blanche McGarity**
	Aug.	Vol. 20, no. 7	**Alma Rubens**
	Sept.	Vol. 20, no. 8	**Madge Kennedy**
	Oct.	Vol. 20, no. 9	**Mildred Harris Chaplin**
	Nov.	Vol. 20, no. 10	**Dorothy Dalton**
	Dec.	Vol. 20, no. 11	**Hope Hampton**
1921	Jan.	Vol. 20, no. 12	**Mary Pickford**
	Feb.	Vol. 21, no. 1	**Norma Talmadge**
	March	Vol. 21, no. 2	**Ruth Roland**
	April	Vol. 21, no. 3	**Pearl White**
	May	Vol. 21, no. 4	**Gladys Lesley**
	June	Vol. 21, no. 5	**Vivian Martin**
	July	Vol. 21, no. 6	**Renée Adorée**
	Sept.	Vol. 22, no. 8	**Douglas Fairbanks**
	Oct.	Vol. 22, no. 9	**Colleen Moore**
	Nov.	Vol. 22, no. 10	**Constance Talmadge**
	Dec.	Vol. 22, no. 11	**Dorothy Phillips**
1922	Jan.	Vol. 22, no. 12	**Mabel Normand**
	Feb.	Vol. 23, no. 1	**Rudolph Valentino**
	March	Vol. 23, no. 2	**Mary Pickford**
	April	Vol. 23, no. 3	**Leatrice Joy**
	May	Vol. 23, no. 4	**Gloria Swanson**
	June	Vol. 23, no. 5	**Dorothy Orth**
	July	Vol. 23, no. 6	**Harold Lloyd**
	Aug.	Vol. 24, no. 7	**Claire Windsor**
	Sept.	Vol. 24, no. 8	**Wesley Barrie**
	Oct.	Vol. 24, no. 9	**Marie Prevost**
	Nov.	Vol. 24, no. 10	**Richard Barthelmess**
	Dec.	Vol. 24, no. 11	**Dorothy Phillips**
1923	Jan.	Vol. 24, no. 12	**Jackie Coogan**
	Feb.	Vol. 25, no. 1	**Norma Talmadge**
	March	Vol. 25, no. 2	**Madge Kennedy**
	April	Vol. 25, no. 3	**Lillian Gish**

YEAR	MONTH	REF. No.	COVER STAR
	May	Vol. 25, no. 4	**Nazimova**
	June	Vol. 25, no. 5	**Pauline Starke**
	July	Vol. 25, no. 6	**Dorothy Gish**
	Aug.	Vol. 26, no. 7	**Bebe Daniels**
	Sept.	Vol. 26, no. 8	**Rudolph Valentino Nazimova**
	Oct.	Vol. 26, no. 9	**Marion Davies**
	Nov.	Vol. 26, no. 10	**Gloria Swanson**
	Dec.	Vol. 26, no. 11	**Ramon Novarro**
1924	Jan.	Vol. 26, no. 12	**Nita Naldi**
	Feb.	Vol. 27, no. 1	**Leatrice Joy**
	March	Vol. 27, no. 2	**Mae Murray**
	April	Vol. 27, no. 3	**William S. Hart**
	May	Vol. 27, no. 4	**Barbara La Marr**
	June	Vol. 27, no. 5	**Mary Pickford**
	July	Vol. 27, no. 6	**Norma Talmadge**
	Aug.	Vol. 28, no. 7	**Leatrice Joy**
	Sept.	Vol. 28, no. 8	**Mary Pickford Douglas Fairbanks**
	Oct.	Vol. 28, no. 9	**Richard Dix**
	Nov.	Vol. 28, no. 10	**Alice Terry**
	Dec.	Vol. 28, no. 11	**Viola Dana**
1925	Jan.	Vol. 28, no. 12	**Blanche Sweet**
	Feb.	Vol. 29, no. 1	**Betty Blythe**
	March	Vol. 29, no. 2	**Ben Lyon**
	April	Vol. 29, no. 3	**Pola Negri**
	May	Vol. 29, no. 4	**Colleen Moore**
	June	Vol. 29, no. 5	**Gloria Swanson**
	July	Vol. 29, no. 6	**Esther Ralston Mary Brian**
	Aug.	Vol. 30, no. 7	**Corinne Griffith**
	Sept.	Vol. 30, no. 8	**Alma Rubens**
	Oct.	Vol. 30, no. 9	**Mabel Normand**
	Nov.	Vol. 30, no. 10	**May McAvoy**
	Dec.	Vol. 30, no. 11	**Lillian Gish**
1926	Jan.	Vol. 30, no. 12	**Dorothy Devore**
	Feb.	Vol. 31, no. 1	**Mary Astor**
	March	Vol. 31, no. 2	**Leatrice Joy**
	April	Vol. 31, no. 3	**Doris Kenyon**
	May	Vol. 31, no. 4	**Bebe Daniels**
	June	Vol. 31, no. 5	**Ramon Novarro**
	July	Vol. 31, no. 6	**Eleanor Boardman**
	Aug.	Vol. 32, no. 1	**Pola Negri**
	Sept.	Vol. 32, no. 2	**Rudolph Valentino**
	Oct.	Vol. 32, no. 3	**Estelle Taylor**
	Nov.	Vol. 32, no. 4	**Gloria Swanson**
	Dec.	Vol. 32, no. 5	**Corinne Griffith**
1927	Jan.	Vol. 32, no. 6	**Colleen Moore**
	Feb.	Vol. 33, no. 1	**Ramon Novarro**

YEAR	MONTH	REF. No.	COVER STAR
	March	Vol. 33, no. 2	**Norma Shearer**
	April	Vol. 33, no. 3	**Lya De Putti**
	May	Vol. 33, no. 4	**Patsy Ruth Miller**
	June	Vol. 33, no. 5	**Gilda Gray**
	July	Vol. 33, no. 6	**Gloria Lloyd**
	Aug.	Vol. 34, no. 1	**Dolores Costello**
	Sept.	Vol. 34, no. 2	**Betty Bronson**
	Oct.	Vol. 34, no. 3	**Mary Brian**
	Nov.	Vol. 34, no. 4	**Vilma Banky**
	Dec.	Vol. 34, no. 5	**Greta Garbo**
1928	Jan.	Vol. 34, no. 6	**Laura La Plante**
	Feb.	Vol. 35, no. 1	**Lois Moran**
	March	Vol. 35, no. 2	**Joan Crawford**
	April	Vol. 35, no. 3	**Esther Ralston**
	May	Vol. 35, no. 4	**Jacqueline Logan**
	June	Vol. 35, no. 5	**Janet Gaynor**
	July	Vol. 35, no. 6	**Molly O'Day**
	Aug.	Vol. 36, no. 1	**Norma Shearer**
	Sept.	Vol. 36, no. 2	**Billie Dove**
	Oct.	Vol. 36, no. 3	**Dorothy Devore**
	Nov.	Vol. 36, no. 4	**Madge Bellamy**
	Dec.	Vol. 36, no. 5	**Anita Page**
1929	Jan.	Vol. 36, no. 6	**Laura La Plante**
	Feb.	Vol. 37, no. 1	**Marian Nixon**
	March	Vol. 37, no. 2	**Lina Basquette**
	April	Vol. 37, no. 3	**Colleen Moore**
	May	Vol. 37, no. 4	**Phyllis Haver**
	June	Vol. 37, no. 5	**Mary Duncan**
	July	Vol. 37, no. 6	**May McAvoy**
	Aug.	Vol. 38, no. 1	**Josephine Dunn**
	Sept.	Vol. 38, no. 2	**Fay Wray**
	Oct.	Vol. 38, no. 3	**Sue Carol**
	Nov.	Vol. 38, no. 4	**Lupe Velez**
	Dec.	Vol. 38, no. 5	**Mary Brian**
1930	Jan.	Vol. 38, no. 6	**Laura La Plante**
	Feb.	Vol. 39, no. 1	**Norma Shearer**
	March	Vol. 39, no. 2	**Alice White**
	April	Vol. 39, no. 3	**Janet Gaynor**
	May	Vol. 39, no. 4	**Greta Garbo**
	June	Vol. 39, no. 5	**Mary Nolan**
	July	Vol. 39, no. 6	**Kay Francis**
	Aug.	Vol. 40, no. 1	**Catherine Dale Owen**
	Sept.	Vol. 40, no. 2	**Clara Bow**
	Oct.	Vol. 40, no. 3	**Bessie Love**
	Nov.	Vol. 40, no. 4	**Helen Twelvetrees**
	Dec.	Vol. 40, no. 5	**Ann Harding**
1931	Jan.	Vol. 40, no. 6	**Lois Moran**
	Feb.	Vol. 41, no. 1	**Gloria Swanson**
	March	Vol. 41, no. 2	**Greta Garbo**
	April	Vol. 41, no. 3	**Marlene Dietrich**
	May	Vol. 41, no. 4	**Bebe Daniels**
	June	Vol. 41, no. 5	**Laura La Plante**

YEAR	MONTH	REF. No.	COVER STAR
	July	Vol. 41, no. 6	**Ruth Chatterton**
	Aug.	Vol. 42, no. 1	**Constance Bennett**
	Sept.	Vol. 42, no. 2	**Joan Crawford**
	Oct.	Vol. 42, no. 3	**Billie Dove**
	Nov.	Vol. 42, no. 4	**Carole Lombard**
	Dec.	Vol. 42, no. 5	**Marlene Dietrich**
1932	Jan.	Vol. 42, no. 6	**Greta Garbo**
	Feb.	Vol. 43, no. 1	**Anita Page**
	March	Vol. 43, no. 2	**Joan Bennett**
	April	Vol. 43, no. 3	**Miriam Hopkins**
	May	Vol. 43, no. 4	**Myrna Loy**
	June	Vol. 43, no. 5	**Jeanette MacDonald**
	July	Vol. 43, no. 6	**Sylvia Sidney**
	Aug.	Vol. 44, no. 1	**Marian Marsh**
	Sept.	Vol. 44, no. 2	**Joan Crawford**
	Oct.	Vol. 44, no. 3	**Ann Dvorak**
	Nov.	Vol. 44, no. 4	**Clara Bow**
	Dec.	Vol. 44, no. 5	**Constance Bennett**
1933	Jan.	Vol. 44, no. 6	**Lupe Velez**
	Feb.	Vol. 45, no. 1	**Loretta Young**
	March	Vol. 45, no. 2	**Katharine Hepburn**
	April	Vol. 45, no. 3	**Jean Harlow**
	May	Vol. 45, no. 4	**Claudette Colbert**
	June	Vol. 45, no. 5	**Helen Hayes**
	July	Vol. 45, no. 6	**Glenda Farrell**
	Aug.	Vol. 46, no. 1	**Sally Eilers**
	Sept.	Vol. 46, no. 2	**Mary Pickford**
	Oct.	Vol. 46, no. 3	**Adrienne Ames**
	Nov.	Vol. 46, no. 4	**Madge Evans**
	Dec.	Vol. 46, no. 5	**Bette Davis**
1934	Jan.	Vol. 46, no. 6	**Joan Crawford**
	Feb.	Vol. 47, no. 1	**Lilian Harvey**
	March	Vol. 47, no. 2	**Myrna Loy**
	April	Vol. 47, no. 3	**Katharine Hepburn Robert Young**
	May	Vol. 47, no. 4	**Anna Sten**
	June	Vol. 47, no. 5	**Sylvia Sidney**
	July	Vol. 47, no. 6	**Margaret Sullavan**
	Aug.	Vol. 48, no. 1	**Evelyn Venable**
	Sept.	Vol. 48, no. 2	**Glenda Farrell**
	Oct.	Vol. 48, no. 3	**Mary Brian**
	Nov.	Vol. 48, no. 4	**Carole Lombard**
	Dec.	Vol. 48, no. 5	**Constance Bennett**
1935	Jan.	Vol. 48, no. 6	**Ginger Rogers**
	Feb.	Vol. 49, no. 1	**Fay Wray**
	March	Vol. 49, no. 2	**Joan Crawford**
	April	Vol. 49, no. 3	**Loretta Young**

YEAR	MONTH	REF. No.	COVER STAR
	May	Vol. 49, no. 4	**Bette Davis**
	June	Vol. 49, no. 5	**Marlene Dietrich**
	July	Vol. 49, no. 6	**Jean Harlow**
	Aug	Vol. 50, no. 1	**Janet Gaynor**
	Sept.	Vol. 50, no. 2	**Katharine Hepburn**
	Oct.	Vol. 50, no. 3	**Dolores Del Rio**
	Nov.	Vol. 50, no. 4	**Claudette Colbert**
	Dec.	Vol. 50, no. 5	**Ann Sothern**
1936	Jan.	Vol. 50, no. 6	**Myrna Loy**
	Feb.	Vol. 51, no. 1	**Ginger Rogers**
	March	Vol. 51, no. 2	**Shirley Temple**
	April	Vol. 51, no. 3	**Bette Davis**
	May	Vol. 51, no. 4	**Jean Harlow**
	June	Vol. 51, no. 5	**Claudette Colbert**
	July	Vol. 51, no. 6	**Carole Lombard**
	Aug.	Vol. 52, no. 1	**Katharine Hepburn**
	Sept.	Vol. 52, no. 2	**Anita Louise**
	Oct.	Vol. 52, no. 3	**Norma Shearer**
	Nov.	Vol. 52, no. 4	**Ginger Rogers**
	Dec.	Vol. 52, no. 5	**Joan Crawford**
1937	Jan.	Vol. 52, no. 6	**Greta Garbo Robert Taylor**
	Feb.	Vol. 53, no. 1	**Simone Simon**
	March	Vol. 53, no. 2	**Jean Arthur**
	April	Vol. 53, no. 3	**Olivia De Havilland**
	May	Vol. 53, no. 4	**Madeleine Carroll**
	June	Vol. 53, no. 5	**Jeanette MacDonald**
	July	Vol. 53, no. 6	**Marlene Dietrich**
	Aug.	Vol. 54, no. 1	**Jean Harlow**
	Sept.	Vol. 54, no. 2	**Ginger Rogers**
	Oct.	Vol. 54, no. 3	**Sonja Henie Tyrone Power**
	Nov.	Vol. 54, no. 4	**Bette Davis**
	Dec.	Vol. 54, no. 5	**Frances Farmer**
1938	Jan.	Vol. 54, no. 6	**Carole Lombard**
	Feb.	Vol. 55, no. 1	**Katharine Hepburn**
	March	Vol. 55, no. 2	**Myrna Loy**
	April	Vol. 55, no. 3	**Loretta Young**
	May	Vol. 55, no. 4	**Paulette Goddard**
	June	Vol. 55, no. 5	**Robert Taylor**
	July	Vol. 55, no. 6	**Priscilla Lane**
	Aug.	Vol. 56, no. 1	**Deanna Durbin**
	Sept.	Vol. 56, no. 2	**Clark Gable**
	Oct.	Vol. 56, no. 3	**Claudette Colbert**
	Nov.	Vol. 56, no. 4	**Errol Flynn**
	Dec.	Vol. 56, no. 5	**Sonja Henie**

YEAR	MONTH	REF. No.	COVER STAR
1939	Jan.	Vol. 56, no. 6	**Tyrone Power**
	Feb.	Vol. 57, no. 1	**Hedy Lamarr**
	March	Vol. 57, no. 2	**Fred Astaire Ginger Rogers**
	April	Vol. 57, no. 3	**Priscilla Lane**
	May	Vol. 57, no. 4	**Olivia De Havilland**
	June	Vol. 57, no. 5	**Myrna Loy**
	July	Vol. 57, no. 6	**Tyrone Power Alice Faye**
	Aug.	Vol. 58, no. 1	**Gary Cooper**
	Sept.	Vol. 58, no. 2	**Ginger Rogers**
	Oct.	Vol. 58, no. 3	**Charles Boyer**
	Nov.	Vol. 58, no. 4	**Jean Arthur**
	Dec.	Vol. 58, no. 5	**Joan Bennett**
1940	Jan.	Vol. 58, no. 6	**Priscilla Lane**
	Feb.	Vol. 59, no. 1	**Robert Taylor**
	March	Vol. 59, no. 2	**Sonja Henie**
	April	Vol. 59, no. 3	**Laurence Olivier**
	May	Vol. 59, no. 4	**Joan Blondell**
	June	Vol. 59, no. 5	**Spencer Tracy**
	July	Vol. 59, no. 6	**Alice Faye**
	Aug.	Vol. 60, no. 1	**Brenda Marshall**
	Sept.	Vol. 60, no. 2	**Carole Lombard**
	Oct.	Vol. 60, no. 3	**Deanna Durbin**
	Nov.	Vol. 60, no. 4	**Loretta Young**
	Dec.	Vol. 60, no. 5	**Paulette Goddard**
1941	Jan.	Vol. 60, no. 6	**Gene Tierney**
	Feb.	Vol. 61, no. 1	**Clark Gable Vivien Leigh**
	March	Vol. 61, no. 2	**Ida Lupino**
	April	Vol. 61, no. 3	**Mickey Rooney Judy Garland**
	May	Vol. 61, no. 4	**Olivia De Havilland**
	June	Vol. 61, no. 5	**Robert Taylor**
	July	Vol. 61, no. 6	**Betty Grable**
	Aug.	Vol. 62, no. 1	**Veronica Lake**
	Sept.	Vol. 62, no. 2	**Clark Gable**
	Oct.	Vol. 62, no. 3	**Rita Hayworth**
	Nov.	Vol. 62, no. 4	**Deanna Durbin**
	Dec.	Vol. 62, no. 5	**Claudette Colbert**
1942	Jan.	Vol. 62, no. 6	**Olivia De Havilland**
	Feb.	Vol. 63, no. 1	**Jeanette MacDonald Gene Raymond**
	March	Vol. 63, no. 2	**Gene Tierney**
	April	Vol. 63, no. 3	**Paulette Goddard John Wayne**
	May	Vol. 63, no. 4	**Linda Darnell**
	June	Vol. 63, no. 5	**Shirley Temple**
	July	Vol. 63, no. 6	**Ann Rutherford**
	Aug.	Vol. 64, no. 1	**Donna Reed**
	Sept.	Vol. 64, no. 2	**Veronica Lake**
	Oct.	Vol. 64, no. 3	**Janet Blair**
	Nov.	Vol. 64, no. 4	**Joan Leslie**
	Dec.	Vol. 64, no. 5	**Deanna Durbin**
1943	Jan.	Vol. 64, no. 6	**Paulette Goddard**
	Feb.	Vol. 65, no. 1	**Clark Gable**
	March	Vol. 65, no. 2	**Greer Garson**
	April	Vol. 65, no. 3	**Gary Cooper Ingrid Bergman**
	May	Vol. 65, no. 4	**Ann Sheridan**
	June	Vol. 65, no. 5	**Ginger Rogers and husband**
	July	Vol. 65, no. 6	**Rita Hayworth**
	Aug.	Vol. 66, no. 1	**Dolores Moran**
	Sept.	Vol. 66, no. 2	**Deanna Durbin**
	Oct.	Vol. 66, no. 3	**Harry James Betty Grable**
	Nov.	Vol. 66, no. 4	**Robert Taylor**
	Dec.	Vol. 66, no. 5	**Alan Ladd**
1944	Jan.	Vol. 66, no. 6	**Maureen O'Hara**
	Feb.	Vol. 67, no. 1	**Clark Gable**
	March	Vol. 67, no. 2	**Ginger Rogers**
	April	Vol. 67, no. 3	**Greer Garson**
	May	Vol. 67, no. 4	**Deanna Durbin**
	June	Vol. 67, no. 5	**Special war bonds cover**
	July	Vol. 67, no. 6	**Jennifer Jones**
	Aug.	Vol. 68, no. 1,	**Ginger Rogers**
	Sept.	Vol. 68, no. 2	**Katharine Hepburn**
	Oct.	Vol. 68, no. 3	**Lena Horne**
	Nov.	Vol. 68, no. 4	**Dennis Morgan**
	Dec.	Vol. 68, no. 5	**Laraine Day**
1945	Jan.	Vol. 68, no. 6	**Cary Grant**
	Feb.	Vol. 69, no. 1	**Margaret O'Brien**
	March	Vol. 69, no. 2	**Ingrid Bergman**
	April	Vol. 69, no. 3	**Linda Darnell**
	May	Vol. 69, no. 4	**Alan Ladd**
	June	Vol. 69, no. 5	**Lauren Bacall**
	July	Vol. 69, no. 6	**Esther Williams**
	Aug.	Vol. 70, no. 1	**John Payne**
	Sept.	Vol. 70, no. 2	**Maureen O'Hara**
	Oct.	Vol. 70, no. 3	**Joan Leslie**
	Nov.	Vol. 70, no. 4	**Van Johnson**
	Dec.	Vol. 70, no. 5	**Deanna Durbin**
1946	Jan.	Vol. 70, no. 6	**Rita Hayworth and daughter**
	Feb.	Vol. 71, no. 1	**Gregory Peck**
	March	Vol. 71, no. 2	**Shirley Temple**
	April	Vol. 71, no. 3	**Gene Tierney**
	May	Vol. 71, no. 4	**Lana Turner**
	June	Vol. 71, no. 5	**Guy Madison**
	July	Vol. 71, no. 6	**Maureen O'Hara**
	Aug.	Vol. 72, no. 1	**June Allyson**

YEAR	MONTH	REF. No.	COVER STAR
	Sept.	Vol. 72, no. 2	**Joan Leslie**
	Oct.	Vol. 72, no. 3	**Tyrone Power**
	Nov.	Vol. 72, no. 4	**Jane Wyman**
	Dec.	Vol. 72, no. 5	**Donna Reed**
1947	Jan.	Vol. 72, no. 6	**James Stewart**
	Feb.	Vol. 73, no. 1	**Virginia Mayo**
	March	Vol. 73, no. 2	**Joan Crawford**
	April	Vol. 73, no. 3	**Van Johnson**
	May	Vol. 73, no. 4	**Susan Hayward**
	June	Vol. 73, no. 5	**Jennifer Jones**
	July	Vol. 73, no. 6	**Diana Lynn**
	Aug.	Vol. 74, no. 1	**Rita Hayworth**
	Sept.	Vol. 74, no. 2	**Esther Williams**
	Oct.	Vol. 74, no. 3	**Betty Grable**
	Nov.	Vol. 74, no. 4	**Linda Darnell**
	Dec.	Vol. 74, no. 5	**Ingrid Bergman**
1948	Jan.	Vol. 74, no. 6	**Barbara Stanwyck**
	Feb.	Vol. 75, no. 1	**Joan Crawford**
	March	Vol. 75, no. 2	**Susan Hayward**
	April	Vol. 75, no. 3	**Jeanne Crain**
	May	Vol. 75, no. 4	**Rita Hayworth**
	June	Vol. 75, no. 5	**Lana Turner**
	July	Vol. 75, no. 6	**June Haver**
	Aug.	Vol. 76, no. 1	**Shirley Temple and baby**
	Sept.	Vol. 76, no. 2	**Loretta Young**
	Oct.	Vol. 76, no. 3	**Esther Williams**
	Nov.	Vol. 76, no. 4	**Ava Gardner**
	Dec.	Vol. 76, no. 5	**Ingrid Bergman**
1949	Jan.	Vol. 76, no. 6	**June Allyson**
	Feb.	Vol. 77, no. 1	**Shirley Temple and baby**
	March	Vol. 77, no. 2	**Elizabeth Taylor**
	April	Vol. 77, no. 3	**Jane Wyman**
	May	Vol. 77, no. 4	**Jane Russell**
	June	Vol. 77, no. 5	**Betty Grable**
	July	Vol. 77, no. 6	**Shirley Temple and baby**
	Aug.	Vol. 78, no. 1	**Ann Blyth**
	Sept.	Vol. 78, no. 2	**June Haver**
	Oct.	Vol. 78, no. 3	**Esther Williams**
	Nov.	Vol. 78, no. 4	**Jane Powell**
	Dec.	Vol. 78, no. 5	**Jeanne Crain**
1950	Jan.	Vol. 78, no. 6	**Ava Gardner**
	Feb.	Vol. 79, no. 1	**June Allyson**
	March	Vol. 79, no. 2	**Doris Day**
	April	Vol. 79, no. 3	**Elizabeth Taylor**
	May	Vol. 79, no. 4	**Jane Russell**
	June	Vol. 79, no. 5	**Ann Blyth**
	July	Vol. 79, no. 6	**Jane Powell**
	Aug.	Vol. 80, no. 1	**Betty Grable**
	Sept.	Vol. 80, no. 2	**Jeanne Crain**

YEAR	MONTH	REF. No.	COVER STAR
	Oct.	Vol. 80, no. 3	**Janet Leigh**
	Nov.	Vol. 80, no. 4	**Shirley Temple**
	Dec.	Vol. 80, no. 5	**Esther Williams**
1951	Jan.	Vol. 80, no. 6	**June Allyson**
	Feb.	Vol. 81, no. 1	**Elizabeth Taylor**
	March	Vol. 81, no. 2	**Jane Powell**
	April	Vol. 81, no. 3	**Ava Gardner**
	May	Vol. 81, no. 4	**Ann Blyth**
	June	Vol. 81, no. 5	**Janet Leigh**
	July	Vol. 81, no. 6	**June Haver**
	Aug.	Vol. 82, no. 1	**Elizabeth Taylor**
	Sept.	Vol. 82, no. 2	**Doris Day**
	Oct.	Vol. 82, no. 3	**Janet Leigh**
	Nov.	Vol. 82, no. 4	**Ava Gardner**
	Dec.	Vol. 82, no. 5	**Ann Blyth**
1952	Jan.	Vol. 82, no. 6	**June Allyson**
	Feb.	Vol. 83, no. 1	**June Haver**
	March	Vol. 83, no. 2	**Jane Powell**
	April	Vol. 83, no. 3	**Elizabeth Taylor**
	May	Vol. 83, no. 4	**Janet Leigh**
	June	Vol. 83, no. 5	**Doris Day**
	July	Vol. 83 no. 6	**Ann Blyth**
	Aug.	Vol. 84, no. 1	**Debbie Reynolds**
	Sept.	Vol. 84, no. 2	**June Allyson**
	Oct.	Vol. 84, no. 3	**Elizabeth Taylor**
	Nov.	Vol. 84, no. 4	**Ava Gardner**
	Dec.	Vol. 84, no. 5	**Ann Blyth**
1953	Jan	Vol. 84, no. 6	**Marilyn Monroe**
	Feb.	Vol. 85, no. 1	**Elizabeth Taylor**
	March	Vol. 85, no. 2	**Janet Leigh**
	April	Vol. 85, no. 3	**Debbie Reynolds**
	May	Vol. 85, no. 4	**Ann Blyth**
	June	Vol. 85, no. 5	**June Allyson**
	July	Vol. 85, no. 6	**Doris Day**
	Aug.	Vol. 86, no. 1	**Jane Powell**
	Sept.	Vol. 86, no. 2	**Ann Blyth**
	Oct.	Vol. 86, no. 3	**Janet Leigh**
	Nov.	Vol. 86, no. 4	**Marilyn Monroe**
	Dec.	Vol. 86, no. 5	**Debbie Reynolds**
1954	Jan.	Vol. 86, no. 6	**Janet Leigh** **Elizabeth Taylor** **Jane Powell** **Doris Day** **Ann Blyth** **Debbie Reynolds** **June Allyson** **Marilyn Monroe**
	Feb.	Vol. 87, no. 1	**Audrey Hepburn**
	March	Vol. 87, no. 2	**Elizabeth Taylor**
	April	Vol. 87, no. 3	**Tony Curtis** **Janet Leigh**
	May	Vol. 87, no. 4	**Lucille Ball** **Desi Arnaz**
	June	Vol. 87, no. 5	**June Allyson**

YEAR	MONTH	REF. No.	COVER STAR
	July	Vol. 87, no. 6	**Ann Blyth**
	Aug.	Vol. 88, no. 1	**Doris Day**
	Sept.	Vol. 88, no. 2	**Jane Powell**
	Oct.	Vol. 88, no. 3	**Janet Leigh**
	Nov.	Vol. 88, no. 4	**Debbie Reynolds**
	Dec.	Vol. 88, no. 5	**Ann Blyth**
1955	Jan.	Vol. 88, no. 6	**Elizabeth Taylor**
	Feb.	Vol. 89, no. 530*	**Janet Leigh**
	March	Vol. 89, no. 531	**Grace Kelly**
	April	Vol. 89, no. 532	**June Allyson**
	May	Vol. 89, no. 533	**Debbie Reynolds Eddie Fisher**
	June	Vol. 89, no. 534	**Doris Day**
	July	Vol. 89, no. 535	**Ann Blyth**
	Aug.	Vol. 90, no. 536	**Janet Leigh**
	Sept.	Vol. 90, no. 537	**Debbie Reynolds**
	Oct.	Vol. 90, no. 538	**Ann Blyth**
	Nov.	Vol. 90, no. 539	**Grace Kelly**
	Dec.	Vol. 90, no. 540	**June Allyson**
1956	Jan.	Vol. 45*, no. 541	**Debbie Reynolds Eddie Fisher**
	Feb.	Vol. 45, no. 542	**Elizabeth Taylor**
	March	Vol. 45, no. 543	**Marlon Brando**
	April	Vol. 45, no. 544	**Janet Leigh Tony Curtis**
	May	Vol. 45, no. 545	**Kim Novak**
	June	Vol. 45, no. 546	**Debbie Reynolds Eddie Fisher**
	July	Vol. 45, no. 547	**Shirley Jones**
	Aug.	Vol. 45, no. 548	**Natalie Wood**
	Sept.	Vol. 45, no. 549	**Doris Day**
	Oct.	Vol. 45, no. 550	**Kim Novak**
	Nov.	Vol. 45, no. 551	**Elizabeth Taylor**
	Dec.	Vol. 45, no. 552	**Debbie Reynolds**
1957	Jan.	Vol. 46, no. 553	**Natalie Wood**
	Feb.	Vol. 46, no. 554	**Janet Leigh**
	March	Vol. 46, no. 555	**Elizabeth Taylor**
	April	Vol. 47, no. 555*	**Debbie Reynolds Eddie Fisher Carrie Fisher**
	May	Vol. 47, no. 556	**Kim Novak**
	June	Vol. 47, no. 557	**Natalie Wood**

YEAR	MONTH	REF. No.	COVER STAR
	July	Vol. 47, no. 558	**Elizabeth Taylor**
	Aug.	Vol. 47, no. 559	**Debbie Reynolds**
	Sept.	Vol. 47, no. 560	**Janet Leigh**
	Oct.	Vol. 47, no. 561	**Natalie Wood**
	Nov.	Vol. 47, no. 562	**Deborah Kerr**
	Dec.	Vol. 47, no. 563	**Natalie Wood Robert Wagner**
1958	Jan.	Vol. 48, no. 564	**Debbie Reynolds**
	Feb.	Vol. 48, no. 565	**Elizabeth Taylor**
	March	Vol. 48, no. 566	**Doris Day**
	April	Vol. 48, no. 567	**Natalie Wood**
	May	Vol. 48, no. 568	**Janet Leigh**
	June	Vol. 48, no. 569	**Elizabeth Taylor**
	July	Vol. 48, no. 570	**Natalie Wood**
	Aug.	Vol. 48, no. 571	**Debbie Reynolds, Eddie Fisher and children**
	Sept.	Vol. 48, no. 572	**Elizabeth Taylor**
	Oct.	Vol. 48, no. 573	**Kim Novak**
	Nov.	Vol. 48, no. 574	**Tony Curtis Janet Leigh**
	Dec.	Vol. 48, no. 575	**Debbie Reynolds, Eddie Fisher Elizabeth Taylor**
1959	Jan.	Vol. 49, no. 576	**Debbie Reynolds**
	Feb.	Vol. 49, no. 577	**Doris Day**
	March	Vol. 49, no. 578	**Ricky Nelson**
	April	Vol. 49, no. 579	**Dick Clark and family**
	May	Vol. 49, no. 580	**Debbie Reynolds**
	June	Vol. 49, no. 581	**Pat Boone and wife**
	July	Vol. 49, no. 582	**Elizabeth Taylor Eddie Fisher**
	Aug.	Vol. 49, no. 583	**Janet Leigh**
	Sept.	Vol. 49, no. 584	**Debbie Reynolds Bob Neal**
	Oct.	Vol. 49, no. 585	**Doris Day**
	Nov.	Vol. 49, no. 586	**Debbie Reynolds Glenn Ford**
	Dec.	Vol. 49, no. 587	**Fabian Annette Funicello**

PHOTOPLAY (American) 1911 – 80

Although *Photoplay* started in 1911, it was not until seven years later that it began to challenge its rival, *Motion Picture*, as one of the leading fan magazines of the day. James R. Quirk edited a gossipy and fashion-conscious journal in the style of the great women's magazines of America. Early covers of film stills gave way to art portraits; Charles Sheldon and Earl Christy were their most popular illustrators. These were matched by the superb photographic covers of the late thirties by George Hurrell and Paul Hesse. Fine examples of Hurrell's work are the Temple and Lamarr covers of May 1938 and January 1939 respectively. Hesse continued to dominate through to the forties with fine frameable covers that are today fetching high prices at auctions. Published by the Macfadden Group Inc., *Photoplay* merged with *Movie Mirror* in January 1941. Quirk edited the magazine until November 1932. Succeeding editors were Kathryn Dougherty, Ruth Waterbury, Ernest Heyn, Helen Gilmore, Adele Whiteley Fletcher, Tony Gray, Ann Higginbotham, Isabel Moore and Evelyn Pain.

Selected issues only. *Discrepancy in numbering.

YEAR	MONTH	REF. No.	COVER STAR
1914	Jan.	Vol. 5, no. 2	**Mary Pickford Owen Moore**
	Sept.	Vol. 6, no. 4	**Mary Pickford**
	Oct.	Vol. 6, no. 5	**Pearl White**
	Nov.	Vol. 6, no. 6	**Florence Lawrence**
	Dec.	Vol. 7, no. 1	**Lillian and Dorothy Gish**
1916	Jan.	Vol. 9, no. 2	**Pearl White**
1917	May	Vol. 11, no. 6	**Theda Bara**
	Sept.	Vol. 12, no. 4	**Mae Marsh**
1919	Nov.	Vol. 16, no. 6	**Lillian Gish**
1920	Oct.	Vol. 18, no. 5	**Mary Pickford**
1923	Jan.	Vol. 23, no. 2	**Douglas Fairbanks**
	Feb.	Vol. 23, no. 3	**Pola Negri**
	Aug.	Vol. 24, no. 3	**Marion Davies**
1924	March	Vol. 25, no. 4	**Pola Negri**
	Nov.	Vol. 26, no. 6	**Jackie Coogan**

YEAR	MONTH	REF. No.	COVER STAR
1925	May	Vol. 27, no. 6	**Norma Shearer**
	Aug.	Vol. 28, no. 3	**Dorothy Gish**
1926	Feb.	Vol. 29, no. 3	**Bebe Daniels**
	April	Vol. 29, no. 5	**Vilma Banky**
1927	Feb.	Vol. 31, no. 3	**Louise Brooks**
	Oct.	Vol. 32, no. 5	**Dolores Costello**
	Dec.	Vol. 33, no. 1	**Joan Crawford**
1928	Feb.	Vol. 33, no. 3	**Clara Bow**
	May	Vol. 33, no. 6	**Greta Garbo**
	June	Vol. 34, no. 1	**Marion Davies**
	Sept.	Vol. 34, no. 4	**Gloria Swanson**
	Dec.	Vol. 35, no. 1	**Janet Gaynor**
1929	March	Vol. 35, no. 4	**Marion Davies**
	April	Vol. 35, no. 5	**Clara Bow**
	July	Vol. 36, no. 2	**Bessie Love**
	Aug.	Vol. 36, no. 3	**Greta Garbo**
	Oct.	Vol. 36, no. 5	**Anita Page**
	Nov.	Vol. 36, no. 6	**Janet Gaynor**

YEAR	MONTH	REF. No.	COVER STAR
1930	March	Vol. 37, no. 4	**Joan Crawford**
	April	Vol. 37, no. 5	**Norma Shearer**
	July	Vol. 38, no. 2	**Jeanette MacDonald**
	Sept.	Vol. 38, no. 4	**Joan Bennett**
	Oct.	Vol. 38, no. 5	**Bebe Daniels**
1931	Jan.	Vol. 39, no. 2	**Clara Bow**
	April	Vol. 39, no. 5	**Janet Gaynor**
			Charles Farrell
	Oct.	Vol. 40, no. 5	**Joan Crawford**
	Dec.	Vol. 41, no. 1	**Jean Harlow**
1932	Jan.	Vol. 41, no. 2	**Greta Garbo**
			Clark Gable
	Feb.	Vol. 41, no. 3	**Mary Astor**
	March	Vol. 41, no. 4	**Miriam Hopkins**
	April	Vol. 41, no. 5	**Norma Shearer**
	Aug.	Vol. 42, no. 3	**Jean Harlow**
	Sept.	Vol. 42, no. 4	**Tallulah Bankhead**
			Gary Cooper
	Oct.	Vol. 42, no. 5	**Irene Dunne**
	Dec.	Vol. 43, no. 1	**Janet Gaynor**
1933	Feb.	Vol. 43, no. 3	**Joan Bennett**
	March	Vol. 43, no. 4	**Claudette Colbert**
	April	Vol. 43, no. 5	**Norma Shearer**
	June	Vol. 44, no. 1	**Bette Davis**
	July	Vol. 44, no. 2	**Helen Hayes**
	Oct.	Vol. 44, no. 5	**Ruby Keeler**
	Nov.	Vol. 44, no. 6	**Marlene Dietrich**
	Dec.	Vol. 45, no. 1	**Ann Harding**
1934	Jan.	Vol. 45, no. 2	**Joan Crawford**
	Feb.	Vol. 45, no. 3	**Kay Francis**
	March	Vol. 45, no. 4	**Norma Shearer**
	April	Vol. 45, no. 5	**Katharine Hepburn**
	May	Vol. 45, no. 6	**Claudette Colbert**
	June	Vol. 46, no. 1	**Carole Lombard**
	Aug.	Vol. 46, no. 3	**Janet Gaynor**
	Sept.	Vol. 46, no. 4	**Dolores Del Rio**
	Oct.	Vol. 46, no. 5	**Irene Dunne**
	Nov.	Vol. 46, no. 6	**Margaret Sullavan**
	Dec.	Vol. 47, no. 1	**Greta Garbo**
1935	Jan.	Vol. 47, no. 2	**Shirley Temple**
	Feb.	Vol. 47, no. 3	**Myrna Loy**
	March	Vol. 47, no. 4	**Loretta Young**
	May	Vol. 47, no. 6	**Jean Harlow**
	June	Vol. 48, no. 1	**Irene Dunne**
	July	Vol. 48, no. 2	**Joan Bennett**
	Oct.	Vol. 48, no. 5	**Joan Crawford**
	Nov.	Vol. 48, no. 6	**Carole Lombard**
1936	Jan.	Vol. 49, no. 2	**Norma Shearer**
	Feb.	Vol. 49, no. 3	**Ginger Rogers**
	March	Vol. 49, no. 4	**Shirley Temple**
	April	Vol. 49, no. 5	**Joan Crawford**
	May	Vol. 49, no. 6	**Myrna Loy**
	June	Vol. 50, no. 1	**Dick Powell**
			Marion Davis
	July	Vol. 50, no. 1*	**Claudette Colbert**
	Aug.	Vol. 50, no. 2	**Bette Davis**
	Sept.	Vol. 50, no. 3	**Katharine Hepburn**
	Oct.	Vol. 50, no. 4	**Norma Shearer**
	Nov.	Vol. 50, no. 5	**Carole Lombard**
	Dec.	Vol. 50, no. 6	**Shirley Temple**
1937	Jan.	Vol. 51, no. 1	**Ginger Rogers**
	Feb.	Vol. 51, no. 2	**Joan Crawford**
	March	Vol. 51, no. 3	**Jean Harlow**
	April	Vol. 51, no. 4	**Ginger Rogers**
	May	Vol. 51, no. 5	**Jean Harlow**
			Robert Taylor
	June	Vol. 51, no. 6	**Shirley Temple**
	July	Vol. 51, no. 7	**Jeanette MacDonald**
	Aug.	Vol. 51, no. 8	**Claudette Colbert**
	Sept.	Vol. 51, no. 9	**Myrna Loy**
	Oct.	Vol. 51, no. 10	**Joan Crawford**
	Nov.	Vol. 51, no. 11	**Shirley Temple**
	Dec.	Vol. 51, no. 12	**Loretta Young**
1938	Jan.	Vol. 52, no. 1	**Irene Dunne**
	Feb.	Vol. 52, no. 2	**Ginger Rogers**
	March	Vol. 52, no. 3	**Sonja Henie**
	April	Vol. 52, no. 4	**Carole Lombard**
	May	Vol. 52, no. 5	**Shirley Temple**
	June	Vol. 52, no. 6	**Claudette Colbert**
	July	Vol. 52, no. 7	**Clark Gable**
	Aug.	Vol. 52, no. 8	**Myrna Loy**
	Sept.	Vol. 52, no. 9	**Jeanette MacDonald**
	Oct.	Vol. 52, no. 10	**Bette Davis**
	Nov.	Vol. 52, no. 11	**Deanna Durbin**
	Dec.	Vol. 52, no. 12	**Tyrone Power**
1939	Jan.	Vol. 53, no. 1	**Hedy Lamarr**
	Feb.	Vol. 53, no. 2	**Claudette Colbert**
	March	Vol. 53, no. 3	**Sonja Henie**
	April	Vol. 53, no. 4	**Norma Shearer**
	May	Vol. 53, no. 5	**Ginger Rogers**
	June	Vol. 53, no. 6	**Bette Davis**
	July	Vol. 53, no. 7	**Priscilla Lane**
	Aug.	Vol. 53, no. 8	**Alice Faye**
	Sept.	Vol. 53, no. 9	**Shirley Temple**
	Oct.	Vol. 53, no. 10	**Gary Cooper**
	Nov.	Vol. 53, no. 11	**Hedy Lamarr**
	Dec.	Vol. 53, no. 12	**Myrna Loy**
1940	Jan.	Vol. 53,* no. 1	**Carole Lombard**
	Feb.	Vol. 53, no. 2	**Clark Gable**
	March	Vol. 53, no. 3	**Olivia De Havilland**
	April	Vol. 53, no. 4	**Tyrone Power**
	May	Vol. 53, no. 5	**Deanna Durbin**
	June	Vol. 53, no. 6	**Jeanette MacDonald**
	July	Vol. 53, no. 7	**Ann Sheridan**
	Aug.	Vol. 53, no. 8	**Bette Davis**
	Sept.	Vol. 53, no. 9	**Ginger Rogers**
	Oct.	Vol. 53, no. 10	**Claudette Colbert**

YEAR	MONTH	REF. No.	COVER STAR
	Nov.	Vol. 53, no. 11	**Paulette Goddard**
	Dec.	Vol. 53, no. 12	**Judy Garland**
1941	Jan.	Vol. 18,* no. 2	**Rosalind Russell**
	Feb.	Vol. 18, no. 3	**Bette Davis**
	March	Vol. 18, no. 4	**Ginger Rogers**
	April	Vol. 18, no. 5	**Hedy Lamarr**
	May	Vol. 18, no. 6	**Alice Faye**
	June	Vol. 19, no. 1	**Deanna Durbin**
	July	Vol. 19, no. 2	**Dorothy Lamour**
	Aug.	Vol. 19, no. 3	**Judy Garland**
	Sept.	Vol. 19, no. 4	**Olivia De Havilland**
	Oct.	Vol. 19, no. 5	**Irene Dunne**
	Nov.	Vol. 19, no. 6	**Claudette Colbert**
	Dec.	Vol. 20, no. 1	**Lana Turner**
1942	Jan.	Vol. 20, no. 2	**Barbara Stanwyck**
	Feb.	Vol. 20, no. 3	**Ann Sothern**
	March	Vol. 20, no. 4	**Bette Davis**
	April	Vol. 20, no. 5	**Joan Fontaine**
	May	Vol. 20, no. 6	**Betty Grable**
	June	Vol. 21, no. 1	**Ann Sheridan**
	July	Vol. 21, no. 2	**Judy Garland**
	Sept.	Vol. 21, no. 4	**Priscilla Lane**
	Oct.	Vol. 21, no. 5	**Deanna Durbin**
	Nov.	Vol. 21, no. 6	**Ginger Rogers**
	Dec.	Vol. 22, no. 1	**Greer Garson**
1943	Jan.	Vol. 22, no. 2	**Hedy Lamarr**
	Feb.	Vol. 22, no. 3	**Rita Hayworth**
	March	Vol. 22, no. 4	**Lana Turner**
	April	Vol. 22, no. 5	**Gene Tierney**
	May	Vol. 22, no. 6	**Veronica Lake**
	June	Vol. 23, no. 1	**Betty Grable**
	July	Vol. 23, no. 2	**Judy Garland**
	Aug.	Vol. 23, no. 3	**Janet Blair**
	Sept.	Vol. 23, no 4	**Olivia De Havilland**
	Oct.	Vol. 23, no. 5	**Ingrid Bergman**
	Nov.	Vol. 23, no. 6	**Ann Sheridan**
	Dec.	Vol. 24, no. 1	**Paulette Goddard**
1945	Jan.	Vol. 26, no. 2	**Ingrid Bergman**
	Feb.	Vol. 26, no. 3	**Joan Fontaine**
	March	Vol. 26, no. 4	**Shirley Temple**
	April	Vol. 26, no. 5	**June Allyson**
	May	Vol. 26, no. 6	**Greer Garson**
	June	Vol. 27, no. 1	**Lauren Bacall**
	July	Vol. 27, no. 2	**Anne Baxter**
	Aug.	Vol. 27, no. 3	**Diana Lynn**
	Sept.	Vol. 27, no. 4	**Rita Hayworth**
	Oct.	Vol. 27, no. 5	**Maureen O'Hara**
	Nov.	Vol. 27, no. 6	**Judy Garland**
	Dec.	Vol. 28, no. 1	**Claudette Colbert**
1946	Jan.	Vol. 28, no. 2	**Margaret O'Brien**
	Feb.	Vol. 28, no. 3	**Van Johnson**
	March	Vol. 28, no. 4	**Gene Tierney**
	April	Vol. 28, no. 5	**Jennifer Jones**
	May	Vol. 28, no. 6	**Jeanne Crain**

YEAR	MONTH	REF. No.	COVER STAR
	June	Vol. 29, no. 1	**Ingrid Bergman**
	July	Vol. 29, no. 2	**Esther Williams**
	Aug.	Vol. 29, no. 3	**June Allyson**
	Sept.	Vol. 29, no. 4	**Cornel Wilde**
	Oct.	Vol. 29, no. 5	**Lana Turner**
	Nov.	Vol. 29, no. 6	**Betty Grable**
	Dec.	Vol. 30, no. 1	**Tyrone Power**
1947	Jan.	Vol. 30, no. 2	**Greer Garson**
	Feb.	Vol. 30, no. 3	**Ingrid Bergman**
	March	Vol. 30, no. 4	**Bing Crosby**
	April	Vol. 30, no. 5	**Jeanne Crain**
	May	Vol. 30, no. 6	**June Allyson**
	June	Vol. 31, no. 1	**Shirley Temple**
	July	Vol. 31, no. 2	**Esther Williams**
	Aug.	Vol. 31, no. 3	**Lana Turner**
	Sept.	Vol. 31, no. 4	**Jennifer Jones**
	Oct.	Vol. 31, no. 5	**Olivia De Havilland**
	Nov.	Vol. 31, no. 6	**Gene Tierney**
	Dec.	Vol. 32, no. 1	**Joan Caulfield**
1948	Jan.	Vol. 32, no. 2	**June Haver**
	Feb.	Vol. 32, no. 3	**Ingrid Bergman**
	March	Vol. 32, no. 4	**Linda Darnell**
	April	Vol. 32, no. 5	**Betty Grable**
	May	Vol. 32, no. 6	**June Allyson**
	June	Vol. 33, no. 1	**Lana Turner**
	July	Vol. 33, no. 2	**Esther Williams**
	Aug.	Vol. 33, no. 3	**Shirley Temple**
	Sept.	Vol. 33, no. 4	**Alan Ladd**
	Oct.	Vol. 33, no. 5	**Jeanne Crain**
	Nov.	Vol. 33, no. 6	**Rita Hayworth**
	Dec.	Vol. 34, no. 1	**Ava Gardner**
1949	Jan.	Vol. 34, no. 2	**Esther Williams**
	Feb.	Vol. 34, no. 3	**Lana Turner**
	March	Vol. 34, no. 4	**Bing Crosby and sons**
	April	Vol. 34, no. 5	**Betty Grable**
	May	Vol. 34, no. 6	**Jane Wyman**
	June	Vol. 35, no. 1	**June Allyson**
	July	Vol. 35, no. 2	**Jane Powell**
	Aug.	Vol. 35, no. 3	**Shirley Temple**
	Sept.	Vol. 35, no. 4	**Esther Williams**
	Oct.	Vol. 35, no. 5	**Rita Hayworth**
	Nov.	Vol. 35, no. 6	**June Haver**
	Dec.	Vol. 36, no. 1	**Ingrid Bergman**
1950	Jan.	Vol. 37,* no. 1	**Elizabeth Taylor**
	Feb.	Vol. 37, no. 2	**Esther Williams**
	March	Vol. 37, no. 3	**Jane Wyman** **James Stewart**
	April	Vol. 37, no. 4	**Janet Leigh**
	May	Vol. 37, no. 5	**Jeanne Crain and sons**
	June	Vol. 37, no. 6	**Elizabeth Taylor**
	July	Vol. 38, no. 1	**June Allyson** **Dick Powell**
	Aug.	Vol. 38, no. 2	**Esther Williams**

YEAR	MONTH	REF. No.	COVER STAR
	Sept.	Vol. 38, no. 3	**Alan Ladd**
	Oct.	Vol. 38, no. 4	**Elizabeth Taylor**
	Nov.	Vol. 38, no. 5	**Shirley Temple**
	Dec.	Vol. 38, no. 6	**June Allyson**
1951	Jan.	Vol. 39, no. 1	**Lana Turner**
	Feb.	Vol. 39, no. 2	**Jane Powell**
	March	Vol. 39, no. 3	**Betty Hutton**
	April	Vol. 39, no. 4	**Esther Williams**
	May	Vol. 39, no. 5	**Elizabeth Taylor**
	June	Vol. 39, no. 6	**Betty Grable**
	July	Vol. 40, no. 1	**Ava Gardner**
	Aug.	Vol. 40, no. 2	**Doris Day**
	Sept.	Vol. 40, no. 3	**Jane Powell**
	Oct.	Vol. 40, no. 4	**Elizabeth Taylor**
	Nov.	Vol. 40, no. 5	**June Allyson and baby**
	Dec.	Vol. 40, no. 6	**Janet Leigh**
1952	Jan.	Vol. 41, no. 1	**Esther Williams**
	Feb.	Vol. 41, no. 2	**Ava Gardner**
	March	Vol. 41, no. 3	**Doris Day**
	April	Vol. 41, no. 4	**Jane Powell**
	May	Vol. 41, no. 5	**Elizabeth Taylor**
	June	Vol. 41, no. 6	**June Allyson**
	July	Vol. 42, no. 1	**Betty Grable**
	Aug.	Vol. 42, no. 2	**Esther Williams**
	Sept.	Vol. 42, no. 3	**Ann Blyth**
	Oct.	Vol. 42, no. 4	**Rita Hayworth**
	Nov.	Vol. 42, no. 5	**Elizabeth Taylor**
	Dec.	Vol. 42, no. 6	**Doris Day**
1953	Jan.	Vol. 43, no. 1	**Debbie Reynolds**
	Feb.	Vol. 43, no. 2	**Marilyn Monroe**
	March	Vol. 43, no. 3	**Jane Powell**
	April	Vol. 43, no. 4	**Esther Williams**
	May	Vol. 43, no. 5	**Tony Curtis** **Janet Leigh**
	June	Vol. 43, no. 6	**Ann Blyth**
	July	Vol. 44, no. 1	**Elizabeth Taylor and child**
	Aug.	Vol. 44, no. 2	**Doris Day**
	Sept.	Vol. 44, no. 3	**Debbie Reynolds**
	Oct.	Vol. 44, no. 4	**Janet Leigh**
	Nov.	Vol. 44, no. 5	**Piper Laurie**
	Dec.	Vol. 44, no. 6	**Marilyn Monroe**
1954	Jan.	Vol. 45, no. 1	**Esther Williams**
	Feb.	Vol. 45, no. 2	**Elizabeth Taylor**
	March	Vol. 45, no. 3	**Debbie Reynolds**
	April	Vol. 45, no. 4	**Alan Ladd** **Marilyn Monroe** **Robert Wagner**
	May	Vol. 45, no. 5	**June Allyson**
	June	Vol. 45, no. 6	**Janet Leigh**
	July	Vol. 46, no. 1	**Doris Day**
	Aug.	Vol. 46, no. 2	**Terry Moore**
	Sept.	Vol. 46, no. 3	**Rock Hudson**
	Oct.	Vol. 46, no. 4	**Tony Curtis** **Janet Leigh**

YEAR	MONTH	REF. No.	COVER STAR
	Nov.	Vol. 46, no. 5	**Debbie Reynolds**
	Dec.	Vol. 46, no. 6	**Elizabeth Taylor**
1955	Jan.	Vol. 47, no. 1	**Janet Leigh**
	Feb.	Vol. 47, no. 2	**Doris Day**
	March	Vol. 47, no. 3	**June Allyson**
	April	Vol. 47, no. 4	**Grace Kelly**
	May	Vol. 47, no. 5	**Debbie Reynolds**
	June	Vol. 47, no. 6	**Janet Leigh**
	July	Vol. 48, no. 1	**Jane Powell**
	Aug.	Vol. 48, no. 2	**Elizabeth Taylor and son**
	Sept.	Vol. 48, no. 3	**Tony Curtis**
	Oct.	Vol. 48, no. 4	**Doris Day**
	Nov.	Vol. 48, no. 5	**Kim Novak**
	Dec.	Vol. 48, no. 6	**Jane Russell**
1956	Jan.	Vol. 49, no. 1	**Ann Blyth**
	Feb.	Vol. 49, no. 2	**Debbie Reynolds**
	March	Vol. 49, no. 3	**Shirley Jones**
	April	Vol. 49, no. 4	**Grace Kelly**
	May	Vol. 49, no. 5	**Mitzi Gaynor**
	June	Vol. 49, no. 6	**Natalie Wood**
	July	Vol. 50, no. 1	**Kim Novak**
	Aug.	Vol. 50, no. 2	**Sheree North**
	Sept.	Vol. 50, no. 3	**Alan Ladd**
	Oct.	Vol. 50, no. 4	**Marilyn Monroe**
	Nov.	Vol. 50, no. 5	**Kim Novak**
	Dec.	Vol. 50, no. 6	**Natalie Wood**
1957	Jan.	Vol. 51, no. 1	**Elizabeth Taylor**
	Feb.	Vol. 51, no. 2	**Rock Hudson**
	March	Vol. 51, no. 3	**Jayne Mansfield**
	April	Vol. 51, no. 4	**Kim Novak**
	May	Vol. 51, no. 5	**Joan Collins**
	June	Vol. 51, no. 6	**Pier Angeli**
	July	Vol. 52, no. 1	**Elvis Presley**
	Aug.	Vol. 52, no. 2	**Natalie Wood**
	Sept.	Vol. 52, no. 3	**Tommy Sands**
	Oct.	Vol. 52, no. 4	**Elizabeth Taylor**
	Nov.	Vol. 52, no. 5	**Kim Novak**
	Dec.	Vol. 52, no. 6	**Natalie Wood** **Robert Wagner**
1958	Jan.	Vol. 53, no. 1	**Debbie Reynolds**
	Feb.	Vol. 53, no. 2	**Rock Hudson**
	March	Vol. 53, no. 3	**Deborah Kerr**
	April	Vol. 53, no. 4	**Pat Boone**
	May	Vol. 53, no. 5	**Ricky Nelson**
	June	Vol. 53, no. 6	**Elizabeth Taylor**
	July	Vol. 54, no. 1	**Natalie Wood**
	Aug.	Vol. 54, no. 2	**Janet Leigh**
	Sept.	Vol. 54, no. 3	**Eddie Fisher, Debbie Reynolds and children**
	Oct.	Vol. 54, no. 4	**Elvis Presley**
	Nov.	Vol. 54, no. 5	**Tony Curtis** **Janet Leigh**
	Dec.	Vol. 54, no. 6	**Debbie Reynolds**

Motion Picture

OCTOBER

1 Shilling

The Women
In *their* Lives

Another Startling
Ghost Story

Sue Carol

MARLAND
STONE

The Stars *and th* ... olly ... ood Diet

1. Sue Carol, *Motion Picture*, October 1929, vol. XXXVIII, no. 3

2. Charlie Chaplin, *Film Pictorial,* 14 March 1936, vol. 9, no. 212

3. Bette Davis, *Photoplay,* June 1939, vol. LIII, no. 6

TIME

THE WEEKLY NEWSMAGAZINE

SCARLETT O'HARA

To Dave & Myron, Vivien Leigh.

(Cinema)

4. Vivien Leigh, *Time*, 25 December 1939, vol. 34, no. 26.

5. Ava Gardner, *Look*, 22 November 1949, vol. 13, no. 24

6. Elizabeth Taylor, *Cinémonde*, 25 October 1956, no. 1159

Bryan Adams, Def Leppard, Dylan and the Dead

Rolling Stone

ISSUE 508 • SEPTEMBER 10TH, 1987 • U.K. £1.90 • $1.95

MADONNA
On Being a Star

EXPOSING CONTRAGATE
The Unknown Heroes

AUDIO EXTRA

DAT VS. CD
The Battle Is Now

SPECIAL ISSUE

WHERE ARE THEY NOW?
Delaney and Bonnie, Dr. Hook, Sopwith Camel, The Turtles and More

7. Madonna, *Rolling Stone,* 10 September 1987, issue 508

GWEN FARRAR
MAE WEST (PARAMOUNT)
2.
GRETA GARBO (M-G-M)
3.
BING CROSBY (PARAMOUNT)
4.
RAQUEL TORRES
6.
MARIE DRESSLER (M-G-M)
7.
JOAN CRAWFORD (M-G-M)
8.
MERLE OBERON (LONDON FILMS)
DOLORES DEL RIO (RADIO)
10.
CICELY COURTNEIDGE
11.
JEANETTE MACDONALD (M-G-M)
12.
JACK BUCHANAN (A BRITISH & DOMINION STAR)
CLAUDETTE COLBERT (COLUMBIA)
14.
KATHARINE HEPBURN (RADIO STAR)
15.
CARL BRISSON
16.
MARY CLARE

JEAN HARLOW (M-G-M)
17.
WALLACE BEERY (M-G-M)
18.
MAURICE CHEVALIER (M-G-M)
19.
MARGOT GRAHAME
20.
TALLULAH BANKHEAD
21.
ELIZABETH ALLAN
22.
GRACIE FIELDS
23.
HEATHER ANGEL
24.
SYLVIA SYDNEY (PARAMOUNT)
25.
MADELEINE CARROLL (A GAUMONT BRITISH STAR)
26.
DIANA WYNYARD
27.
NORMA SHEARER (M-G-M)
28
WENDY BARRIE
29.
ANNA NEAGLE
30.
RALPH LYNN
31.
WINIFRED SHOTTER
32

33. JESSIE MATTHEWS

34. RAYMOND MASSEY

35. IDA LUPINO (PARAMOUNT)

36. HERBERT MARSHALL

37. MYRNA LOY (M-G-M)

38. EVELYN LAYE

39. FRANCIS LEDERER

40. CAROLE LOMBARD (M-G-M)

41. JANET GAYNOR (FOX STAR)

42. CHARLES LAUGHTON

43. ELISSA LANDI (COLUMBIA)

44. DOUGLAS FAIRBANKS Jnr (LONDON FILMS)

45. JUNE

46. CLARK GABLE (COLUMBIA)

47. MARLENE DIETRICH (PARAMOUNT)

48. LILIAN HARVEY (FOX STAR)

10. Larry Parks and Evelyn Keyes in *The Jolson Story* on the dust jacket of the annual *Film Review*, 1946-47

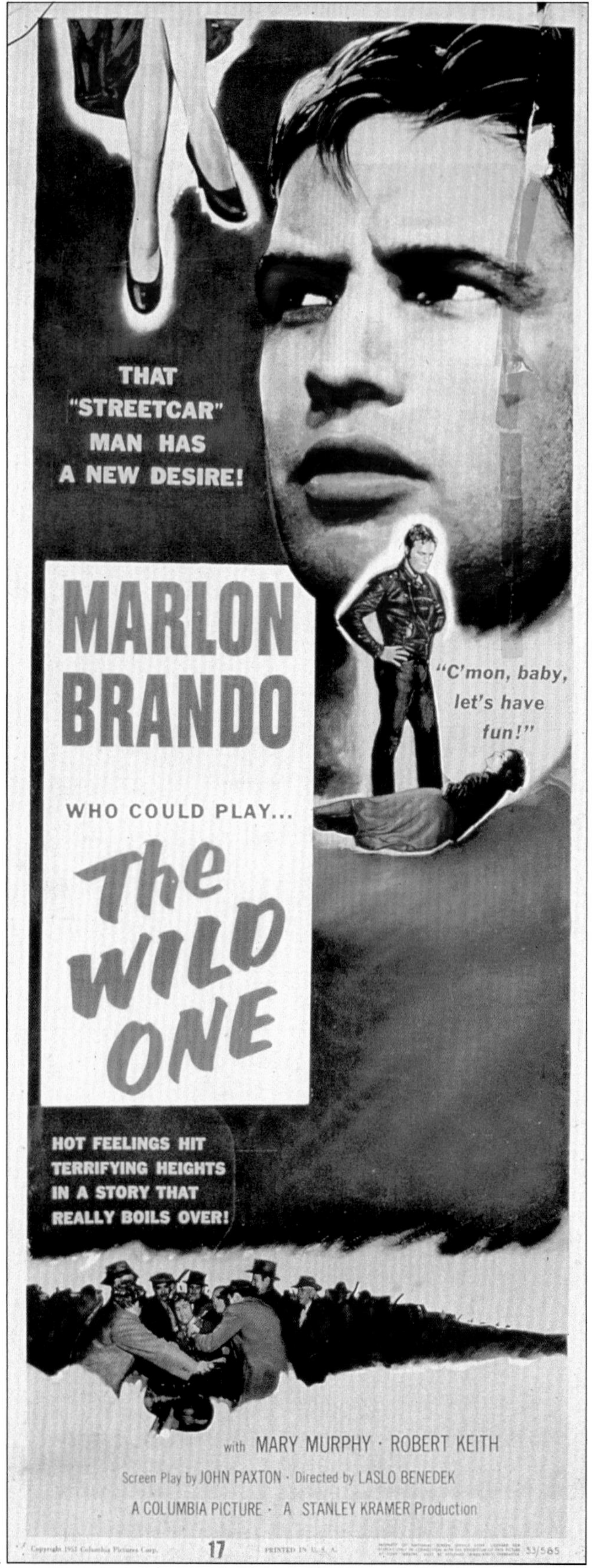

11. Poster for *The Wild One* with Marlon Brando, 1954

12. Poster for *Rebel without a Cause* with James Dean, 1955 (right, above)

13. Poster for *Jailhouse Rock*, 1957, and *It happened at the World's Fair*, 1962, with Elvis Presley (right, below)

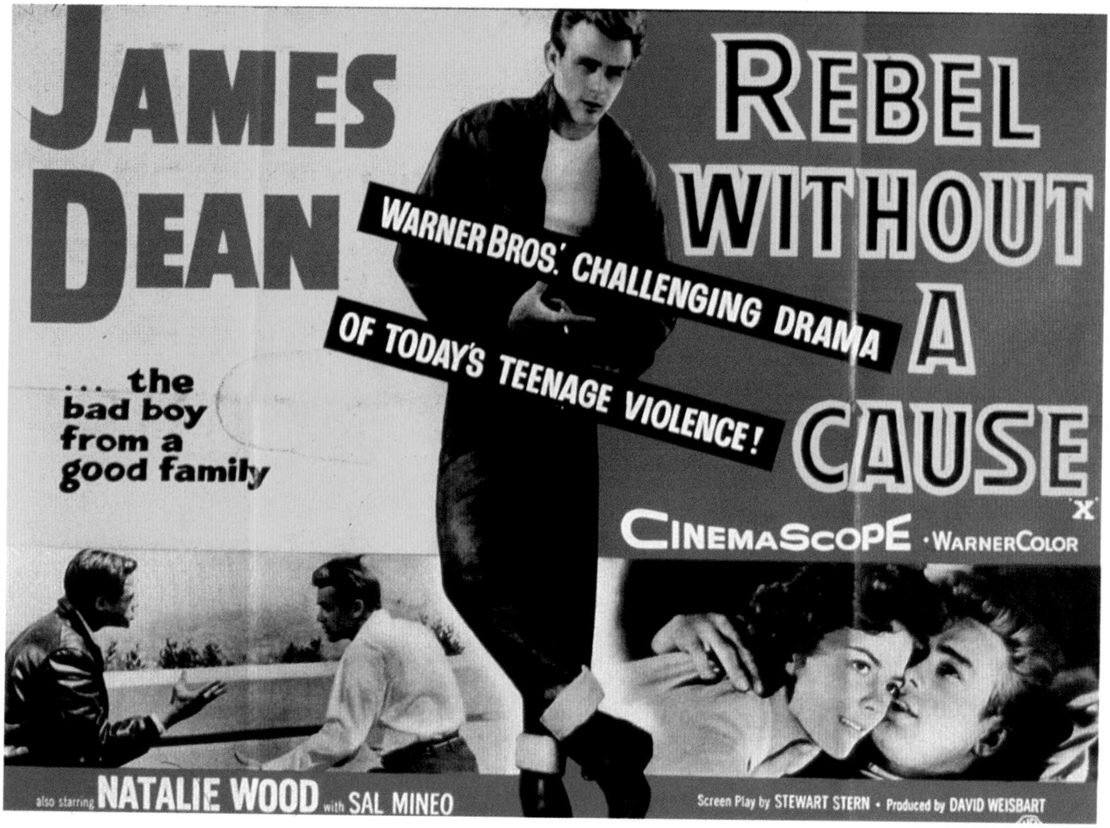

JAMES DEAN

REBEL WITHOUT A CAUSE

WARNER BROS.' CHALLENGING DRAMA OF TODAY'S TEENAGE VIOLENCE!

... the bad boy from a good family

'X'

CINEMASCOPE · WARNERCOLOR

also starring NATALIE WOOD with SAL MINEO

Screen Play by STEWART STERN · Produced by DAVID WEISBART

ELVIS

IN HIS 2 BIGGEST SINGING SWINGING HITS!

M-G-M presents
ELVIS PRESLEY
IN
"JAIL-HOUSE ROCK"
'A'
With JUDY TYLER
DEAN JONES
Directed by Richard Thorpe
Produced by Pandro S. Berman

M-G-M Presents ELVIS PRESLEY IN
"It Happened at the World's Fair"
'U'
A Ted Richmond Production in PANAVISION & METROCOLOR
With JOAN O'BRIEN · GARY LOCKWOOD

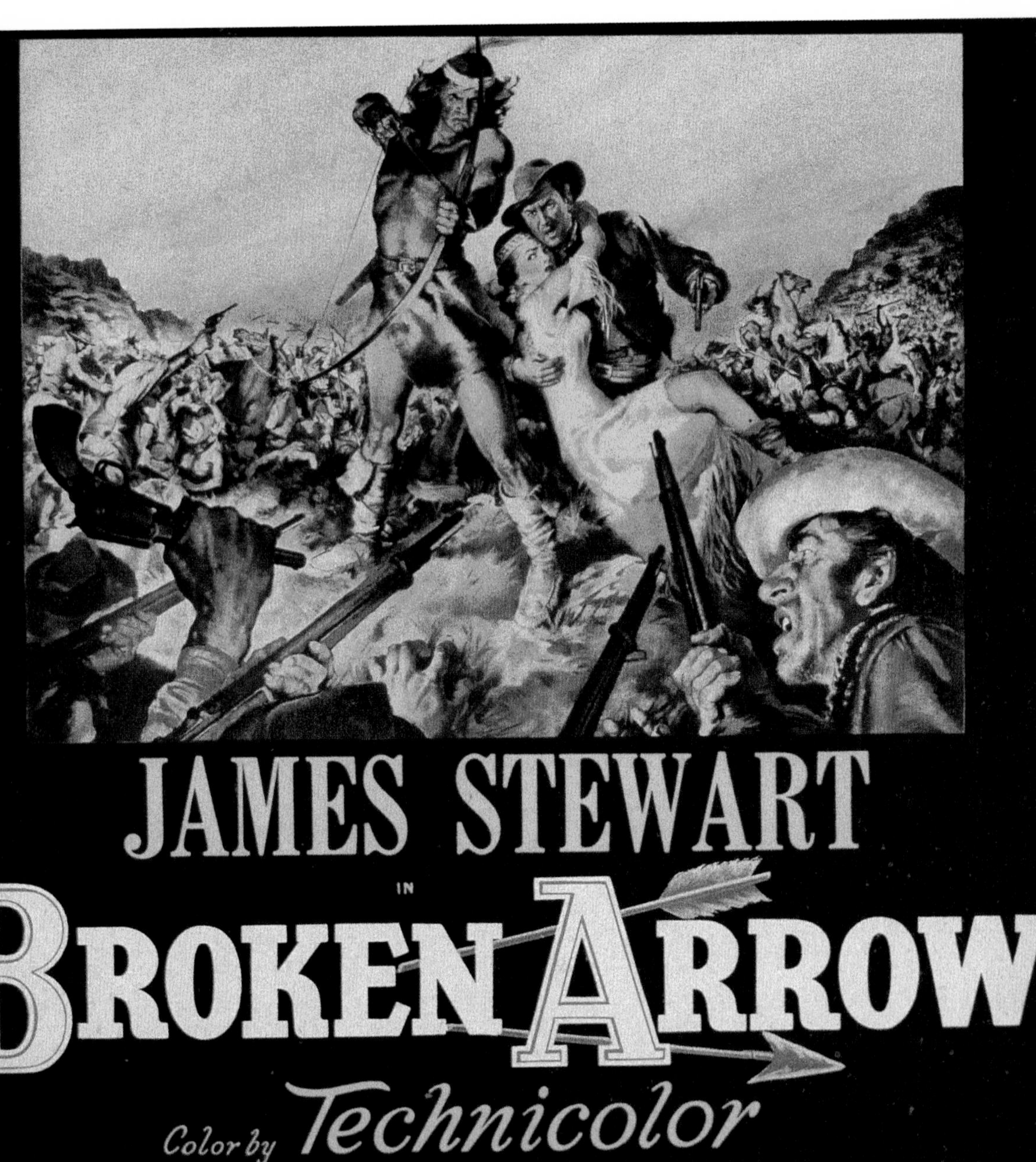

14. Poster for *Broken Arrow* with James Stewart, 1950

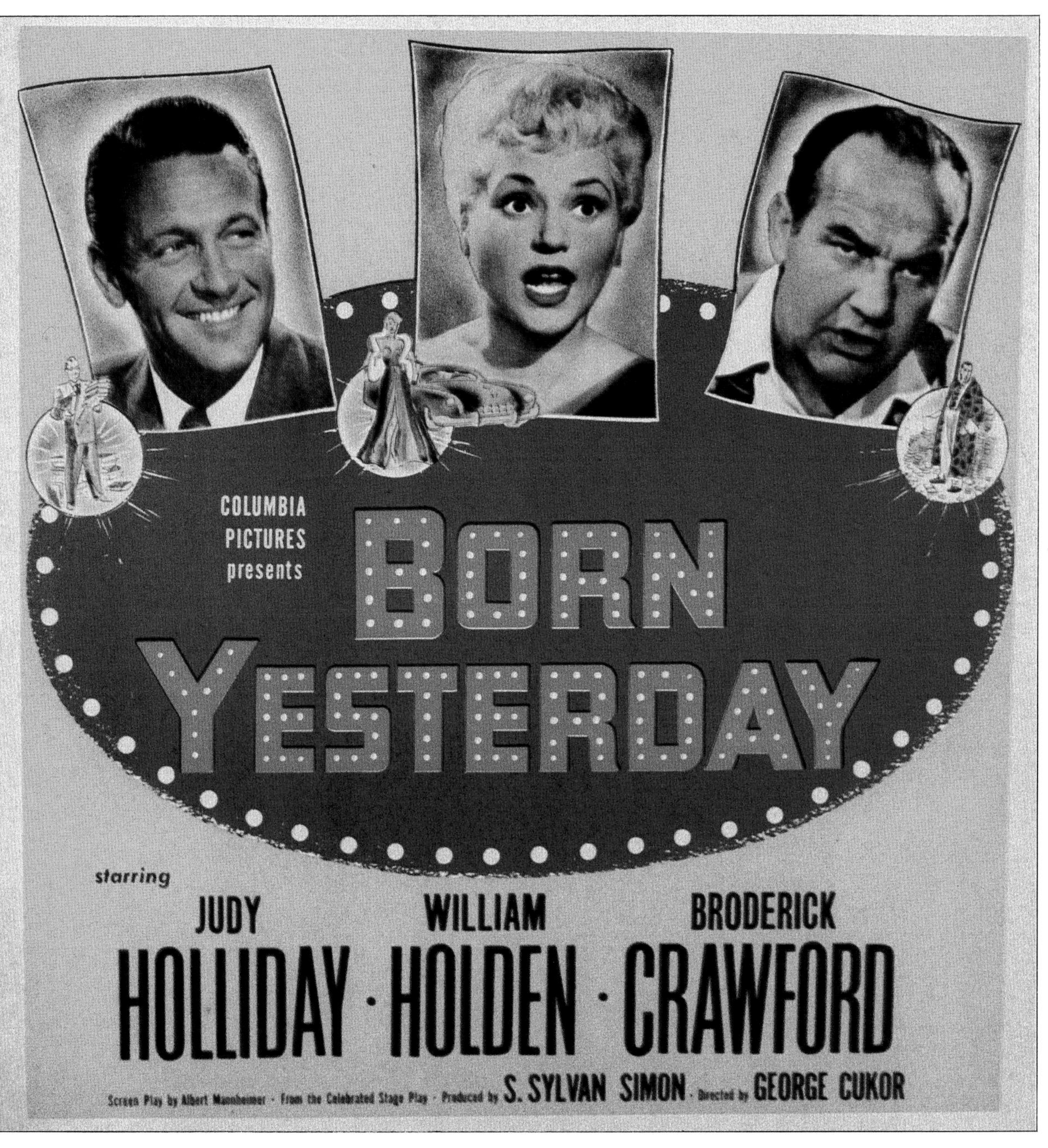

15. Poster for *Born Yesterday*, 1950

16. *Laurel and Hardy* by Royal Doulton

PHOTOPLAY (British) 1950 –

A special arrangement with the proprietors of American *Photoplay* magazine allowed many of its exclusive features, illustrated articles, and colour plates to be incorporated in the British edition. In addition there was complete coverage of British films and personalities. Collectors should note that three excellent full-page colour plates appeared in each issue, from the mid-fifties to the early sixties, and suffered the fate of being unstapled, cut by scissors, and pinned to bedroom walls by film fans. Complete editions of *Photoplay* from this period are therefore now difficult to find. The covers were colourful pin-ups. The colour plates disappeared in 1961 and the magazine was never quite the same again. No July issue was published in 1959. Editors have been Mae Murray, Roderick Mann, and Ken Ferguson. There were various title changes: *Photoplay Film Monthly*, from February 1968; *Photoplay Film & TV Scene*, from January 1978; *Photoplay*, from November 1980; *Photoplay Movies & Video*, from April 1981. In April 1989 *Photoplay* was dropped altogether from the title and the magazine was renamed *Film Monthly*. *Hence change in volume numbers. It is published by Argus Publications.

YEAR	MONTH	REF. No.	COVER STAR
1950	March	Vol. 1, no. 1	***The Elusive Pimpernel***
	April	Vol. 1, no. 2	**Patricia Dainton**
	May	Vol. 1, no. 3	**Frank Sinatra**
			Betty Garrett
	June	Vol. 1, no. 4	**Betty Hutton**
			Louis Jourdan
	July	Vol. 1, no. 5	**Barbara Bates**
	Aug.	Vol. 1, no. 6	**Gene Tierney**
	Sept.	Vol. 1, no. 7	**Adele Jergens**
	Oct.	Vol. 1, no. 8	**Susan Shaw**
	Nov.	Vol. 1, no. 9	**Mario Cabre**
	Dec.	Vol. 1, no. 10	**Barbara Murray**
1951	Jan.	Vol. 2, no. 1	**Faith Domergue**
			Robert Mitchum
	Feb.	Vol. 2, no. 2	**Anthony Dexter**
			Eleanor Parker
	March	Vol. 2, no. 3	**Dolores Moran**
	April	Vol. 2, no. 4	**Nadia Gray**
	May	Vol. 2, no. 5	**Elizabeth Taylor**
	June	Vol. 2, no. 6	**Debra Paget**
	July	Vol. 2, no. 7	**Jeanne Crain**
	Aug.	Vol. 2, no. 8	**Esther Williams**
	Sept.	Vol. 2, no. 9	**Piper Laurie**
	Oct.	Vol. 2, no. 10	**Arlene Dahl**
	Nov.	Vol. 2, no. 11	**Ann Blyth**
	Dec.	Vol. 2, no. 12	**Nadia Gray**
1952	Jan.	Vol. 3, no. 1	**June Haver**
	Feb.	Vol. 3, no. 2	**Glynis Johns**
	March	Vol. 3, no. 3	**Linda Darnell**
			Tab Hunter
	April	Vol. 3, no. 4	**Mitzi Gaynor**
	May	Vol. 3, no. 5	**Marina Berti**
	June	Vol. 3, no. 6	**Joan Greenwood**
	July	Vol. 3, no. 7	**Janet Leigh**
	Aug.	Vol. 3, no. 8	**Gloria Grahame**
	Sept.	Vol. 3, no. 9	**Rhonda Fleming**
	Oct.	Vol. 3, no. 10	**Debra Paget**
	Nov.	Vol. 3, no. 11	**Marilyn Monroe**
	Dec.	Vol. 3, no. 12	**Vera-Ellen**
1953	Jan.	Vol. 4, no. 1	**Ava Gardner**
	Feb.	Vol. 4, no. 2	**Jean Peters**
	March	Vol. 4, no. 3	**Zsa Zsa Gabor**

YEAR	MONTH	REF. No.	COVER STAR
	April	Vol. 4, no. 4	**Gene Tierney**
	May	Vol. 4, no. 5	**Mari Blanchard**
	June	Vol. 4, no. 6	**Jeanne Crain**
	July	Vol. 4, no. 7	**Debbie Reynolds**
	Aug.	Vol. 4, no. 8	**Marilyn Monroe**
	Sept.	Vol. 4, no. 9	**Elizabeth Taylor**
	Oct.	Vol. 4, no. 10	**Susan Hayward**
	Nov.	Vol. 4, no. 11	**Debra Paget**
	Dec.	Vol. 4, no. 12	**Janet Leigh**
1954	Jan.	Vol. 5, no. 1	**Diana Dors**
	Feb.	Vol. 5, no. 2	**Elaine Stewart**
	March	Vol. 5, no. 3	**Marilyn Monroe**
	April	Vol. 5, no. 4	**Ursula Thiess**
	May	Vol. 5, no. 5	**Jane Russell**
	June	Vol. 5, no. 6	**Janet Leigh**
	July	Vol. 5, no. 7	**Elaine Stewart**
	Aug.	Vol. 5, no. 8	**Sheree North**
	Sept.	Vol. 5, no. 9	**Anne Baxter**
	Oct.	Vol. 5, no. 10	**Lana Turner**
	Nov.	Vol. 5, no 11	**Rita Moreno**
	Dec.	Vol. 5, no 12	**Marilyn Monroe**
1955	Jan.	Vol. 6, no. 1	**Jane Powell**
	Feb.	Vol. 6, no. 2	**Ruth Hampton**
	March	Vol. 6, no. 3	**Joanne Dru**
	April	Vol. 6, no. 4	**Barbara Ruick**
	May	Vol. 6, no. 5	**Janet Leigh**
	June	Vol. 6, no. 6	**Mamie Van Doren**
	July	Vol. 6, no. 7	**Marilyn Monroe**
	Aug.	Vol. 6, no. 8	**Jill Adams**
	Sept.	Vol. 6, no. 9	**Sue Evans**
	Oct.	Vol. 6, no. 10	**Ann Miller**
	Nov.	Vol. 6, no. 11	**Joan Collins**
	Dec.	Vol. 6, no. 12	**Eunice Gayson**
1956	Jan.	Vol. 7, no. 1	**Jeanne Crain**
	Feb.	Vol. 7, no. 2	**Janet Leigh**
	March	Vol. 7, no. 3	**Sabrina**
	April	Vol. 7, no. 4	**Anita Ekberg**
	May	Vol. 7, no. 5	**Jackie Lane**
	June	Vol. 7, no. 6	**Diana Dors**
	July	Vol. 7, no. 7	**Cyd Charisse**
	Aug.	Vol. 7, no. 8	**Marilyn Monroe**
	Sept.	Vol. 7, no. 9	**Belinda Lee**
	Oct.	Vol. 7, no. 10	**Myrna Hansen**
	Nov.	Vol. 7, no. 11	**Anita Ekberg**
	Dec.	Vol. 7, no. 12	**Mitzi Gaynor**
1957	Jan.	Vol. 8, no. 1	**Shirley Deane**
	Feb.	Vol. 8, no. 2	**Jayne Mansfield**
	March	Vol. 8, no. 3	**Elsa Martinelli**
	April	Vol. 8, no. 4	**Barbara Lang**
	May	Vol. 8, no. 5	**Sophia Loren**
	June	Vol. 8, no. 6	**Jackie Lane**
	July	Vol. 8, no. 7	**Rita Moreno**
	Aug.	Vol. 8, no. 8	**Jayne Mansfield**
	Sept.	Vol. 8, no. 9	**Betty Brosmer**

YEAR	MONTH	REF. No.	COVER STAR
	Oct.	Vol. 8, no. 10	**Kathy Grant**
	Nov.	Vol. 8, no. 11	**Tina Louise**
	Dec.	Vol. 8, no. 12	**Mamie Van Doren**
1958	Jan.	Vol. 9, no. 1	**Kay Kendall**
	Feb.	Vol. 9, no. 2	**Anita Ekberg**
	March	Vol. 9, no. 3	**Judy Bamber**
	April	Vol. 9, no. 4	**Betty Brosmer**
	May	Vol. 9, no. 5	**Kathy Gabriel**
	June	Vol. 9, no. 6	**Anne Heywood**
	July	Vol. 9, no. 7	**Vikki Dougan**
	Aug.	Vol. 9, no. 8	**Mamie Van Doren**
	Sept.	Vol. 9, no. 9	**Barbara Lang**
	Oct.	Vol. 9, no. 10	**Brigitte Bardot**
	Nov.	Vol. 9, no. 11	**Carole Lesley**
	Dec.	Vol. 9, no. 12	**Tina Louise**
1959	Jan.	Vol. 10, no. 1	**Cyd Charisse**
	Feb.	Vol. 10, no. 2	**Elvis Presley**
	March	Vol. 10, no. 3	**Sabrina**
	April	Vol. 10, no. 4	**Eve Eden**
	May	Vol. 10, no. 5	**Barbara Lang**
	June	Vol. 10, no. 6	**Tommy Steele**
	Aug.	Vol. 10, no. 7	**Mollie Ann Bourn**
	Sept.	Vol. 10, no. 8	**Joan Collins**
	Oct.	Vol. 10, no. 9	**Robert Horton**
	Nov.	Vol. 10, no. 10	**Elvis Presley**
	Dec.	Vol. 10, no. 11	**Joy Reynolds**
1960	Jan.	Vol. 11, no. 1	**Brigitte Bardot**
	Feb.	Vol. 11, no. 2	**Cliff Richard**
	March	Vol. 11, no. 3	**Maggie Pierce**
	April	Vol. 11, no. 4	**Brigitte Bardot**
	May	Vol. 11, no. 5	**Adam Faith**
	June	Vol. 11, no. 6	**Marty Wilde**
	July	Vol. 11, no. 7	**James Garner**
	Aug.	Vol. 11, no. 8	**James Arness**
	Sept.	Vol. 11, no 9	**Tina Louise**
	Oct.	Vol. 11, no. 10	**Debbie Reynolds**
	Nov.	Vol. 11, no. 11	**Mylene Demongeot**
	Dec.	Vol. 11, no. 12	**Suzy Parker**
1961	Jan.	Vol. 12, no. 1	**Roger Moore**
	Feb.	Vol. 12, no. 2	**Marlon Brando**
	March	Vol. 12, no. 3	**Elke Sommer**
	April	Vol. 12, no. 4	**Gina Lollobrigida**
	May	Vol. 12, no. 5	**Jess Conrad**
	June	Vol. 12, no. 6	**Anita Ekberg**
	July	Vol. 12, no. 7	**Chelo Alonso**
	Aug.	Vol. 12, no. 8	**Maggie Pierce**
	Sept.	Vol. 12, no. 9	**Yvette Mimieux**
	Oct.	Vol. 12, no. 10	**Giorgia Moll**
	Nov.	Vol. 12, no. 11	**Elvis Presley**
	Dec.	Vol. 12, no. 12	**Jackie Jones**
1962	Jan.	Vol. 13, no. 1	**Carole Wells**
	Feb.	Vol. 13, no. 2	**Tuesday Weld**
	March	Vol. 13, no. 3	**Billy Fury**
	April	Vol. 13, no. 4	**Elizabeth Taylor**
	May	Vol. 13, no. 5	**Elvis Presley**

YEAR	MONTH	REF. No.	COVER STAR
	June	Vol. 13, no. 6	**Jackie Lane**
	July	Vol. 13, no. 7	**Isabel Corey**
	Aug.	Vol. 13, no. 8	**Nancy Kovak**
	Sept.	Vol. 13, no. 9	**Rosanna Schiaffino**
	Oct.	Vol. 13, no. 10	**Hayley Mills**
	Nov.	Vol. 13, no. 11	**Elvis Presley**
	Dec.	Vol. 13, no. 12	**Sophia Loren**
1963	Jan.	Vol. 14, no. 1	**Elsa Martinelli**
	Feb.	Vol. 14, no. 2	**Cliff Richard**
	March	Vol. 14, no. 3	**The Shadows**
	April	Vol. 14, no. 4	**Richard Chamberlain**
	May	Vol. 14, no. 5	**Frank Ifield**
	June.	Vol. 14, no. 6	**Elvis Presley**
	July	Vol. 14, no. 7	**Cliff Richard**
	Aug.	Vol. 14, no. 8	**Billy Fury**
	Sept.	Vol. 14, no. 9	**Kim Tracy**
	Oct.	Vol. 14, no. 10	**Jet Harris**
			Tony Meehan
	Nov.	Vol. 14, no. 11	**The Beatles**
	Dec.	Vol. 14, no. 12	**Craig Douglas**
1964	Jan.	Vol. 15, no. 1	**Billy Fury**
	Feb.	Vol. 15, no. 2	**Billy J. Kramer**
	March	Vol. 15, no. 3	**Ringo Starr**
	April	Vol. 15, no. 4	**Dave Clark**
	May	Vol. 15, no. 5	**Swinging Blue Jeans**
	June	Vol. 15, no. 6	**Paul McCartney**
	July	Vol. 15, no. 7	**Cliff Richard**
			Susan Hampshire
	Aug.	Vol. 15, no. 8	**Sean Connery**
			Shirley Eaton
	Sept.	Vol. 15, no. 9	**Cilla Black**
	Oct.	Vol. 15, no. 10	**Natalie Wood**
			Steve McQueen
	Nov.	Vol. 15, no. 11	**Sean Connery**
	Dec.	Vol. 15, no. 12	**Richard Burton**
			Sue Lyon
1965	Jan.	Vol. 16, no. 1	**George Peppard**
			Carroll Baker,
	Feb.	Vol. 16, no. 2	**Audrey Hepburn**
	March	Vol. 16, no. 3	**Peter O'Toole**
	April	Vol. 16, no. 4	**Doris Day**
			Peter Sellers
			Britt Ekland
	May	Vol. 16, no. 5	**Gene Barry**
	June	Vol. 16, no. 6	**Carroll Baker**
			Richard Burton
			Elizabeth Taylor
	July	Vol. 16, no. 7	**Claudine Auger**
	Aug.	Vol. 16, no. 8	**Elke Sommer**
			Ann-Margret
	Sept.	Vol. 16, no. 9	**Raquel Welch**
	Oct.	Vol. 16, no. 10	**Ursula Andress**
	Nov.	Vol. 16, no. 11	**Claudine Auger**
	Dec.	Vol. 16, no. 12	**Jocelyn Lane**

YEAR	MONTH	REF. No.	COVER STAR
1966	Jan.	Vol. 17, no. 1	**Senta Berger**
	Feb.	Vol. 17, no. 2	**Suzy Kendall**
	March	Vol. 17, no. 3	**Jill St John**
	April	Vol. 17, no. 4	**Sharon Tate**
	May	Vol. 17, no. 5	**Matt Helm's Slaygirls**
	June	Vol. 17, no. 6	**Monica Vitti**
	July	Vol. 17, no. 7	**Marisa Mell**
	Aug.	Vol. 17, no. 8	**Raquel Welch**
	Sept.	Vol. 17, no. 9	**Jacqueline Bisset**
	Oct.	Vol. 17, no. 10	**Mylene Demongeot**
	Nov.	Vol. 17, no. 11	**Natalie Wood**
	Dec.	Vol. 17, no. 12	**Sean Connery**
			Sylvia Koscina
1967	Jan.	Vol. 18, no. 1	**Virna Lisi**
	Feb.	Vol. 18, no. 2	**Adam West**
	March	Vol. 18, no. 3	**Ann-Margret**
	April	Vol. 18, no. 4	**Raquel Welch**
	May	Vol. 18, no. 5	**Martine Beswick**
	June	Vol. 18, no. 6	**Ursula Andress**
	July	Vol. 18, no. 7	**Sean Connery**
	Aug.	Vol. 18, no. 8	**Julie Andrews**
	Sept.	Vol. 18, no. 9	**Sophia Loren**
	Oct.	Vol. 18, no. 10	**Stella Stevens**
	Nov.	Vol. 18, no. 11	**Julie Christie**
	Dec.	Vol. 18, no. 12	**Omar Sharif**
1968	Jan.	Vol. 19, no. 1	**Rex Harrison**
	Feb.	Vol. 19, no. 2	**Jane Fonda**
	March	Vol. 19, no. 3	**Pamela Tiffin**
	April	Vol. 19, no. 4	**Faye Dunaway**
	May	Vol. 19, no. 5	**Sylvia Koscina**
	June	Vol. 19, no. 6	**Charlotte Rampling**
	July	Vol. 19, no. 7	**Claudine Auger**
	Aug.	Vol. 19, no. 8	**Julie Andrews**
	Sept.	Vol. 19, no. 9	**Stella Stevens**
	Oct.	Vol. 19, no. 10	**Nancy Sinatra**
	Nov.	Vol. 19, no. 11	**Claudia Cardinale**
			Warren Mitchell
	Dec.	Vol. 19, no. 12	**Raquel Welch**
1969	Jan.	Vol. 20, no. 1	**Beba Loncar**
	Feb.	Vol. 20, no. 2	**Kate O'Mara**
	March	Vol. 20, no. 3	**Robert Mitchum**
	April	Vol. 20, no. 4	**Gina Lollobrigida**
			Jean-Louis Trintignant
	May	Vol. 20, no. 5	**Sophia Loren and baby**
	June	Vol. 20, no. 6	**Gregory Peck**
	July	Vol. 20, no. 7	**Rock Hudson**
	Aug.	Vol. 20, no. 8	**Elizabeth Taylor**
			Mia Farrow
	Sept.	Vol. 20, no. 9	**Omar Sharif**
	Oct.	Vol. 20, no. 10	**Paul Newman**
			Lynn Redgrave
	Nov.	Vol. 20, no. 11	**Sydne Rome**
			James Coburn
	Dec.	Vol. 20, no. 12	**Peter O'Toole**
			Petula Clark

YEAR	MONTH	REF. No.	COVER STAR
1970	Jan.	Vol. 21, no. 1	**Barbra Streisand**
	Feb.	Vol. 21, no. 2	**Michael Caine**
			Candice Bergen
	March	Vol. 21, no. 3	**Richard Burton**
	April	Vol. 21, no. 4	**Paul Newman**
	May	Vol. 21, no. 5	**Clint Eastwood**
	June	Vol. 21, no. 6	**Candice Bergen**
			Bekim Fehmiu
	July	Vol. 21, no. 7	**John Wayne**
	Aug.	Vol. 21, no. 8	**Raquel Welch**
	Sept.	Vol. 21, no. 9	**Erika Raffael**
	Oct.	Vol. 21, no. 10	**Michael Crawford**
			Genevieve Gilles
	Nov.	Vol. 21, no. 11	**Rock Hudson**
			Julie Andrews
	Dec.	Vol. 21, no. 12	**Rod Steiger**
1971	Jan.	Vol. 22, no. 1	**Robert Mitchum**
			Sarah Miles
			Christopher Jones
	Feb.	Vol. 22, no. 2	**Peter O'Toole**
	March	Vol. 22, no. 3	**Steve McQueen**
	April	Vol. 22, no. 4	**Julie Ege**
	May,	Vol. 22, no. 5	**Elizabeth Taylor**
	June	Vol. 22, no. 6	**Joan Collins**
	July	Vol. 22, no. 7	**Susan Hampshire**
	Aug.	Vol. 22, no. 8	**Sophia Loren**
	Sept.	Vol. 22, no. 9	**Glenda Jackson**
	Oct.	Vol. 22, no. 10	**Robert Redford**
	Nov.	Vol. 22, no. 11	**Raquel Welch**
	Dec.	Vol. 22, no. 12	**William Holden**
			Ryan O'Neal
1972	Jan.	Vol. 23, no. 1	**Sean Connery**
			Lana Wood
	Feb.	Vol. 23, no. 2	**Michael Caine**
			Elizabeth Taylor
	March	Vol. 23, no. 3	**Christopher Gable**
			Twiggy
	April	Vol. 23, no. 4	**Vanessa Redgrave**
	May	Vol. 23, no. 5	**Yul Brynner**
			Daliah Lavi
	June	Vol. 23, no. 6	**Liza Minnelli**
			Joel Grey
	July	Vol. 23, no. 7	**Robert Redford**
	Aug.	Vol. 23, no. 8	**Natalie Wood**
			Robert Wagner
	Sept.	Vol. 23, no. 9	**Raquel Welch**
	Oct.	Vol. 23, no. 10	**Marlon Brando**
	Nov.	Vol. 23, no. 11	**Sophia Loren**
	Dec.	Vol. 23, no. 12	**Sarah Miles**
1973	Jan.	Vol. 24, no. 1	**Charles Bronson**
			Jill Ireland
	Feb.	Vol. 24, no. 2	**Burt Reynolds**
	March	Vol. 24, no. 3	**Steve McQueen**
			Ali MacGraw
	April	Vol. 24, no. 4	**Peter Finch**
			Liv Ullmann

YEAR	MONTH	REF. No.	COVER STAR
	May	Vol. 24, no. 5	**Peter Finch**
			Glenda Jackson
	June	Vol. 24, no. 6	**Elke Sommer**
	July	Vol. 24, no. 7	**Victor Garber**
	Aug.	Vol. 24, no. 8	**Roger Moore**
	Sept.	Vol. 24, no. 9	**Ted Neeley**
	Oct.	Vol. 24, no. 10	**Burt Reynolds**
	Nov.	Vol. 24, no. 11	**James Coburn**
	Dec.	Vol. 24, no. 12	**Paul Newman**
1974	Jan.	Vol. 25, no. 1	**John Phillip Law**
	Feb.	Vol. 25, no. 2	**Paul Newman**
			Robert Redford
	March	Vol. 25, no. 3	**Peter Sellers**
	April	Vol. 25, no. 4	**Steve McQueen**
	May	Vol. 25, no. 5	**Robert Redford**
			Mia Farrow
			Linda Blair
			Ellen Burstyn
	June	Vol. 25, no. 6	**Al Pacino**
	July	Vol. 25, no. 7	**Roger Moore**
			Britt Ekland
	Aug.	Vol. 25, no. 8	**Ann-Margret**
	Sept.	Vol. 25, no. 9	**Charlotte Rampling**
	Oct.	Vol. 25, no. 10	**Dennis Weaver**
	Nov.	Vol. 25, no. 11	**David Essex**
			James Coburn
	Dec.	Vol. 25, no. 12	**Christopher Lee**
			James Caan
			Albert Finney
1975	Jan.	Vol. 26, no. 1	**Roger Moore**
	Feb.	Vol. 26, no. 2	**Charlton Heston**
	March	Vol. 26, no. 3	**Steve McQueen**
	April	Vol. 26, no. 4	**Barbra Streisand**
	May	Vol. 26, no. 5	**Burt Reynolds**
			Roger Daltrey
	June	Vol. 26, no. 6	**Robert Redford**
	July	Vol. 26, no. 7	**Warren Beatty**
	Aug.	Vol. 26, no. 8	**James Caan**
	Sept.	Vol. 26, no. 9	**Clint Eastwood**
	Oct.	Vol. 26, no. 10	**James Caan**
	Nov.	Vol. 26, no. 11	**Peter Sellers**
	Dec.	Vol. 26, no. 12	**John Wayne**
			Katharine Hepburn
1976	Jan.	Vol. 27, no. 1	***Jaws***
	Feb.	Vol. 27, no. 2	**Liza Minnelli**
	March	Vol. 27, no. 3	**Ryan O'Neal**
			Marisa Berenson
	April	Vol. 27, no. 4	**Valerie Perrine**
	May	Vol. 27, no. 5	**Diana Ross**
	June	Vol. 27, no. 6	**Lee Marvin**
	July	Vol. 27, no. 7	**Georges Guetary**
	Aug.	Vol. 27, no. 8	**Robert Redford**
	Sept.	Vol. 27, no. 9	**Paul Newman**
	Oct.	Vol. 27, no. 10	**Kris Kristofferson**
	Nov.	Vol. 27, no. 11	**Raquel Welch**
			Harvey Keitel

YEAR	MONTH	REF. No.	COVER STAR
	Dec.	Vol. 27, no. 12	**David Soul**
1977	Jan.	Vol. 28, no. 1	**Barbra Streisand** **Kris Kristofferson**
	Feb.	Vol. 28, no. 2	***King Kong***
	March	Vol. 28, no. 3	**Kris Kristofferson**
	April	Vol. 28, no. 4	**Roger Moore** **Barbara Bach**
	May	Vol. 28, no. 5	**Farrah Fawcett-Majors** **Kate Jackson** **Jaclyn Smith**
	June	Vol. 28, no. 6	**Sylvester Stallone** **Talia Shire**
	July	Vol. 28, no. 7	***A Bridge Too Far***
	Aug.	Vol. 28, no. 8	**Roger Moore**
	Sept.	Vol. 28, no. 9	**Evel Knievel**
	Oct.	Vol. 28, no. 10	**Robert De Niro** **Liza Minnelli**
	Nov.	Vol. 28, no. 11	**Michelle Phillips** **Rudolf Nureyev**
	Dec.	Vol. 28, no. 12	**Al Pacino**
1978	Jan.	Vol. 29, no. 1	**Artoo Detoo and See Threepio**
	Feb.	Vol. 29, no. 2	**Harrison Ford**
	March	Vol. 29, no. 3	**Clint Eastwood**
	April	Vol. 29, no. 4	**Kris Kristofferson** **Jaclyn Smith**
	May	Vol. 29, no. 5	**John Travolta** **Karen Gorney**
	June	Vol. 29, no. 6	**Oliver Tobias**
	July	Vol. 29, no. 7	**John Travolta**
	Aug.	Vol. 29, no. 8	**Henry Winkler**
	Sept.	Vol. 29, no. 9	**Nick Nolte** **Olivia De Havilland**
	Oct.	Vol. 29, no. 10	**John Travolta** **Olivia Newton-John**
	Nov.	Vol. 29, no. 11	**Robert Mitchum** **Peter Ustinov**
	Dec.	Vol. 29, no. 12	**The Bee Gees** **Peter Frampton**
1979	Jan.	Vol. 30, no. 1	**Christopher Reeve**
	Feb.	Vol. 30, no. 2	**Olivia Newton-John**
	March	Vol. 30, no. 3	**Anthony Hopkins**
	April	Vol. 30, no. 4	**Robert De Niro**
	May	Vol. 30, no. 5	**Diana Ross**
	June	Vol. 30, no. 6	**Sophia Loren**
	July	Vol. 30, no. 7	**Roger Moore** **Lois Chiles**
	Aug.	Vol. 30, no. 8	**William Katt** **Tom Berenger**
	Sept.	Vol. 30, no. 9	**Ryan O'Neal** **Barbra Streisand**
	Oct.	Vol. 30, no. 10	**Frank Langella**
	Nov.	Vol. 30, no. 11	**Joan Collins**
	Dec.	Vol. 30, no. 12	**Paul Newman**

YEAR	MONTH	REF. No.	COVER STAR
1980	Jan.	Vol. 31, no. 1	**Leonard Nimoy**
	Feb.	Vol. 31, no. 2	**Clint Eastwood**
	March	Vol. 31, no. 3	**Bette Midler**
	April	Vol. 31, no. 4	**David Essex**
	May	Vol. 31, no. 5	**Nine small pictures of stars**
	June	Vol. 31, no. 6	***The Empire Strikes Back***
	July	Vol. 31, no. 7	***All That Jazz***
	Aug.	Vol. 31, no. 8	**Clint Eastwood**
	Sept.	Vol. 31, no. 9	**Sophia Loren**
	Oct.	Vol. 31, no. 10	**Olivia Newton-John**
	Nov.	Vol. 31, no. 11	**Jack Nicholson**
	Dec.	Vol. 31, no. 12	**Linda Gray**
1981	Jan.	Vol. 32, no. 1	**Sam Jones** **Melody Anderson**
	Feb.	Vol. 32, no. 2	**Clint Eastwood**
	March	Vol. 32, no. 3	**Elizabeth Taylor**
	April	Vol. 32, no. 4	**Robin Williams** **Shelley Duvall**
	May	Vol. 32, no. 5	**Christopher Reeve**
	June	Vol. 32, no. 6	**Jack Nicholson** **Jessica Lange**
	July	Vol. 32, no. 7	**Terence Stamp**
	Aug.	Vol. 32, no. 8	**Burt Reynolds** **Farrah Fawcett**
	Sept.	Vol. 32, no. 9	**Harrison Ford**
	Oct.	Vol. 32, no. 10	***History of the World – Part 1***
	Nov.	Vol. 32, no. 11	**Bo Derek** **Miles O'Keefe**
	Dec.	Vol. 32, no. 12	**John Travolta**
1982	Jan.	Vol. 33, no. 1	**Faye Dunaway**
	Feb.	Vol. 33, no. 2	**Peter Falk** **Vicki Frederick** **Laurene Landon**
	March	Vol. 33, no. 3	**Brooke Shields**
	April	Vol. 33, no. 4	**Diane Keaton** **Warren Beatty**
	May	Vol. 33, no. 5	**Burt Reynolds** **Rachel Ward**
	June	Vol. 33, no. 6	**Jamie Lee Curtis** **Al Pacino**
	July	Vol. 33, no. 7	**Christopher Reeve**
	Aug.	Vol. 33, no. 8	**Albert Finney**
	Sept.	Vol. 33, no. 9	**Sylvester Stallone** **Talia Shire**
	Oct.	Vol. 33, no. 10	**Harrison Ford**
	Nov.	Vol. 33, no. 11	**Dolly Parton**
	Dec.	Vol. 33, no. 12	***E.T.***
1983	Jan.	Vol. 34, no. 1	**Peter Sellers**
	Feb.	Vol. 34, no. 2	**Sylvester Stallone**
	March	Vol. 34, no. 3	**Goldie Hawn** **Burt Reynolds**
	April	Vol. 34, no. 4	**Faye Dunaway**

YEAR	MONTH	REF. No.	COVER STAR
	May	Vol. 34, no. 5	**Meryl Streep**
	June	Vol. 34, no. 6	**Dudley Moore**
	July	Vol. 34, no. 7	***Return of the Jedi***
	Aug.	Vol. 34, no. 8	**Christopher Reeve**
	Sept.	Vol. 34, no. 9	**Roy Scheider**
	Oct.	Vol. 34, no. 10	**John Travolta**
	Nov.	Vol. 34, no. 11	**Richard Gere** **Valerie Kaprisky**
	Dec.	Vol. 34, no. 12	**Ann-Margret**
1984	Jan.	Vol. 35, no. 1	**Sean Connery** **Kim Basinger**
	Feb.	Vol. 35, no. 2	**Clint Eastwood**
	March	Vol. 35, no. 3	**Al Pacino**
	April	Vol. 35, no. 4	**Barbra Streisand**
	May	Vol. 35, no. 5	**Tom Selleck**
	June	Vol. 35, no. 6	**Paul Newman**
	July	Vol. 35, no. 7	**Harrison Ford**
	Aug.	Vol. 35, no. 8	**Helen Slater**
	Sept.	Vol. 35, no. 9	**Leonard Nimoy**
	Oct.	Vol. 35, no. 10	**Michelle Johnson** **Michael Caine**
	Nov.	Vol. 35, no. 11	**Arnold Schwarzenegger**
	Dec.	Vol. 35, no. 12	***The Gremlins***
1985	Jan.	Vol. 36, no. 1	**Lance Guest** **Catherine Mary Stewart** **Francesca Annis** **Sting**
	Feb.	Vol. 36, no. 2	**Dolly Parton**
	March	Vol. 36, no. 3	**Kris Kristofferson**
	April	Vol. 36, no. 4	***2010***
	May	Vol. 36, no. 5	**Richard Gere**
	June	Vol. 36, no. 6	**Harrison Ford**
	July	Vol. 36, no. 7	**Mel Gibson** **Diane Keaton**
	Aug.	Vol. 36, no. 8	**Jamie Lee Curtis**
	Sept.	Vol. 36, no. 9	**Christopher Lambert**
	Oct.	Vol. 36, no. 10	**Tina Turner** **Mel Gibson**
	Nov.	Vol. 36, no. 11	**Meryl Streep**
	Dec.	Vol. 36, no. 12	**Christopher Lloyd**
1986	Jan.	Vol. 37, no. 1	**Kevin Kline**
	Feb.	Vol. 37, no. 2	**Al Pacino**
	March	Vol. 37, no. 3	**Robert Redford**
	April	Vol. 37, no. 4	**Eddie O'Connell**
	May	Vol. 37, no. 5	**Kathleen Turner**
	June	Vol. 37, no. 6	**James Cagney**
	July	Vol. 37, no. 7	**Sally Field** **James Garner**
	Aug.	Vol. 37, no. 8	**Sylvester Stallone**
	Sept.	Vol. 37, no 9	***Aliens***
	Oct.	Vol. 37, no. 10	**Goldie Hawn**
	Nov.	Vol. 37, no. 11	**Bette Midler**
	Dec.	Vol. 37, no. 12	**David Bowie**

YEAR	MONTH	REF. No.	COVER STAR
1987	Jan.	Vol. 38, no. 1	**Jack Nicholson**
	Feb.	Vol. 38, no. 2	***The Fly***
	March	Vol. 38, no. 3	**Harrison Ford**
	April	Vol. 38, no. 4	**Paul Newman**
	May	Vol. 38, no. 5	***Platoon***
	June	Vol. 38, no. 6	**Burt Reynolds**
	July	Vol. 38, no. 7	**Timothy Dalton**
	Aug.	Vol. 38, no. 8	**Bruce Willis**
	Sept.	Vol. 38, no. 9	**Mel Gibson**
	Oct.	Vol. 38, no. 10	**Eddie Murphy**
	Nov.	Vol. 38, no. 11	**Robert Englund**
	Dec.	Vol. 38, no. 12	**Jack Nicholson** **Cher** **Susan Sarandon** **Michelle Pfeiffer**
1988	Jan.	Vol. 39, no. 1	***Robocop*** ***Spaceballs***
	Feb.	Vol. 39, no. 2	**Glenn Close** **Michael Douglas**
	March	Vol. 39, no. 3	**Richard Dreyfuss** **Emilio Estevez**
	April	Vol. 39, no. 4	**Tom Berenger**
	May	Vol. 39, no. 5	**Tom Selleck** **Steve Guttenberg** **Ted Danson**
	June	Vol. 39, no. 6	**Kim Basinger**
	July	Vol. 39, no. 7	**Paul Hogan** **Linda Kozlowski**
	Aug.	Vol. 39, no. 8	**Gary Oldman** **Theresa Russell**
	Sept.	Vol. 39, no. 9	**Sylvester Stallone**
	Oct.	Vol. 39, no. 10	**Phil Collins** **Julie Walters**
	Nov.	Vol. 39, no. 11	**John Cleese** **Jamie Lee Curtis** **Kevin Kline** **Michael Palin**
	Dec.	Vol. 39, no. 12	**Bob Hoskins and Roger Rabbit**
1989	Jan.	Vol. 40, no. 1	**Charlie Sheen** **Emilio Estevez**
	Feb.	Vol. 40, no. 2	**Tom Cruise**
	March	Vol. 40, no. 3	**Jodie Foster**
	April	Vol. 1,* no. 1	**Clint Eastwood**
	May	Vol. 1, no. 2	**Melanie Griffith**
	June	Vol. 1, no. 3	**Timothy Dalton**
	July	Vol. 1, no. 4	**Harrison Ford**
	Aug.	Vol. 1, no. 5	**Jack Nicholson**
	Sept.	Vol. 1, no. 6	**Mel Gibson**
	Oct.	Vol. 1, no. 7	**Kris Kristofferson** **Cheryl Ladd**
	Nov.	Vol. 1, no. 8	**Yahoo Serious**
	Dec.	Vol. 1, no. 9	**Bill Murray** **Dan Aykroyd** **Harold Ramis** **Rick Moranis**

PICTURE SHOW 1919 – 60

This bluetone covered weekly eventually became the popular filmgoer's read every Tuesday. Published by the Amalgamated Press, it was the first British film magazine to offer its readers souvenirs of their favourite stars as prizes in simple competitions; Valentino's fur hat, worn by him in *The Eagle*, was the first awarded prize. Early covers gave prominence to the title of the leading article inside the magazine, while later covers featured star couples in black and white stills with one colour – yellow, red, green, orange, blue or whatever the colour the logo banner happened to be that week – prominently displayed in a shirt or dress of one of the stars. In 1932, the first of four silver prints with black photogravure was given away in a series of 'Famous Lovers of History'.

There were special summer and Christmas issues, free souvenir booklets, and star albums during the thirties. *Picture Show* finally became the best-valued 16 pages filmgoers could buy: couple cover, gossip page, star souvenirs to be won, book reviews, story adaptation, full-page signed photograph, illustrated centre spread of current films, film reviews, previews, studio news, and a life story of a star with postcard-size picture that could be cut out and pasted on a postcard. No wonder these magazines are becoming increasingly difficult to find complete and uncut.

Collectors should note that due to paper shortage during the war *Picture Show* appeared fortnightly from 13 September 1941 to 25 June 1949. Teasers began to creep in on the covers during the fifties. By 28 March 1959 there was a title change to *Picture Show & TV Mirror*, reverting back to *Picture Show* on 17 September 1960. The last of the banner covers appeared with the issue of 14 February 1959. The magazine finally went into decline with the increasing coverage of television and a new editorial policy that attempted to mix films with photojournalism. No one was ever credited for editing the magazine.

Due to an industrial strike, no issues were published from 27 June to 15 August 1959.

YEAR	MONTH	REF. No.	COVER STAR
1919	3 May	Vol. 1, no. 1	**Charlie Chaplin**
	10 May	Vol. 1, no. 2	**Mabel Normand**
	17 May	Vol. 1, no. 3	**Mildred Harris**
	24 May	Vol. 1, no. 4	**Douglas Fairbanks**
	31 May	Vol. 1, no. 5	**Jewel Carmen**
	7 June	Vol. 1, no. 6	**Tom Mix**
	14 June	Vol. 1, no. 7	**Alma Taylor**
	21 June	Vol. 1, no. 8	**Charles Ray**
	28 June	Vol. 1, no. 9	**Dorothy Gish**
	5 July	Vol. 1, no. 10	**Roscoe Arbuckle**
	12 July	Vol. 1, no. 11	**Mary Miles Minter**

YEAR	MONTH	REF. No.	COVER STAR
	19 July	Vol. 1, no. 12	**Eddie Polo**
	26 July	Vol. 1, no. 13	**Carmel Myers**
	2 Aug.	Vol. 1, no. 14	**William Russell**
	9 Aug.	Vol. 1, no. 15	**Ruth Roland**
	16 Aug.	Vol. 1, no. 16	**George Walsh**
	23 Aug.	Vol. 1, no. 17	**Dorothy Dalton**
	30 Aug.	Vol. 1, no. 18	**William Duncan**
	6 Sept.	Vol. 1, no. 19	**Norma Talmadge**
	13 Sept.	Vol. 1, no. 20	**E.K. Lincoln**
	20 Sept.	Vol. 1, no. 21	**Marie Doro**
	27 Sept.	Vol. 1, no. 22	**Dustin Farnum**

YEAR	MONTH	REF. No.	COVER STAR
	4 Oct.	Vol. 1, no. 23	**Bessie Love**
	11 Oct.	Vol. 1, no. 24	**Harold Lloyd**
	18 Oct.	Vol. 1, no. 25	**Geraldine Farrar**
	25 Oct.	Vol. 1, no. 26	**Owen Moore**
	1 Nov.	Vol. 2, no. 27	**Jane Novak**
	8 Nov.	Vol. 2, no. 28	**Montagu Love**
	15 Nov.	Vol. 2, no. 29	**Marie Prevost**
	22 Nov.	Vol. 2, no. 30	**Monroe Salisbury**
	29 Nov.	Vol. 2, no. 31	**Pearl White**
	6 Dec.	Vol. 2, no. 32	**Lee Moran**
	13 Dec.	Vol. 2, no. 33	**Mae Marsh**
	20 Dec.	Vol. 2, no. 34	**William S. Hart**
	27 Dec.	Vol. 2, no. 35	**Francesca Bertini**
1920	3 Jan.	Vol. 2, no. 36	**Sessue Hayakawa**
	10 Jan.	Vol. 2, no. 37	**Queenie Thomas**
	17 Jan.	Vol. 2, no. 38	**James Knight**
	24 Jan.	Vol. 2, no. 39	**Anita Stewart**
	31 Jan.	Vol. 2, no. 40	**Larry Semon**
	7 Feb.	Vol. 2, no. 41	**Dorothy Phillips**
	14 Feb.	Vol. 2, no. 42	**Henry Edwards**
	21 Feb.	Vol. 2, no. 43	**Mary Pickford**
	28 Feb.	Vol. 2, no. 44	**Eddie Lyons**
	6 March	Vol. 2, no. 45	**Pauline Frederick**
	13 March	Vol. 2, no. 46	**Madge Kennedy** **Tom Moore**
	20 March	Vol. 2, no. 47	**Charles Ray**
	27 March	Vol. 2, no. 48	**Jack Dempsey** **Anna Q. Nilsson**
	3 April	Vol. 2, no. 49	**Mildred Harris**
	10 April	Vol. 2, no. 50	**Marguerite Clark and husband**
	17 April	Vol. 2, no. 51	**Pauline Frederick**
	24 April	Vol. 2, no. 52	**Warren Kerrigan and family**
	1 May	Vol. 3, no. 53	**Katharine MacDonald** **Milton Sims**
	8 May	Vol. 3, no. 54	**William S. Hart**
	15 May	Vol. 3, no. 55	**Priscilla Dean**
	22 May	Vol. 3, no. 56	**Constance, Norma, and Natalie Talmadge**
	29 May	Vol. 3, no. 57	**Edna May** **A.E. Mason** **Maurice Elvey**
	5 June	Vol. 3, no. 58	**Nazimova**
	12 June	Vol. 3, no. 59	**Margery Daw**
	19 June	Vol. 3, no. 60	**Filming wild animals at Selig zoo**
	26 June	Vol. 3, no. 61	**Douglas Fairbanks**
	3 July	Vol. 3, no. 62	**Tom Mix** **Pearl White** **Charlie Chaplin**
	10 July	Vol. 3, no. 63	**Ann May** **Charles Ray**
	17 July	Vol. 3, no. 64	**Mary Pickford**
	24 July	Vol. 3, no. 65	**Mae Marsh and baby**
	31 July	Vol. 3, no. 66	**Fatty Arbuckle**
	7 Aug.	Vol. 3, no. 67	**Myrtle Lind**
	14 Aug.	Vol. 3, no. 68	**Tom Moore** **Peaches Jackson**
	21 Aug.	Vol. 3, no. 69	**Georges Carpentier** **Faire Binney**
	28 Aug.	Vol. 3, no. 70	**Seena Owen** **Princess Pat**
	4 Sept.	Vol. 3, no. 71	**Eddie Lyons** **Lee Moran**
	11 Sept.	Vol. 3, no. 72	**Sir Thomas Lipton** **Anna Q. Nilsson** **Lord Dewar**
	18 Sept.	Vol. 3, no. 73	**Mary Pickford**
	25 Sept.	Vol. 3, no. 74	**Shirley Mason** **Viola Dana**
	2 Oct.	Vol. 3, no. 75	**Ora Carew**
	9 Oct.	Vol. 3, no. 76	**Norma, Natalie, Constance Talmadge**
	16 Oct.	Vol. 3, no. 77	**Frank Mayo**
	23 Oct.	Vol. 3, no. 78	**Helene Chadwick**
	30 Oct.	Vol. 4, no. 79	**Solving the wallpaper question**
	6 Nov.	Vol. 4, no. 80	**'Snooky' the chimp**
	13 Nov.	Vol. 4, no. 81	**Wesley Barrie** **Aaron Mitchell** **Walter Chung**
	20 Nov.	Vol. 4, no. 82	**Mabel Normand**
	27 Nov.	Vol. 4, no. 83	**Wallace Reid** **Bebe Daniels**
	4 Dec.	Vol. 4, no. 84	**Priscilla Dean**
	11 Dec.	Vol. 4, no. 85	**Leonora Hughes**
	18 Dec.	Vol. 4, no. 86	**Antonio Moreno** **Viola Dana** **Eddie Polo**
	25 Dec.	Vol. 4, no. 87	**Bebe Daniels**
1921	1 Jan.	Vol. 4, no. 88	**Gladys Walton**
	8 Jan.	Vol. 4, no. 89	**Violet Hopson** **Stewart Rome** **Gregory Scott**
	15 Jan.	Vol. 4, no. 90	**Jackie Coogan**
	22 Jan.	Vol. 4, no. 91	**Edith Roberts**
	29 Jan.	Vol. 4, no. 92	**George K. Arthur**
	5 Feb.	Vol. 4, no. 93	**Ruth Roland**
	12 Feb.	Vol. 4, no. 94	**Mary Pickford** **Douglas Fairbanks**
	19 Feb.	Vol. 4, no. 95	**Nick Cogley**
	26 Feb.	Vol. 4, no. 96	**Dorothy Gish** **James Rennie**
	5 March	Vol. 4, no. 97	**Shirley Mason**

YEAR	MONTH	REF. No.	COVER STAR
	12 March	Vol. 4, no. 98	**Johnny Jones**
	19 March	Vol. 4, no. 99	**Thomas Meighan** **Betty Compson**
	26 March	Vol. 4, no. 100	**Mary Pickford** **Herbert Ralston**
	2 April	Vol. 4, no. 101	**Charlie Chaplin** **Jackie Coogan**
	9 April	Vol. 4, no. 102	**Hilda Bayley**
	16 April	Vol. 4, no. 103	**Pearl White** **Wallace McCutcheon**
	23 April	Vol. 4, no. 104	**John Henry Jr**
	30 April	Vol. 5, no. 105	**Charlie Chaplin** **Mary Pickford** **Douglas Fairbanks**
	7 May	Vol. 5, no. 106	**Sessue Hayakawa and wife**
	14 May	Vol. 5, no. 107	**Nazimova**
	21 May	Vol. 5, no. 108	**Norma Talmadge**
	28 May	Vol. 5, no. 109	**Wallace Reid and family**
	4 June	Vol. 5, no. 110	**Viola Dana** **Shirley Mason**
	11 June	Vol. 5, no. 111	**Vivia Ogden** **Emily Fitzroy**
	18 June	Vol. 5, no. 112	**May Allison** **Wyndham Standing**
	25 June	Vol. 5, no. 113	**Shirley Mason**
	2 July	Vol. 5, no. 114	**Bebe Daniels** **Harrison Ford**
	9 July	Vol. 5, no. 115	**Douglas Fairbanks**
	16 July	Vol. 5, no. 116	**Norma Talmadge** **Marion Davies**
	23 July	Vol. 5, no. 117	**Mary Miles Minter**
	30 July	Vol. 5, no. 118	**Doris Keane** **Basil Sydney**
	6 Aug.	Vol. 5, no. 119	**A Mack Sennett bathing beauty**
	13 Aug.	Vol. 5, no. 120	**Tom Mix** **Victoria Forde**
	20 Aug.	Vol. 5, no. 121	**Buster Keaton** **Natalie Talmadge**
	27 Aug.	Vol. 5, no. 122	**Charlie Chaplin** **Jackie Coogan**
	3 Sept.	Vol. 5, no. 123	**Wallace Reid** **Agnes Ayres**
	10 Sept.	Vol. 5, no. 124	**May McAvoy** **Walter Hiers**
	17 Sept.	Vol. 5, no. 125	**Betsy Ann Hisle**
	24 Sept.	Vol. 5, no. 126	**Mary Pickford**
	1 Oct.	Vol. 5, no. 127	**Violet Hopson**
	8 Oct.	Vol. 5, no. 128	**Charlie Chaplin**
	15 Oct.	Vol. 5, no. 129	**Girls' cinema**
	22 Oct.	Vol. 5, no. 130	**Tom Moore**
	29 Oct.	Vol. 6, no. 131	**Clara Kimball Young**

YEAR	MONTH	REF. No.	COVER STAR
	5 Nov.	Vol. 6, no. 132	**Gloria Swanson**
	12 Nov.	Vol. 6, no. 133	**Mary Pickford** **Douglas Fairbanks** **Margaret De La Motte**
	19 Nov.	Vol. 6, no. 134	**Jackie Coogan**
	26 Nov.	Vol. 6, no. 135	**Colleen Moore**
	3 Dec.	Vol. 6, no. 136	**Constance Binney**
	10 Dec.	Vol. 6, no. 137	**Pauline Frederick**
	17 Dec.	Vol. 6, no. 138	**Dorothy Phillips** **Gertrude Olmsted**
	24 Dec.	Vol. 6, no. 139	**Jane Novak** **'Snowy' Baker**
	31 Dec.	Vol. 6, no. 140	**Phyllis Bedells** **Edouard Espinosa** **Jack Morrison**
1922	7 Jan.	Vol. 6, no. 141	**Will Rogers** **Jeanette Treboal**
	14 Jan.	Vol. 6, no. 142	**Gladys Walton** **Carmen Phillips**
	21 Jan.	Vol. 6, no. 143	**Irene Castle**
	28 Jan.	Vol. 6, no. 144	**Douglas Fairbanks**
	4 Feb.	Vol. 6, no. 145	**Martin Johnson and wife**
	11 Feb.	Vol. 6, no. 146	**Charles Ray** **Ethel Shannon**
	18 Feb.	Vol. 6, no. 147	**Mary Pickford**
	25 Feb.	Vol. 6, no. 148	**'Sunshine' Sammy**
	4 March	Vol. 6, no. 149	**Lon Chaney**
	11 March	Vol. 6, no. 150	**Lady Diana Manners** **Victor McLaglen**
	18 March	Vol. 6, no. 151	**Charlie Chaplin**
	25 March	Vol. 6, no. 152	**Betty Blythe**
	1 April	Vol. 6, no. 153	**'Snowy' Baker** **Pauline Frederick**
	8 April	Vol. 6, no. 154	**Mary Pickford** **Geraldine Farrar** **John Pialoglou** **Constance Talmadge** **Lou Tellegen**
	15 April	Vol. 6, no. 155	***The Fire of London*** ***Orphans of the Storm***
	22 April	Vol. 6, no. 156	***The Sign on the Door*** ***The Charm School***
	29 April	Vol. 6, no. 157	**Lady Doris Stapleton** **Poppy Wyndham** **Lady Diana Manners**
	6 May	Vol. 6, no. 158	**Mary Pickford** **Constance Talmadge** **Lillian Gish**

YEAR	MONTH	REF. No.	COVER STAR
	13 May	Vol. 6, no. 159	**William Desmond and family**
	20 May	Vol. 6, no. 160	**'Sunshine' Sammy**
			Pat Moore
			Richard Headrick
			Jackie Coogan
	27 May	Vol. 7, no. 161	**Eille Norwood**
	3 June	Vol. 7, no. 162	**Fay Compton**
	10 June	Vol. 7 no. 163	**Jack Dempsey**
			Georges Carpentier
			Victor McLaglen
	17 June	Vol. 7, no. 164	**Talmadge sisters**
			Matheson Lang
			Charlie Chaplin
	24 June	Vol. 7, no. 165	**Gish sisters**
	1 July	Vol. 7, no. 166	**Mary Miles Minter**
			Tony Moreno
			Mae Murray
			Eugene O'Brien
	8 July	Vol. 7, no. 167	**Jackie Coogan**
	15 July	Vol. 7, no. 168	**Screen animals**
	22 July	Vol. 7, no. 169	**Alla Nazimova**
			Mary Pickford
			Alma Taylor
	29 July	Vol. 7, no. 170	**William S. Hart**
			Natalie Talmadge
	5 Aug.	Vol. 7, no. 171	**Carlyle Blackwell**
			Edna Mayo
			Lina Cavalieri
			Evelyn Nesbit
			G.M. Anderson
	12 Aug.	Vol. 7, no. 172	**Irene Castle**
			Sessue Hayakawa
			Chrissie White
			Marie Prevost
	19 Aug.	Vol. 7, no. 173	**Ruth Roland**
			Sadie Bennett
			Betty Compson
			Irene Castle
			Tremaine
			Annette Kellerman
	26 Aug.	Vol. 7, no. 174	**Eddie Polo**
			Will Duncan
			Charles Hutchinson
	2 Sept.	Vol. 7, no. 175	**Suzanne Lenglen and father**
	9 Sept.	Vol. 7, no. 176	**Kathlyn Williams**
			Hobart Bosworth
			Florence Turner
			Maurice Costello
	16 Sept.	Vol. 7, no. 177	**Violet Hopson**
			Stewart Rome
			Mary Pickford
			Lloyd Coogan
	23 Sept.	Vol. 7, no. 178	**Pola Negri**
			Pearl White
			Virginia Pearson
			Mary Thurman
			Alice Joyce
	30 Sept.	Vol. 7, no. 179	**James Kirkwood**
			Anna Q. Nilsson
			Henry Edwards
	7 Oct.	Vol. 7, no. 180	**Pictures of the year**
	14 Oct.	Vol. 7, no. 181	**Mildred Harris**
			Milton Sills
			Mary Dibley
	21 Oct.	Vol. 7, no. 182	**Sir John Herschell**
	28 Oct.	Vol. 8, no. 183	**The world's most wonderful film school**
	4 Nov.	Vol. 8, no. 184	**Victor McLaglen**
			Cecil Humphreys
			Annette Benson
			Adrian Brunel
			Georges Carpentier
			Rex McDougall
	11 Nov.	Vol. 8, no. 185	**Edith Johnson**
			Mae Marsh
			Corinne Griffith
	18 Nov.	Vol. 8, no. 186	***My Strange Life***
	25 Nov.	Vol. 8, no. 187	**Louise Fazenda**
			Charlie Chaplin
			Buster Keaton
			Jimmy Aubrey
			Billy Bevan
	2 Dec.	Vol. 8, no. 188	**Douglas Fairbanks**
			Orrin Johnson
			M. Aime Simon-Girard
	9 Dec.	Vol. 8, no. 189	**Emory Johnson**
			Bebe Daniels
	16 Dec.	Vol. 8, no. 190	**Artist's drawing**
	23 Dec.	Vol. 8, no. 191	**Erich Von Stroheim**
			Mary Pickford
			Priscilla Dean
	30 Dec.	Vol. 8, no. 192	**Mary Miles Minter**
1923	6 Jan.	Vol. 8, no. 193	**Claire Windsor**
			Eleanor Boardman
			Helen Ferguson
			Patsy Ruth Miller
	13 Jan.	Vol. 8, no. 194	**Constance and Norma Talmadge**
			May McAvoy
	20 Jan.	Vol. 8, no. 195	**The perils of picture making**
	27 Jan.	Vol. 8, no. 196	**Screen scoundrels**
	3 Feb.	Vol. 8, no. 197	**Ruth Roland**

YEAR	MONTH	REF. No.	COVER STAR
	10 Feb.	Vol. 8, no. 198	**Scenes that make a film**
	17 Feb.	Vol. 8, no. 199	**Charlie Chaplin**
	24 Feb.	Vol. 8, no. 200	**Bringing the South Pole to the pictures**
	3 March	Vol. 8, no. 201	**Rudolph Valentino**
			Theda Bara
			Pola Negri
			Maurice Costello
	10 March	Vol. 8, no. 202	**Pola Negri**
	17 March	Vol. 8, no. 203	**Mary Pickford**
			Thomas Meighan
			Victor McLaglen
			Chrissie White
	24 March	Vol. 8, no. 204	**Money and the pictures**
	31 March	Vol. 8, no. 205	**Fiction favourites filmed**
	7 April	Vol. 8, no. 206	**A picture in the making**
	14 April	Vol. 8, no. 207	**Famous characters that gain film fame**
	21 April	Vol. 8, no. 208	**Wonder women of the world!**
	28 April	Vol. 9, no. 209	**Walter Hiers**
			Mary Pickford
			Nazimova
			Phyllis Haver
			Elmo Lincoln
	5 May	Vol. 9, no. 210	**Gambling with death!**
	12 May	Vol. 9, no. 211	**Clothes and the camera**
	19 May	Vol. 9, no. 212	**Tense moments**
	26 May	Vol. 9, no. 213	**Dressing the hair for films**
	2 June	Vol. 9, no. 214	**Doubles made by the camera**
	9 June	Vol. 9, no. 215	**Little laughtermakers**
	16 June	Vol. 9, no. 216	**The seesaw of screen stardom**
	23 June	Vol. 9, no. 217	**American stars in British pictures**
	30 June	Vol. 9, no. 218	**Don't envy the cinema star!**
	7 July	Vol. 9, no. 219	**Famous stars that draw no wages**
	14 July	Vol. 9, no. 220	**Harold Lloyd**
			Gish sisters
			Carol Dempster
	21 July	Vol. 9, no. 221	**Rudolph Valentino**
			Alice Calhoun
			Ramon Novarro
			Kathryn Key
	28 July	Vol. 9, no. 222	**Spotting the stars**
	4 Aug.	Vol. 9, no. 223	**Eleanor Boardman**
	11 Aug.	Vol. 9, no. 224	**Eleanor Boardman**
	18 Aug.	Vol. 9, no. 225	**Eleanor Boardman**
			Barbara La Marr
			Mae Busch
	25 Aug.	Vol. 9, no. 226	**Pictures for posterity**
	1 Sept.	Vol. 9, no. 227	**Wallace Reid**
			Dorothy Davenport
	8 Sept.	Vol. 9, no. 228	**Back to the pictures**
	15 Sept.	Vol. 9, no. 229	**Rudolph Valentino**
	22 Sept.	Vol. 9, no. 230	**Rudolph Valentino**
	29 Sept.	Vol. 9, no. 231	**The screen's best-sellers**
	6 Oct.	Vol. 9, no. 232	**Rudolph Valentino**
	13 Oct.	Vol. 9, no. 233	**Types that make money**
	20 Oct.	Vol. 9, no. 234	**Mary Pickford**
			Priscilla Dean
			Agnes Ayres
			Gladys Walton
	27 Oct.	Vol. 10, no. 235	**Making their fortunes safe**
	3 Nov.	Vol. 10, no. 236	**Elinor Glyn**
	10 Nov.	Vol. 10, no. 237	**Charlie Chaplin**
			Douglas Fairbanks
			Rudolph Valentino
			Fay Compton
	17 Nov.	Vol. 10, no. 238	**Our prince helps British pictures**
	24 Nov.	Vol. 10, no. 239	**Rudolph Valentino**
			Erich Von Stroheim
			Madge Kennedy
			Mary Pickford
			Douglas Fairbanks
	1 Dec.	Vol. 10, no. 240	**The secrets of the stars**
	8 Dec.	Vol. 10, no. 241	**Uncredited film scene**
	15 Dec.	Vol. 10, no. 242	**Why don't we keep them here?**
	22 Dec.	Vol. 10, no. 243	**Erich Von Stroheim**
			Mary Philbin
			Zasu Pitts
	29 Dec.	Vol. 10, no. 244	**My funniest Xmas**
1924	5 Jan.	Vol. 10, no. 245	**May McAvoy**
	12 Jan.	Vol. 10, no. 246	**Before they were famous**
	19 Jan.	Vol. 10, no. 247	**Pola Negri**
			William S. Hart
			Lillian Gish
			Mae Murray
	26 Jan.	Vol. 10, no. 248	**They really play in pictures**

YEAR	MONTH	REF. No.	COVER STAR
	2 Feb.	Vol. 10, no. 249	**Wanda Hawley** **Alice Calhoun** **Earle Williams**
	9 Feb.	Vol. 10, no. 250	**What we've got in pictures**
	16 Feb.	Vol. 10, no. 251	**British screenplays from British books**
	23 Feb.	Vol. 10, no. 252	**Love stories that live through the ages**
	1 March	Vol. 10, no. 253	**Douglas Fairbanks** **Matheson Lang** **Nigel Barrie**
	8 March	Vol. 10, no. 254	**Comic relief**
	15 March	Vol. 10, no. 255	**Filming the depths of the ocean**
	22 March	Vol. 10, no. 256	**Conrad Nagel** **Pola Negri** **Rudolph Valentino** **Alice Terry** **Ramon Novarro**
	29 March	Vol. 10, no. 257	**Where men are veiled**
	5 April	Vol. 10, no. 258	**Felix the Cat**
	12 April	Vol. 10, no. 259	**The story of the screen**
	19 April	Vol. 10, no. 260	**Sensational spectacles**
	26 April	Vol. 11, no. 261	**Elinor Glyn** **Pola Negri**
	3 May	Vol. 11, no. 262	**Buster Keaton** **Jackie Coogan** **Charlie Chaplin** **Louise Fazenda**
	10 May	Vol. 11, no. 263	**Will they follow father's footsteps?**
	17 May	Vol. 11, no. 264	**Can your dog act?**
	24 May	Vol. 11, no. 265	**Mary Pickford** **Rudolph Valentino** **Jackie Coogan** **Baby Peggy**
	31 May	Vol. 11, no. 266	**Where age beats youth**
	7 June	Vol. 11, no. 267	**The drama of the Old Testament**
	14 June	Vol. 11, no. 268	**Gloria Swanson** **Blanche Sweet** **Norma Talmadge**
	21 June	Vol. 11, no. 269	**Is the artistic picture popular?**
	28 June	Vol. 11, no. 270	**Betty Balfour** **Dorothy Gish** **Alma Taylor** **Fay Compton** **Lillian Gish** **Ivy Duke** **Mary Pickford** **Norma Talmadge**
	5 July	Vol. 11, no. 271	**Rudolph Valentino** **Bebe Daniels**
	12 July	Vol. 11, no. 272	***Camille*** ***The Invisible Fear*** ***Yolanda***
	19 July	Vol. 11, no. 273	**Morals and the movies**
	26 July	Vol. 11 no. 274	**The world's most fascinating men**
	2 Aug.	Vol. 11, no. 275	**The magic of the movies**
	9 Aug.	Vol. 11, no. 276	**Dipping in the past**
	16 Aug.	Vol. 11, no. 277	**Constance Binney** **Mae Murray** **Ramon Novarro**
	23 Aug.	Vol. 11, no. 278	**How to improve your tennis**
	30 Aug.	Vol. 11, no. 279	**Does Nature know best?**
	6 Sept.	Vol. 11, no. 280	**Lessons in love**
	13 Sept.	Vol. 11, no. 281	**Ivor Novello** **Rod La Rocque** **Rudolph Valentino** **André L. Daven**
	20 Sept.	Vol. 11, no. 282	**Scenes that thrill the actors**
	27 Sept.	Vol. 11, no. 283	**Jackie Coogan**
	4 Oct.	Vol. 11, no. 284	**Pola Negri** **Shirley Mason** **Ramon Novarro**
	11 Oct.	Vol. 11, no. 285	**Rudolph Valentino** **Doris Kenyon**
	18 Oct.	Vol. 11, no. 286	**Film figures**
	25 Oct.	Vol. 12, no. 287	**Accidents worth fortunes**
	1 Nov.	Vol. 12, no. 288	**Gloria Swanson** **Betty Compson** **Ivy Duke**
	8 Nov.	Vol. 12, no. 289	**The universe in pictures**
	15 Nov.	Vol. 12, no. 290	**Douglas Fairbanks** **Adolphe Menjou** **Milton Sills**
	22 Nov.	Vol. 12, no. 291	**Norma Talmadge**
	29 Nov.	Vol. 12, no. 292	**Pola Negri** **Gloria Swanson**
	6 Dec.	Vol. 12, no. 293	**Baby Peggy**
	13 Dec.	Vol. 12, no. 294	**Famous sea stories screened**
	20 Dec.	Vol. 12, no. 295	**Jack Dempsey**
	27 Dec.	Vol. 12, no. 296	**Ivor Novello** **Leslie Henson** **Ivy Duke**
1925	3 Jan.	Vol. 12, no. 297	**Wallace Beery** **Rudolph Valentino** **Percy Marmont** **Otis Skinner**

YEAR	MONTH	REF. No.	COVER STAR
	10 Jan.	Vol. 12, no. 298	Shots that save life
	17 Jan.	Vol. 12, no. 299	Douglas MacLean Harold Lloyd Dorothy Devore
	24 Jan.	Vol. 12, no. 300	A few years ago
	31 Jan.	Vol. 12, no. 301	Wresting the last secrets from Mother Earth
	7 Feb.	Vol. 12, no. 302	Films that made them famous
	14 Feb.	Vol. 12, no. 303	Once they lined up for pay
	21 Feb.	Vol. 12, no. 304	Gloria Swanson Nita Naldi Rudolph Valentino
	28 Feb.	Vol. 12, no. 305	Constance Bennett Lucille Ricksen Clara Bow
	7 March	Vol. 12, no. 306	Monte Blue Julanne Johnston Jack Holt
	14 March	Vol. 12, no. 307	Ernest Torrence Wallace Beery Adolphe Menjou
	21 March	Vol. 12, no. 308	When the stars grow cold!
	28 March	Vol. 12, no. 309	Risking life for thirty shillings a day
	4 April	Vol. 12, no. 310	Rudolph Valentino Gloria Swanson Norma Talmadge
	11 April	Vol. 12, no. 311	Conrad Nagel Constance Talmadge Agnes Ayres
	18 April	Vol. 12, no. 312	Alice Lake Patsy Ruth Miller Conway Tearle
	25 April	Vol. 13, no. 313	Why we like 'em
	2 May	Vol. 13, no. 314	Bringing back the past in pictures
	9 May	Vol. 13, no. 315	Tom Mix Jack Holt Buck Jones
	16 May	Vol. 13, no. 316	Lon Chaney Eleanor Boardman George K. Arthur
	23 May	Vol. 13, no. 317	They call it art
	30 May	Vol. 13, no. 318	Rudolph Valentino Tom Mix Norma Talmadge Lillian Gish
	6 June	Vol. 13, no. 319	Miracles of the cinema
	13 June	Vol. 13, no. 320	Norma and Constance Talmadge

YEAR	MONTH	REF. No.	COVER STAR
	13 June (*cont.*)		Eva and Jane Novak Lillian and Dorothy Gish
	20 June	Vol. 13, no. 321	Enid Bennett Wallace Beery Lon Chaney
	27 June	Vol. 13, no. 322	Colleen Moore Lois Wilson Mary Carr Mary Pickford
	4 July	Vol. 13, no. 323	Larry Semon Ramon Novarro
	11 July	Vol. 13, no. 324	Superstitions of the successful
	18 July	Vol. 13, no. 325	Thomas Meighan Ben Lyon Jack Gilbert Eleanor Boardman
	25 July	Vol. 13, no. 326	Juliette Compton Ivor Novello Isabel Jeans Betty Balfour
	1 Aug.	Vol. 13, no. 327	Mary Philbin Baby Peggy Nita Naldi
	8 Aug.	Vol. 13, no. 328	What is the ideal picture?
	15 Aug.	Vol. 13, no. 329	Tom Mix Fred Thomson
	22 Aug.	Vol. 13, no. 330	Charlie Chaplin Norma Shearer Lon Chaney Constance Talmadge Ronald Colman
	29 Aug.	Vol. 13, no. 331	Ronald Colman George K. Arthur Walter Tennyson George O'Brien
	5 Sept.	Vol. 13, no. 332	Big month in the movies!
	12 Sept.	Vol. 13, no. 333	Mary Miles Minter Mary Pickford George Walsh
	19 Sept.	Vol. 13, no. 334	Fashions in heroes
	26 Sept.	Vol. 13, no. 335	Queer people in pictures
	3 Oct.	Vol. 13, no. 336	Douglas Fairbanks Bebe Daniels
	10 Oct.	Vol. 13, no. 337	Sybil Rhoda
	17 Oct.	Vol. 13, no. 338	Lillian Gish Lon Chaney Mary Brian Betty Bronson
	24 Oct.	Vol. 14, no. 339	Tom Mix Mabel Ballin Blanche Sweet Stuart Holmes

YEAR	MONTH	REF. No.	COVER STAR
	31 Oct.	Vol. 14, no. 340	**John Gilbert**
			Mae Murray
			Mary Brough
			Louise Fazenda
	7 Nov.	Vol. 14, no. 341	**Charlie Chaplin**
	14 Nov.	Vol. 14, no. 342	**Edith Yorke**
			Edythe Chapman
			Mary Carr
	21 Nov.	Vol. 14, no. 343	**Harry Langdon**
	28 Nov.	Vol. 14, no. 344	**Rudolph Valentino**
	5 Dec.	Vol. 14, no. 345	**Dorothy Gish**
			Randle Ayrton
	12 Dec.	Vol. 14, no. 346	**Lillian Gish**
	19 Dec.	Vol. 14, no. 347	**Ernest Torrence**
	26 Dec.	Vol. 14, no. 348	**Eleanor Boardman**
1926	2 Jan.	Vol. 14, no. 349	**Aileen Pringle**
	9 Jan.	Vol. 14, no. 350	**Betty Balfour**
			George Hackathorne
	16 Jan.	Vol. 14, no. 351	**Mary Pickford**
	23 Jan.	Vol. 14, no. 352	**Mae Murray**
			John Gilbert
	30 Jan.	Vol. 14, no. 353	**Godfrey Tearle**
			Marjorie Hume
	6 Feb.	Vol. 14, no. 354	**Ronald Colman**
			Blanche Sweet
	13 Feb.	Vol. 14, no. 355	**Ivor Novello**
	20 Feb.	Vol. 14, no. 356	**Rudolph Valentino**
	27 Feb.	Vol. 14, no. 357	**Buster Keaton**
	6 March	Vol. 14, no. 358	**James Cruze**
			Betty Compson
			Ivor Novello
	13 March	Vol. 14, no. 359	**Dorothy Gish**
			Norma Talmadge
	20 March	Vol. 14, no. 360	**Belle Bennett**
			Lois Moran
			Richard Barthelmess
	27 March	Vol. 14, no. 361	**Improve your dancing**
	3 April	Vol. 14, no. 362	**Ramon Novarro**
	10 April	Vol. 14, no. 363	**Steve Donoghue**
	17 April	Vol. 14, no. 364	**Constance Talmadge**
			Ronald Colman
	24 April	Vol. 15, no. 365	**Douglas Fairbanks**
			Mary Astor
	1 May	Vol. 15, no. 366	**Gertrude Olmsted**
			Ricardo Cortez
	8 May	Vol. 15, no. 367	**Norma Talmadge**
	15 May	Vol. 15, no. 368	**John Gilbert**
			Lillian Gish
	22 May	Vol. 15, no. 369	**Virginia Valli**
			John Stuart
	29 May/ 5 June	Vol. 15, no. 370	**Basil Rathbone**
			Mae Murray
	12 June	Vol. 15, no. 371	**Jaques Catelain**
			Huguette Duflos
	19 June	Vol. 15, no. 372	**William Haines**
			Sally O'Neill
	26 June	Vol. 15, no. 373	**Lya De Putti**
	3 July	Vol. 15, no. 374	**Dorothy Gish**
	10 July	Vol. 15, no. 375	**Donald Crisp**
			Douglas Fairbanks
	17 July	Vol. 15, no. 376	**Rudolph Valentino**
			Vilma Banky
	24 July	Vol. 15, no. 377	**Aggie Herring**
	31 July	Vol. 15, no. 378	**John Gilbert**
			Renée Adorée
	7 Aug.	Vol. 15, no. 379	**Success from simplicity**
	14 Aug.	Vol. 15, no. 380	**Corinne Griffith**
	21 Aug.	Vol. 15, no. 381	**Lillian Gish**
			Lars Hansen
	28 Aug.	Vol. 15, no. 382	**Alice Terry**
	4 Sept.	Vol. 15, no. 383	**Tim Holt**
			Jack Holt
			Conrad Nagel
	11 Sept.	Vol. 15, no. 384	**Rod La Rocque**
	18 Sept.	Vol. 15, no. 385	**Lillian Rich**
	25 Sept.	Vol. 15, no. 386	**Norma Talmadge**
			Eugene O'Brien
	2 Oct.	Vol. 15, no. 387	**Harold Lloyd**
	9 Oct.	Vol. 15, no. 388	**Fisher White**
			Betty Balfour
	16 Oct.	Vol. 15, no. 389	**Karl Dane**
	23 Oct.	Vol. 15, no. 390	**Irene Rich**
			May McAvoy
	30 Oct.	Vol. 16, no. 391	**Mabel Normand**
	6 Nov.	Vol. 16, no. 392	**Louise Fazenda**
	13 Nov.	Vol. 16, no. 393	**John Stuart**
			Estelle Brody
	20 Nov.	Vol. 16, no. 394	**Rudolph Valentino**
			Vilma Banky
	27 Nov.	Vol. 16, no. 395	**Ivor Novello**
			Nina Vanna
	4 Dec.	Vol. 16, no. 396	**Anna Q. Nilsson**
	11 Dec.	Vol. 16, no. 397	**Charlie Chaplin**
	18 Dec.	Vol. 16, no. 398	**John Gilbert**
			Lillian Gish
	25 Dec.	Vol. 16, no. 399	**Betty Bronson**
1927	1 Jan.	Vol. 16, no. 400	**Douglas Fairbanks**
			Billie Dove
	8 Jan.	Vol. 16, no. 401	**Ramon Novarro**
	15 Jan.	Vol. 16, no. 402	**Ronald Colman**
			Vilma Banky
	22 Jan.	Vol. 16, no. 403	**Harold Lloyd**
	29 Jan.	Vol. 16, no. 404	**Clara Bow**
	5 Feb.	Vol. 16, no. 405	**Adolphe Menjou**
	12 Feb.	Vol. 16, no. 406	**Douglas Fairbanks**
			Ricardo Cortez
	19 Feb.	Vol. 16, no. 407	**Olive Borden**
	26 Feb.	Vol. 16, no. 408	**Richard Dix**
	5 March	Vol. 16, no. 409	**June**
	12 March	Vol. 16, no. 410	**Ivor Novello**

YEAR	MONTH	REF. No.	COVER STAR
	19 March	Vol. 16, no. 411	**Reginald Denny Laura La Plante**
	26 March	Vol. 16, no. 412	**Ronald Colman Ralph Forbes**
	2 April	Vol. 16, no. 413	**Vilma Banky Ronald Colman**
	9 April	Vol. 16, no. 414	**Billie Dove Bert Lytell**
	16 April	Vol. 16, no. 415	**Corinne Griffith Einar Hanson**
	23 April	Vol. 16, no. 416	**Who is your favourite screen lover?**
	30 April	Vol. 17, no. 417	**Dorothy Gish Henri Bosc**
	7 May	Vol. 17, no. 418	**Grock**
	14 May	Vol. 17, no. 419	**Norma Talmadge**
	21 May	Vol. 17, no. 420	**Dorothy Gish**
	28 May	Vol. 17, no. 421	**Vilma Banky**
	4 June	Vol. 17, no. 422	**Corinne Griffith**
	11 June	Vol. 17, no. 423	**Lois Moran**
	18 June	Vol. 17, no. 424	**Lya De Putti**
	25 June	Vol. 17, no. 425	**Richard Dix**
	2 July	Vol. 17, no. 426	**Milton Sills Doris Kenyon**
	9 July	Vol. 17, no. 427	**Renée Adorée**
	16 July	Vol. 17, no. 428	**Brigitte Helm**
	23 July	Vol. 17, no. 429	**Roaring lions and wedding bells**
	30 July	Vol. 17, no. 430	**Constance Talmadge**
	6 Aug.	Vol. 17, no. 431	**Norma Shearer**
	13 Aug.	Vol. 17, no. 432	**Dolores Del Rio**
	20 Aug.	Vol. 17, no. 433	**The romance of the bathing girls**
	27 Aug.	Vol. 17, no. 434	**Rudolph Valentino**
	3 Sept.	Vol. 17, no. 435	**John Gilbert Lillian Gish**
	10 Sept.	Vol. 17, no. 436	**Pola Negri George Siegmann James Hall**
	17 Sept.	Vol. 17, no. 437	**Estelle Brody**
	24 Sept.	Vol. 17, no. 438	**Greta Garbo**
	1 Oct.	Vol. 17, no. 439	**Brigitte Helm**
	8 Oct.	Vol. 17, no. 440	**Betty Balfour**
	15 Oct.	Vol. 17, no. 441	**Stars for sale**
	22 Oct.	Vol. 17, no. 442	**John Barrymore Mary Astor**
	29 Oct.	Vol. 18, no. 443	**May McAvoy Ramon Novarro**
	5 Nov.	Vol. 18, no. 444	**Victor McLaglen Dolores Del Rio**
	12 Nov.	Vol. 18, no. 445	**Lest we forget**
	19 Nov.	Vol. 18, no. 446	**Colleen Moore Donald Reed**
	26 Nov.	Vol. 18, no. 447	**Adolphe Menjou Greta Nissen**
	3 Dec.	Vol. 18, no. 448	**Lya De Putti Joseph Schildkraut**
	10 Dec.	Vol. 18, no. 449	**A Christmas hamper of good wishes**
	17 Dec.	Vol. 18, no. 450	**Ronald Colman Vilma Banky**
	24 Dec.	Vol. 18, no. 451	**Charlie Chaplin**
	31 Dec.	Vol. 18, no. 452	**Betty Bronson Ben Lyon Richard Dix John Gilbert Colleen Moore Lloyd Hughes Laura La Plante Constance Talmadge Betty Balfour Victor McLagen**
1928	7 Jan.	Vol. 18, no. 453	**Picture show calendar**
	14 Jan.	Vol. 18, no. 454	**Victor McLaglen**
	21 Jan.	Vol. 18, no. 455	**Syd Chaplin**
	28 Jan.	Vol. 18, no. 456	**Richard Colman Vilma Banky**
	4 Feb.	Vol. 18, no. 457	**Rod La Rocque Dolores Del Rio**
	11 Feb.	Vol. 18, no. 458	**Reginald Denny and family**
	18 Feb.	Vol. 18, no. 459	**Janet Gaynor Charles Farrell**
	25 Feb.	Vol. 18, no. 460	**Lya De Putti**
	3 March	Vol. 18, no. 461	**Dolores Del Rio**
	10 March	Vol. 18, no. 462	***Chang***
	17 March	Vol. 18, no. 463	**Norma Talmadge Gilbert Roland**
	24 March	Vol. 18, no. 464	**Janet Gaynor Charles Farrell**
	31 March	Vol. 18, no. 465	**Ted MacNamara Sammy Cohen**
	7 April	Vol. 18, no. 466	**Ramon Novarro Joan Crawford**
	14 April	Vol. 18, no. 467	**Ivor Novello Mabel Poulton**
	21 April	Vol. 18, no. 468	**Laura La Plante**
	28 April	Vol. 19, no. 469	**Ronald Colman Vilma Banky**
	5 May	Vol. 19, no. 470	**Victor McLaglen Dolores Del Rio**
	12 May	Vol. 19, no. 471	**Hollywood's foreign legion**
	19 May	Vol. 19, no. 472	**Adolphe Menjou Kathryn Carver**
	26 May	Vol. 19, no. 473	**Pola Negri**
	2 June	Vol. 19, no. 474	**Ladies prefer?**
	9 June	Vol. 19, no. 475	**Buster Keaton**
	16 June	Vol. 19, no. 476	**Lupe Velez**
	23 June	Vol. 19, no. 477	**Betty Balfour John Gilbert**

YEAR	MONTH	REF. No.	COVER STAR
	30 June	Vol. 19, no. 478	**Ronald Colman** **Clara Bow**
	7 July	Vol. 19, no. 479	**Laura La Plante** **Carl Brisson**
	14 July	Vol. 19, no. 480	**Ivor Novello** **Pola Negri**
	21 July	Vol. 19, no. 481	**Adolphe Menjou** **Bebe Daniels**
	28 July	Vol. 19, no. 482	**Ramon Novarro** **Renée Adorée**
	4 Aug.	Vol. 19, no. 483	**Betty Nuthall**
	11 Aug.	Vol. 19, no. 484	**Ethlyne Clair** **Barbara Kent** **Barbara Worth**
	18 Aug.	Vol. 19, no. 485	**Dorothy Gish**
	25 Aug.	Vol. 19, no. 486	**Jetta Goudal** **Victor Varconi**
	1 Sept.	Vol. 19, no. 487	**Mary Pickford**
	8 Sept.	Vol. 19, no. 488	**Janet Gaynor** **Clara Bow**
	15 Sept.	Vol. 19, no. 489	**Victor Varconi**
	22 Sept.	Vol. 19, no. 490	**Janet Gaynor** **George O'Brien**
	29 Sept.	Vol. 19, no. 491	**Gloria Swanson** **Raoul Walsh**
	6 Oct.	Vol. 19, no. 492	**Mabel Poulton** **Ivor Novello**
	13 Oct.	Vol. 19, no. 493	**Dolores Del Rio** **Warner Baxter**
	20 Oct.	Vol. 19, no. 494	**Charlie Chaplin**
	27 Oct.	Vol. 20, no. 495	**Douglas Fairbanks** **Lupe Velez**
	3 Nov.	Vol. 20, no. 496	**Ramon Novarro** **Marceline Day** **Rod La Rocque**
	10 Nov.	Vol. 20, no. 497	**Lillian Gish**
	17 Nov.	Vol. 20, no. 498	**Percy Marmont**
	24 Nov.	Vol. 20, no. 499	**Camilla Horn** **John Barrymore**
	1 Dec.	Vol. 20, no. 500	**May McAvoy** **Alec B. Francis** **Edward Everett Horton**
	8 Dec.	Vol. 20, no. 501	**Pictures – the best entertainment**
	15 Dec.	Vol. 20, no. 502	**George Bancroft** **Evelyn Brent** **Neil Hamilton**
	22 Dec.	Vol. 20, no. 503	**Leatrice Joy**
	29 Dec.	Vol. 20, no. 504	**Geoffrey Miller**
1929	5 Jan.	Vol. 20, no. 505	**Picture show calendar**
	12 Jan.	Vol. 20, no. 506	**Greta Garbo** **John Gilbert**
	19 Jan.	Vol. 20, no. 507	**Carl Brisson** **Lillian Hall-Davis**
	26 Jan.	Vol. 20, no. 508	**Jameson Thomas** **Evelyn Brent** **George Bancroft** **Isabel Jeans**
	2 Feb.	Vol. 20, no. 509	**Teddy Brown**
	9 Feb.	Vol. 20, no. 510	**Ronald Colman** **Vilma Banky**
	16 Feb.	Vol. 20, no. 511	**Janet Gaynor** **Charles Farrell**
	23 Feb.	Vol. 20, no. 512	**Ramon Novarro** **Norma Shearer**
	2 March	Vol. 20, no. 513	**Greta Garbo** **Lars Hanson**
	9 March	Vol. 20, no. 514	**Clive Brook** **George Bancroft** **Evelyn Brent**
	16 March	Vol. 20, no. 515	**Marion Davies**
	23 March	Vol. 20, no. 516	**Lon Chaney** **Renée Adorée** **Ralph Forbes**
	30 March	Vol. 20, no. 517	**The price of stardom**
	6 April	Vol. 20, no. 518	**Lucky 13**
	13 April	Vol. 20, no. 519	**Ivor Novello** **Evelyn Holt**
	20 April	Vol. 20, no. 520	**Rin-Tin-Tin**
	27 April	Vol. 21, no. 521	**Phyllis Haver** **Jean Hersholt**
	4 May	Vol. 21, no. 522	**Henry Victor** **Lillian Hall-Davis** **Walter Byron**
	11 May	Vol. 21, no. 523	**Norma Shearer** **Ralph Forbes**
	18 May	Vol. 21, no. 524	**Clarence Muse** **Stepin Fetchit**
	25 May	Vol. 21, no. 525	**Charles Rogers** **Mary Brian** **Chester Conklin**
	1 June	Vol. 21, no. 526	**Phyllis Haver**
	8 June	Vol. 21, no. 527	**Dolores Costello**
	15 June	Vol. 21, no. 528	**Corinne Griffith**
	22 June	Vol. 21, no. 529	**Gary Cooper** **Lupe Velez**
	29 June	Vol. 21, no. 530	**Buster Keaton**
	6 July	Vol. 21, no. 531	**Kenneth McLaglen**
	13 July	Vol. 21, no. 532	**George O'Brien** **Lois Moran**
	20 July	Vol. 21, no. 533	**Laura La Plante**
	27 July	Vol. 21, no. 534	**John Stuart** **Estelle Brody**
	3 Aug.	Vol. 21, no. 535	**Betty Compson** **George Bancroft**
	10 Aug.	Vol. 21, no. 536	**Clara Bow**
	17 Aug.	Vol. 21, no. 537	**Anna May Wong**
	24 Aug.	Vol. 21, no 538	**Dolores Del Rio** **Leroy Mason**
	31 Aug.	Vol. 21, no. 539	**Lon Chaney** **Nils Asther** **Loretta Young**

YEAR	MONTH	REF. No.	COVER STAR
	7 Sept.	Vol. 21, no. 540	**John Gilbert** **Greta Garbo**
	14 Sept.	Vol. 21, no. 541	**Joseph Schildkraut** **Laura La Plante**
	21 Sept.	Vol. 21, no. 542	**Victor McLaglen**
	28 Sept.	Vol. 21, no. 543	**Moran and Mack**
	5 Oct.	Vol. 21, no. 544	**Ronald Colman** **Lili Damita**
	12 Oct.	Vol. 21, no. 545	**Marion Davies** **Nils Asther**
	19 Oct.	Vol. 22, no. 546	**Colleen Moore** **Gary Cooper**
	26 Oct.	Vol. 22, no. 547	**Jameson Thomas** **Estelle Brody**
	2 Nov.	Vol. 22, no. 548	**Billie Dove** **Antonio Moreno**
	9 Nov.	Vol. 22, no. 549	**Laura La Plante**
	16 Nov.	Vol. 22, no. 550	**The cinema and peace**
	23 Nov.	Vol. 22, no. 551	**Douglas Fairbanks** **Norma Talmadge** **Emil Jannings**
	30 Nov.	Vol. 22, no. 552	**Lupe Velez**
	7 Dec.	Vol. 22, no. 553	**Victor McLaglen** **Lily Damita** **Edmund Lowe**
	14 Dec.	Vol. 22, no. 554	**Norma Talmadge** **Gilbert Roland**
	21 Dec.	Vol. 22, no. 555	**John Gilbert**
	28 Dec.	Vol. 22, no. 556	**Clara Bow**
1930	4 Jan.	Vol. 22, no. 557	**Picture show calendar**
	11 Jan.	Vol. 22, no. 558	**Norma Shearer**
	18 Jan.	Vol. 22, no. 559	**Douglas Fairbanks Jr** **Joan Crawford**
	25 Jan.	Vol. 22, no. 560	**Conrad Nagel** **Greta Garbo**
	1 Feb.	Vol. 22, no. 561	**John Boles** **Bebe Daniels**
	8 Feb.	Vol. 22, no. 562	**Anna May Wong**
	15 Feb.	Vol. 22, no. 563	**Janet Gaynor**
	22 Feb.	Vol. 22, no. 564	**Betty Compson**
	1 March	Vol. 22, no. 565	**Greta Garbo**
	8 March	Vol. 22, no. 566	**Joan Crawford**
	15 March	Vol. 22, no. 567	**Gloria Swanson**
	22 March	Vol. 22, no. 568	**Ruth Chatterton**
	29 March	Vol. 22, no. 569	**Reginald Denny**
	5 April	Vol. 22, no. 570	***The Mississippi Gambler***
	12 April	Vol. 22, no. 571	**Ivor Novello**
	19 April	Vol. 22, no. 572	**Billie Dove**
	26 April	Vol. 23, no. 573	**Carl Brisson** **Madeleine Carroll**
	3 May	Vol. 23, no. 574	**Gary Cooper** **Mary Brian** **Richard Arlen**
	10 May	Vol. 23, no. 575	**Charles Rogers** **Mary Brian**
	17 May	Vol. 23, no. 576	**John Boles** **Carlotta King**
	24 May	Vol. 23, no. 577	**Janet Gaynor** **Charles Farrell**
	31 May	Vol. 23, no. 578	**Ramon Novarro** **Dorothy Janis**
	7 June	Vol. 23, no. 579	**Nancy Carroll**
	14 June	Vol. 23, no. 580	**Monte Blue** **Lupe Velez**
	21 June	Vol. 23, no. 581	**Gloria Swanson**
	28 June	Vol. 23, no. 582	**Evelyn Brent**
	5 July	Vol. 23, no. 583	**Joan Bennett** **Anthony Bushell**
	12 July	Vol. 23, no. 584	**Lilyan Tashman**
	19 July	Vol. 23, no. 585	**Greta Garbo**
	26 July	Vol. 23, no. 586	**James Hall** **Clara Bow**
	2 Aug.	Vol. 23, no. 587	**John Boles** **Vivienne Segal**
	9 Aug.	Vol. 23, no. 588	**Norma Shearer** **Johnny Mack Brown**
	16 Aug.	Vol. 23, no. 589	**John Garrick** **Helen Chandler**
	23 Aug.	Vol. 23, no. 590	**John Boles** **Laura La Plante**
	30 Aug.	Vol. 23, no. 591	**Dorothy Mackaill**
	6 Sept.	Vol. 23, no. 592	**Chester Morris**
	13 Sept.	Vol. 23, no. 593	**John Gilbert** **Catherine Dale Owen**
	20 Sept.	Vol. 23, no. 594	**Ramon Novarro** **Dorothy Jordan**
	27 Sept.	Vol. 23, no. 595	**John Boles** **Bebe Daniels**
	4 Oct.	Vol. 23, no. 596	**William Boyd**
	11 Oct.	Vol. 23, no. 597	**Betty Balfour**
	18 Oct.	Vol. 23, no. 598	**Maurice Chevalier** **Jeanette MacDonald**
	25 Oct.	Vol. 24, no. 599	**Ralph Lynn** **Winifred Shotter**
	1 Nov.	Vol. 24, no. 600	**Greta Garbo**
	8 Nov.	Vol. 24, no. 601	**Clive Brook** **Ruth Chatterton**
	15 Nov.	Vol. 24, no. 602	**Colin Clive** **David Manners**
	22 Nov.	Vol. 24, no. 603	**Loretta Young** **Grant Withers**
	29 Nov.	Vol. 24, no. 604	**Ann Harding** **James Rennie**
	6 Dec.	Vol. 24, no. 605	**Lupe Velez**
	13 Dec.	Vol. 24, no. 606	**Maurice Chevalier**
	20 Dec.	Vol. 24, no. 607	**Janet Gaynor** **Charles Farrell**
	27 Dec.	Vol. 24, no. 608	**Madeleine Carroll**

YEAR	MONTH	REF. No.	COVER STAR
1931	3 Jan.	Vol. 24, no. 609	**Picture show calendar**
	10 Jan.	Vol. 24, no. 610	***Song Of The Flame***
	17 Jan.	Vol. 24, no. 611	**Jeanette MacDonald**
	24 Jan.	Vol. 24, no. 612	**Edna Best** **Owen Nares**
	31 Jan.	Vol. 24, no. 613	**Ralph Forbes** **Ruth Chatterton** **Basil Rathbone**
	7 Feb.	Vol. 24, no. 614	**Walter Pidgeon** **Vivienne Segal**
	14 Feb.	Vol. 24, no. 615	**Lew Ayres**
	21 Feb.	Vol. 24, no. 616	**Marlene Dietrich**
	28 Feb.	Vol. 24, no. 617	**Ann Harding** **Robert Ames**
	7 March	Vol. 24, no. 618	**The dog hero of *Scrags***
	14 March	Vol. 24, no. 619	**John Boles** **Lupe Velez**
	21 March	Vol. 24, no. 620	**Marion Davies**
	28 March	Vol. 24, no. 621	**Greta Garbo** **Gavin Gordon**
	4 April	Vol. 24, no. 622	**Charlie Chaplin** **Virginia Cherrill**
	11 April	Vol. 24, no. 623	**Polly Moran** **Marie Dressler**
	18 April	Vol. 24, no. 624	**Robert Montgomery**
	25 April	Vol. 25, no. 625	**Madeleine Carroll** **Frank Lawton**
	2 May	Vol. 25, no. 626	**George Arliss**
	9 May	Vol. 25, no. 627	**Ronald Colman** **John Rogers**
	16 May	Vol. 25, no. 628	**Leslie Henson** **Heather Thatcher**
	23 May	Vol. 25, no. 629	**Joan Crawford** **Kent Douglas**
	30 May	Vol. 25, no. 630	**Walter Pidgeon** **Vivienne Segal**
	6 June	Vol. 25, no. 631	**Janet Gaynor** **Charles Farrell**
	13 June	Vol. 25, no. 632	**John Boles**
	20 June	Vol. 25, no. 633	**Betty Compson**
	27 June	Vol. 25, no. 634	**Johnny Mack Brown** **Kay Johnson**
	4 July	Vol. 25, no. 635	**Robert Montgomery** **Greta Garbo**
	11 July	Vol. 25, no. 636	**Charles Bickford** **Kay Johnson**
	18 July	Vol. 25, no. 637	**Mary Brian** **Richard Arlen**
	25 July	Vol. 25, no. 638	**Mary Pickford**
	1 Aug.	Vol. 25, no. 639	**Kay Francis**
	8 Aug.	Vol. 25, no. 640	**Owen Nares** **Jacqueline Logan** **Jack Raine**

YEAR	MONTH	REF. No.	COVER STAR
	15 Aug.	Vol. 25, no. 641	**Janet Gaynor** **Charles Farrell**
	22 Aug.	Vol. 25, no. 642	**Greta Garbo** **Lewis Stone**
	29 Aug.	Vol. 25, no. 643	**Joan Crawford**
	5 Sept.	Vol. 25, no. 644	**Ruth Chatterton** **Clive Brook**
	12 Sept.	Vol. 25, no. 645	**Richard Dix** **Irene Dunne**
	19 Sept.	Vol. 25, no. 646	**Seymour Hicks**
	26 Sept.	Vol. 25, no. 647	**Ralph Lynn** **Mary Brough**
	3 Oct.	Vol. 25, no. 648	**Ann Harding** **Conrad Nagel**
	10 Oct.	Vol. 25, no. 649	**Laughter week**
	17 Oct.	Vol. 25, no. 650	**Norma Shearer** **Neil Hamilton**
	24 Oct.	Vol. 26, no. 651	**Harry Carey** **Duncan Renaldo** **Edwina Booth**
	31 Oct.	Vol. 26, no. 652	**Ronald Colman** **Loretta Young**
	7 Nov.	Vol. 26, no. 653	**George Arliss**
	14 Nov.	Vol. 26, no. 654	**Tony Bruce** **Carl Harbord**
	21 Nov.	Vol. 26, no. 655	**Gary Cooper**
	28 Nov.	Vol. 26, no. 656	**Norma Shearer**
	5 Dec.	Vol. 26, no. 657	**John Boles** **Lois Wilson** **Genevieve Tobin**
	12 Dec.	Vol. 26, no. 658	**Conchita Montenegro**
	19 Dec.	Vol. 26, no. 659	**Jean Harlow**
	26 Dec.	Vol. 26, no. 660	**Kathryn Crawford**
1932	2 Jan.	Vol. 26, no. 661	**Picture show calendar**
	9 Jan.	Vol. 26, no. 662	**Norma Shearer** **Clark Gable**
	16 Jan.	Vol. 26, no. 663	**Ramon Novarro**
	23 Jan.	Vol. 26, no. 664	**Douglas Fairbanks Jr** **Rose Hobart**
	30 Jan.	Vol. 26, no. 665	**Constance Bennett**
	6 Feb.	Vol. 26, no. 666	**Marion Davies** **Leslie Howard**
	13 Feb.	Vol. 26, no. 667	**Edna Best** **Herbert Marshall**
	20 Feb.	Vol. 26, no. 668	**William Powell** **Carole Lombard**
	27 Feb.	Vol. 26, no. 669	**Janet Gaynor** **Charles Farrell**
	5 March	Vol. 26, no. 670	**Renate Muller** **Owen Nares**
	12 March	Vol. 26, no. 671	**Madeleine Carroll**
	19 March	Vol. 26, no. 672	**Sylvia Sidney** **William Collier Jr**
	26 March	Vol. 26, no. 673	**Madge Evans** **Clark Gable**

YEAR	MONTH	REF. No.	COVER STAR
	2 April	Vol. 26, no. 674	Alan Mowbray Kay Francis
	9 April	Vol. 26, no. 675	Greta Garbo Clark Gable
	16 April	Vol. 26, no. 676	Henry Garat Lilian Harvey Gibb McLaughlin
	23 April	Vol. 27, no. 677	Clive Brook Marlene Dietrich
	30 April	Vol. 27, no. 678	James Dunn Sally Eilers
	7 May	Vol. 27, no. 679	Greta Garbo
	14 May	Vol. 27, no. 680	Neil Hamilton Helen Hayes
	21 May	Vol. 27, no. 681	Leo Carrillo
	28 May	Vol. 27, no. 682	Colin Clive
	4 June	Vol. 27, no. 683	Ronald Colman Helen Hayes
	11 June	Vol. 27, no. 684	Dorothy Jordan Paul Lukas
	18 June	Vol. 27, no. 685	Barbara Stanwyck Adolphe Menjou
	25 June	Vol. 27, no. 686	Laurel and Hardy
	2 July	Vol. 27, no. 687	Dolores Del Rio Leo Carrillo
	9 July	Vol. 27, no. 688	George Bancroft Juliette Compton
	16 July	Vol. 27, no. 689	Lil Dagover Warren William
	23 July	Vol. 27, no. 690	Ann Todd Ian Hunter
	30 July	Vol. 27, no. 691	Frances Dee Charles Ruggles
	6 Aug.	Vol. 27, no. 692	Robert Montgomery Madge Evans
	13 Aug.	Vol. 27, no. 693	Joan Barry Walter Byron Jack Hulbert Anne Grey Herbert Marshall John Stuart
	20 Aug.	Vol. 27, no. 694	Joan Crawford
	27 Aug.	Vol. 27, no. 695	Maurice Chevalier Jeanette MacDonald
	3 Sept.	Vol. 27, no. 696	Ralph Lynn Robertson Hare Tom Walls
	10 Sept.	Vol. 27, no. 697	Jack Hulbert Cicely Courtneidge
	17 Sept.	Vol. 27, no. 698	Jack Buchanan Anna Neagle
	24 Sept.	Vol. 27, no. 699	Fredric March Rose Hobart
	1 Oct.	Vol. 27, no. 700	Greta Garbo Ramon Novarro
	8 Oct.	Vol. 27, no. 701	Marlene Dietrich Clive Brook
	15 Oct.	Vol. 27, no. 702	Fredric March Kay Francis
	22 Oct.	Vol. 28, no. 703	Sylvia Sidney Chester Morris
	29 Oct.	Vol. 28, no. 704	Frances Dee Douglas Fairbanks Jr
	5 Nov.	Vol. 28, no. 705	Joan Crawford Robert Montgomery
	12 Nov.	Vol. 28, no. 706	Constance Bennett Neil Hamilton
	19 Nov.	Vol. 28, no. 707	Charles Farrell Janet Gaynor
	26 Nov.	Vol. 28, no. 708	Gracie Fields
	3 Dec.	Vol. 28, no. 709	John Boles Irene Dunne
	10 Dec.	Vol. 28, no. 710	Nora Swinburne
	17 Dec.	Vol. 28, no. 711	Ivor Novello Elizabeth Allan
	24 Dec.	Vol. 28, no. 712	Judy Kelly Molly Lamont Hal Gordon
	31 Dec.	Vol. 28, no. 713	Norma Shearer Leslie Howard
1933	7 Jan.	Vol. 28, no. 714	Anna Neagle Henry Edwards
	14 Jan.	Vol. 28, no. 715	Jeanette MacDonald Maurice Chevalier
	21 Jan.	Vol. 28, no. 716	Jessie Matthews
	28 Jan.	Vol. 28, no. 717	Greta Garbo John Barrymore
	4 Feb.	Vol. 28, no. 718	Marion Davies Robert Montgomery
	11 Feb.	Vol. 28, no. 719	Joan Barry Harold Huth
	18 Feb.	Vol. 28, no. 720	Irene Dunne John Boles
	25 Feb.	Vol. 28, no. 721	Zita Johann Richard Arlen
	4 March	Vol. 28, no. 722	Jean Harlow Clark Gable
	11 March	Vol. 28, no. 723	Harold Lloyd Constance Cummings
	18 March	Vol. 28, no. 724	Norma Shearer Clark Gable
	25 March	Vol. 28, no. 725	Kay Francis William Powell
	1 April	Vol. 28, no. 726	Herbert Marshall
	8 April	Vol. 28, no. 727	Harold Huth Joan Barry
	15 April	Vol. 28, no. 728	Kay Francis Ronald Colman
	22 April	Vol. 29, no. 729	John Barrymore Katharine Hepburn
	29 April	Vol. 29, no. 730	Maurice Chevalier

YEAR	MONTH	REF. No.	COVER STAR
	6 May	Vol. 29, no. 731	**Kay Francis** **Herbert Marshall**
	13 May	Vol. 29, no. 732	**Warren William** **Lili Damita**
	20 May	Vol. 29, no. 733	**Sylvia Sidney** **Cary Grant**
	27 May	Vol. 29, no. 734	**Irene Dunne** **Phillips Holmes**
	3 June	Vol. 29, no. 735	**Edward G. Robinson** **Bebe Daniels**
	10 June	Vol. 29, no. 736	**W.C. Fields** **Alison Skipworth**
	17 June	Vol. 29, no. 737	**Dorothy Bouchier** **Harry Milton**
	24 June	Vol. 29, no. 738	**Herbert Marshall** **Sari Maritza**
	1 July	Vol. 29, no. 739	**George O'Brien**
	8 July	Vol. 29, no. 740	**Tala Birell** **Melvyn Douglas**
	15 July	Vol. 29, no. 741	**Edmund Lowe** **Wynne Gibson**
	22 July	Vol. 29, no. 742	**Edna May Oliver** **James Gleason** **Robert Armstrong** **Mae Clarke** **Donald Cook**
	29 July	Vol. 29, no. 743	**Fredric March** **Claudette Colbert**
	5 Aug.	Vol. 29, no. 744	**Leslie Howard** **Myrna Loy**
	12 Aug.	Vol. 29, no. 745	**Janet Gaynor** **Lew Ayres**
	19 Aug.	Vol. 29, no. 746	**Clark Gable** **Carole Lombard**
	26 Aug.	Vol. 29, no. 747	**Truth in interviewing**
	2 Sept.	Vol. 29, no. 748	**Maurice Chevalier** **Baby Leroy**
	9 Sept.	Vol. 29, no. 749	**Gilbert Roland** **Constance Bennett**
	16 Sept.	Vol. 29, no. 750	**Gene Raymond** **Loretta Young**
	23 Sept.	Vol. 29, no. 751	**Jack Hulbert** **Tamara Desni**
	30 Sept.	Vol. 29, no. 752	**Fredric March** **Elissa Landi**
	7 Oct.	Vol. 29, no. 753	**Vilma Banky** **Luis Trenker**
	14 Oct.	Vol. 29, no. 754	**Diana Wynyard** **Clive Brook**
	21 Oct.	Vol. 30, no. 755	**George Brent** **Kay Francis**
	28 Oct.	Vol. 30, no. 756	**Gary Cooper** **Helen Hayes**
	4 Nov.	Vol. 30, no. 757	**Katharine Hepburn** **Colin Clive**
	11 Nov.	Vol. 30, no. 758	**Leslie Howard** **Mary Pickford**
	18 Nov.	Vol. 30, no. 759	**Anna Neagle** **Fernand Gravet**
	25 Nov.	Vol. 30, no. 760	**Madeleine Carroll** **Conrad Veidt**
	2 Dec.	Vol. 30, no. 761	**Marion Davies**
	9 Dec.	Vol. 30, no. 762	**Sylvia Sidney** **Donald Cook**
	16 Dec.	Vol. 30, no. 763	**Joel McCrea** **Irene Dunne**
	23 Dec.	Vol. 30, no. 764	**Lilian Harvey** **John Boles**
	30 Dec.	Vol. 30, no. 765	**Tom Walls** **Ralph Lynn**
1934	6 Jan.	Vol. 30, no. 766	**Conrad Veidt** **Anne Grey**
	13 Jan.	Vol. 30, no. 767	**Franchot Tone** **Miriam Hopkins**
	20 Jan.	Vol. 30, no. 768	**Randolph Scott** **Verna Hillie**
	27 Jan.	Vol. 30, no. 769	**Marlene Dietrich**
	3 Feb.	Vol. 30, no. 770	**Marie Dressler** **Wallace Beery**
	10 Feb.	Vol. 30, no. 771	**Elissa Landi** **Ronald Colman**
	17 Feb.	Vol. 30, no. 772	**Billie Burke**
	24 Feb.	Vol. 30, no. 773	**George Raft** **Helen Vinson**
	3 March	Vol. 30, no. 774	**Conrad Veidt**
	10 March	Vol. 30, no. 775	**Gary Cooper** **Frances Farmer**
	17 March	Vol. 30, no. 776	**Ann Dvorak** **Maurice Chevalier**
	24 March	Vol. 30, no. 777	**Katharine Hepburn** **Adolphe Menjou**
	31 March	Vol. 30, no. 778	**Claudette Colbert** **David Manners**
	7 April	Vol. 30, no. 779	**Jack Hulbert**
	14 April	Vol. 30, no. 780	**Leslie Howard** **Heather Angel**
	21 April	Vol. 31, no. 781	**Cary Grant** **Mae West**
	28 April	Vol. 31, no. 782	**W.C. Fields** **Alison Skipworth** **Baby Leroy**
	5 May	Vol. 31, no. 783	**Jessie Matthews** **Esmond Knight**
	12 May	Vol. 31, no. 784	**Ivor Novello** **Fay Compton**
	19 May	Vol. 31, no. 785	**Katharine Hepburn**
	26 May	Vol.·31, no. 786	**Ramon Novarro** **Jeanette MacDonald**
	2 June	Vol. 31, no. 787	**Marion Davies** **Bing Crosby**
	9 June	Vol. 31, no. 788	**Constance Bennett** **Gilbert Roland**
	16 June	Vol. 31, no. 789	**Wynne Gibson** **Preston Foster**

YEAR	MONTH	REF. No.	COVER STAR
	23 June	Vol. 31, no. 790	**Fredric March**
			Miriam Hopkins
			Gary Cooper
	30 June	Vol. 31, no. 791	**Paul Lukas**
			Elissa Landi
	7 July	Vol. 31, no. 792	**John Boles**
			Rosemary Ames
	14 July	Vol. 31, no. 793	**William Powell**
			Bette Davis
	21 July	Vol. 31, no. 794	**Herbert Marshall**
			Claudette Colbert
	28 July	Vol. 31, no. 795	**Clive Brook**
			Irene Dunne
	4 Aug.	Vol. 31, no. 796	**Robert Montgomery**
			Elizabeth Allan
	Holiday special		**Diana Napier**
	11 Aug.	Vol. 31, no. 797	**Janet Gaynor**
			Robert Young
	18 Aug.	Vol. 31, no. 798	**Miriam Hopkins**
	25 Aug.	Vol. 31, no. 799	**Conrad Veidt**
			Mary Ellis
			John Stuart
	1 Sept.	Vol. 31, no. 800	**Marion Davies**
			Gary Cooper
	8 Sept.	Vol. 31, no. 801	**Greta Garbo**
			John Gilbert
	15 Sept.	Vol. 31, no. 802	**Marlene Dietrich**
			John Lodge
			Sam Jaffe
	21 Sept.	Vol. 31, no. 803	**Norma Shearer**
			Herbert Marshall
	28 Sept.	Vol. 31, no. 804	**Jessie Matthews**
	6 Oct.	Vol. 31, no. 805	**Ramon Novarro**
			Lupe Velez
	13 Oct.	Vol. 31, no. 806	**Anna May Wong**
	20 Oct.	Vol. 32, no. 807	**Carl Brisson**
			Kitty Carlisle
	27 Oct.	Vol. 32, no. 808	**George Arliss**
	3 Nov.	Vol. 32, no. 809	**Fredric March and Norma Shearer**
			Anna Neagle and Cedric Hardwicke
			Claudette Colbert and Henry Wilcoxon
			Douglas Fairbanks and Merle Oberon
	10 Nov.	Vol. 32, no. 810	**Matheson Lang**
			Nova Pilbeam
	17 Nov.	Vol. 32, no. 811	**William Powell**
			Myrna Loy
	24 Nov.	Vol. 32, no. 812	**Irene Dunne**
			Richard Dix
	Christmas special		**Margaret Lindsay**
			Gloria Stuart
			Tom Brown
	1 Dec.	Vol. 32, no. 813	**Evelyn Laye**
	8 Dec.	Vol. 32, no. 814	**Myrna Loy**
			George Brent
	15 Dec.	Vol. 32, no. 815	**Una Merkel**
			Stuart Erwin
	22 Dec.	Vol. 32, no. 816	**Norma Shearer**
	29 Dec.	Vol. 32, no. 817	**Richard Tauber**
1935	5 Jan.	Vol. 32, no. 818	**Madeleine Carroll**
			Clive Brook
	12 Jan.	Vol. 32, no. 819	**Conrad Veidt**
			Joan Maude
	19 Jan.	Vol. 32, no. 820	**Grace Moore**
			Tullio Carminati
	26 Jan.	Vol. 32, no. 821	**Anna Neagle**
	2 Feb.	Vol. 32, no. 822	**Jeanette MacDonald**
			Maurice Chevalier
	9 Feb.	Vol. 32, no. 823	**Helen Hayes**
			Brian Aherne
	16 Feb.	Vol. 32, no. 824	**Madeleine Carroll**
			Franchot Tone
	23 Feb.	Vol. 32, no. 825	**Ronald Colman**
			Loretta Young
	2 March	Vol. 32, no. 826	**Robert Donat**
			Elissa Landi
	9 March	Vol. 32, no. 827	**Merle Oberon**
	16 March	Vol. 32, no. 828	**Greta Garbo**
			Herbert Marshall
	23 March	Vol. 32, no. 829	**Leslie Howard**
			Bette Davis
	30 March	Vol. 32, no. 830	**Charles Boyer**
			Jean Parker
	6 April	Vol. 32, no. 831	**Joan Crawford**
			Robert Montgomery
			Clark Gable
	13 April	Vol. 32, no. 832	**Fred Astaire**
			Ginger Rogers
	20 April	Vol. 33, no. 833	**Nancy Carroll**
			George Murphy
	27 April	Vol. 33, no. 834	**Jean Parker**
			Russell Hardie
	4 May	Vol. 33, no. 835	**Ann Harding**
			Brian Aherne
	11 May	Vol. 33, no. 836	**Ramon Novarro**
			Evelyn Laye
	18 May	Vol. 33, no. 837	**Irene Dunne**
			John Boles
	25 May	Vol. 33, no. 838	**Bing Crosby**
			Kitty Carlisle
	1 June	Vol. 33, no. 839	**Helen Hayes**
			Robert Montgomery
	8 June	Vol. 33, no. 840	**Grace Moore**
	15 June	Vol. 33, no. 841	**Gary Cooper**
			Franchot Tone
			Richard Cromwell
	22 June	Vol. 33, no. 842	**Claudette Colbert**
			Fred MacMurray
			Ray Milland

YEAR	MONTH	REF. No.	COVER STAR
	29 June	Vol. 33, no. 843	**Cary Grant**
			Myrna Loy
	6 July	Vol. 33, no. 844	**Warren William**
			Barbara Stanwyck
	13 July	Vol. 33, no. 845	**Paul Lukas**
			Rosalind Russell
	20 July	Vol. 33, no. 846	**Ginger Rogers**
			Francis Lederer
	27 July	Vol. 33, no. 847	**Frances Day**
	3 Aug.	Vol. 33, no. 848	**Randolph Scott**
			Ann Sheridan
	Holiday special		**Ruby Keeler**
			Dick Powell
	10 Aug.	Vol. 33, no. 849	**Johnny Weissmuller**
			Una Merkel
	17 Aug.	Vol. 33, no. 850	**Katharine Hepburn**
			John Beal
	24 Aug.	Vol. 33, no. 851	**Leslie Howard**
			Kay Francis
	31 Aug.	Vol. 33, no. 852	**John Boles**
			Gloria Swanson
	7 Sept.	Vol. 33, no. 853	**Madeleine Carroll**
	14 Sept.	Vol. 33, no. 854	**Ronald Colman**
			Loretta Young
	21 Sept.	Vol. 33, no. 855	**Frank Lawton**
			Madge Evans
	28 Sept.	Vol. 33, no. 856	**Leslie Howard**
	5 Oct.	Vol. 33, no. 857	**Maurice Chevalier**
	12 Oct.	Vol. 34, no. 858	**Jeanette MacDonald**
			Nelson Eddy
	19 Oct.	Vol. 34, no. 859	**Elizabeth Bergner**
	26 Oct.	Vol. 34, no. 860	**Margaret Sullavan**
	2 Nov.	Vol. 34, no. 861	**Mary Ellis**
			Tullio Carminati
	9 Nov.	Vol. 34, no. 862	**Loretta Young**
			Charles Boyer
	16 Nov.	Vol. 34, no. 863	**John Mills**
	23 Nov.	Vol. 34, no. 864	**Robert Donat**
			Madeleine Carroll
	30 Nov.	Vol. 34, no. 865	**Katharine Hepburn**
			Charles Boyer
	Christmas special		**Gary Cooper**
			Anna Sten
	7 Dec.	Vol. 34, no. 866	**Bing Crosby**
			Mary Boland
	14 Dec.	Vol. 34, no. 867	**Victor McLaglen**
			Margot Grahame
	21 Dec.	Vol. 34, no. 868	**Madge Evans**
	28 Dec.	Vol. 34, no. 869	**Shirley Temple**
1936	4 Jan.	Vol. 34, no. 870	**Clark Gable**
			Jean Harlow
	11 Jan.	Vol. 34, no. 871	**Greta Garbo**
			Fredric March
	18 Jan.	Vol. 34, no. 872	**Grace Moore**
			Michael Bartlett
	25 Jan.	Vol. 34, no. 873	**Henry Wilcoxon**
			Loretta Young
	1 Feb.	Vol. 34, no. 874	**Molly Lamont**
			Theodore Newton
	8 Feb.	Vol. 34, no. 875	**Anna Neagle**
	15 Feb.	Vol. 34, no. 876	**Joel McCrea**
			Miriam Hopkins
	22 Feb.	Vol. 34, no. 877	**Gail Patrick**
			Dean Jagger
	29 Feb.	Vol. 34, no. 878	**Lee Tracy**
			Grace Bradley
			Roscoe Karns
	7 March	Vol. 34, no. 879	**Fredric March**
			Merle Oberon
			Herbert Marshall
	14 March	Vol. 34, no. 880	**Robert Donat**
			Jean Parker
	21 March	Vol. 34, no. 881	**Gary Cooper**
			Ann Harding
	28 March	Vol. 34, no. 882	**Randolph Scott**
			Margaret Sullavan
	4 April	Vol. 34, no. 883	**Robert Taylor**
			Eleanor Powell
	11 April	Vol. 34, no. 884	**Wendy Barrie**
			John Howard
	18 April	Vol. 35, no. 885	**Spencer Tracy**
			Jean Harlow
	25 April	Vol. 35, no. 886	**Gladys Swarthout**
			John Boles
	2 May	Vol. 35, no. 887	**Ronald Colman**
	9 May	Vol. 35, no. 888	**Errol Flynn**
	16 May	Vol. 35, no. 889	**Mala and Lotus**
	23 May	Vol. 35, no. 890	**Herbert Marshall**
			Jean Arthur
	30 May	Vol. 35, no. 891	**Charlotte Wynters**
			Richard Arlen
	6 June	Vol. 35, no. 892	**Fred Astaire**
			Ginger Rogers
	13 June	Vol. 35, no. 893	**George Houston**
			Josephine Hutchinson
	20 June	Vol. 35, no. 894	**Mae West**
			Victor McLaglen
	27 June	Vol. 35, no. 895	**Katharine Hepburn**
			Brian Aherne
	4 July	Vol. 35, no. 896	**Margaret Sullavan**
			James Stewart
	11 July	Vol. 35, no. 897	**Joan Bennett**
			Fred MacMurray
	18 July	Vol. 35, no. 898	**Jan Kiepura**
			Gladys Swarthout
	25 July	Vol. 35, no. 899	**June Clyde**
			Billy Milton
	1 Aug.	Vol. 35, no. 900	**Tom Keene**
			Katharine De Mille
	8 Aug.	Vol. 35, no. 901	**Marlene Dietrich**
			Gary Cooper
	Holiday special		**Jean Parker**

YEAR	MONTH	REF. No.	COVER STAR
	15 Aug.	Vol. 35, no. 902	**Loretta Young** **Franchot Tone**
	22 Aug.	Vol. 35, no. 903	**Elissa Landi** **Douglas Fairbanks Jr**
	29 Aug.	Vol. 35, no. 904	**Nova Pilbeam** **John Mills**
	5 Sept.	Vol. 35, no. 905	**Miriam Hopkins** **Joel McCrea**
	12 Sept.	Vol. 35, no. 906	**Anna Neagle** **Arthur Tracy**
	19 Sept.	Vol. 35, no. 907	**Bette Davis** **Leslie Howard**
	26 Sept.	Vol. 35, no. 908	**Charles Laughton** **Clark Gable** **Movita**
	3 Oct.	Vol. 35, no. 909	**Henry Fonda** **Sylvia Sidney**
	10 Oct.	Vol. 35, no. 910	**Ronald Colman** **Elizabeth Allan**
	17 Oct.	Vol. 35, no. 911	**Gary Cooper** **Jean Arthur**
	24 Oct.	Vol. 36, no. 912	**Shirley Temple** **Guy Kibbee**
	Autumn Special	Vol. 36, no. 913	**Ann Harding** **Walter Abel**
	31 Oct.	Vol. 36, no. 914	**Nelson Eddy** **Jeanette MacDonald**
	7 Nov.	Vol. 36, no. 915	**Katharine Hepburn** **Fredric March**
	14 Nov.	Vol. 36, no. 916	**Carole Lombard** **Fred MacMurray**
	21 Nov.	Vol. 36, no. 917	**Grace Moore** **Franchot Tone**
	28 Nov.	Vol. 36, no. 918	**Charles Collins** **Steffi Duna**
	Christmas special		**Fred Astaire** **Ginger Rogers**
	5 Dec.	Vol. 36, no. 919	**Marlene Dietrich**
	12 Dec.	Vol. 36, no. 920	**Randolph Scott** **Frances Drake**
	19 Dec.	Vol. 36, no. 921	**John Howard** **Frances Farmer**
	26 Dec.	Vol. 36, no. 922	**Shirley Temple**
1937	2 Jan.	Vol. 36, no. 923	**Robert Taylor** **Greta Garbo**
	9 Jan.	Vol. 36, no. 924	**Clark Gable** **Jeanette MacDonald**
	16 Jan.	Vol. 36, no. 925	**Cary Grant** **Franchot Tone** **Jean Harlow**
	23 Jan.	Vol. 36, no. 926	**Gertrude Michael** **Ray Milland**
	30 Jan.	Vol. 36, no. 927	**Robert Taylor** **Joan Crawford**

YEAR	MONTH	REF. No.	COVER STAR
	6 Feb.	Vol. 36, no. 928	**Robert Montgomery** **Madge Evans**
	13 Feb.	Vol. 36, no. 929	**Walter Huston** **Ruth Chatterton**
	20 Feb.	Vol. 36, no. 930	**Dick Powell** **Marion Davies**
	27 Feb.	Vol. 36, no. 931	**Loretta Young** **Don Ameche**
	6 March	Vol. 36, no. 932	**John Boles** **Rosalind Russell**
	13 March	Vol. 36, no. 933	**Barbara Stanwyck** **Preston Foster**
	20 March	Vol. 36, no. 934	**Kay Francis**
	27 March	Vol. 36, no. 935	**Leslie Howard** **Norma Shearer**
	3 April	Vol. 36, no. 936	**Shirley Temple** **Frank Morgan**
	10 April	Vol. 37, no. 937	**Merle Oberon** **Brian Aherne**
	17 April	Vol. 37, no. 938	**Gary Cooper** **Madeleine Carroll**
	24 April	Vol. 37, no. 939	**Clark Gable** **Joan Crawford**
	1 May	Vol. 37, no. 940	**Johnny Weissmuller** **Maureen O'Sullivan**
	8 May	Vol. 37, no. 941	**Ann Sothern** **Gene Raymond**
	15 May	Vol. 37, no. 942	**Eleanore Whitney** **Tom Brown**
	22 May	Vol. 37, no. 943	**Barbara Stanwyck** **Joel McCrea**
	29 May	Vol. 37, no. 944	**Wendy Barrie** **Lawrence Tibbett**
	5 June	Vol. 37, no. 945	**Ann Harding** **Basil Rathbone**
	12 June	Vol. 37, no. 946	**Lily Pons** **Gene Raymond**
	19 June	Vol. 37, no. 947	**Mae Clarke** **James Cagney**
	26 June	Vol. 37, no. 948	**Gary Cooper** **Jean Arthur**
	3 July	Vol. 37, no. 949	**Robert Taylor**
	10 July	Vol. 37, no. 950	**Melvyn Douglas** **Virginia Bruce**
	17 July	Vol. 37, no. 951	**Fred MacMurray** **Claudette Colbert**
	24 July	Vol. 37, no. 952	**Dick Powell** **Joan Blondell**
	31 July	Vol. 37, no. 953	**Jean Harlow** **Robert Taylor**
	7 Aug.	Vol. 37, no. 954	**Edward Arnold** **Francine Larrimore**
	14 Aug.	Vol. 37, no. 955	**Henry Fonda** **Annabella**
	21 Aug.	Vol. 37, no. 956	**Sonja Henie** **Don Ameche**

YEAR	MONTH	REF. No.	COVER STAR
	Holiday special		**Joan Blondell**
			Dick Powell
	28 Aug.	Vol. 37, no. 957	**Vivien Leigh**
			Conrad Veidt
	4 Sept.	Vol. 37, no. 958	**Greta Garbo**
	11 Sept.	Vol. 37, no. 959	**Madeleine Carroll**
			Tyrone Power
	18 Sept.	Vol. 37, no. 960	**Eleanor Powell**
			James Stewart
	25 Sept.	Vol. 37, no. 961	**Eleanor Powell**
	2 Oct.	Vol. 37, no. 962	**Tyrone Power**
	9 Oct.	Vol. 38, no. 963	**Joan Crawford**
	16 Oct.	Vol. 38, no. 964	**Ronald Colman**
	23 Oct.	Vol. 38, no. 965	**Gracie Fields**
	30 Oct.	Vol. 38, no. 966	**Robert Taylor**
			Barbara Stanwyck
	6 Nov.	Vol. 38, no. 967	**Jean Harlow**
			Clark Gable
	13 Nov.	Vol. 38, no. 968	**Clark Gable**
			Myrna Loy
	20 Nov.	Vol. 38, no. 969	**Vivien Leigh**
			Rex Harrison
	27 Nov.	Vol. 38, no. 970	**William Powell**
			Luise Rainer
	4 Dec.	Vol. 38, no. 971	**Gilbert Roland**
			Dorothy Lamour
	11 Dec.	Vol. 38, no. 972	**Shirley Temple**
	18 Dec.	Vol. 38, no. 973	**Jeanette MacDonald**
			Gene Raymond
	25 Dec.	Vol. 38, no. 974	**Spencer Tracy**
	Christmas special		**Deanna Durbin**
1938	1 Jan.	Vol. 38, no. 975	**Tyrone Power**
			Loretta Young
	8 Jan.	Vol. 38, no. 976	**Marlene Dietrich**
			Robert Donat
	15 Jan.	Vol. 38, no. 977	**Janet Gaynor**
			Fredric March
	22 Jan.	Vol. 38, no. 978	**Randolph Scott**
			Irene Dunne
	29 Jan.	Vol. 38, no. 979	**Frances Farmer**
			Fred MacMurray
	5 Feb.	Vol. 38, no. 980	**Madeleine Carroll**
			Francis Lederer
	12 Feb.	Vol. 38, no. 981	**Gary Cooper**
			Frances Dee
	19 Feb.	Vol. 38, no. 982	**Jeanette MacDonald**
			Allan Jones
	26 Feb.	Vol. 38, no. 983	**Leslie Howard**
			Olivia De Havilland
	5 March	Vol. 38, no. 984	**Robert Young**
			Joan Crawford
			Franchot Tone
	12 March	Vol. 38, no. 985	**Ronald Colman**
			Nancy Carroll

YEAR	MONTH	REF. No.	COVER STAR
	19 March	Vol. 38, no. 986	**Adolphe Menjou**
			Katharine Hepburn
	26 March	Vol. 38, no. 987	**Robert Benchley**
			Robert Montgomery
			Rosalind Russell
	2 April	Vol. 38, no. 988	**Cary Grant**
			Irene Dunne
	9 April	Vol. 39, no. 989	**Greta Garbo**
	16 April	Vol. 39, no. 990	**Shirley Temple**
			Jean Hersholt
	23 April	Vol. 39, no. 991	**Tyrone Power**
			Loretta Young
	30 April	Vol. 39, no. 992	**Nova Pilbeam**
			Derrick De Marney
	7 May	Vol. 39, no. 993	**Grace Moore**
			Melvyn Douglas
	14 May	Vol. 39, no. 994	**Myrna Loy**
			Franchot Tone
	21 May	Vol. 39, no. 995	**Ramon Novarro**
			Lola Lane
	28 May	Vol. 39, no. 996	**Joel McCrea**
			Frances Dee
	4 June	Vol. 39, no. 997	**Hugh Williams**
			Margaret Lockwood
	11 June	Vol. 39, no. 998	**Brian Aherne**
			Olivia De Havilland
	Summer special		**Larry Crabbe**
			Betty Grable
	18 June	Vol. 39, no. 999	**Fred MacMurray**
			Carole Lombard
	25 June	Vol. 39, no. 1000	**George Murphy**
			Alice Faye
	2 July	Vol. 39, no. 1001	**Fredric March**
			Franciska Gaal
	9 July	Vol. 39, no. 1002	**Leif Erickson**
			Dorothy Lamour
	16 July	Vol. 39, no. 1003	**Richard Arlen**
			Mary Astor
	23 July	Vol. 39, no. 1004	**Gene Raymond**
			Ann Sothern
	30 July	Vol. 39, no. 1005	**Shirley Temple**
			Randolph Scott
	6 Aug.	Vol. 39, no. 1006	**James Stewart**
			Ann Rutherford
	13 Aug.	Vol. 39, no. 1007	**Cary Grant**
			Katharine Hepburn
	20 Aug.	Vol. 39, no. 1008	**Edna Best**
			Ralph Richardson
	27 Aug.	Vol. 39, no. 1009	**Spencer Tracy**
			Joan Crawford
	3 Sept.	Vol. 39, no. 1010	**Maureen O'Sullivan**
			Robert Taylor
	10 Sept.	Vol. 39, no. 1011	**Jeanette MacDonald**
			Nelson Eddy
	17 Sept.	Vol. 39, no. 1012	**Gary Cooper**
			Claudette Colbert

YEAR	MONTH	REF. No.	COVER STAR
	24 Sept.	Vol. 39, no. 1013	**Clark Gable**
			Myrna Loy
			Spencer Tracy
	1 Oct.	Vol. 39, no. 1014	**Alice Faye**
			Tyrone Power
	8 Oct.	Vol. 40, no. 1015	**Robert Taylor**
			Margaret Sullavan
	15 Oct.	Vol. 40, no. 1016	**Luise Rainer**
			Robert Young
	22 Oct.	Vol. 40, no. 1017	**Fred MacMurray**
			Harriet Hilliard
	29 Oct.	Vol. 40, no. 1018	**Gracie Fields**
	5 Nov.	Vol. 40, no. 1019	**Shirley Ross**
			John Howard
	12 Nov.	Vol. 40, no. 1020	**James Stewart**
			Margaret Sullavan
	Christmas special		**Cary Grant**
			Doris Nolan
	19 Nov.	Vol. 40, no. 1021	**Dorothy Lamour**
			Ray Milland
	26 Nov.	Vol. 40, no. 1022	**Robert Taylor**
			Maureen O'Sullivan
	3 Dec.	Vol. 40, no. 1023	**Melvyn Douglas**
			Florence Rice
	10 Dec.	Vol. 40, no. 1024	**Jean Parker**
	17 Dec.	Vol. 40, no. 1025	**Ellen Drew**
			Fred MacMurray
	24 Dec.	Vol. 40, no. 1026	**Anna Neagle**
			Anton Walbrook
	31 Dec.	Vol. 40, no. 1027	**Olivia De Havilland**
			Errol Flynn
1939	7 Jan.	Vol. 40, no. 1028	**Gracie Fields**
	14 Jan.	Vol. 40, no. 1029	**Joan Bennett**
			Randolph Scott
	21 Jan.	Vol. 40, no. 1030	**Douglas Fairbanks Jr**
			Danielle Darrieux
	28 Jan.	Vol. 40, no. 1031	**Deanna Durbin**
			Melvyn Douglas
	4 Feb.	Vol. 40, no. 1032	**Norma Shearer**
			Tyrone Power
	11 Feb.	Vol. 40, no. 1033	**Ronald Colman**
			Frances Dee
	18 Feb.	Vol. 40, no. 1034	**Sonja Henie**
			Richard Greene
	25 Feb.	Vol. 40, no. 1035	**Fredric March**
			Virginia Bruce
	4 March	Vol. 40, no. 1036	**Robert Donat**
			Rosalind Russell
	11 March	Vol. 40, no. 1037	**James Stewart**
			Jean Arthur
	18 March	Vol. 40, no. 1038	**Jeffrey Lynn**
			Priscilla Lane
	25 March	Vol. 40, no. 1039	**Paulette Goddard**
			Janet Gaynor
			Douglas Fairbanks Jr

YEAR	MONTH	REF. No.	COVER STAR
	1 April	Vol. 40, no. 1040	**Michael Redgrave**
			Elizabeth Bergner
	8 April	Vol. 41, no. 1041	**Fernand Gravet**
			Luise Rainer
	15 April	Vol. 41, no. 1042	**Loretta Young**
			Richard Greene
	22 April	Vol. 41, no. 1043	**Gary Cooper**
			Merle Oberon
	29 April	Vol. 41, no. 1044	**Jeanette MacDonald**
			Nelson Eddy
	6 May	Vol. 41, no. 1045	**Patric Knowles**
			Olivia De Havilland
			Rosalind Russell
			Errol Flynn
	13 May	Vol. 41, no. 1046	**Olympe Bradna**
			Ray Milland
	20 May	Vol. 41, no. 1047	**Robert Taylor**
			Florence Rice
	27 May	Vol. 41, no. 1048	**Madeleine Carroll**
			Fred MacMurray
	3 June	Vol. 41, no. 1049	**Dorothy Lamour**
			Lloyd Nolan
	10 June	Vol. 41, no. 1050	**J. Carrol Naish**
			Patricia Morison
	17 June	Vol. 41, no. 1051	**Bette Davis**
			Errol Flynn
	24 June	Vol. 41, no. 1052	**Eleanor Powell**
			Robert Young
	1 July	Vol. 41, no. 1053	**Olivia De Havilland**
			John Payne
	8 July	Vol. 41, no. 1054	**Melvyn Douglas**
			Virginia Bruce
	15 July	Vol. 41, no. 1055	**Nelson Eddy and wife**
	22 July	Vol. 41, no. 1056	**Errol Flynn**
			Lili Damita
	29 July	Vol. 41, no. 1057	**Virginia Bruce**
			Nelson Eddy
	5 Aug.	Vol. 41, no. 1058	**Brian Aherne**
			June Lang
	12 Aug.	Vol. 41, no. 1059	**Isa Miranda**
			Ray Milland
	19 Aug.	Vol. 41, no. 1060	**Tyrone Power**
			Nancy Kelly
	26 Aug.	Vol. 41, no. 1061	**Valerie Hobson**
			Laurence Olivier
	2 Sept.	Vol. 41, no. 1062	**John Clements**
			June Duprez
	9 Sept.	Vol. 41, no. 1063	**Norma Shearer**
			Clark Gable
	16 Sept.	Vol. 41, no. 1064	**Deanna Durbin**
			Nan Grey
			Charles Winniger
			Helen Parrish
	23 Sept.	Vol. 41, no. 1065	**Bette Davis**
			George Brent

YEAR	MONTH	REF. No.	COVER STAR
	30 Sept.	Vol. 41, no. 1066	**Sally Gray** **Lupino Lane**
	7 Oct.	Vol. 42, no. 1067	**Kenny Baker** **Jean Colin**
	14 Oct.	Vol. 42, no. 1068	**Ray Milland** **Gary Cooper** **Robert Preston**
	21 Oct.	Vol. 42, no. 1069	**Irene Dunne** **Fred MacMurray**
	28 Oct.	Vol. 42, no. 1070	**Greer Garson** **Robert Donat**
	4 Nov.	Vol. 42, no. 1071	**Laurence Olivier** **Merle Oberon**
	11 Nov.	Vol. 42, no. 1072	**Cary Grant** **Jean Arthur**
	18 Nov.	Vol. 42, no. 1073	**Barbara Stanwyck** **Joel McCrea**
	25 Nov.	Vol. 42, no. 1074	**Anna Neagle** **George Sanders**
	2 Dec.	Vol. 42, no. 1075	**Errol Flynn** **Olivia De Havilland**
	9 Dec.	Vol. 42, no. 1076	**William Powell** **Myrna Loy** **William Anthony Poulsen**
	16 Dec.	Vol. 42, no. 1077	**Robert Young** **Ruth Hussey**
	23 Dec.	Vol. 42, no. 1078	**Warner Baxter** **Loretta Young**
	30 Dec.	Vol. 42, no. 1079	**Douglas Fairbanks Jr** **Margaret Lockwood**
1940	6 Jan.	Vol. 42, no. 1080	**Deanna Durbin** **Robert Stack**
	13 Jan.	Vol. 42, no. 1081	**Charles Boyer** **Irene Dunne**
	20 Jan.	Vol. 42, no. 1082	**Hedy Lamarr** **Robert Taylor**
	27 Jan.	Vol. 42, no. 1083	**Fred MacMurray** **Madeleine Carroll**
	3 Feb.	Vol. 42, no. 1084	**William Holden** **Barbara Stanwyck**
	10 Feb.	Vol. 42, no. 1085	**Tyrone Power** **Myrna Loy**
	17 Feb.	Vol. 42, no. 1086	**Merle Oberon** **Rex Harrison**
	24 Feb.	Vol. 42, no. 1087	**Ray Milland** **Ellen Drew**
	2 March	Vol. 42, no. 1088	**Deanna Durbin** **Robert Stack**
	9 March	Vol. 42, no. 1089	**Lana Turner** **Richard Carlson**
	16 March	Vol. 42, no. 1090	**Gary Cooper** **Andrea Leeds**
	23 March	Vol. 42, no. 1091	**Richard Greene** **Brenda Joyce**

YEAR	MONTH	REF. No.	COVER STAR
	30 March	Vol. 42, no. 1092	**Alice Faye** **Don Ameche**
	6 April	Vol. 43, no. 1093	**Greta Garbo** **Melvyn Douglas**
	13 April	Vol. 43, no. 1094	**James Stewart** **Marlene Dietrich**
	20 April	Vol. 43, no. 1095	**William Powell** **Myrna Loy**
	27 April	Vol. 43, no. 1096	**Nelson Eddy** **Ilona Massey**
	4 May	Vol. 43, no. 1097	**David Niven** **Olivia De Havilland**
	11 May	Vol. 43, no. 1098	**Henry Fonda** **Claudette Colbert**
	18 May	Vol. 43, no. 1099	**Ann Morriss** **George Murphy**
	25 May	Vol. 43, no. 1100	**Mickey Rooney** **Ann Rutherford**
	1 June	Vol. 43, no. 1101	**Karen Verne** **Rex Harrison** **Mavis Clair**
	8 June	Vol. 43, no. 1102	**Preston Foster** **Ellen Drew** **William Henry**
	15 June	Vol. 43, no. 1103	**Melvyn Douglas** **Joan Blondell**
	22 June	Vol. 43, no. 1104	**John Howard** **Dolores Del Rio**
	29 June	Vol. 43, no. 1105	**Cary Grant** **Rosalind Russell** **Ralph Bellamy**
	6 July	Vol. 43, no. 1106	**Alastair Sim** **Diana Churchill** **Barry K. Barnes**
	13 July	Vol. 43, no. 1107	**Fred MacMurray** **Barbara Stanwyck**
	20 July	Vol. 43, no. 1108	**Patricia Morison** **Ray Milland**
	27 July	Vol. 43, no. 1109	**Dorothy Lamour** **Robert Preston**
	3 Aug.	Vol. 43, no. 1110	**Spencer Tracy** **Hedy Lamarr**
	10 Aug.	Vol. 43, no. 1111	**Joel McCrea** **Ginger Rogers**
	17 Aug.	Vol. 43, no. 1112	**Robert Cummings** **Laraine Day**
	24 Aug.	Vol. 43, no. 1113	**Eleanor Powell** **Fred Astaire**
	31 Aug.	Vol. 43, no. 1114	**Margaret Lockwood** **Rex Harrison**
	7 Sept.	Vol. 43, no. 1115	**Anna Neagle** **Ray Milland**
	14 Sept.	Vol. 43, no. 1116	**Laurence Olivier** **Joan Fontaine**
	21 Sept.	Vol. 43, no. 1117	**Don Ameche** **Edward Arnold**

YEAR	MONTH	REF. No.	COVER STAR
	21 Sept. (*cont.*)		**Alice Faye** **Warren William** **Henry Fonda**
	28 Sept.	Vol. 43, no. 1118	**Gary Cooper** **Doris Davenport**
	5 Oct.	Vol. 44, no. 1119	**Bette Davis** **Errol Flynn**
	12 Oct.	Vol. 44, no. 1120	**Margaret Sullavan** **James Stewart**
	19 Oct.	Vol. 44, no. 1121	**Janice Logan** **Thomas Coley**
	26 Oct.	Vol. 44, no. 1122	**Judy Garland** **Mickey Rooney**
	2 Nov.	Vol. 44, no. 1123	**Miriam Hopkins** **Errol Flynn**
	9 Nov.	Vol. 44, no. 1124	**Robert Montgomery** **Constance Cummings**
	16 Nov.	Vol. 44, no. 1125	**Greer Garson** **Laurence Olivier**
	23 Nov.	Vol. 44, no. 1126	**Nelson Eddy** **Jeanette MacDonald**
	30 Nov.	Vol. 44, no. 1127	**Joel McCrea** **Laraine Day**
	7 Dec.	Vol. 44, no. 1128	**Robert Taylor** **Vivien Leigh**
	14 Dec.	Vol. 44, no. 1129	**Jack Benny** **Ellen Drew**
	21 Dec.	Vol. 44, no. 1130	**Fredric March** **Joan Crawford**
	28 Dec.	Vol. 44, no. 1131	**Robert Cummings** **Deanna Durbin**
1941	4 Jan.	Vol. 44, no. 1132	**Dick Powell** **Joan Blondell**
	11 Jan.	Vol. 44, no. 1133	**Judy Garland** **Mickey Rooney**
	18 Jan.	Vol. 44, no. 1134	**Loretta Young** **Melvyn Douglas**
	25 Jan.	Vol. 44, no. 1135	**Linda Darnell** **Tyrone Power**
	1 Feb.	Vol. 44, no. 1136	**Mary Martin** **Bing Crosby**
	8 Feb.	Vol. 44, no. 1137	**Mary Beth Hughes** **Cesar Romero**
	15 Feb.	Vol. 44, no. 1138	**Patricia Morison** **Betty Brewer** **Fred MacMurray**
	22 Feb.	Vol. 44, no. 1139	**Betty Grable** **Don Ameche**
	1 March	Vol. 44, no. 1140	**Tyrone Power** **Linda Darnell**
	8 March	Vol. 44, no. 1141	**June Duprez** **John Justin** **Sabu** **Conrad Veidt**
	15 March	Vol. 44, no. 1142	**Melvyn Douglas** **Myrna Loy**
	22 March	Vol. 44, no. 1143	**Mischa Auer** **Deanna Durbin**
	29 March	Vol. 44, no. 1144	**Richard Carlson** **Anna Neagle** **Victor Mature**
	5 April	Vol. 45, no. 1145	**Madeleine Carroll** **Gary Cooper**
	12 April	Vol. 45, no. 1146	**Robert Taylor** **Norma Shearer**
	19 April	Vol. 45, no. 1147	**Walter Pidgeon** **Ruth Hussey** **Robert Taylor**
	26 April	Vol. 45, no. 1148	**Clark Gable** **Hedy Lamarr**
	3 May	Vol. 45, no. 1149	**Claudette Colbert** **Ray Milland**
	10 May	Vol. 45, no. 1150	**Peggy Moran** **Franchot Tone**
	17 May	Vol. 45, no. 1151	**John Carroll** **Diana Lewis** **Marx Brothers**
	24 May	Vol. 45, no. 1152	**Paulette Goddard** **Fred Astaire**
	31 May	Vol. 45, no. 1153	**Cary Grant** **Katharine Hepburn** **James Stewart**
	7 June	Vol. 45, no. 1154	**Fredric March** **Betty Field**
	14 June	Vol. 45, no. 1155	**Ginger Rogers** **Dennis Morgan**
	21 June	Vol. 45, no. 1156	**Madeleine Carroll** **Fred MacMurray**
	28 June	Vol. 45, no. 1157	**Diana Wynyard** **Michael Redgrave**
	5 July	Vol. 45, no. 1158	**Virginia Bruce** **John Howard**
	12 July	Vol. 45, no. 1159	**Deanna Durbin** **Robert Stack**
	19 July	Vol. 45, no. 1160	**Ann Sheridan** **George Brent**
	26 July	Vol. 45, no. 1161	**Henry Fonda** **Barbara Stanwyck**
	2 Aug.	Vol. 45, no. 1162	**Merle Oberon** **Melvyn Douglas**
	9 Aug.	Vol. 45, no. 1163	**Cary Grant** **Irene Dunne**
	16 Aug.	Vol. 45, no. 1164	**Robert Montgomery** **Ingrid Bergman**
	23 Aug.	Vol. 45, no. 1165	**Bob Hope** **Dorothy Lamour** **Bing Crosby**
	30 Aug.	Vol. 45, no. 1166	**Preston Foster** **Patricia Morison** **Richard Dix**
	13 Sept.	Vol. 45, no. 1167	**George Montgomery** **Mary Beth Hughes**
	27 Sept.	Vol. 45, no. 1168	**Bruce Cabot** **Marlene Dietrich**

YEAR	MONTH	REF. No.	COVER STAR
	11 Oct.	Vol. 45, no. 1169	**Charles Boyer Olivia De Havilland**
	25 Oct.	Vol. 45, no. 1170	**Bette Davis George Brent**
	8 Nov.	Vol. 46, no. 1171	**Bob Hope Paulette Goddard**
	22 Nov.	Vol. 46, no. 1172	**Glynis Johns Anton Walbrook Leslie Howard Laurence Olivier Raymond Massey Eric Portman**
	6 Dec.	Vol. 46, no. 1173	**Dorothy Lewis James Ellison**
	20 Dec.	Vol. 46, no. 1174	**Mary Martin Don Ameche**
1942	3 Jan.	Vol. 46, no. 1175	**Betty Grable Don Ameche**
	17 Jan.	Vol. 46, no. 1176	**Ona Munson John Wayne**
	31 Jan.	Vol. 46, no. 1177	**Veronica Lake Joel McCrea**
	14 Feb.	Vol. 46, no. 1178	**Gary Cooper Joan Leslie**
	28 Feb.	Vol. 46, no. 1179	**Fred MacMurray Mary Martin**
	14 March	Vol. 46, no. 1180	**Melvyn Douglas Greta Garbo**
	28 March	Vol. 46, no. 1181	**Tyrone Power Rita Hayworth**
	11 April	Vol. 46, no. 1182	**John Wayne Joan Blondell**
	25 April	Vol. 46, no. 1183	**Anne Shirley James Craig**
	9 May	Vol. 46, no. 1184	**Dana Andrews Anne Baxter**
	23 May	Vol. 46, no. 1185	**Madeleine Carroll Sterling Hayden**
	6 June	Vol. 46, no. 1186	**Loretta Young Fredric March**
	20 June	Vol. 46, no. 1187	**Paulette Goddard Ray Milland**
	4 July	Vol. 46, no. 1188	**Eddie Bracken William Holden Dorothy Lamour**
	18 July	Vol. 46, no. 1189	**Paul Henreid Michele Morgan**
	1 Aug.	Vol. 46, no. 1190	**Kathryn Grayson John Carroll**
	15 Aug.	Vol. 46, no. 1191	**Fred MacMurray Rosalind Russell**
	29 Aug.	Vol. 46, no. 1192	**Bing Crosby Virginia Dale Fred Astaire**
	12 Sept.	Vol. 46, no. 1193	**Rosamund John Leslie Howard**
	26 Sept.	Vol. 46, no. 1194	**Claudette Colbert Joel McCrea Rudy Vallee**
	10 Oct.	Vol. 46, no. 1195	**Norma Shearer Robert Taylor George Sanders**
	24 Oct.	Vol. 46, no. 1196	**Nelson Eddy Jeanette MacDonald**
	7 Nov.	Vol. 47, no. 1197	**Tyrone Power Joan Fontaine**
	21 Nov.	Vol. 47, no. 1198	**Ray Milland Betty Field**
	5 Dec.	Vol. 47, no. 1199	**Susan Hayward Fred MacMurray**
	19 Dec.	Vol. 47, no. 1200	**Bob Hope Dorothy Lamour Bing Crosby**
1943	2 Jan.	Vol. 47, no. 1201	**Maria Montez Jon Hall**
	16 Jan.	Vol. 47, no. 1202	**Lana Turner Clark Gable**
	30 Jan.	Vol. 47, no. 1203	**Ann Sothern Dan Dailey**
	13 Feb.	Vol. 47, no. 1204	**Teresa Wright Gary Cooper**
	27 Feb.	Vol. 47, no. 1205	**Ann Dvorak Eric Portman**
	13 March	Vol. 47, no. 1206	**Greer Garson Ronald Colman**
	27 March	Vol. 47, no. 1207	**Humphrey Bogart Mary Astor**
	10 April	Vol. 47, no. 1208	**Maureen O'Hara Henry Fonda**
	24 April	Vol. 47, no. 1209	**Betty Hutton Bob Hope**
	8 May	Vol. 47, no. 1210	**Fred MacMurray Claudette Colbert**
	22 May	Vol. 47, no. 1211	**Loretta Young Brian Aherne**
	5 June	Vol. 47, no. 1212	**Ann Sothern Melvyn Douglas**
	19 June	Vol. 47, no. 1213	**Charles Boyer Rita Hayworth**
	3 July	Vol. 47, no. 1214	**Macdonald Carey Betty Rhodes**
	17 July	Vol. 47, no. 1215	**Fred MacMurray Rosalind Russell**
	31 July	Vol. 47, no. 1216	**Jack Oakie Alice Faye John Payne**
	14 Aug.	Vol. 47, no. 1217	**Dorothy Lamour Bob Hope**
	28 Aug.	Vol. 47, no. 1218	**James Mason Margaret Lockwood**
	11 Sept.	Vol. 47, no. 1219	**Tyrone Power Anne Baxter**

YEAR	MONTH	REF. No.	COVER STAR
	25 Sept.	Vol. 47, no. 1220	**Red Skelton** **Lucille Ball**
	9 Oct.	Vol. 47, no. 1221	**Deanna Durbin** **Joseph Cotten**
	23 Oct.	Vol. 47, no. 1222	**Bing Crosby** **Marjorie Reynolds**
	6 Nov.	Vol. 48, no. 1223	**Gene Tierney** **Don Ameche**
	20 Nov.	Vol. 48, no. 1224	**Valerie Hobson** **Robert Donat**
	4 Dec.	Vol. 48, no. 1225	**Richard Greene** **Anna Neagle**
	18 Dec.	Vol. 48, no. 1226	**Judy Garland** **Mickey Rooney**
1944	1 Jan.	Vol. 48, no. 1227	**Sonja Henie** **Geary Steffen**
	15 Jan	Vol. 48, no. 1228	**Fred Astaire** **Joan Leslie**
	29 Jan.	Vol. 48, no. 1229	**Robert Young** **Betty Grable** **Reginald Gardiner**
	12 Feb.	Vol. 48, no. 1230	**Lassie** **Roddy McDowall**
	28 Feb.	Vol. 48, no. 1231	**Betty Hutton** **Dorothy Lamour** **Diana Lynn** **Mimi Chandler**
	11 March	Vol. 48, no. 1232	**Luise Rainer** **Arturo De Cordova**
	25 March	Vol. 48, no. 1233	**Nelson Eddy** **Susanna Foster**
	8 April	Vol. 48, no. 1234	**Franchot Tone** **Deanna Durbin**
	22 April	Vol. 48, no. 1235	**Paulette Goddard** **Fred MacMurray**
	6 May	Vol. 48, no. 1236	**William Powell** **Hedy Lamarr**
	20 May	Vol. 48, no. 1237	**Robert Ryan** **Ginger Rogers**
	3 June	Vol. 48, no. 1238	**Joel McCrea** **Maureen O'Hara**
	17 June	Vol. 48, no. 1239	**Margaretta Scott** **James Mason** **Phyllis Calvert** **Stewart Granger**
	1 July	Vol. 48, no. 1240	**Robert Cummings** **Olivia De Havilland**
	15 July	Vol. 48, no. 1241	**Dick Powell** **Lucille Ball** **Bert Lahr**
	29 July	Vol. 48, no. 1242	**Gary Cooper** **Ingrid Bergman**
	12 Aug.	Vol. 48, no. 1243	**David Niven** **Penelope Ward**
	26 Aug.	Vol. 48, no. 1244	**Sergeant John Sweet** **Sheila Sim**
	9 Sept.	Vol. 48, no. 1245	**Lee Bowman** **Rita Hayworth** **Gene Kelly**
	23 Sept.	Vol. 48, no. 1246	**Cary Grant** **Ted Donaldson** **Janet Blair**
	7 Oct.	Vol. 48, no. 1247	**Irene Dunne** **Alan Marshal**
	21 Oct.	Vol. 48, no. 1248	**Dickie Moore** **Linda Darnell**
	4 Nov.	Vol. 49, no. 1249	**Toumanova** **Gregory Peck**
	18 Nov.	Vol. 49, no. 1250	**Richard Greene** **Patricia Medina**
	2 Dec.	Vol. 49, no. 1251	**Eleanor Parker** **Paul Henreid**
	16 Dec.	Vol. 49, no. 1252	**Jess Barker** **Ann Miller**
	30 Dec.	Vol. 49, no. 1253	**Maria Montez** **Peter Coe**
1945	13 Jan.	Vol. 49, no. 1254	**Belita**
	27 Jan.	Vol. 49, no. 1255	**Ronald Colman** **Marlene Dietrich**
	10 Feb.	Vol. 49, no. 1256	**Arturo De Cordova** **Joan Fontaine**
	24 Feb.	Vol. 49, no. 1257	**Peggy Ryan** **Donald O'Connor** **Jack Oakie**
	10 March	Vol. 49, no. 1258	**William Powell** **Myrna Loy**
	24 March	Vol. 49, no. 1259	**Irene Dunne** **Charles Boyer**
	7 April	Vol. 49, no. 1260	**Deanna Durbin** **Robert Paige**
	21 April	Vol. 49, no. 1261	**Joseph Cotten** **Claudette Colbert**
	5 May	Vol. 49, no. 1262	**Vivian Blaine** **Michael O'Shea**
	19 May	Vol. 49, no. 1263	**Laraine Day** **Alan Marshal**
	2 June	Vol. 49, no. 1264	**Judy Garland** **Robert Walker**
	16 June	Vol. 49, no. 1265	**Dorothy Lamour** **Arturo De Cordova**
	30 June	Vol. 49, no. 1266	**Spencer Tracy** **Katharine Hepburn**
	14 July	Vol. 49, no. 1267	**Lauren Bacall** **Humphrey Bogart**
	28 July	Vol. 49, no. 1268	**Alan Ladd** **Gail Russell**
	11 Aug.	Vol. 49, no. 1269	**Joseph Cotten** **Ginger Rogers**
	25 Aug.	Vol. 49, no. 1270	**Peter Graves** **Patricia Medina**
	8 Sept.	Vol. 49, no. 1271	**Sonja Henie** **Michael O'Shea**

YEAR	MONTH	REF. No.	COVER STAR
	22 Sept.	Vol. 49, no. 1272	**Gene Tierney** **John Hodiak**
	6 Oct.	Vol. 49, no. 1273	**Ginger Rogers** **Walter Pidgeon**
	20 Oct.	Vol. 49, no. 1274	**Robert Donat** **Deborah Kerr**
	3 Nov.	Vol. 50, no. 1275	**Lassie** **June Lockhart** **Peter Lawford**
	17 Nov.	Vol. 50, no. 1276	**June Allyson** **Robert Walker**
	1 Dec.	Vol. 50, no. 1277	**Fred MacMurray** **Joan Leslie**
	15 Dec.	Vol. 50, no. 1278	**Gary Cooper** **Loretta Young**
	29 Dec.	Vol. 50, no. 1279	**Fred Astaire** **Lucille Bremer**
1946	12 Jan.	Vol. 50, no. 1280	**Joseph Cotten** **Jennifer Jones**
	26 Jan.	Vol. 50, no. 1281	**Margaret Lockwood** **James Mason**
	9 Feb.	Vol. 50, no. 1282	**Esther Williams** **Van Johnson** **Tommy Dorsey**
	23 Feb.	Vol. 50, no. 1283	**Celia Johnson** **Trevor Howard**
	9 March	Vol. 50, no. 1284	**Kathryn Grayson** **Frank Sinatra** **Gene Kelly**
	23 March	Vol. 50, no. 1285	**Arturo De Cordova** **Dorothy Lamour**
	6 April	Vol. 50, no. 1286	**Maureen O'Hara** **Paul Henreid**
	20 April	Vol. 50, no. 1287	**Ingrid Bergman** **Gary Cooper**
	4 May	Vol. 50, no. 1288	**Judy Garland** **John Hodiak**
	18 May	Vol. 50, no. 1289	**Kent Taylor** **Maria Montez**
	1 June	Vol. 50, no. 1290	**Jean Kent** **Stewart Granger**
	15 June	Vol. 50, no. 1291	**Zachary Scott** **Faye Emerson**
	29 June	Vol. 50, no. 1292	**Margaret Lockwood** **Ian Hunter**
	13 July	Vol. 50, no. 1293	**Michael Redgrave** **Valerie Hobson**
	27 July	Vol. 50, no. 1294	**Mark Stevens** **Joan Fontaine**
	10 Aug.	Vol. 50, no. 1295	**Gregory Peck** **Ingrid Bergman**
	24 Aug.	Vol. 50, no. 1296	**Deborah Kerr** **Trevor Howard**
	7 Sept.	Vol. 50, no. 1297	**Olivia De Havilland** **Paul Henreid**

YEAR	MONTH	REF. No.	COVER STAR
	21 Sept.	Vol. 50, no. 1298	**Lucille Ball** **John Hodiak**
	5 Oct.	Vol. 50, no. 1299	**Merle Oberon** **Turhan Bey**
	19 Oct.	Vol. 50, no. 1300	**Fred MacMurray** **Anne Baxter**
	2 Nov.	Vol. 51, no. 1301	**Barbara Stanwyck** **Robert Cummings**
	16 Nov.	Vol. 51, no. 1302	**Donna Reed** **Tom Drake**
	30 Nov.	Vol. 51, no. 1303	**Phyllis Calvert** **Stewart Granger**
	14 Dec.	Vol. 51, no. 1304	**Guy Madison** **Dorothy McGuire**
	28 Dec.	Vol. 51, no. 1305	**Robert Taylor** **Katharine Hepburn**
1947	11 Jan.	Vol. 51, no. 1306	**Belita** **Barry Sullivan**
	25 Jan.	Vol. 51, no. 1307	**Bette Davis** **Glenn Ford**
	8 Feb.	Vol. 51, no. 1308	**Margaret Lockwood** **Dennis Price**
	22 Feb.	Vol. 51, no. 1309	**Claudette Colbert** **Walter Pidgeon**
	8/22 March	Vol. 51, nos. 1310/11	**Paulette Goddard** **Fred MacMurray**
	5 April	Vol. 51, no. 1312	**Ronald Howard** **Barbara White**
	19 April	Vol. 51, no. 1313	**Cary Grant** **Ingrid Bergman**
	3 May	Vol. 51, no. 1314	**Ginger Rogers** **David Niven**
	17 May	Vol. 51, no. 1315	**Richard Attenborough** **Jean Kent**
	31 May	Vol. 51, no. 1316	**Donna Reed** **James Stewart**
	14 June	Vol. 51, no. 1317	**Dick Haymes** **Betty Grable**
	28 June	Vol. 51, no. 1318	**Van Johnson** **June Allyson**
	12 July	Vol. 51, no. 1319	**Patricia Roc** **Maxwell Reed**
	26 July	Vol. 51, no. 1320	**Maureen O'Hara** **Cornel Wilde**
	9 Aug.	Vol. 51, no. 1321	**James Mason** **Pamela Kellino**
	23 Aug.	Vol. 51, no. 1322	**Deborah Kerr** **Clark Gable**
	6 Sept.	Vol. 51, no. 1323	**Anna Neagle** **Michael Wilding**
	20 Sept.	Vol. 51, no. 1324	**Dermot Walsh** **Margaret Lockwood**
	4 Oct.	Vol. 51, no. 1325	**John Mills** **Joan Greenwood**

YEAR	MONTH	REF. No.	COVER STAR
	18 Oct.	Vol. 51, no. 1326	**Gregory Peck** **Jennifer Jones**
	1 Nov.	Vol. 52, no. 1327	**Henry Fonda** **Barbara Bel Geddes**
	15 Nov.	Vol. 52, no. 1328	**Dennis Price** **Margaret Lockwood**
	29 Nov.	Vol. 52, no. 1329	**Kieron Moore** **Margaret Johnston**
	13 Dec.	Vol. 52, no. 1330	**Maureen O'Hara** **John Payne**
	27 Dec.	Vol. 52, no. 1331	**Gene Kelly** **Judy Garland**
1948	10 Jan.	Vol. 52, no. 1332	**Ava Gardner** **Fred MacMurray**
	24 Jan.	Vol. 52, no. 1333	**Burt Lancaster** **Lizabeth Scott**
	7 Feb.	Vol. 52, no. 1334	**Veronica Lake** **Alan Ladd**
	21 Feb.	Vol. 52, no. 1335	**Paulette Goddard** **Michael Wilding**
	6 March	Vol. 52, no. 1336	**Siobhan McKenna** **Maxwell Reed**
	20 March	Vol. 52, no. 1337	**Valerie Hobson** **Stewart Granger**
	3 April	Vol. 52, no. 1338	**Frederic March** **Myrna Loy** **Dana Andrews** **Teresa Wright** **Hoagy Carmichael**
	17 April	Vol. 52, no. 1339	**Ray Milland** **Maureen O'Sullivan**
	1 May	Vol. 52, no. 1340	**Dennis Price** **Mila Parely**
	15 May	Vol. 52, no. 1341	**Peggy Cummins** **Rex Harrison**
	29 May	Vol. 52, no. 1342	**Griffith Jones** **Glynis Johns**
	12 June	Vol. 52, no. 1343	**Susan Hayward** **Bill Williams**
	26 June	Vol. 52, no. 1344	**John McCallum** **Greta Gynt**
	10 July	Vol. 52, no. 1345	**June Allyson** **Van Johnson**
	24 July	Vol. 52, no. 1346	**Robert Young** **Maureen O'Hara** **Clifton Webb**
	7 Aug.	Vol. 52, no. 1347	**Hazel Court** **Dermot Walsh**
	21 Aug.	Vol. 52, no. 1348	**Cornel Wilde** **Ginger Rogers**
	4 Sept.	Vol. 52, no. 1349	**Robert Helpmann** **Moira Shearer** **Leonide Massine**
	18 Sept.	Vol. 52, no. 1350	**Anna Neagle** **Michael Wilding**

YEAR	MONTH	REF. No.	COVER STAR
	2 Oct.	Vol. 52, no. 1351	**Cornel Wilde** **Linda Darnell**
	16 Oct.	Vol. 52, no. 1352	**Stewart Granger** **Joan Greenwood**
	30 Oct.	Vol. 52, no. 1353	**Douglas Fairbanks Jr** **Maria Montez**
	13 Nov.	Vol. 53, no. 1354	**Clark Gable** **Lana Turner**
	27 Nov.	Vol. 53, no. 1355	**Burgess Meredith** **Paulette Goddard**
	11 Dec.	Vol. 53, no. 1356	**Jack Warner** **Susan Shaw** **Kathleen Harrison** **Petula Clark** **Jimmy Hanley** **Jane Hylton**
	25 Dec.	Vol. 53, no. 1357	**Michael Wilding** **Ingrid Bergman**
1949	8 Jan.	Vol. 53, no. 1358	**Margaret Leighton** **David Niven**
	22 Jan.	Vol. 53, no. 1359	**Mai Zetterling** **Robert Beatty**
	5 Feb.	Vol. 53, no. 1360	**Anna Neagle** **Nicholas Phipps**
	19 Feb.	Vol. 53, no. 1361	**Tyrone Power** **Anne Baxter**
	5 March	Vol. 53, no. 1362	**Ann Todd** **Gregory Peck**
	19 March	Vol. 53, no. 1363	**Greer Garson** **Walter Pidgeon**
	2 April	Vol. 53, no. 1364	**Danny Kaye** **Virginia Mayo**
	16 April	Vol. 53, no. 1365	**Ida Lupino** **Cornel Wilde**
	30 April	Vol. 53, no. 1366	**John Wayne** **Laraine Day**
	14 May	Vol. 53, no. 1367	**Margaret Lockwood** **Sid Field**
	28 May	Vol. 53, no. 1368	**David Niven** **Teresa Wright**
	11 June	Vol. 53, no. 1369	**Kathryn Grayson** **Frank Sinatra**
	25 June	Vol. 53, no. 1370	**Robert Stack** **Wanda Hendrix**
	9 July	Vol. 53, no. 1371	**Tom Drake** **Janet Leigh** **Lassie**
	16 July	Vol. 53, no. 1372	**Jeffrey Lynn** **Jeanne Crain**
	23 July	Vol. 53, no. 1373	**Barbara Stanwyck** **Robert Preston**
	30 July	Vol. 53, no. 1374	**Carol Marsh** **David Tomlinson**
	6 Aug.	Vol. 53, no. 1375	**Ann Sheridan** **Gary Cooper**

YEAR	MONTH	REF. No.	COVER STAR
	13 Aug.	Vol. 53, no. 1376	**Betty Grable** **Douglas Fairbanks Jr**
	20 Aug.	Vol. 53, no. 1377	**Mickey Rooney** **Judy Garland**
	27 Aug.	Vol. 53, no. 1378	**Peter Ustinov** **Maria Denis**
	3 Sept.	Vol. 53, no. 1379	**Paul Dupuis** **Margaret Lockwood**
	10 Sept.	Vol. 53, no. 1380	**Peggy Cummins** **Richard Greene**
	17 Sept.	Vol. 53, no. 1381	**Anna Neagle** **Michael Wilding**
	24 Sept.	Vol. 53, no. 1382	**Elizabeth Taylor** **Robert Taylor**
	1 Oct.	Vol. 53, no. 1383	**Jane Wyman** **James Stewart**
	8 Oct.	Vol. 53, no. 1384	**Laurence Olivier** **Jean Simmons**
	15 Oct.	Vol. 53, no. 1385	**Valerie Hobson** **Richard Todd**
	22 Oct.	Vol. 53, no. 1386	**Danny Kaye** **Virginia Mayo**
	29 Oct.	Vol. 53, no. 1387	**Fred Astaire** **Ginger Rogers**
	5 Nov.	Vol. 53, no. 1388	**Ronald Reagan** **Richard Todd** **Patricia Neal**
	12 Nov.	Vol. 53, no. 1389	**Errol Flynn** **Viveca Lindfors**
	19 Nov.	Vol. 53, no. 1390	**Michael Denison** **Patricia Plunket**
	26 Nov.	Vol. 53, no. 1391	**Judy Garland** **Van Johnson**
	3 Dec.	Vol. 53, no. 1392	**Glenn Ford** **Terry Moore**
	10 Dec.	Vol. 53, no. 1393	**June Allyson** **Peter Lawford**
	17 Dec.	Vol. 53, no. 1394	**Gregory Peck** **Ava Gardner**
	24 Dec.	Vol. 53, no. 1395	**Errol Flynn** **Greer Garson**
	31 Dec.	Vol. 53, no. 1396	**Bob Hope** **Rhonda Fleming**
1950	7 Jan.	Vol. 54, no. 1397	**Michael Wilding** **Ingrid Bergman** **Joseph Cotten**
	14 Jan.	Vol. 54, no. 1398	**Terry Moore** **Ben Johnson**
	21 Jan.	Vol. 54, no. 1399	**Wanda Hendrix** **Alan Ladd**
	28 Jan.	Vol. 54, no. 1400	**Mario Lanza** **Kathryn Grayson**
	4 Feb.	Vol. 54, no. 1401	**John Mills** **Valerie Hobson**
	11 Feb.	Vol. 54, no. 1402	**Louis Jourdan** **Jennifer Jones**
	18 Feb.	Vol. 54, no. 1403	**Larry Parks** **Barbara Hale**
	25 Feb.	Vol. 54, no. 1404	**Tyrone Power** **Wanda Hendrix**
	4 March	Vol. 54, no. 1405	**Rory Calhoun** **Coleen Gray**
	11 March	Vol. 54, no. 1406	**Trevor Howard** **Anouk**
	18 March	Vol. 54, no. 1407	**Ricardo Montalban** **Esther Williams**
	25 March	Vol. 54, no. 1408	**Ivan Desny** **Ann Todd**
	1 April	Vol. 54, no. 1409	**Margaret Leighton** **Noel Coward**
	8 April	Vol. 54, no. 1410	**Eleanor Parker** **Humphrey Bogart**
	15 April	Vol. 54, no. 1411	**Susan Hayward** **Dana Andrews**
	22 April	Vol. 54, no. 1412	**Sonja Henie** **Michael Kirby**
	29 April	Vol. 54, no. 1413	**Betty Grable** **Cesar Romero**
	6 May	Vol. 54, no. 1414	**Edward Underdown** **Helen Cherry**
	13 May	Vol. 54, no. 1415	**Jean Kent** **Guy Rolfe**
	20 May	Vol. 54, no. 1416	**Mario Vitale** **Ingrid Bergman**
	27 May	Vol. 54, no. 1417	**Mark Stevens** **Betsy Drake**
	3 June	Vol. 54, no. 1418	**Robert Walker** **Joan Leslie**
	10 June	Vol. 54, no. 1419	**Lon McCallister** **Shirley Temple**
	17 June	Vol. 54, no. 1420	**Robert Walker** **Ava Gardner**
	24 June	Vol. 54, no. 1421	**Barbara Stanwyck** **James Mason**
	1 July	Vol. 54, no. 1422	**Robert Taylor** **Arlene Dahl**
	8 July	Vol. 55, no. 1423	**Cathy O'Donnell** **Farley Granger**
	15 July	Vol. 55, no. 1424	**Clark Gable** **Loretta Young**
	22 July	Vol. 55, no. 1425	**Errol Flynn** **Alexis Smith**
	29 July	Vol. 55, no. 1426	**Anne Baxter** **Dan Dailey**
	5 Aug.	Vol. 55, no. 1427	**David Tomlinson** **Jean Simmons**
	12 Aug.	Vol. 55, no. 1428	**Vera-Ellen** **Gene Kelly**
	19 Aug.	Vol. 55, no. 1429	**Peggy Cummins** **Richard Greene**
	26 Aug.	Vol. 55, no. 1430	**Marlene Dietrich** **Richard Todd**
	2 Sept.	Vol. 55, no. 1431	**Dennis Price** **Gisele Preville**

YEAR	MONTH	REF. No.	COVER STAR
	9 Sept.	Vol. 55, no. 1432	**Douglas Fairbanks Jr** **Glynis Johns**
	16 Sept.	Vol. 55, no. 1433	**Barbara Bates** **Danny Kaye**
	23 Sept.	Vol. 55, no. 1434	**Tyrone Power** **Cecile Aubry**
	30 Sept.	Vol. 55, no. 1435	**Anna Neagle** **Trevor Howard**
	7 Oct.	Vol. 55, no. 1436	**Howard Keel** **Betty Hutton**
	14/21/28 Oct/4 Nov.	Vol. 55, nos. 1437/38/39/40	**Valentina Cortesa** **Richard Greene**
	11 Nov.	Vol. 55, no. 1441	**Jean Simmons** **David Farrar**
	18 Nov.	Vol. 55, no. 1442	**Sheila Manahan** **Hugh Cross**
	25 Nov.	Vol. 55, no. 1443	**Barbara Hale** **James Stewart** **Natalie Wood** **Tommy Rettig**
	2 Dec.	Vol. 55, no. 1444	**Ray Milland** **Lana Turner**
	9 Dec.	Vol. 55, no. 1445	**Linda Darnell** **Cornel Wilde**
	16 Dec.	Vol. 55, no. 1446	**Fred Astaire** **Vera-Ellen**
	23/30 Dec.	Vol. 55, nos. 1447/8	**Bing Crosby** **Nancy Olson**
1951	6 Jan.	Vol. 56, no. 1449	**Joseph Cotten** **Joan Fontaine**
	13 Jan.	Vol. 56, no. 1450	**Dane Clark** **Margaret Lockwood**
	20 Jan.	Vol. 56, no. 1451	**Bette Davis** **Gary Merrill**
	27 Jan.	Vol. 56, no. 1452	**Phyllis Calvert** **Edward Underdown**
	3 Feb.	Vol. 56, no. 1453	**Kirk Douglas** **Jane Wyman**
	10 Feb.	Vol. 56, no. 1454	**Barbara Stanwyck** **Clark Gable**
	17 Feb.	Vol. 56, no. 1455	**June Haver** **William Lundigan**
	24 Feb.	Vol. 56, no. 1456	**Alan Ladd** **Mona Freeman**
	3 March	Vol. 56, no. 1457	**James Mason** **Ava Gardner**
	10 March	Vol. 56, no. 1458	**Dulcie Gray** **Michael Denison**
	17 March	Vol. 56, no. 1459	**Errol Flynn** **Laurette Luez**
	24 March	Vol. 56, no. 1460	**Hedy Lamarr** **Victor Mature**
	31 March	Vol. 56, no. 1461	**Michael Rennie** **Constance Smith**
	7 April	Vol. 56, no. 1462	**Stewart Granger** **Ann Blyth**

YEAR	MONTH	REF. No.	COVER STAR
	14 April	Vol. 56, no. 1463	**Richard Todd** **Glynis Johns**
	21 April	Vol. 56, no. 1464	**Viveca Lindfors** **Christopher Kent**
	28 April	Vol. 56, no. 1465	**Bob Hope** **Marilyn Maxwell**
	5 May	Vol. 56, no. 1466	**Douglas Fairbanks Jr** **Yolande Donlan**
	12 May	Vol. 56, no. 1467	**Doris Day** **Gordon MacRae**
	19 May	Vol. 56, no. 1468	**Ray Milland** **Patricia Roc**
	26 May	Vol. 56, no. 1469	**Fred Astaire** **Jane Powell**
	2 June	Vol. 56, no. 1470	**Gary Cooper** **Jane Greer**
	9 June	Vol. 56, no. 1471	**Roy Rogers** **Gail Davis**
	16 June	Vol. 56, no. 1472	**Kathryn Grayson** **Mario Lanza**
	23 June	Vol. 56, no. 1473	**Joan Evans** **Farley Granger**
	30 June	Vol. 56, no. 1474	**Irene Dunne** **Fred MacMurray**
	7 July	Vol. 57, no. 1475	**Jan Sterling** **Kirk Douglas**
	14 July	Vol. 57, no. 1476	**William Lundigan** **Susan Hayward**
	21 July	Vol. 57, no. 1477	**Danny Kaye** **Gene Tierney**
	28 July	Vol. 57, no. 1478	**Louis Jourdan** **Debra Paget**
	4 Aug.	Vol. 57, no. 1479	**Yvonne De Carlo** **Peter Ustinov**
	11 Aug.	Vol. 57, no. 1480	**Marge and Gower Champion**
	18 Aug.	Vol. 57, no. 1481	**Fernando Lamas** **Jane Powell** **Vic Damone**
	25 Aug.	Vol. 57, no. 1482	**Piper Laurie** **Tony Curtis**
	1 Sept.	Vol. 57, no. 1483	**Alan Ladd** **Lizabeth Scott**
	8 Sept.	Vol. 57, no. 1484	**Vera-Ellen** **David Niven**
	15 Sept.	Vol. 57, no. 1485	**Michael Wilding** **Greer Garson** **Fernando Lamas**
	22 Sept.	Vol. 57, no. 1486	**Kathryn Grayson** **Howard Keel**
	29 Sept.	Vol. 57, no. 1487	**Gregory Peck** **Virginia Mayo**
	6 Oct.	Vol. 57, no. 1488	**Donald O'Connor** **Piper Laurie**
	13 Oct.	Vol. 57, no. 1489	**Peter Hanson** **Barbara Rush**
	20 Oct.	Vol. 57, no. 1490	**Gene Kelly** **Leslie Caron**

YEAR	MONTH	REF. No.	COVER STAR
	27 Oct.	Vol. 57, no. 1491	**David Niven** **Glynis Johns**
	3 Nov.	Vol. 57, no. 1492	**Jan Sterling** **Ray Milland**
	10 Nov.	Vol. 57, no. 1493	**Derek Farr** **Joan Greenwood** **Nigel Patrick**
	17 Nov.	Vol. 57, no. 1494	**Corinne Calvet** **Joseph Cotten**
	24 Nov.	Vol. 57, no. 1495	**Ricardo Montalban** **Cyd Charisse**
	1 Dec.	Vol. 57, no. 1496	**John Derek** **Jody Lawrance**
	8 Dec.	Vol. 57, no. 1497	**Rory Calhoun** **Betty Grable**
	15 Dec.	Vol. 57, no. 1498	**Bob Hope** **Hedy Lamarr**
	22 Dec.	Vol. 57, no. 1499	**Vera-Ellen**
	29 Dec.	Vol. 57, no. 1500	**Susan Hayward** **Gregory Peck**
1952	5 Jan.	Vol. 58, no. 1501	**Farley Granger** **Peggy Dow**
	12 Jan.	Vol. 58, no. 1502	**John McCallum** **Pauline Stroud**
	19 Jan.	Vol. 58, no. 1503	**Pier Angeli** **Stewart Granger**
	26 Jan.	Vol. 58, no. 1504	**Montgomery Clift** **Elizabeth Taylor**
	2 Feb.	Vol. 58, no. 1505	**William Talman** **Virginia Huston**
	9 Feb.	Vol. 58, no. 1506	**Elizabeth Taylor** **Larry Parks**
	16 Feb.	Vol. 58, no. 1507	**Louis Jourdan** **Jean Peters**
	23 Feb.	Vol. 58, no. 1508	**Joan Fontaine** **Ray Milland**
	1 March	Vol. 58, no. 1509	**Kerima** **Trevor Howard**
	8 March	Vol. 58, no. 1510	**Humphrey Bogart** **Katharine Hepburn**
	15 March	Vol. 58, no. 1511	**Mitzi Gaynor** **Dale Robertson**
	22 March	Vol. 58, no. 1512	**Donna Reed** **John Derek**
	29 March	Vol. 58, no. 1513	**Betty Hutton** **Cornel Wilde**
	5 April	Vol. 58, no. 1514	**Constance Smith** **Richard Widmark**
	12 April	Vol. 58, no. 1515	**Joan Rice** **Richard Todd**
	19 April	Vol. 58, no. 1516	**Linda Darnell** **Tab Hunter**
	26 April	Vol. 58, no. 1517	**Marlon Brando** **Jean Peters**
	3 May	Vol. 58, no. 1518	**Debbie Reynolds** **Gene Kelly**

YEAR	MONTH	REF. No.	COVER STAR
	10 May	Vol. 58, no. 1519	**Victor Mature** **Jane Russell**
	17 May	Vol. 58, no. 1520	**Doris Day** **Gordon MacRae**
	24 May	Vol. 58, no. 1521	**Jeff Chandler** **Susan Cabot**
	31 May	Vol. 58, no. 1522	**Rod Cameron** **Adele Mara**
	7 June	Vol. 58, no. 1523	**Alan Young** **Dinah Shore**
	14 June	Vol. 58, no. 1524	**Edward Underdown** **Claude Farell**
	21 June	Vol. 58, no. 1525	**Joan Crawford** **Dennis Morgan**
	28 June	Vol. 58, no. 1526	**Howard Keel** **Dorothy McGuire** **Fred MacMurray**
	5 July	Vol. 59, no. 1527	**Susan Stephen** **Brian Worth**
	12 July	Vol. 59, no. 1528	**Stewart Granger** **Cyd Charisse**
	19 July	Vol. 59, no. 1529	**John Wayne** **Maureen O'Hara**
	26 July	Vol. 59, no. 1530	**George Cole** **Peggy Cummins**
	2 Aug.	Vol. 59, no. 1531	**Laurence Olivier** **Jennifer Jones**
	9 Aug.	Vol. 59, no. 1532	**Joan Rice** **James Donald**
	16 Aug.	Vol. 59, no. 1533	**Ruth Roman** **Errol Flynn**
	23 Aug.	Vol. 59, no. 1534	**Ginger Rogers** **Fred Allen**
	30 Aug.	Vol. 59, no. 1535	**Anna Neagle**
	6 Sept.	Vol. 59, no. 1536	**Elizabeth Taylor** **Robert Taylor**
	13 Sept.	Vol. 59, no. 1537	**Judy Holliday** **Aldo Ray**
	20 Sept.	Vol. 59, no. 1538	**Rita Hayworth** **Glenn Ford**
	27 Sept.	Vol. 59, no. 1539	**Gregory Peck** **Ann Blyth**
	4 Oct.	Vol. 59, no. 1540	**Bing Crosby** **Jane Wyman**
	11 Oct.	Vol. 59, no. 1541	**Valerie Hobson** **Nigel Patrick**
	18 Oct.	Vol. 59, no. 1542	**Constance Smith** **Jeffrey Hunter**
	25 Oct.	Vol. 59, no. 1543	**Jack Hawkins** **Claudette Colbert**
	1 Nov.	Vol. 59, no. 1544	**Richard Todd** **Merle Oberon**
	8 Nov.	Vol. 59, no. 1545	**Richard Todd** **Eva Bartok**
	15 Nov.	Vol. 59, no. 1546	**Lana Turner** **Fernando Lamas**
	22 Nov.	Vol. 59, no. 1547	**Peter Hammond** **Susan Stephen**

YEAR	MONTH	REF. No.	COVER STAR
	29 Nov.	Vol. 59, no. 1548	**Gary Merrill**
			Linda Darnell
	6 Dec.	Vol. 59, no. 1549	**Fred MacMurray**
			Eleanor Parker
	13 Dec.	Vol. 59, no. 1550	**Jeff Chandler**
			Suzan Ball
	20 Dec.	Vol. 59, no. 1551	**Marge and Gower Champion**
	27 Dec.	Vol. 59, no. 1552	**Danny Kaye**
			Jeanmaire
1953	3 Jan.	Vol. 60, no. 1553	**Lilli Palmer**
			Rex Harrison
	10 Jan.	Vol. 60, no. 1554	**Valerie Hobson**
			Edward Underdown
	17 Jan.	Vol. 60, no. 1555	**Ricardo Montalban**
			Shelley Winters
	24 Jan.	Vol. 60, no. 1556	**Alan Ladd**
			Patricia Medina
	31 Jan.	Vol. 60, no. 1557	**Margaret Lockwood**
			Michael Wilding
	7 Feb.	Vol. 60, no. 1558	**Gregory Peck**
			Ava Gardner
	14 Feb.	Vol. 60, no. 1559	**Louis Jourdan**
			Joan Fontaine
	21 Feb.	Vol. 60, no. 1560	**John Mills**
			Eva Bergh
	28 Feb.	Vol. 60, no. 1561	**Richard Burton**
			Olivia De Havilland
	7 March	Vol. 60, no. 1562	**Van Johnson**
			Dawn Addams
	14 March	Vol. 60, no. 1563	**Dirk Bogarde**
			Dinah Sheridan
	21 March	Vol. 60, no. 1564	**Robert Taylor**
			Eleanor Parker
	28 March	Vol. 60, no. 1565	**Van Heflin**
			Eric Portman
			Wanda Hendrix
	4 April	Vol. 60, no. 1566	**Doris Day**
			Ray Bolger
	11 April	Vol. 60, no. 1567	**Constance Smith**
			Cornel Wilde
	18 April	Vol. 60, no. 1568	**Alan Ladd**
			Arlene Dahl
	25 April	Vol. 60, no. 1569	**Virginia McKenna**
			Donald Sinden
	2 May	Vol. 60, no. 1570	**Mitzi Gaynor**
			Bob Graham
	9 May	Vol. 60, no. 1571	**James Stewart**
			Janet Leigh
	16 May	Vol. 60, no. 1572	**Rock Hudson**
			Yvonne De Carlo
	23 May	Vol. 60, no. 1573	**Kirk Douglas**
			Pier Angeli
	30 May	Vol. 60, no. 1574	**Queen Elizabeth II**

YEAR	MONTH	REF. No.	COVER STAR
	6 June	Vol. 60, no. 1575	**Gene Tierney**
			Clark Gable
	13 June	Vol. 60, no. 1576	**Glenn Ford**
			Anne Vernon
	20 June	Vol. 60, no. 1577	**Fred MacMurray**
			Vera Ralston
	27 June	Vol. 60, no. 1578	**Betty Grable**
			Dale Robertson
	4 July	Vol. 61, no. 1579	**Kay Kendall**
			Cesar Romero
	11 July	Vol. 61, no. 1580	**Arlene Dahl**
			Ray Milland
	18 July	Vol. 61, no. 1581	**William Holden**
			Ginger Rogers
			Paul Douglas
	25 July	Vol. 61, no. 1582	**Wendy Hiller**
			Michael Rennie
	1 Aug.	Vol. 61, no. 1583	**Yvonne De Carlo**
			Alec Guinness
	8 Aug.	Vol. 61, no. 1584	**Jean Simmons**
			Stewart Granger
	15 Aug.	Vol. 61, no. 1585	**Jeanmaire**
			Farley Granger
			Danny Kaye
	22 Aug.	Vol. 61, no. 1586	**Dinah Sheridan**
			John Gregson
			Kenneth More
			Kay Kendall
	29 Aug.	Vol. 61, no. 1587	**Kirk Douglas**
			Molly Vitale
	5 Sept.	Vol. 61, no. 1588	**Stewart Granger**
			Rita Hayworth
	12 Sept.	Vol. 61, no. 1589	**Leslie Caron**
			Mel Ferrer
	19 Sept.	Vol. 61, no. 1590	**Peggy Cummins**
			Terence Morgan
	26 Sept.	Vol. 61, no. 1591	**Robert Taylor**
			Deborah Kerr
	3 Oct.	Vol. 61, no. 1592	**Audrey Hepburn**
			Gregory Peck
	10 Oct.	Vol. 61, no. 1593	**John McCallum**
			Patrice Munsel
	17 Oct.	Vol. 61, no. 1594	**Margaret Lockwood**
			Wendell Corey
	24 Oct.	Vol. 61, no. 1595	**Richard Todd**
			Glynis Johns
	31 Oct.	Vol. 61, no. 1596	**Errol Flynn**
			Beatrice Campbell
	7 Nov.	Vol. 61, no. 1597	**Valerie Hobson**
			Philip Friend
	14 Nov.	Vol. 61, no. 1598	**Claire Bloom**
			James Mason
	21 Nov.	Vol. 61, no. 1599	**Glenn Ford**
			Julia Adams
	28 Nov.	Vol. 61, no. 1600	**Debbie Reynolds**
			Bobby Van
	5 Dec.	Vol. 61, no. 1601	**Mari Blanchard**
			Victor Mature

YEAR	MONTH	REF. No.	COVER STAR
	12 Dec.	Vol. 61, no. 1602	**Jeanne Crain** **Elliott Reid**
	19 Dec.	Vol. 61, no. 1603	**Esther Williams** **Fernando Lamas**
	26 Dec.	Vol. 61, no. 1604	**Tony Curtis** **Janet Leigh**
1954	2 Jan.	Vol. 62, no. 1605	**Ricardo Montalban** **Lana Turner**
	9 Jan.	Vol. 62, no. 1606	**Clark Gable** **Ava Gardner**
	16 Jan.	Vol. 62, no. 1607	**Charlton Heston** **Mary Sinclair**
	23 Jan.	Vol. 62, no. 1608	**Piper Laurie** **Rock Hudson**
	30 Jan.	Vol. 62, no. 1609	**Deborah Kerr** **Burt Lancaster**
	6 Feb.	Vol. 62, no. 1610	**Robert Taylor** **Ann Blyth** **Stewart Granger**
	13 Feb.	Vol. 62, no. 1611	**Gregory Peck** **Jane Griffiths**
	20 Feb.	Vol. 62, no. 1612	**Fred Astaire** **Cyd Charisse**
	27 Feb.	Vol. 62, no. 1613	**Julia Adams** **Stephen McNally**
	6 March	Vol. 62, no. 1614	**June Allyson** **James Stewart**
	13 March	Vol. 62, no. 1615	**David Niven** **Peggy Cummins**
	20 March	Vol. 62, no. 1616	**Doris Day** **Howard Keel**
	27 March	Vol. 62, no. 1617	**Vera Ralston** **John Russell** **Joan Leslie**
	3 April	Vol. 62, no. 1618	**Cornel Wilde** **Jean Wallace**
	10 April	Vol. 62, no. 1619	**Margaret Leighton** **Laurence Harvey**
	17 April	Vol. 62, no. 1620	**Kathryn Grayson** **Howard Keel**
	24 April	Vol. 62, no. 1621	**Gene Barry** **Joanne Gilbert**
	1 May	Vol. 62, no. 1622	**Kenneth More** **Suzanne Cloutier**
	8 May	Vol. 62, no. 1623	**Bob Hope** **Joan Fontaine** **Basil Rathbone**
	15 May	Vol. 62, no. 1624	**Van Johnson** **Esther Williams**
	22 May	Vol. 62, no. 1625	**Barbara Stanwyck** **Gary Merrill**
	29 May	Vol. 62, no. 1626	**Janet Leigh** **Robert Wagner**
	5 June	Vol. 62, no. 1627	**Lucille Ball** **Desi Arnaz**
	12 June	Vol. 62, no. 1628	**Danny Kaye** **Mai Zetterling**
	19 June	Vol. 62, no. 1629	**Anne Baxter** **Lyle Bettger**
	26 June	Vol. 62, no. 1630	**Aldo Ray** **Rita Hayworth**
	3 July	Vol. 63, no. 1631	**Marge and Gower Champion**
	10 July	Vol. 63, no. 1632	**William Holden** **Eleanor Parker**
	17 July	Vol. 63, no. 1633	**Joan Crawford** **Sterling Hayden**
	24 July	Vol. 63, no. 1634	**Betta St John** **Ricardo Montalban**
	31 July	Vol. 63, no. 1635	**Shirley Booth** **Robert Ryan**
	7 Aug.	Vol. 63, no. 1636	**Yvonne De Carlo** **Barry Fitzgerald** **David Niven**
	14 Aug.	Vol. 63, no. 1637	**Maureen O'Hara** **Macdonald Carey**
	21 Aug.	Vol. 63, no. 1638	**Debbie Reynolds** **Dick Powell**
	28 Aug.	Vol. 63, no. 1639	**Ray Milland** **Grace Kelly**
	4 Sept.	Vol. 63, no. 1640	**Elizabeth Taylor** **Peter Finch**
	11 Sept.	Vol. 63, no. 1641	**Jack Hawkins** **Glynis Johns**
	18 Sept.	Vol. 63, no. 1642	**Maggie McNamara** **Louis Jourdan**
	25 Sept.	Vol. 63, no. 1643	**Marilyn Monroe** **Robert Mitchum**
	2 Oct.	Vol. 63, no. 1644	**Lisa Gaye** **Audie Murphy**
	9 Oct.	Vol. 63, no. 1645	**Ava Gardner** **Robert Taylor**
	16 Oct.	Vol. 63, no. 1646	**Odile Versois** **David Knight**
	23 Oct.	Vol. 63, no. 1647	**William Holden** **Audrey Hepburn**
	30 Oct.	Vol. 63, no. 1648	**Susan Shentall** **Laurence Harvey**
	6 Nov.	Vol. 63, no. 1649	**Eva Marie Saint** **Marlon Brando**
	13 Nov.	Vol. 63, no. 1650	**Tony Curtis** **Janet Leigh**
	20 Nov.	Vol. 63, no. 1651	**Dirk Bogarde** **Susan Stephen**
	27 Nov.	Vol. 63, no. 1652	**Ronald Shiner** **Margaret Rutherford**
	4 Dec.	Vol. 63, no. 1653	**Shelley Winters** **John Gregson**
	11 Dec.	Vol. 63, no. 1654	**Robert Wagner** **Jean Peters**
	18 Dec.	Vol. 63, no. 1655	**Gary Cooper** **Susan Hayward**
	25 Dec.	Vol. 63, no. 1656	**Bing Crosby** **Vera-Ellen**

YEAR	MONTH	REF. No.	COVER STAR
	25 Dec. (cont.)		Rosemary Clooney Danny Kaye
1955	1 Jan.	Vol. 64, no. 1657	Elizabeth Taylor Stewart Granger
	8 Jan.	Vol. 64, no. 1658	Virginia Mayo Laurence Harvey
	15 Jan.	Vol. 64, no. 1659	Terence Morgan Hildegarde Neff
	22 Jan.	Vol. 64, no. 1660	Norman Wisdom Joan Rice
	29 Jan.	Vol. 64, no. 1661	Errol Flynn Anna Neagle
	5 Feb.	Vol. 64, no. 1662	Linda Darnell Rick Jason
	12 Feb.	Vol. 64, no. 1663	William Holden Grace Kelly
	19 Feb.	Vol. 64, no. 1664	Odile Versois Alec Guinness
	26 Feb.	Vol. 64, no. 1665	Howard Keel Jane Powell
	5 March	Vol. 64, no. 1666	Dorothy Dandridge Harry Belafonte
	12 March	Vol. 64, no. 1667	Alan Ladd Audrey Dalton
	19 March	Vol. 64, no. 1668	David Knight Margo Lorenz
	26 March	Vol. 64, no. 1669	Jane Russell Richard Egan
	2 April	Vol. 64, no. 1670	Grace Kelly Stewart Granger
	9 April	Vol. 64, no. 1671	Marlon Brando Jean Simmons
	16 April	Vol. 64, no. 1672	Doris Day Frank Sinatra
	23 April	Vol. 64, no. 1673	Bing Crosby Grace Kelly
	30 April	Vol. 64, no. 1674	Elaine Stewart John Derek
	7 May	Vol. 64, no. 1675	Rock Hudson Barbara Rush
	14 May	Vol. 64, no. 1676	Jean Peters Richard Todd
	21 May	Vol. 64, no. 1677	Rex Harrison Kay Kendall
	28 May	Vol. 64, no. 1678	Tyrone Power Susan Hayward
	4 June	Vol. 64, no. 1679	James Mason Judy Garland
	11 June	Vol. 64, no. 1680	Robert Taylor Eleanor Parker
	18 June	Vol. 64, no. 1681	Tony Curtis Colleen Miller
	25 June	Vol. 64, no. 1682	Richard Burton Maggie McNamara
	2 July	Vol. 65, no. 1683	Gene Kelly Cyd Charisse

YEAR	MONTH	REF. No.	COVER STAR
	9 July	Vol. 65, no. 1684	Charlton Heston Donna Reed
	16 July	Vol. 65, no. 1685	Rock Hudson Anne Baxter
	23 July	Vol. 65, no. 1686	Virginia Leith Richard Egan
	30 July	Vol. 65, no. 1687	Peter Finch Joanne Dru Errol Flynn
	6 Aug.	Vol. 65, no. 1688	Fred Astaire Leslie Caron
	13 Aug.	Vol. 65, no. 1689	June Allyson James Stewart
	20 Aug.	Vol. 65, no. 1690	Joe Robinson Diana Dors
	27 Aug.	Vol. 65, no. 1691	John Wayne Lana Turner
	3 Sept.	Vol. 65, no. 1692	Eleanor Parker Glenn Ford
	10 Sept.	Vol. 65, no. 1693	Marilyn Monroe Tom Ewell
	17 Sept.	Vol. 65, no. 1694	Jean Simmons Stewart Granger
	24 Sept.	Vol. 65, no. 1695	John Gregson Susan Stephen
	1 Oct.	Vol. 65, no. 1696	Kirk Douglas Silvano Mangano
	8 Oct.	Vol. 65, no. 1697	Dirk Bogarde Margaret Lockwood
	15 Oct.	Vol. 65, no. 1698	James Dean Julie Harris
	22 Oct.	Vol. 65, no. 1699	Betty Garrett Jack Lemmon
	29 Oct.	Vol. 65, no. 1700	Charlton Heston Jane Wyman
	5 Nov.	Vol. 65, no. 1701	Margaret Johnston Jack Hawkins
	12 Nov.	Vol. 65, no. 1702	Katharine Hepburn Rossano Brazzi
	19 Nov.	Vol. 65, no. 1703	Jeanne Crain George Nader
	26 Nov.	Vol. 65, no. 1704	Shirley Yamaguchi Robert Ryan Robert Stack
	3 Dec.	Vol. 65, no. 1705	Robert Cummings Betty Grable
	10 Dec.	Vol. 65, no. 1706	Leslie Caron Michael Wilding
	17 Dec.	Vol. 65, no. 1707	Richard Todd Joan Collins
	24 Dec.	Vol. 65, no. 1708	Alan Ladd June Allyson
	31 Dec.	Vol. 65, no. 1709	Gene Kelly Cyd Charisse Michael Kidd Dolores Gray Dan Dailey

YEAR	MONTH	REF. No.	COVER STAR
1956	7 Jan.	Vol. 66, no. 1710	**Mel Ferrer** **Anton Walbrook** **Ludmilla Tcherina** **Michael Redgrave**
	14 Jan.	Vol. 66, no. 1711	**William Holden** **Jennifer Jones**
	21 Jan.	Vol. 66 no. 1712	**Peter Finch** **Glynis Johns**
	28 Jan.	Vol. 66, no. 1713	**Anna Neagle** **Errol Flynn**
	4 Feb.	Vol. 66, no. 1714	**Frank Sinatra** **Debbie Reynolds**
	11 Feb.	Vol. 66, no. 1715	**Dorothy McGuire** **Glenn Ford**
	18 Feb.	Vol. 66, no. 1716	**Joan Collins** **Farley Granger**
	25 Feb.	Vol. 66, no. 1717	**Donna Reed** **Steve Allen**
	3/10/17/24/ 31 March 7/14 April	Vol. 66, nos. 1718/19/20/21/ 22/23/24	**Laurence Olivier** **Claire Bloom**
	21 April	Vol. 66, no. 1725	**Grace Kelly**
	28 April	Vol. 66, no. 1726	**Anne Francis** **Cornel Wilde** **Michael Wilding**
	5 May	Vol. 66, no. 1727	**George Baker** **Belinda Lee**
	12 May	Vol. 66, no. 1728	**Kathryn Grayson** **Oreste**
	19 May	Vol. 66, no. 1729	**Max Bygraves** **Patricia Driscoll**
	26 May	Vol. 66, no. 1730	**Grace Kelly** **Alec Guinness**
	2 June	Vol. 66, no. 1731	**Shirley Jones** **Gordon MacRae**
	9 June	Vol. 66, no. 1732	**Arlene Dahl** **Phil Carey**
	16 June	Vol. 66, no. 1733	**Guy Rolfe** **Phyllis Calvert** **Patrick Barr**
	23 June	Vol. 66, no. 1734	**Van Johnson** **Jane Wyman**
	30 June	Vol. 66, no. 1735	**Walter Pidgeon** **Anne Francis** **Paul Newman**
	7 July	Vol. 67, no. 1736	**George Nader** **Virginia Mayo**
	14 July	Vol. 67, no. 1737	**Jody Lawrance** **John Derek**
	21 July	Vol. 67, no. 1738	**Denholm Elliott** **Susan Stephen**
	28 July	Vol. 67, no. 1739	**Tyrone Power** **Kim Novak**
	4 Aug.	Vol. 67, no. 1740	**Burt Lancaster** **Gina Lollobrigida** **Tony Curtis**
	11 Aug.	Vol. 67, no. 1741	**Gregory Peck** **Jennifer Jones**

YEAR	MONTH	REF. No.	COVER STAR
	18 Aug.	Vol. 67, no. 1742	**Katharine Hepburn** **Bob Hope**
	25 Aug.	Vol. 67, no. 1743	**Dana Wynter** **Richard Todd**
	1 Sept.	Vol. 67, no. 1744	**Ava Gardner** **Stewart Granger**
	8 Sept.	Vol. 67, no. 1745	**Gordon MacRae** **Shirley Jones**
	15 Sept.	Vol. 67, no. 1746	**Deborah Kerr** **Yul Brynner**
	22 Sept.	Vol. 67, no. 1747	**Jean Simmons** **Marlon Brando**
	29 Sept.	Vol. 67, no. 1748	**Terence Morgan** **Mylene Nicole***
	6 Oct.	Vol. 67, no. 1749	**James Mason** **Barbara Rush**
	13 Oct.	Vol. 67, no. 1750	**Marilyn Monroe** **Don Murray**
	20 Oct.	Vol. 67, no. 1751	**David Niven** **Genevieve Page**
	27 Oct.	Vol. 67, no. 1752	**June Allyson** **Jack Lemmon**
	3 Nov.	Vol. 67, no. 1753	**John Gregson** **Anthony Quayle** **Bernard Lee** **Ian Hunter** **Peter Finch**
	10 Nov.	Vol. 67, no. 1754	**Glynis Johns** **Rossano Brazzi**
	17 Nov.	Vol. 67, no. 1755	**Bob Hope** **Eva Marie Saint**
	24 Nov.	Vol. 67, no. 1756	**Donald Sinden** **Muriel Pavlow**
	1 Dec.	Vol. 67, no. 1757	**Mel Ferrer** **Audrey Hepburn**
	8 Dec.	Vol. 67, no. 1758	**Mark Richman** **Phyllis Love**
	15 Dec.	Vol. 67, no. 1759	**Odile Versois** **Anthony Steel**
	22 Dec.	Vol. 67, no. 1760	**Bing Crosby** **Grace Kelly** **Frank Sinatra** **Celeste Holm**
	29 Dec.	Vol. 67, no. 1761	**Martin and Lewis** **Pat Crowley**
1957	5 Jan.	Vol. 68, no. 1762	**William Holden** **Virginia Leith**
	12 Jan.	Vol. 68, no. 1763	**Rock Hudson** **Elizabeth Taylor**
	19 Jan.	Vol. 68 no. 1764	**Michael Rennie** **Ginger Rogers**
	26 Jan.	Vol. 68, no. 1765	**Anita Ekberg** **Victor Mature**
	2 Feb.	Vol. 68, no. 1766	**Rock Hudson** **Martha Hyer**

*Later known as Mylene Demongeot.

YEAR	MONTH	REF. No.	COVER STAR
	9 Feb.	Vol. 68, no. 1767	**Katharine Hepburn** **Burt Lancaster**
	16 Feb.	Vol. 68, no. 1768	**Janette Scott** **John Fraser**
	23 Feb.	Vol. 68, no. 1769	**Sal Mineo** **Susan Volkman**
	2 March	Vol. 68, no. 1770	**Helen Hayes** **Yul Brynner** **Ingrid Bergman**
	9 March	Vol. 68, no. 1771	**Jennifer Jones** **Bill Travers**
	16 March	Vol. 68, no. 1772	**Donald Sinden** **Muriel Pavlow** **Dirk Bogarde**
	23 March	Vol. 68, no. 1773	**Jack Hawkins** **Arlene Dahl**
	30 March	Vol. 68, no. 1774	**Doris Day** **Louis Jourdan**
	6 April	Vol. 68, no. 1775	**Betta St John** **William Sylvester**
	13 April	Vol. 68, no. 1776	**Ann Todd** **Michael Redgrave**
	20 April	Vol. 68, no. 1777	**Gregory Peck** **Lauren Bacall**
	27 April	Vol. 68, no. 1778	**Fred Astaire** **Audrey Hepburn**
	4 May	Vol. 68, no. 1779	**Virginia Mayo** **Alan Ladd**
	11 May	Vol. 68, no. 1780	**Tony Martin** **Vera-Ellen** **Rhonda Fleming**
	18 May	Vol. 68, no. 1781	**Alan Ladd** **Sophia Loren**
	25 May	Vol. 68, no. 1782	**Bill Travers** **Virginia McKenna**
	1 June	Vol. 68, no. 1783	**Machiko Kyo** **Marlon Brando** **Glenn Ford**
	8 June	Vol. 68, no. 1784	**Robert Mitchum** **Rita Hayworth** **Jack Lemmon**
	15 June	Vol. 68, no. 1785	**Kieron Moore** **Diane Cilento**
	22 June	Vol. 68, no. 1786	**Jean Seberg** **Richard Todd**
	29 June	Vol. 68, no. 1787	**Clark Gable** **Vivien Leigh**
	6 July	Vol. 69, no. 1788	**Laurence Olivier** **Marilyn Monroe**
	13 July	Vol. 69, no. 1789	**Shirley MacLaine** **David Niven** **Cantinflas**
	20 July	Vol. 69, no. 1790	**Trevor Howard** **Elsa Martinelli**
	27 July	Vol. 69, no. 1791	**Joan Collins** **Stephen Boyd**
	3 Aug.	Vol. 69, no. 1792	**Fred Astaire** **Cyd Charisse**

YEAR	MONTH	REF. No.	COVER STAR
	10 Aug.	Vol. 69, no. 1793	**Audrey Hepburn** **Gary Cooper**
	17 Aug.	Vol. 69, no. 1794	**Heather Sears** **Lee Patterson**
	24 Aug.	Vol. 69, no. 1795	**Deborah Kerr** **John Kerr**
	31 Aug.	Vol. 69, no. 1796	**Wendell Corey** **Lizabeth Scott** **Elvis Presley**
	7 Sept.	Vol. 69, no. 1797	**Cary Grant** **Deborah Kerr**
	14 Sept.	Vol. 69, no. 1798	**Frankie Vaughan** **Carole Lesley**
	21 Sept.	Vol. 69, no. 1799	**Dirk Bogarde** **Barbara Murray**
	28 Sept.	Vol. 69, no. 1800	**Stephen Boyd** **Anna Gaylor**
	5 Oct.	Vol. 69, no. 1801	**Tony Randall** **Jayne Mansfield**
	12 Oct.	Vol. 69, no. 1802	**Cary Grant** **Sophia Loren** **Frank Sinatra**
	19 Oct.	Vol. 69, no. 1803	**June Allyson** **David Niven**
	26 Oct.	Vol. 69, no. 1804	**David Niven** **Ava Gardner** **Stewart Granger**
	2 Nov.	Vol. 69, no. 1805	**Ian Carmichael** **Sharon Acker**
	9 Nov.	Vol. 69, no. 1806	**Gene Kelly** **Mitzi Gaynor** **Kay Kendall** **Taina Elg**
	16 Nov.	Vol. 69, no. 1807	**Natalie Wood** **Efrem Zimbalist Jr**
	23 Nov.	Vol. 69, no. 1808	**Don Murray** **Eva Marie Saint**
	30 Nov.	Vol. 69, no. 1809	**Debra Paget** **John Derek**
	7 Dec.	Vol. 69, no. 1810	**Jeanne Crain** **Frank Sinatra**
	14 Dec.	Vol. 69, no. 1811	**Tony Britton** **Sylvia Syms**
	21 Dec.	Vol. 69, no. 1812	**Doris Day** **John Raitt**
	28 Dec.	Vol. 69, no. 1813	**Ingrid Bergman** **Cary Grant**
1958	4 Jan.	Vol. 70, no. 1814	**Ann Blyth** **Paul Newman**
	11 Jan.	Vol. 70, no. 1815	**Judy Meredith** **John Saxon**
	18 Jan.	Vol. 70, no. 1816	**Louis Jourdan** **Belinda Lee**
	25 Jan.	Vol. 70, no. 1817	**Peter Finch** **Mary Ure**

YEAR	MONTH	REF. No.	COVER STAR
	1 Feb.	Vol. 70, no. 1818	**Terry-Thomas** **Shirley Eaton** **Georgina Cookson**
	8 Feb.	Vol. 70, no. 1819	**Adele Leigh** **Harry Secombe**
	15 Feb.	Vol. 70, no. 1820	**Cary Grant** **Jayne Mansfield**
	22 Feb.	Vol. 70, no. 1821	**Jack Lemmon** **Anna Kashfi**
	1 March	Vol. 70, no. 1822	**Judy Tyler** **Elvis Presley**
	8 March	Vol. 70, no. 1823	**Janette Scott** **Ian Carmichael**
	15 March	Vol. 70, no. 1824	**Richard Todd** **Juliette Greco**
	22 March	Vol. 70, no. 1825	**Dirk Bogarde** **Dorothy Tutin**
	29 March	Vol. 70, no. 1826	**Anna Magnani** **Anthony Franciosa**
	5 April	Vol. 70, no. 1827	**Virginia McKenna** **Alain Saury**
	12 April	Vol. 70, no. 1828	**Marlon Brando** **Miiko Taka**
	19 April	Vol. 70, no. 1829	**June Laverick** **Tommy Steele**
	26 April	Vol. 70, no. 1830	**Rossano Brazzi** **Mitzi Gaynor**
	3 May	Vol. 70, no. 1831	**Diane Varsi** **Russ Tamblyn**
	10 May	Vol. 70, no. 1832	**Giorgia Moll** **Audie Murphy**
	17 May	Vol. 70, no. 1833	**Doris Day** **Clark Gable**
	24 May	Vol. 70, no. 1834	**Mario Lanza** **Marisa Allasio**
	31 May	Vol. 70, no. 1835	**Lili Gentle** **Tommy Sands**
	7 June	Vol. 70, no. 1836	**Dan Duryea** **Patty McCormack** **Mary Fickett**
	14 June	Vol. 70, no. 1837	**Susan Strasberg** **Henry Fonda**
	21 June	Vol. 70, no. 1838	**Glenn Ford** **Shirley MacLaine**
	28 June	Vol. 70, no. 1839	**Natalie Wood** **Gene Kelly**
	5 July	Vol. 71, no. 1840	**Gary Cooper** **Suzy Parker**
	12 July	Vol. 71, no. 1841	**Mel Ferrer** **Dana Wynter**
	19 July	Vol. 71, no. 1842	**Clint Walker** **Virginia Mayo**
	26 July	Vol. 71, no. 1843	**Yul Brynner** **Maria Schell**
	2 Aug.	Vol. 71, no. 1844	**William Holden** **Sophia Loren**
	9 Aug.	Vol. 71, no. 1845	**Sylvia Syms** **George Baker**

YEAR	MONTH	REF. No.	COVER STAR
	16 Aug.	Vol. 71, no. 1846	**Yoko Tani** **Dirk Bogarde**
	23 Aug.	Vol. 71, no. 1847	**Betsy Drake** **Richard Todd**
	30 Aug.	Vol. 71, no. 1848	**Kim Novak** **James Stewart**
	6 Sept.	Vol. 71, no. 1849	**Belinda Lee** **Michael Craig**
	13 Sept.	Vol. 71, no. 1850	**Frankie Vaughan** **Jackie Lane**
	20 Sept.	Vol. 71, no. 1851	**Elizabeth Taylor** **Montgomery Clift**
	27 Sept.	Vol. 71, no. 1852	**Elvis Presley**
	4 Oct.	Vol. 71, no. 1853	**Pier Angeli** **Danny Kaye**
	11 Oct.	Vol. 71, no. 1854	**Kieron Moore**
	18 Oct.	Vol. 71, no. 1855	**Joan Fontaine** **Rossano Brazzi**
	25 Oct.	Vol. 71, no. 1856	**Cary Grant** **Ingrid Bergman**
	1 Nov.	Vol. 71, no. 1857	**Virginia McKenna** **Bill Travers**
	8 Nov.	Vol. 71, no. 1858	**May Britt** **Robert Mitchum**
	15 Nov.	Vol. 71, no. 1859	**John Wayne** **Eiko Ando**
	22 Nov.	Vol. 71, no. 1860	**Frankie Vaughan** **Dirk Bogarde** **Elvis Presley** **Marlon Brando**
	29 Nov.	Vol. 71, no. 1861	**Paul Newman** **Elizabeth Taylor**
	6 Dec.	Vol. 71, no. 1862	**Tony Britton** **Vanessa Redgrave**
	13 Dec.	Vol. 71, no. 1863	**Jennifer Jayne** **Forrest Tucker**
	20 Dec.	Vol. 71, no. 1864	**John Saxon** **Sandra Dee**
	27 Dec.	Vol. 71, no. 1865	**Kenneth More** **Jayne Mansfield**
1959	3 Jan.	Vol. 72, no. 1866	**Linda Cristal**
	10 Jan.	Vol. 72, no. 1867	**Bob Fosse** **Gwen Verdon**
	17 Jan.	Vol. 72, no. 1868	**Gary Cooper** **Julie London**
	24 Jan.	Vol. 72, no. 1869	**Ingrid Bergman** **Curt Jurgens**
	31 Jan.	Vol. 72, no. 1870	**Sophia Loren** **Cary Grant**
	7 Feb.	Vol. 72, no. 1871	**Pat Boone**
	14 Feb.	Vol. 72, no. 1872	**June Allyson** **Jeff Chandler**
	21 Feb.	Vol. 72, no. 1873	**Robert Taylor** **Cyd Charisse**
	28 Feb.	Vol. 72, no. 1874	**Juliette Greco** **Trevor Howard**

YEAR	MONTH	REF. No.	COVER STAR
	7 March	Vol. 72, no. 1875	**Leslie Caron**
			Louis Jourdan
	14 March	Vol. 72, no. 1876	**Elizabeth Mueller**
			Robert Mitchum
	21 March	Vol. 72, no. 1877	**Frankie Vaughan**
			Janette Scott
	28 March	Vol. 72, no. 1878	**Joanne Woodward**
			Paul Newman
	4 April	Vol. 72, no. 1879	**Gary Cooper**
			Maria Schell
	11 April	Vol. 72, no. 1880	**Heather Sears**
			Laurence Harvey
	18 April	Vol. 72, no. 1881	**Yul Brynner**
			Deborah Kerr
	25 April	Vol. 72, no. 1882	**Don Murray**
	2 May	Vol. 72, no. 1883	**Dirk Bogarde**
	9 May	Vol. 72, no. 1884	**Ricky Nelson**
	16 May	Vol. 72, no. 1885	**John Gavin**
			Lana Turner
	23 May	Vol. 72, no. 1886	**Shirley MacLaine**
			Frank Sinatra
	30 May	Vol. 72, no. 1887	**Victor Mature**
	6 June	Vol. 72, no. 1888	**John Saxon**
	13 June	Vol. 72, no. 1889	**Rossano Brazzi**
			Deborah Kerr
	20 June	Vol. 72, no. 1890	**Audrey Hepburn**
	22 Aug.	Vol. 73, no. 1891	**Fess Parker**
			Tina Louise
	29 Aug.	Vol. 73, no. 1892	**Tab Hunter**
	5 Sept.	Vol. 73, no. 1893	**Frankie Vaughan**
	12 Sept.	Vol. 73, no. 1894	**Terry Moore**
			Sal Mineo
	19 Sept.	Vol. 73, no. 1895	**MyleneDemongeot**
	26 Sept.	Vol. 73, no. 1896	**Hardy Kruger**
	3 Oct.	Vol. 73, no. 1897	**Anne Aubrey**
			Robert Taylor
	10 Oct.	Vol. 73, no. 1898	**Cliff Robertson**
			Sandra Dee
			James Darren
	17 Oct.	Vol. 73, no. 1899	**May Britt**
	24 Oct.	Vol. 73, no. 1900	**Sophia Loren**
	31 Oct.	Vol. 73, no. 1901	**Doris Day**
			Rock Hudson
	7 Nov.	Vol. 73, no. 1902	**Eva Bartok**
	14 Nov.	Vol. 73, no. 1903	**Suzy Parker**
	21 Nov.	Vol. 73, no. 1904	**Yul Brynner**
	28 Nov.	Vol. 73, no. 1905	**Donna Anderson**
	5 Dec.	Vol. 73, no. 1906	**Ava Gardner**
			Anthony Franciosa
	12 Dec.	Vol. 73, no. 1907	**Haya Harareet**
	19 Dec.	Vol. 73, no. 1908	**Brigitte Bardot**
	26 Dec.	Vol. 73, no. 1909	**Marilyn Monroe**
1960	2 Jan.	Vol. 74, no. 1910	**Cliff Richard**
	9 Jan.	Vol. 74, no. 1911	**Janet Leigh**
	16 Jan.	Vol. 74, no. 1912	**Shirley MacLaine**
	23 Jan.	Vol. 74, no. 1913	**David Niven**
	30 Jan.	Vol. 74, no. 1914	**Charlton Heston**
	6 Feb.	Vol. 74, no. 1915	**Troy Donahue**
	13 Feb.	Vol. 74, no. 1916	**Leslie Caron**
	20 Feb.	Vol. 74, no. 1917	**Norman Wisdom**
	27 Feb.	Vol. 74, no. 1918	**Gina Lollobrigida**
	5 March	Vol. 74, no. 1919	**Anthony Newley**
	12 March	Vol. 74, no. 1920	**Sophia Loren**
	19 March	Vol. 74, no. 1921	**Pier Angeli**
	26 March	Vol. 74, no. 1922	**Angie Dickinson**
	2 April	Vol. 74, no. 1923	**Mai Zetterling**
	9 April	Vol. 74, no. 1924	**Michael Craig**
	16 April	Vol. 74, no. 1925	**Yvette Mimieux**
	23 April	Vol. 74, no. 1926	**James Garner**
	30 April	Vol. 74, no. 1927	**Mitzi Gaynor**
	7 May	Vol. 74, no. 1928	**George Hamilton**
	14 May	Vol. 74, no. 1929	**Carole Lesley**
	21 May	Vol. 74, no. 1930	**Elizabeth Taylor**
	28 May	Vol. 74, no. 1931	**Natalie Wood**
	4 June	Vol. 74, no. 1932	**Elizabeth Seal**
	11 June	Vol. 74, no. 1933	**Jane Fonda**
	18 June	Vol. 74, no. 1934	**Dean Stockwell**
	25 June	Vol. 74, no. 1935	**Adam Faith**
	2 July	Vol. 75, no. 1936	**Yoko Tani**
	9 July	Vol. 75, no. 1937	**Leslie Parrish**
			Peter Palmer
	16 July	Vol. 75, no. 1938	**Yvonne Monlaur**
	23 July	Vol. 75, no. 1939	**Sandra Dee**
	30 July	Vol. 75, no. 1940	**Sarah Branch**
	6 Aug.	Vol. 75, no. 1941	**Shirley Anne Field**
	13 Aug.	Vol. 75, no. 1942	**Nancy Kovack**
	20 Aug.	Vol. 75, no. 1943	**Mary Peach**
	27 Aug.	Vol. 75, no. 1944	**Mamie Van Doren**
	3 Sept.	Vol. 75, no. 1945	**Lisa Gastoni**
	10 Sept.	Vol. 75, no. 1946	**May Britt**
	17 Sept.	Vol. 75, no. 1947	**Brigitte Bardot**
	24 Sept.	Vol. 75, no. 1948	**Jayne Mansfield**
	1 Oct.	Vol. 75, no. 1949	**Tuesday Weld**
	8 Oct.	Vol. 75, no. 1950	**Susan Hayward**
	15 Oct.	Vol. 75, no. 1951	**Marilyn Monroe**
	22 Oct.	Vol. 75, no. 1952	**May Britt**
	29 Oct.	Vol. 75, no. 1953	**Sophia Loren**
	5 Nov.	Vol. 75, no. 1954	**MyleneDemongeot**
	12 Nov.	Vol. 75, no. 1955	**Jo Morrow**
	19 Nov.	Vol. 75, no. 1956	**Sandra Dee**
	26 Nov.	Vol. 75, no. 1957	**Shirley Bassey**
	3 Dec.	Vol. 75, no. 1958	**Anne Marie Baumann**
	10 Dec.	Vol. 75, no. 1959	**Elke Sommer**
	17 Dec.	Vol. 75, no. 1960	**Karen Alden**
	24 Dec.	Vol. 75, no. 1961	**Dog wearing Christmas hat**
	31 Dec.	Vol. 75, no. 1962	**Uncredited starlet**

PICTUREGOER 1913 – 60

This British film magazine originally started life as *The Picturegoer* on 11 October 1913, subtitled 'The Picture Theatre Weekly Magazine'; its first cover featured Ellaline Terriss and Seymour Hicks. By 1914 it was amalgamated with *Pictures*, becoming *Pictures And The Picturegoer. The Picturegoer* was relaunched as a monthly in January 1921, continuing in this format until May 1931, when a new series began: *Picturegoer Weekly*.

The forerunners of the weekly *Picturegoer* are of little but academic interest to the collector although it should be noted that some of *The Picturegoer* monthlies are worth seeking: the Louise Brooks cover of 28 August 1928 and the Garbo/Gilbert cover of March 1930 for instance. But it was *Picturegoer Weekly* that really captured its readers with its sepiatone pages, lively gossip, superb pictures and riveting reviews. Edited by S. Rossiter Shepherd and later by Connery Chappell, *Picturegoer* was published by Odhams Press Ltd.

Wonderful sepia star portraits adorned the covers of *Picturegoer* for many years, particularly during the forties, although, owing to government restrictions on the use of paper, it was forced to publish fortnightly from 6 September 1941 to 2 July 1949. A further paper shortage meant that there was no issue for 1 March 1947 either. Its first full-colour cover, of Vera-Ellen, was issued 20 November 1954.

From 1956 *Picturegoer* was edited by Robert Ottaway. By the late fifties *Picturegoer* was devoting more pages to pop music, and when an industrial dispute stopped the presses for seven weeks in 1959 the magazine's fate was sealed. On 23 April 1960 *Picturegoer* appeared for the last time.

The following is a complete entry of the new series of *Picturegoer* 1931–60.

YEAR	MONTH	REF. No.	COVER STAR
1931	30 May	Vol. 1, no. 1	**Marlene Dietrich**
	6 June	Vol. 1, no. 2	**Greta Garbo**
	13 June	Vol. 1, no. 3	**Leila Hyams**
	20 June	Vol. 1, no. 4	**Evalyn Knapp**
	27 June	Vol. 1, no. 5	**Dorothy Lee**
	4 July	Vol. 1, no. 6	**Mary Brian**
	11 July	Vol. 1, no. 7	**Rochelle Hudson**
	18 July	Vol. 1, no. 8	**Nancy Carroll**
	25 July	Vol. 1, no. 9	**Wynne Gibson**
	1 Aug.	Vol. 1, no. 10	**Claire Dodd**
	8 Aug.	Vol. 1, no. 11	**Anita Page**
	15 Aug.	Vol. 1, no. 12	**Maurice Chevalier** **Miriam Hopkins**
	22 Aug.	Vol. 1, no. 13	**Dorothy Jordan**
	29 Aug.	Vol. 1, no. 14	**Gary Cooper**
	5 Sept.	Vol. 1, no. 15	**Marguerite Namara**
	12 Sept.	Vol. 1, no. 16	**Mitzi Green**
	19 Sept.	Vol. 1, no. 17	**Robert Montgomery**
	26 Sept.	Vol. 1, no. 18	**Joan Crawford**
	3 Oct.	Vol. 1, no. 19	**Madeleine Carroll**
	10 Oct.	Vol. 1, no. 20	**Jackie Cooper**
	17 Oct.	Vol. 1, no. 21	**Anna May Wong**
	24 Oct.	Vol. 1, no. 22	**Yvonne Pelletier**
	31 Oct.	Vol. 1, no. 23	**Lillian Bond**

YEAR	MONTH	REF. No.	COVER STAR
	7 Nov.	Vol. 1, no. 24	**Juliette Compton**
	14 Nov.	Vol. 1, no. 25	**John Boles**
	21 Nov.	Vol. 1, no. 26	**Dolores Del Rio**
	28 Nov.	Vol. 1, no. 27	**Ruth Chatterton**
	5 Dec.	Vol. 1, no. 28	**Jack Buchanan**
	12 Dec.	Vol. 1, no. 29	**Rosita Garcia**
	19 Dec.	Vol. 1, no. 30	**Mae Clarke**
	26 Dec.	Vol. 1, no. 31	**Helen Twelvetrees**
	Christmas annual		**Norma Shearer**
1932	2 Jan.	Vol. 1, no. 32	**Marguerite Churchill**
	9 Jan.	Vol. 1, no. 33	**Mary Doran**
	16 Jan.	Vol. 1, no. 34	**Ralph Bellamy**
	23 Jan.	Vol. 1, no. 35	**Charlotte V. Henry**
	30 Jan.	Vol. 1, no. 36	**Mary Astor**
	6 Feb.	Vol. 1, no. 37	**Ann Casson**
	13 Feb.	Vol. 1, no. 38	**Arline Judge**
	20 Feb.	Vol. 1, no. 39	**Sylvia Sidney**
	27 Feb.	Vol. 1, no. 40	**Marlene Dietrich**
	5 March	Vol. 1, no. 41	**Sydney Fox**
	12 March	Vol. 1, no. 42	**Claudette Colbert**
	19 March	Vol. 1, no. 43	**Marion Davies**
	26 March	Vol. 1, no. 44	**Carole Lombard**
	2 April	Vol. 1, no. 45	**Kathryn Crawford**
	9 April	Vol. 1, no. 46	**Dorothy Jordan**
	16 April	Vol. 1, no. 47	**Joyce Compton**
	23 April	Vol. 1, no. 48	**Myrna Loy**
	30 April	Vol. 1, no. 49	**Wynne Gibson**
	7 May	Vol. 1, no. 50	**Helen Hayes**
	14 May	Vol. 1, no. 51	**Nancy Carroll**
	21 May	Vol. 1, no. 52	**Barbara Stanwyck**
	28 May	Vol. 2, no. 53	**Peggy Shannon**
	4 June	Vol. 2, no. 54	**Corinne Griffith**
	11 June	Vol. 2, no. 55	**Joan Bennett**
	18 June	Vol. 2, no. 56	**Helen Twelvetrees** **Eric Linden**
	25 June	Vol. 2, no. 57	**Loretta Young**
	Summer annual		**Claire Dodd** **Adrienne Ames**
	2 July	Vol. 2, no. 58	**Lili Damita** **Charlie Ruggles**
	9 July	Vol. 2, no. 59	**Leila Hyams**
	16 July	Vol. 2, no. 60	**Janet Gaynor**
	23 July	Vol. 2, no. 61	**Madge Evans**
	30 July	Vol. 2, no. 62	**Maureen O'Sullivan**
	6 Aug.	Vol. 2, no. 63	**Dorothy Jordan** **Robert Young**
	13 Aug.	Vol. 2, no. 64	**Karen Morley**
	20 Aug.	Vol. 2, no. 65	**Wynne Gibson**
	27 Aug.	Vol. 2, no. 66	**Sylvia Sidney**

YEAR	MONTH	REF. No.	COVER STAR
	3 Sept.	Vol. 2, no. 67	**Marion Marsh** **Warren William**
	10 Sept.	Vol. 2, no. 68	**Norma Shearer**
	17 Sept.	Vol. 2, no. 69	**Marian Nixon**
	24 Sept.	Vol. 2, no. 70	**Frances Dee**
	1 Oct.	Vol. 2, no. 71	**Greta Garbo** **John Barrymore**
	8 Oct.	Vol. 2, no. 72	**Jeanette MacDonald**
	15 Oct.	Vol. 2, no. 73	**Nora Gregor**
	22 Oct.	Vol. 2, no. 74	**Maurice Chevalier**
	29 Oct.	Vol. 2, no. 75	**Claudette Colbert**
	5 Nov.	Vol. 2, no. 76	**Dolores Del Rio** **Joel McCrea**
	12 Nov.	Vol. 2, no. 77	**Tallulah Bankhead**
	19 Nov.	Vol. 2, no. 78	**Virginia Bruce**
	26 Nov.	Vol. 2, no. 79	**Jean Harlow** **Clark Gable**
	3 Dec.	Vol. 2, no. 80	**Carole Lombard**
	10 Dec.	Vol. 2, no. 81	**Miriam Hopkins**
	17 Dec.	Vol. 2, no. 82	**Constance Bennett** **Phillips Holmes**
	24 Dec.	Vol. 2, no. 83	**Anne Grey**
	31 Dec.	Vol. 2, no. 84	**Claire Dodd**
	Christmas annual		**Jack Buchanan** **Margot Grahame**
1933	7 Jan.	Vol. 2, no. 85	**Irene Dunne**
	14 Jan.	Vol. 2, no. 86	**Nancy Carroll**
	21 Jan.	Vol. 2, no. 87	**Katharine Hepburn**
	28 Jan.	Vol. 2, no. 88	**Renée Gadd**
	4 Feb.	Vol. 2, no. 89	**Una Merkel**
	11 Feb.	Vol. 2, no. 90	**Norma Shearer**
	18 Feb.	Vol. 2, no. 91	**Clara Bow**
	25 Feb.	Vol. 2, no. 92	**Sidney Fox**
	4 March	Vol. 2, no. 93	**Ursula Jeans**
	11 March	Vol. 2, no. 94	**Diana Wynyard**
	18 March	Vol. 2, no. 95	**Evelyn Laye**
	25 March	Vol. 2, no. 96	**Joan Crawford**
	1 April	Vol. 2, no. 97	**Molly Lamont**
	8 April	Vol. 2, no. 98	**Dorothy Hyson**
	15 April	Vol. 2, no. 99	**Heather Angel**
	22 April	Vol. 2, no. 100	**Joan Marsh**
	29 April	Vol. 2, no. 101	**Lilian Harvey**
	6 May	Vol. 2, no. 102	**Myrna Loy**
	13 May	Vol. 2, no. 103	**Wynne Gibson**
	20 May	Vol. 2, no. 104	**Sari Maritza**
	27 May	Vol. 3, no. 105	**Wera Engels**
	3 June	Vol. 3, no. 106	**Bebe Daniels**
	10 June	Vol. 3, no. 107	**Sally Eilers**
	17 June	Vol. 3, no. 108	**Robert Montgomery** **Madge Evans**

YEAR	MONTH	REF. No.	COVER STAR
	24 June	Vol. 3, no. 109	**Thelma Todd**
	Summer annual		**Norma Shearer**
	1 July	Vol. 3, no. 110	**Elissa Landi**
	8 July	Vol. 3, no. 111	**Barbara Stanwyck**
	15 July	Vol. 3, no. 112	**Carole Lombard**
	22 July	Vol. 3, no. 113	**Janet Gaynor**
	29 July	Vol. 3, no. 114	**Glenda Farrell**
	5 Aug.	Vol. 3, no. 115	**Miriam Jordan**
	12 Aug.	Vol. 3, no. 116	**Joan Bennett**
	19 Aug.	Vol. 3, no. 117	**Bette Davis**
	26 Aug.	Vol. 3, no. 118	**Gloria Stuart**
	2 Sept.	Vol. 3, no. 119	**Kathleen Burke**
	9 Sept.	Vol. 3, no. 120	**Sylvia Sidney**
	16 Sept.	Vol. 3, no. 121	**Fredric March** **Elissa Landi**
	23 Sept.	Vol. 3, no. 122	**Ginger Rogers**
	30 Sept.	Vol. 3, no. 123	**Marlene Dietrich**
	7 Oct.	Vol. 3, no. 124	**Nancy Carroll**
	14 Oct.	Vol. 3, no. 125	**Marion Davies**
	21 Oct.	Vol. 3, no. 126	**Eddie Cantor** **Lyda Roberti**
	28 Oct.	Vol. 3, no. 127	**Frances Dee**
	4 Nov.	Vol. 3, no. 128	**Peggy Shannon**
	11 Nov.	Vol. 3, no. 129	**Judith Allen**
	18 Nov.	Vol. 3, no. 130	**Jessie Matthews**
	25 Nov.	Vol. 3, no. 131	**Rochelle Hudson**
	2 Dec.	Vol. 3, no. 132	**Joan Crawford** **Franchot Tone**
	9 Dec.	Vol. 3, no. 133	**Miriam Hopkins**
	16 Dec.	Vol. 3, no. 134	**Frances Farmer**
	23 Dec.	Vol. 3, no. 135	**Elizabeth Allan**
	30 Dec.	Vol. 3, no. 136	**Kay Francis**
	Christmas annual		**Gloria Stuart**
1934	6 Jan.	Vol. 3, no. 137	**Marion Marsh**
	13 Jan.	Vol. 3, no. 138	**Joan Bennett**
	20 Jan.	Vol. 3, no. 139	**Frances Day**
	27 Jan.	Vol. 3, no. 140	**Claudette Colbert** **Ben Lyon**
	3 Feb.	Vol. 3, no. 141	**Warner Baxter** **Margaret Lindsay**
	10 Feb.	Vol. 3, no. 142	**Constance Bennett**
	17 Feb.	Vol. 3, no. 143	**Jean Harlow**
	24 Feb.	Vol. 3, no. 144	**Diana Napier** **Douglas Fairbanks Jr**
	3 March	Vol. 3, no. 145	**Anna Neagle**
	10 March	Vol. 3, no. 146	**Greta Garbo**
	17 March	Vol. 3, no. 147	**Jean Parker**
	24 March	Vol. 3, no. 148	**Merle Oberon**
	31 March	Vol. 3, no. 149	**Helen Mack**
	7 April	Vol. 3, no. 150	**Katharine Hepburn**
	14 April	Vol. 3, no. 151	**Mae West** **Cary Grant**
	21 April	Vol. 3, no. 152	**Gracie Fields**
	28 April	Vol. 3, no. 153	**Elizabeth Bergner**
	5 May	Vol. 3, no. 154	**Anna Neagle** **Cedric Hardwicke**
	12 May	Vol. 3, no. 155	**Joan Bennett** **Douglas S Montgomery**
	19 May	Vol. 3, no. 156	**Margaret Sullavan**
	26 May	Vol. 3, no. 157	**Loretta Young**
	2 June	Vol. 3, no. 158	**Madeleine Carroll**
	9 June	Vol. 4, no. 159	**Douglas Fairbanks Sr** **Benita Hume**
	16 June	Vol. 4, no. 160	**Muriel Evans**
	23 June	Vol. 4, no. 161	**Jessie Matthews**
	30 June	Vol. 4, no. 162	**Shirley Temple**
	Summer annual		**Florine McKinney**
	7 July	Vol. 4, no. 163	**Helen Twelvetrees**
	14 July	Vol. 4, no. 164	**Greta Garbo**
	21 July	Vol. 4, no. 165	**Fay Wray**
	28 July	Vol. 4, no. 166	**Jo Matthews** **Geneva Mitchell**
	4 Aug.	Vol. 4, no. 167	**Claudette Colbert** **Henry Wilcoxon**
	11 Aug.	Vol. 4, no. 168	**Ann Dvorak**
	18 Aug.	Vol. 4, no. 169	**Dolores Del Rio**
	25 Aug.	Vol. 4, no. 170	**Alice Faye**
	1 Sept.	Vol. 4, no. 171	**Greta Garbo** **Ian Keith**
	8 Sept.	Vol. 4, no. 172	**Constance Bennett**
	15 Sept.	Vol. 4, no. 173	**Katharine De Mille**
	22 Sept.	Vol. 4, no. 174	**Anna Neagle**
	29 Sept.	Vol. 4, no. 175	**Binnie Barnes**
	6 Oct.	Vol. 4, no. 176	**Madge Evans**
	13 Oct.	Vol. 4, no. 177	**Laura La Plante**
	20 Oct.	Vol. 4, no. 178	**Gracie Fields**
	27 Oct.	Vol. 4, no. 179	**Nils Asther** **Pat Paterson**
	3 Nov.	Vol. 4, no. 180	**Marthe Eggerth**
	10 Nov.	Vol. 4, no. 181	**Fredric March** **Anna Sten**
	17 Nov.	Vol. 4, no. 182	**Norma Shearer**
	24 Nov.	Vol. 4, no. 183	**Claudette Colbert**
	1 Dec.	Vol. 4, no. 184	**Margaret Sullavan**
	8 Dec.	Vol. 4, no. 185	**Greta Garbo** **Herbert Marshall**
	15 Dec.	Vol. 4, no. 186	**Jackie Cooper**
	22 Dec.	Vol. 4, no. 187	**June Lang**

YEAR	MONTH	REF. No.	COVER STAR
	29 Dec.	Vol. 4, no. 188	**Merle Oberon**
			Leslie Howard
	Christmas annual		**Jeanette MacDonald**
			Maurice Chevalier
1935	5 Jan.	Vol. 4, no. 189	**Joan Crawford**
	12 Jan.	Vol. 4, no. 190	**Fay Wray**
	19 Jan.	Vol. 4, no. 191	**Jeanette MacDonald**
	26 Jan.	Vol. 4, no. 192	**Twenty-four small pictures of film stars**
	2 Feb.	Vol. 4, no. 193	**Adrienne Ames**
	9 Feb.	Vol. 4, no. 194	**Kitty Carlisle**
	16 Feb.	Vol. 4, no. 195	**Myrna Loy**
	23 Feb.	Vol. 4, no. 196	**Jean Harlow**
	2 March	Vol. 4, no. 197	**Greta Garbo**
	9 March	Vol. 4, no. 198	**Katharine Hepburn**
			John Beal
	16 March	Vol. 4, no. 199	**Bette Davis**
	23 March	Vol. 4, no. 200	**Joan Crawford**
	30 March	Vol. 4, no. 201	**Gracie Fields**
	6 April	Vol. 4, no. 202	**Nancy O'Neil**
	13 April	Vol. 4, no. 203	**Jean Parker**
			Russell Hardie
	20 April	Vol. 4, no. 204	**Madeleine Carroll**
			Robert Donat
	27 April	Vol. 4, no. 205	**Wynne Gibson**
	4 May	Vol. 4, no. 206	**Evelyn Laye**
	11 May	Vol. 4, no. 207	**Valerie Hobson**
	18 May	Vol. 4, no. 208	**Carole Lombard**
	25 May	Vol. 4, no. 209	**Paulette Goddard**
	1 June	Vol. 5, no. 210	**Clark Gable**
	8 June	Vol. 5, no. 211	**Mae West**
	15 June	Vol. 5, no. 212	**Greta Garbo**
	22 June	Vol. 5, no. 213	**Margaret Sullavan**
	29 June	Vol. 5, no. 214	**Maureen O'Sullivan**
			Cesar Romero
	Summer annual		**Jean Harlow**
	6 July	Vol. 5, no. 215	**Karen Morley**
	13 July	Vol. 5, no. 216	**Miriam Hopkins**
	20 July	Vol. 5, no. 217	**Anna Sten**
	27 July	Vol. 5, no. 218	**Sally Eilers**
	3 Aug.	Vol. 5, no. 219	**Claudette Colbert**
	10 Aug.	Vol. 5, no. 220	**William Powell**
			Ginger Rogers
	17 Aug.	Vol. 5, no. 221	**Four uncredited starlets**
	24 Aug.	Vol. 5, no. 222	**Helen Vinson**
	31 Aug.	Vol. 5, no. 223	**Maureen O'Sullivan**

YEAR	MONTH	REF. No.	COVER STAR
	7 Sept.	Vol. 5, no. 224	**Constance Bennett**
	14 Sept.	Vol. 5, no. 225	**Madge Evans**
	21 Sept.	Vol. 5, no. 226	**Clark Gable**
			Jean Harlow
	28 Sept.	Vol. 5, no. 227	**Anna Neagle**
	5 Oct.	Vol. 5, no. 228	**Jeanette MacDonald**
	12 Oct.	Vol. 5, no. 229	**Franchot Tone**
	19 Oct.	Vol. 5, no. 230	**Jean Muir**
	26 Oct.	Vol. 5, no. 231	**Mary Ellis**
	2 Nov.	Vol. 5, no. 232	**Myrna Loy**
	9 Nov.	Vol. 5, no. 233	**Heather Angel**
	16 Nov.	Vol. 5, no. 234	**Gail Patrick**
	23 Nov.	Vol. 5, no. 235	**Rochelle Hudson**
	30 Nov.	Vol. 5, no. 236	**Marlene Dietrich**
	7 Dec.	Vol. 5, no. 237	**Charles Laughton**
	14 Dec.	Vol. 5, no. 238	**Binnie Barnes**
	21 Dec.	Vol. 5, no. 239	**Jean Parker**
			Robert Donat
	28 Dec.	Vol. 5, no. 240	**Margaretta Scott**
	Christmas annual		**Grace Moore**
1936	4 Jan.	Vol. 5, no. 241	**Greta Garbo**
	11 Jan.	Vol. 5, no. 242	**Wendy Barrie**
	18 Jan.	Vol. 5, no. 243	**Special double issue and film guide for 1936**
	25 Jan.	Vol. 5, no. 244	**Charlie Chaplin**
	1 Feb.	Vol. 5, no. 245	**Elizabeth Bergner**
			Sophie Stewart
	8 Feb.	Vol. 5, no. 246	**Lily Pons**
	15 Feb.	Vol. 5, no. 247	**Fay Wray**
	22 Feb.	Vol. 5, no. 248	**Jean Harlow**
	29 Feb.	Vol. 5, no. 249	**Katharine Hepburn**
	7 March	Vol. 5, no. 250	**Carole Lombard**
	14 March	Vol. 5, no. 251	**Ann Harding**
	21 March	Vol. 5, no. 252	**Eleanor Powell**
			Robert Taylor
	28 March	Vol. 5, no. 253	**Norma Shearer**
	4 April	Vol. 5, no. 254	**Eleanore Whitney**
	11 April	Vol. 5, no. 255	**Una Merkel**
	18 April	Vol. 5, no. 256	**Claudette Colbert**
	25 April	Vol. 5, no. 257	**Marlene Dietrich**
			Gary Cooper
	2 May	Vol. 5, no. 258	**Dolores Del Rio**
	9 May	Vol. 5, no. 259	**Clark Gable**
	16 May	Vol. 5, no. 260	**Jean Arthur**
	23 May	Vol. 6, no. 261	**Sylvia Sidney**
	30 May	Vol. 6, no. 262	**Ginger Rogers**
	6 June	Vol. 6, no. 263	**Joan Blondell**
	13 June	Vol. 6, no. 264	**Fredric March**
	20 June	Vol. 6, no. 265	**Merle Oberon**

YEAR	MONTH	REF. No.	COVER STAR
	27 June	Vol. 6, no. 266	**Irene Dunne**
	4 July	Vol. 6, no. 267	**Pat Paterson**
	11 July	Vol. 6, no. 268	**Carl Brisson**
	18 July	Vol. 6, no. 269	**Sylvia Sidney**
			Spencer Tracy
	25 July	Vol. 6, no. 270	**Charles Laughton**
	1 Aug.	Vol. 6, no. 271	**Robert Taylor**
	8 Aug.	Vol. 6, no. 272	**Eleanore Whitney**
			Kent Taylor
	15 Aug.	Vol. 6, no. 273	**Jessie Matthews**
	22 Aug.	Vol. 6, no. 274	**Ronald Colman**
			Jane Wyatt
	29 Aug.	Vol. 6, no. 275	**Norma Shearer**
			Leslie Howard
	5 Sept.	Vol. 6, no. 276	**Shirley Temple**
	12 Sept.	Vol. 6, no. 277	**Myrna Loy**
			William Powell
	19 Sept.	Vol. 6, no. 278	**Luise Rainer**
	26 Sept.	Vol. 6, no. 279	**Mary Astor**
	3 Oct.	Vol. 6, no. 280	**Jean Harlow**
	10 Oct.	Vol. 6, no. 281	**Leslie Howard**
	17 Oct.	Vol. 6, no. 282	**Madeleine Carroll**
	24 Oct.	Vol. 6, no. 283	**Anna Lee**
	31 Oct.	Vol. 6, no. 284	**Jane Wyatt**
	7 Nov.	Vol. 6, no. 285	**Eleanor Powell**
	14 Nov.	Vol. 6, no. 286	**Frances Langford**
	21 Nov.	Vol. 6, no. 287	**Jean Harlow**
			Spencer Tracy
	28 Nov.	Vol. 6, no. 288	**Greta Garbo**
			Robert Taylor
	5 Dec.	Vol. 6, no. 289	**Vivien Leigh**
	12 Dec.	Vol. 6, no. 290	**Mary Pickford**
	19 Dec.	Vol. 6, no. 291	**Merle Oberon**
			Brian Aherne
	26 Dec.	Vol. 6, no. 292	**Binnie Barnes**
	Christmas annual		**Ginger Rogers**
1937	2 Jan.	Vol. 6, no. 293	**Eleanor Powell**
	9 Jan.	Vol. 6, no. 294	**Elizabeth Bergner**
	16 Jan.	Vol. 6, no. 295	**Jessie Matthews**
	23 Jan.	Vol. 6, no. 296	**Bette Davis**
	30 Jan.	Vol. 6, no. 297	**Greta Garbo**
	6 Feb.	Vol. 6, no. 298	**Claudette Colbert**
	13 Feb.	Vol. 6, no. 299	**Frances Farmer**
	20 Feb.	Vol. 6, no. 300	**Barbara Stanwyck**
	27 Feb.	Vol. 6, no. 301	**Madge Evans**
	6 March	Vol. 6, no. 302	**Deanna Durbin**
	13 March	Vol. 6, no. 303	**Robert Taylor**
	20 March	Vol. 6, no. 304	**June Knight**
	27 March	Vol. 6, no. 305	**Joan Crawford**
	3 April	Vol. 6, no. 306	**Fred Astaire**
	10 April	Vol. 6, no. 307	**Jean Harlow**
	17 April	Vol. 6, no. 308	**Mary Ellis**
	24 April	Vol. 6, no. 309	**Ann Sothern**
	1 May	Vol. 7, no. 310	**Carole Lombard**
	8 May	Vol. 7, no. 311	**Gracie Fields**
	15 May	Vol. 7, no. 312	**Ginger Rogers**
	22 May	Vol. 7, no. 313	**Gary Cooper**
	29 May	Vol. 7, no. 314	**Loretta Young**
	5 June	Vol. 7, no. 315	**Janet Gaynor**
			Fredric March
	12 June	Vol. 7, no. 316	**Simone Simon**
	19 June	Vol. 7, no. 317	**Marlene Dietrich**
	26 June	Vol. 7, no. 318	**Joan Crawford**
			Franchot Tone
	3 July	Vol. 7, no. 319	**Norma Shearer**
	10 July	Vol. 7, no. 320	**Luise Rainer**
	Summer annual		**Clark Gable**
	17 July	Vol. 7, no. 321	**Claudette Colbert**
	24 July	Vol. 7, no. 322	**Kay Francis**
	31 July	Vol. 7, no. 323	**Anita Louise**
			Olivia De Havilland
	7 Aug.	Vol. 7, no. 324	**Loretta Young**
	14 Aug.	Vol. 7, no. 325	**Jean Rogers**
	21 Aug.	Vol. 7, no. 326	**Clive Brook**
			Margaretta Scott
	28 Aug.	Vol. 7, no. 327	**Merle Oberon**
	4 Sept.	Vol. 7, no. 328	**Robert Taylor**
	11 Sept.	Vol. 7, no. 329	**Eleanor Powell**
	18 Sept.	Vol. 7, no. 330	**Anna Neagle**
	25 Sept.	Vol. 7, no. 331	**Virginia Bruce**
	2 Oct.	Vol. 7, no. 332	**Kay Francis**
	9 Oct.	Vol. 7, no. 333	**Jon Hall**
			Dorothy Lamour
	16 Oct.	Vol. 7, no. 334	**Spencer Tracy**
	23 Oct.	Vol. 7, no. 335	**Pat Paterson**
	30 Oct.	Vol. 7, no. 336	**Ronald Colman**
			Madeleine Carroll
	6 Nov.	Vol. 7, no. 337	**Greta Garbo**
	13 Nov.	Vol. 7, no. 338	**Sonja Henie**
	20 Nov.	Vol. 7, no. 339	**Katharine Hepburn**
	27 Nov.	Vol. 7, no. 340	**Sigrid Gurie**
	4 Dec.	Vol. 7, no. 341	**Carole Lombard**
	11 Dec.	Vol. 7, no. 342	**Robert Taylor**
	18 Dec.	Vol. 7, no. 343	**Greta Garbo**
			Charles Boyer
	25 Dec.	Vol. 7, no. 344	**Deanna Durbin**
	Christmas annual		**Fredric March**
			Janet Gaynor
1938	1 Jan.	Vol. 7, no. 345	**Anton Walbrook**
			Anna Neagle
	8 Jan.	Vol. 7, no. 346	**Nova Pilbeam**
	15 Jan.	Vol. 7, no. 347	**Bette Davis**

YEAR	MONTH	REF. No.	COVER STAR
	22 Jan.	Vol. 7, no. 348	**Tyrone Power**
			Loretta Young
	29 Jan.	Vol. 7, no. 349	**Merle Oberon**
	5 Feb.	Vol. 7, no. 350	**Dorothy Lamour**
	12 Feb.	Vol. 7, no. 351	**Maureen O'Sullivan**
	19 Feb.	Vol. 7, no. 352	**Danielle Darrieux**
	26 Feb.	Vol. 7, no. 353	**Errol Flynn**
	5 March	Vol. 7, no. 354	**Andrea Leeds**
	12 March	Vol. 7, no. 355	**Claudette Colbert**
	19 March	Vol. 7, no. 356	**Katharine Hepburn**
			Cary Grant
	26 March	Vol. 7, no. 357	**Ginger Rogers**
	2 April	Vol. 7, no. 358	**Spencer Tracy**
	9 April	Vol. 7, no. 359	**Vivien Leigh**
	16 April	Vol. 7, no. 360	**Norma Shearer**
	23 April	Vol. 7, no. 361	**Sylvia Sidney**
	30 April	Vol. 7, no. 362	**Clark Gable**
	7 May	Vol. 7, no. 363	**Irene Dunne**
			Douglas Fairbanks Jr
	14 May	Vol. 7, no. 364	**Myrna Loy**
	21 May	Vol. 8, no. 365	**Nelson Eddy**
			Jeanette MacDonald
	28 May	Vol. 8, no. 366	**Robert Taylor**
			Margaret Sullavan
	4 June	Vol. 8, no. 367	**Olivia De Havilland**
			Errol Flynn
	11 June	Vol. 8, no. 368	**Madeleine Carroll**
			Henry Fonda
	18 June	Vol. 8, no. 369	**Rosalind Russell**
	25 June	Vol. 8, no. 370	**Kay Francis**
	2 July	Vol. 8, no. 371	**Sylvia Sidney**
	9 July	Vol. 8, no. 372	**Ginger Rogers**
	16 July	Vol. 8, no. 373	**Robert Donat**
			Rosalind Russell
	23 July	Vol. 8, no. 374	**Robert Taylor**
	Summer annual		**Gary Cooper**
			Claudette Colbert
	30 July	Vol. 8, no 375	**Maureen O'Sullivan**
			John Beal
	6 Aug.	Vol. 8, no. 376	**Danielle Darrieux**
	13 Aug.	Vol. 8, no. 377	**Joan Bennett**
	20 Aug.	Vol. 8, no. 378	**Carole Lombard**
	27 Aug.	Vol. 8, no. 379	**Katharine Hepburn**
	3 Sept.	Vol. 8, no. 380	**Joan Crawford**

YEAR	MONTH	REF. No.	COVER STAR
	10 Sept.	Vol. 8, no. 381	**Bette Davis**
	17 Sept.	Vol. 8, no. 382	**Alice Faye**
			Tyrone Power
	24 Sept.	Vol. 8, no. 383	**Jeanette MacDonald**
			Nelson Eddy
	1 Oct.	Vol. 8, no. 384	**Dorothy Lamour**
	8 Oct.	Vol. 8, no. 385	**Errol Flynn**
	15 Oct.	Vol. 8, no. 386	**Jean Arthur**
	22 Oct.	Vol. 8, no. 387	**Irene Dunne**
	29 Oct.	Vol. 8, no. 388	**Gracie Fields**
	5 Nov.	Vol. 8, no. 389	**Charles Laughton**
			Vivien Leigh
	12 Nov.	Vol. 8, no. 390	**Fredric March**
			Virginia Bruce
	19 Nov.	Vol. 8, no. 391	**Loretta Young**
			Tyrone Power
	26 Nov.	Vol. 8, no. 392	**Norma Shearer**
	3 Dec.	Vol. 8, no. 393	**Priscilla Lane**
	10 Dec.	Vol. 8, no. 394	**Polly Ward**
	17 Dec.	Vol. 8, no. 395	**Lilli Palmer**
	24 Dec.	Vol. 8, no. 396	**Jean Colin**
			Kenny Baker
	31 Dec.	Vol. 8, no. 397	**Gary Cooper**
	Christmas annual		**Norma Shearer**
			Tyrone Power
1939	7 Jan.	Vol. 8, no. 398	**Joan Bennett**
	14 Jan.	Vol. 8, no. 399	**Margaret Sullavan**
	21 Jan.	Vol. 8, no. 400	**Madeleine Carroll**
	28 Jan.	Vol. 8, no. 401	**Carole Lombard**
	4 Feb.	Vol. 8, no. 402	**Ronald Colman**
			Frances Dee
	11 Feb.	Vol. 8, no. 403	**Myrna Loy**
	18 Feb.	Vol. 8, no. 404	**Janet Gaynor**
	25 Feb.	Vol. 8, no. 405	**Norma Shearer**
	4 March	Vol. 8, no. 406	**Alice Faye**
	11 March	Vol. 8, no. 407	**Margaret Lockwood**
			Hugh Sinclair
	18 March	Vol. 8, no. 408	**Constance Bennett**
	25 March	Vol. 8, no. 409	**Joan Crawford**
			James Stewart
	1 April	Vol. 8, no. 410	**Elizabeth Bergner**
	8 April	Vol. 8, no. 411	**John Clements**
			June Duprez
	15 April	Vol. 8, no. 412	**Jean Rogers**
	22 April	Vol. 8, no. 413	**Hedy Lamarr**
	29 April	Vol. 8, no. 414	**Andrea Leeds**
	6 May	Vol. 8, no. 415	**Deanna Durbin**
	13 May	Vol. 8, no. 416	**Susan Hayward**
	20 May	Vol. 9, no. 417	**Ann Sheridan**

YEAR	MONTH	REF. No.	COVER STAR
	27 May	Vol. 9, no. 418	**Madeleine Carroll**
	3 June	Vol. 9, no. 419	**John Wayne Claire Trevor**
	10 June	Vol. 9, no. 420	**Irene Dunne Charles Boyer**
	17 June	Vol. 9, no. 421	**Priscilla Lane**
	24 June	Vol. 9, no. 422	**Bette Davis**
	1 July	Vol. 9, no. 423	**Joan Bennett**
	8 July	Vol. 9, no. 424	**Dorothy Lamour**
	15 July	Vol. 9, no. 425	**Deanna Durbin**
	22 July	Vol. 9, no. 426	**Anna Neagle**
	29 July	Vol. 9, no. 427	**Margaret Lockwood**
	Summer annual		**Carole Lombard**
	5 Aug.	Vol. 9, no. 428	**Greta Garbo**
	12 Aug.	Vol. 9, no. 429	**Myrna Loy**
	19 Aug.	Vol. 9, no. 430	**Virginia Bruce**
	26 Aug.	Vol. 9, no. 431	**Loretta Young**
	2 Sept.	Vol. 9, no. 432	**Joan Crawford James Stewart**
	9 Sept.	Vol. 9, no. 433	**Louis Hayward Joan Bennett**
	16 Sept.	Vol. 9, no. 434	**Tyrone Power Alice Faye**
	23 Sept.	Vol. 9, no. 435	**Annabella**
	30 Sept.	Vol. 9, no. 436	**Dorothy Lamour**
	7 Oct.	Vol. 9, no. 437	**Ann Sothern**
	14 Oct.	Vol. 9, no. 438	**Irene Dunne Fred MacMurray**
	21 Oct.	Vol. 9, no. 439	**Barbara Stanwyck**
	28 Oct.	Vol. 9, no. 440	**Bette Davis**
	4 Nov.	Vol. 9, no. 441	**Robert Donat Greer Garson**
	11 Nov.	Vol. 9, no. 442	**Jean Arthur**
	18 Nov.	Vol. 9, no. 443	**Nancy Kelly Spencer Tracy**
	25 Nov.	Vol. 9, no. 444	**Myrna Loy William Powell**
	2 Dec.	Vol. 9, no. 445	**Valerie Hobson**
	9 Dec.	Vol. 9, no. 446	**Norma Shearer**
	16 Dec.	Vol. 9, no. 447	**Claire Trevor**
	23 Dec.	Vol. 9, no. 448	**Carole Lombard**
	30 Dec.	Vol. 9, no. 449	**Rosemary Lane**
1940	6 Jan.	Vol. 9, no. 450	**Greta Garbo**
	13 Jan.	Vol. 9, no. 451	**Patricia Morison**
	20 Jan.	Vol. 9, no. 452	**Jean Colin**
	27 Jan.	Vol. 9, no. 453	**Andrea Leeds Gary Cooper**
	3 Feb.	Vol. 9, no. 454	**Jane Bryan**
	10 Feb.	Vol. 9, no. 455	**Mary Martin**
	17 Feb.	Vol. 9, no. 456	**Lucille Ball**
	24 Feb.	Vol. 9, no. 457	**Ellen Drew**
	2 March	Vol. 9, no. 458	**Margaret Sullavan**
	9 March	Vol. 9, no. 459	**Linda Darnell**
	16 March	Vol. 9, no. 460	**Alice Faye**
	23 March	Vol. 9, no. 461	**Anne Shirley**
	30 March	Vol. 9, no. 462	**Hedy Lamarr**
	6 April	Vol. 9, no. 463	**Isa Miranda**
	13 April	Vol. 9, no. 464	**Conrad Veidt**
	20 April	Vol. 9, no. 465	**Dorothy Lamour**
	27 April	Vol. 9, no. 466	**Clark Gable Vivien Leigh**
	4 May	Vol. 9, no. 467	**Joan Crawford**
	11 May	Vol. 9, no. 468	**Cary Grant Rosalind Russell**
	18 May	Vol. 9, no. 469	**Robert Donat Bette Davis**
	25 May	Vol. 9, no. 470	**Joan Bennett**
	1 June	Vol. 9, no. 471	**Robert Montgomery Constance Cummings**
	8 June	Vol. 9, no. 472	**Virginia Bruce**
	15 June	Vol. 9, no. 473	**Olympe Bradna**
	22 June	Vol. 9, no. 474	**Loretta Young**
	29 June	Vol. 9, no. 475	**Jane Wyman**
	6 July	Vol. 9, no. 476	**Melvyn Douglas Jean Arthur**
	13 July	Vol. 9, no. 477	**Madeleine Carroll**
	20 July	Vol. 9, no. 478	**Irene Dunne**
	27 July	Vol. 9, no. 479	**Jeanette MacDonald**
	3 Aug	Vol. 9, no. 480	**Phyllis Brooks**
	10 Aug.	Vol. 9, no. 481	**Priscilla Lane**
	17 Aug.	Vol. 9, no. 482	**Barbara Stanwyck**
	24 Aug.	Vol. 9, no. 483	**Joan Blondell**
	31 Aug.	Vol. 9, no. 484	**Margaret Lockwood Rex Harrison**
	7 Sept.	Vol. 9, no. 485	**Carole Lombard**
	14 Sept.	Vol. 9, no. 486	**Olivia De Havilland**
	21 Sept.	Vol. 9, no. 487	**Paulette Goddard**
	28 Sept.	Vol. 9, no. 488	**Rosemary Lane**
	5 Oct.	Vol. 9, no. 489	**Clark Gable Claudette Colbert**
	12 Oct.	Vol. 9, no. 490	**Deanna Durbin**
	19 Oct.	Vol. 9, no. 491	**Ann Sheridan**
	26 Oct.	Vol. 10, no. 492	**Robert Taylor Norma Shearer**
	2 Nov.	Vol. 10, no. 493	**Gail Patrick**
	9 Nov.	Vol. 10, no. 494	**Mary Martin**
	16 Nov.	Vol. 10, no. 495	**Lynn Bari**
	23 Nov.	Vol. 10, no. 496	**Rosalind Russell**
	30 Nov.	Vol. 10, no. 497	**Gary Cooper**
	7 Dec.	Vol. 10, no. 498	**Marlene Dietrich**

YEAR	MONTH	REF. No.	COVER STAR
	14 Dec.	Vol. 10, no. 499	**Sally Gray**
	21 Dec.	Vol. 10, no. 500	**Ann Sothern**
			Edward G. Robinson
	28 Dec.	Vol. 10, no. 501	**Bette Davis**
1941	4 Jan.	Vol. 10, no. 502	**Kay Francis**
	11 Jan.	Vol. 10, no. 503	**Myrna Loy**
			Melvyn Douglas
	18 Jan.	Vol. 10, no. 504	**Paulette Goddard**
			Charlie Chaplin
	25 Jan.	Vol. 10, no. 505	**Wendy Hiller**
			Rex Harrison
	1 Feb.	Vol. 10, no. 506	**Ellen Drew**
	8 Feb.	Vol. 10, no. 507	**Ruth Hussey**
	15 Feb.	Vol. 10, no. 508	**Linda Darnell**
			Tyrone Power
	22 Feb.	Vol. 10, no. 509	**Penny Singleton**
	1 March	Vol. 10, no. 510	**Alice Faye**
	8 March	Vol. 10, no. 511	**Michele Morgan**
	15 March	Vol. 10, no. 512	**Katharine Hepburn**
			James Stewart
	22 March	Vol. 10, no. 513	**Jean Arthur**
	29 March	Vol. 10, no. 514	**Myrna Loy**
	5 April	Vol. 10, no. 515	**Gary Cooper**
			Madeleine Carroll
	12 April	Vol. 10, no. 516	**Ingrid Bergman**
	19 April	Vol. 10, no. 517	**Clark Gable**
			Hedy Lamarr
	26 April	Vol. 10, no. 518	**Margaret Lockwood**
	3 May	Vol. 10, no. 519	**Ann Sheridan**
	10 May	Vol. 10, no. 520	**Wendy Hiller**
	17 May	Vol. 10, no. 521	**Margaret Sullavan**
			Charles Boyer
	24 May	Vol. 10, no. 522	**Rita Hayworth**
	31 May	Vol. 10, no. 523	**Paulette Goddard**
			Fred Astaire
	7 June	Vol. 10, no. 524	**Loretta Young**
	14 June	Vol. 10, no. 525	**Barbara Stanwyck**
	21 June	Vol. 10, no. 526	**Joan Fontaine**
	28 June	Vol. 10, no. 527	**Michael Redgrave**
			Phyllis Calvert
	5 July	Vol. 10, no. 528	**Dorothy Lamour**
	12 July	Vol. 10, no. 529	**Veronica Lake**
	19 July	Vol. 10, no. 530	**Irene Dunne**
	26 July	Vol. 11, no. 531	**Joan Crawford**
	2 Aug.	Vol. 11, no. 532	**Vivien Leigh**
	9 Aug.	Vol. 11, no. 533	**Lana Turner**
	16 Aug.	Vol. 11, no. 534	**Mary Martin**

YEAR	MONTH	REF. No.	COVER STAR
	23 Aug.	Vol. 11, no. 535	**Simone Simon**
	6 Sept.	Vol. 11, no. 536	**Joan Bennett**
	20 Sept.	Vol. 11, no. 537	**Bebe Daniels**
			Ben Lyon
	4 Oct.	Vol. 11, no. 538	**Norma Shearer**
	18 Oct.	Vol. 11, no. 539	**Olivia De Havilland**
	1 Nov.	Vol. 11, no. 540	**Linda Darnell**
	15 Nov.	Vol. 11, no. 541	**Laraine Day**
			Lew Ayres
	29 Nov.	Vol. 11, no. 542	**Lucille Ball**
	13 Dec.	Vol. 11, no. 543	**Betty Grable**
			Tyrone Power
	27 Dec.	Vol. 11, no. 544	**Deanna Durbin**
			Robert Cummings
1942	10 Jan.	Vol. 11, no. 545	**John Clements**
			Ann Todd
	24 Jan.	Vol. 11, no. 546	**Greta Garbo**
	7 Feb.	Vol. 11, no. 547	**Loretta Young**
	21 Feb.	Vol. 11, no. 548	**Joan Fontaine**
	7 March	Vol. 11, no. 549	**Vera Zorina**
	21 March	Vol. 11, no. 550	**Ruth Warwick**
	4 April	Vol. 11, no. 551	**Hedy Lamarr**
	18 April	Vol. 11, no. 552	**John Wayne**
			Paulette Goddard
	2 May	Vol. 11, no. 553	**Myrna Loy**
	16 May	Vol. 11, no. 554	**Spencer Tracy**
			Katharine Hepburn
	30 May	Vol. 11, no. 555	**Deborah Kerr**
	13 June	Vol. 11, no. 556	**Margaret Lockwood**
	27 June	Vol. 11, no. 557	**Bob Hope**
	11 July	Vol. 11, no. 558	**Donna Reed**
	25 July	Vol. 11, no. 559	**Susan Hayward**
	8 Aug.	Vol. 11, no. 560	**Joan Fontaine**
			Tyrone Power
	22 Aug.	Vol. 11, no. 561	**Irene Dunne**
	5 Sept.	Vol. 11, no. 562	**Robert Donat**
			Phyllis Calvert
	19 Sept.	Vol. 11, no. 563	**Noel Coward**
	3 Oct.	Vol. 11, no. 564	**Ann Sheridan**
	17 Oct.	Vol. 11, no. 565	**Clark Gable**
			Lana Turner
	31 Oct.	Vol. 11, no. 566	**Dorothy Lamour**
	14 Nov.	Vol. 11, no. 567	**Gary Cooper**
			Teresa Wright
	28 Nov.	Vol. 11, no. 568	**Cary Grant**
	12 Dec.	Vol. 11, no. 569	**Ann Sothern**
	26 Dec.	Vol. 11, no. 570	**Ginger Rogers**
			Ray Milland
1943	9 Jan.	Vol. 12, no. 571	**Joan Crawford**
	23 Jan.	Vol. 12, no. 572	**Judy Garland**

YEAR	MONTH	REF. No.	COVER STAR
	6 Feb.	Vol. 12, no. 573	**Ronald Colman** **Greer Garson**
	20 Feb.	Vol. 12, no. 574	**Marjorie Reynolds**
	6 March	Vol. 12, no. 575	**Betty Grable** **Victor Mature**
	20 March	Vol. 12, no. 576	**Googie Withers**
	3 April	Vol. 12, no. 577	**Lucille Ball**
	17 April	Vol. 12, no. 578	**Claudette Colbert**
	1 May	Vol. 12, no. 579	**Ida Lupino**
	15 May	Vol. 12, no. 580	**Joan Crawford** **Philip Dorn**
	29 May	Vol. 12, no. 581	**Anna Neagle**
	12 June	Vol. 12, no. 582	**Tyrone Power** **Maureen O'Hara**
	26 June	Vol. 12, no. 583	**John Mills**
	10 July	Vol. 12, no. 584	**Alan Ladd**
	24 July	Vol. 12, no. 585	**Marsha Hunt**
	7 Aug.	Vol. 12, no. 586	**Anne Baxter**
	21 Aug.	Vol. 12, no. 587	**Laraine Day**
	4 Sept.	Vol. 12, no. 588	**Barbara Stanwyck**
	18 Sept.	Vol. 12, no. 589	**Charles Boyer** **Joan Fontaine**
	2 Oct.	Vol. 12, no. 590	**Brian Donlevy**
	16 Oct.	Vol. 12, no. 591	**Deanna Durbin** **Joseph Cotten**
	30 Oct.	Vol. 12, no. 592	**Robert Donat** **Valerie Hobson**
	13 Nov.	Vol. 12, no. 593	**Rosamund John**
	27 Nov.	Vol. 12, no. 594	**Paulette Goddard**
	11 Dec.	Vol. 12, no. 595	**Bob Hope**
	25 Dec.	Vol. 12, no. 596	**Bette Davis**
1944	8 Jan.	Vol. 13, no. 597	**Kathryn Grayson** **Gene Kelly**
	22 Jan.	Vol. 13, no. 598	**Susanna Foster**
	5 Feb.	Vol. 13, no. 599	**Robert Montgomery**
	19 Feb.	Vol. 13, no. 600	**Betty Hutton**
	4 March	Vol. 13, no. 601	**Ann Sheridan**
	18 March	Vol. 13, no. 602	**Hedy Lamarr**
	1 April	Vol. 13, no. 603	**Jennifer Jones**
	15 April	Vol. 13, no. 604	**Ginger Rogers**
	29 April	Vol. 13, no. 605	**Robert Taylor**
	13 May	Vol. 13, no. 606	**Dorothy Lamour**
	27 May	Vol. 13, no. 607	**Sheila Sim**
	10 June	Vol. 13, no. 608	**David Niven**
	24 June	Vol. 13, no. 609	**Maria Montez**
	8 July	Vol. 13, no. 610	**Rita Hayworth**
	22 July	Vol. 13, no. 611	**Tyrone Power**
	5 Aug.	Vol. 13, no. 612	**Linda Darnell**
	19 Aug.	Vol. 13, no. 613	**Robert Donat** **Deborah Kerr**
	2 Sept.	Vol. 13, no. 614	**Barbara Stanwyck**
	16 Sept.	Vol. 13, no. 615	**Humphrey Bogart**
	30 Sept.	Vol. 13, no. 616	**Ingrid Bergman**
	14 Oct.	Vol. 13, no. 617	**Phyllis Calvert** **Stewart Granger**
	28 Oct.	Vol. 13, no. 618	**Bing Crosby**
	11 Nov.	Vol. 13, no. 619	**Vivien Leigh**
	25 Nov.	Vol. 13, no. 620	**Lana Turner**
	9 Dec.	Vol. 13, no. 621	**Betty Grable**
	23 Dec.	Vol. 13, no. 622	**Greer Garson** **Walter Pidgeon**
1945	6 Jan.	Vol. 14, no. 623	**Merle Oberon**
	20 Jan.	Vol. 14, no. 624	**Bette Davis**
	3 Feb.	Vol. 14, no. 625	**Eleanor Parker**
	17 Feb.	Vol. 14, no. 626	**Helen Walker**
	3 March	Vol. 14, no. 627	**Irene Manning**
	17 March	Vol. 14, no. 628	**Myrna Loy**
	31 March	Vol. 14, no. 629	**Gail Russell**
	14 April	Vol. 14, no. 630	**Anton Walbrook**
	28 April	Vol. 14, no. 631	**Deanna Durbin**
	12 May	Vol. 14, no. 632	**Margaret Lockwood**
	26 May	Vol. 14, no. 633	**Stewart Granger**
	9 June	Vol. 14, no. 634	**Katharine Hepburn**
	23 June	Vol. 14, no. 635	**Lauren Bacall**
	7 July	Vol. 14, no. 636	**Françoise Rosay**
	21 July	Vol. 14, no. 637	**Anna Neagle** **Rex Harrison**
	4 Aug.	Vol. 14, no. 638	**Janet Blair**
	18 Aug.	Vol. 14, no. 639	**Joan Fontaine**
	1 Sept.	Vol. 14, no. 640	**Arturo De Cordova** **Betty Hutton**
	15 Sept.	Vol. 14, no. 641	**Van Johnson**
	29 Sept.	Vol. 14, no. 642	**Margaret O'Brien**
	13 Oct.	Vol. 14, no. 643	**Robert Young**
	27 Oct.	Vol. 14, no. 644	**Gary Cooper** **Loretta Young**
	10 Nov.	Vol. 14, no. 645	**Ann Todd**
	24 Nov.	Vol. 14, no. 646	**Ginger Rogers**
	8 Dec.	Vol. 14, no. 647	**Dennis Morgan**
	22 Dec.	Vol. 14, no. 648	**Margaret Lockwood** **James Mason**
1946	5 Jan.	Vol. 15, no. 649	**Googie Withers**
	19 Jan.	Vol. 15, no. 650	**Fred Astaire**
	2 Feb.	Vol. 15, no. 651	**Joan Crawford**
	16 Feb.	Vol. 15, no. 652	**Rita Hayworth**
	2 March	Vol. 15, no. 653	**Gary Cooper** **Ingrid Bergman**
	16 March	Vol. 15, no. 654	**Claudette Colbert**
	30 March	Vol. 15, no. 655	**Lucille Ball**
	13 April	Vol. 15, no. 656	**Jeanne Crain**
	27 April	Vol. 15, no. 657	**Ray Milland**

YEAR	MONTH	REF. No.	COVER STAR
	11 May	Vol. 15, no. 658	**Marsha Hunt**
	25 May	Vol. 15, no. 659	**George Sanders**
	8 June	Vol. 15, no. 660	**Michael Redgrave**
			Rachel Kempson
	22 June	Vol. 15, no. 661	**Pat Kirkwood**
	6 July	Vol. 15, no. 662	**Gregory Peck**
	20 July	Vol. 15, no. 663	**Lizabeth Scott**
	3 Aug.	Vol. 15, no. 664	**Deborah Kerr**
	17 Aug.	Vol. 15, no. 665	**Clark Gable**
	31 Aug.	Vol. 15, no. 666	**Anna Neagle**
			Michael Wilding
	14 Sept.	Vol. 15, no. 667	**Jane Wyman**
	28 Sept.	Vol. 15, no. 668	**Laurence Olivier**
	12 Oct.	Vol. 15, no. 669	**Joan Crawford**
	26 Oct.	Vol. 15, no. 670	**Humphrey Bogart**
			Lauren Bacall
	9 Nov.	Vol. 15, no. 671	**Gregory Peck**
			Jennifer Jones
	23 Nov.	Vol. 15, no. 672	**Anne Crawford**
	7 Dec.	Vol. 15, no. 673	**David Niven**
			Loretta Young
	21 Dec.	Vol. 15, no. 674	**Hedy Lamarr**
1947	4 Jan.	Vol. 16, no. 675	**John Mills**
			Valerie Hobson
	18 Jan.	Vol. 16, no. 676	**Olivia De Havilland**
	1 Feb.	Vol. 16, no. 677	**Greer Garson**
	15 Feb.	Vol. 16, no. 678	**Dennis Price**
	15 March	Vol. 16, no. 679	**Michele Morgan**
	29 March	Vol. 16, no. 680	**Audrey Totter**
	12 April	Vol. 16, no. 681	**Cornel Wilde**
	26 April	Vol. 16, no. 682	**Fredric March**
			Myrna Loy
	10 May	Vol. 16, no. 683	**Jane Wyman**
	24 May	Vol. 16, no. 684	**Gregory Peck**
			Claude Jarman Jr
	7 June	Vol. 16, no. 685	**Anne Baxter**
	21 June	Vol. 16, no. 686	**Patricia Roc**
	5 July	Vol. 16, no. 687	**Alan Ladd**
	19 July	Vol. 16, no. 688	**Anna Neagle**
	2 Aug.	Vol. 16, no. 689	**Van Johnson**
			Janet Leigh
	16 Aug.	Vol. 16, no. 690	**Vivien Leigh**
	30 Aug.	Vol. 16, no. 691	**Gary Cooper**
	13 Sept.	Vol. 16, no. 692	**Joan Fontaine**
	27 Sept.	Vol. 16, no. 693	**Lana Turner**
	11 Oct.	Vol. 16, no. 694	**Lizabeth Scott**
			John Hodiak
	25 Oct.	Vol. 16, no. 695	**Tyrone Power**
	8 Nov.	Vol. 16, no. 696	**Deborah Kerr**
			Walter Pidgeon
	22 Nov.	Vol. 16, no. 697	**Cary Grant**
	6 Dec.	Vol. 16, no. 698	**Alexis Smith**
	20 Dec.	Vol. 16, no. 699	**Jennifer Jones**
1948	3 Jan.	Vol. 17, no. 700	**Carole Landis**
	17 Jan.	Vol. 17, no. 701	**Bing Crosby**
	31 Jan.	Vol. 17, no. 702	**Ava Gardner**
	14 Feb.	Vol. 17, no. 703	**John Mills**
	28 Feb.	Vol. 17, no. 704	**Barbara White**
	13 March	Vol. 17, no. 705	**Edana Romney**
	27 March	Vol. 17, no. 706	**Danny Kaye**
	10 April	Vol. 17, no. 707	**Rita Hayworth**
	24 April	Vol. 17, no. 708	**Laurence Olivier**
	8 May	Vol. 17, no. 709	**Jack Warner**
	22 May	Vol. 17, no. 710	**Jeanette MacDonald**
			José Iturbi
	5 June	Vol. 17, no. 711	**Eleanor Parker**
	19 June	Vol. 17, no. 712	**Margaret Johnston**
	3 July	Vol. 17, no. 713	**Gregory Peck**
			Dorothy McGuire
	17 July	Vol. 17, no. 714	**Clark Gable**
	31 July	Vol. 17, no. 715	**Veronica Lake**
	14 Aug.	Vol. 17, no. 716	**Spencer Tracy**
	28 Aug.	Vol. 17, no. 717	**Ingrid Bergman**
	11 Sept.	Vol. 17, no. 718	**Joan Greenwood**
	25 Sept.	Vol. 17, no. 719	**Gail Russell**
	9 Oct.	Vol. 17, no. 720	**Betty Hutton**
	23 Oct.	Vol. 17, no. 721	**David Niven**
	6 Nov.	Vol. 17, no. 722	**Judy Garland**
	20 Nov.	Vol. 17, no. 723	**Marlene Dietrich**
	4 Dec.	Vol. 17, no. 724	**Jane Wyman**
	18 Dec.	Vol. 17, no. 725	**Mai Zetterling**
1949	1 Jan.	Vol. 18, no. 726	**Elizabeth Taylor**
			Robert Taylor
	15 Jan.	Vol. 18, no. 727	**Jane Powell**
	29 Jan.	Vol. 18, no. 728	**Susan Hayward**
	12 Feb.	Vol. 18, no. 729	**Humphrey Bogart**
	26 Feb.	Vol. 18, no. 730	**Deborah Kerr**
	12 March	Vol. 18, no. 731	**Maureen O'Hara**
	26 March	Vol. 18, no. 732	**Teresa Wright**
	9 April	Vol. 18, no. 733	**Gene Tierney**
			Tyrone Power
	23 April	Vol. 18, no. 734	**Alan Ladd**
	7 May	Vol. 18, no. 735	**Sid Field**
	21 May	Vol. 18, no. 736	**Arlene Dahl**
	4 June	Vol. 18, no. 737	**Jean Simmons**
			Stewart Granger
	18 June	Vol. 18, no. 738	**June Allyson**
	2 July	Vol. 18, no. 739	**Barbara Stanwyck**
	9 July	Vol. 18, no. 740	**Betty Grable**
	16 July	Vol. 18, no. 741	**Frank Sinatra**
	23 July	Vol. 18, no. 742	**Jennifer Jones**
	30 July	Vol. 18, no. 743	**Lena Horne**
	6 Aug.	Vol. 18, no. 744	**Jeanne Crain**

YEAR	MONTH	REF. No.	COVER STAR
	13 Aug.	Vol. 18, no. 745	**Cyd Charisse**
	20 Aug.	Vol. 18, no. 746	**Danny Kaye**
	27 Aug.	Vol. 18, no. 747	**Yvonne De Carlo**
	3 Sept.	Vol. 18, no. 748	**Clifton Webb**
	10 Sept.	Vol. 18, no. 749	**Sally Gray**
			Robert Newton
	17 Sept.	Vol. 18, no. 750	**Clark Gable**
	24 Sept.	Vol. 18, no. 751	**Ann Sheridan**
			Cary Grant
	1 Oct.	Vol. 18, no. 752	**Jean Simmons**
	8 Oct.	Vol. 18, no. 753	**Glynis Johns**
	15 Oct.	Vol. 18, no. 754	**Van Johnson**
	22 Oct.	Vol. 18, no. 755	**Olivia De Havilland**
			Leo Genn
	29 Oct.	Vol. 18, no. 756	**Susan Hayward**
			Richard Conte
	5 Nov.	Vol. 18, no. 757	**Abbott and Costello**
	12 Nov.	Vol. 18, no. 758	**Robert Mitchum**
	19 Nov.	Vol. 18, no. 759	**Lea Padovani**
			Sam Wanamaker
	26 Nov.	Vol. 18, no. 760	**Bob Hope**
	3 Dec.	Vol. 18, no. 761	**Petula Clark**
	10 Dec.	Vol. 18, no. 762	**Ava Gardner**
			Gregory Peck
	17 Dec.	Vol. 18, no. 763	**Virginia Mayo**
	24 Dec.	Vol. 18, no. 764	**Jean Simmons**
	31 Dec.	Vol. 18, no. 765	**Joan Crawford**
1950	7 Jan.	Vol. 19, no. 766	**Diana Lynn**
	14 Jan.	Vol. 19, no. 767	**Valentina Cortesa**
			Spencer Tracy
	21 Jan.	Vol. 19, no. 768	**Gary Cooper**
	28 Jan.	Vol. 19, no. 769	**June Haver**
	4 Feb.	Vol. 19, no. 770	**Robert Donat**
	11 Feb.	Vol. 19, no. 771	**Esther Williams**
			Ricardo Montalban
	18 Feb.	Vol. 19, no. 772	**Ann Todd**
	25 Feb.	Vol. 19, no. 773	**Dan Dailey**
	4 March	Vol. 19, no. 774	**Susan Hayward**
	11 March	Vol. 19, no. 775	**Doris Day**
	18 March	Vol. 19, no. 776	**Maureen O'Hara**
	25 March	Vol. 19, no. 777	**Margaret Lockwood**
	1 April	Vol. 19, no. 778	**Bing Crosby**
	8 April	Vol. 19, no. 779	**Richard Attenborough**
	15 April	Vol. 19, no. 780	**Corinne Calvet**
	22 April	Vol. 19, no. 781	**Van Heflin**
	29 April	Vol. 19, no. 782	**Alan Ladd**
	6 May	Vol. 19, no. 783	**Joanne Dru**
	13 May	Vol. 19, no. 784	**Ingrid Bergman**
	20 May	Vol. 19, no. 785	**Mercedes McCambridge**

YEAR	MONTH	REF. No.	COVER STAR
	27 May	Vol. 19, no. 786	**Richard Todd**
	3 June	Vol. 19, no. 787	**Robert Newton**
			Bobby Driscoll
	10 June	Vol. 19, no. 788	**Cornell Borchers**
	17 June	Vol. 19, no. 789	**Gene Tierney**
	24 June	Vol. 19, no. 790	**John Hodiak**
	1 July	Vol. 19, no. 791	**Rhonda Fleming**
	8 July	Vol. 20, no. 792	**Googie Withers**
			Richard Widmark
	15 July	Vol. 20, no. 793	**Loretta Young**
			Clark Gable
	22 July	Vol. 20, no. 794	**Betsy Drake**
			Robert Young
	29 July	Vol. 20, no. 795	**Ginger Rogers**
			Dennis Morgan
	5 Aug.	Vol. 20, no. 796	**Rex Harrison**
			Lilli Palmer
	12 Aug.	Vol. 20, no. 797	**John Derek**
			Diana Lynn
	19 Aug;.	Vol. 20, no. 798	**Barbara Murray**
	26 Aug.	Vol. 20, no. 799	**Jane Wyman**
	2 Sept.	Vol. 20, no. 800	**Patricia Dainton**
	9 Sept.	Vol. 20, no. 801	**Cecile Aubry**
	16 Sept.	Vol. 20, no. 802	**Danny Kaye**
			Barbara Bates
	23 Sept.	Vol. 20, no. 803	**Elizabeth Taylor**
	30 Sept.	Vol. 20, no. 804	**Olivia De Havilland**
	7 Oct.	Vol. 20, no. 805	**Betty Hutton**
	14 Oct.	Vol. 20, no. 806	**Esther Williams**
	21 Oct.	Vol. 20, no. 807	**Joan Fontaine**
	28 Oct.	Vol. 20, no. 808	**Cathy O'Donnell**
	4 Nov.	Vol. 20, no. 809	**Jennifer Jones**
	11 Nov.	Vol. 20, no. 810	**Hedy Lamarr**
			George Sanders
	18 Nov.	Vol. 20, no. 811	**David Niven**
	25 Nov.	Vol. 20, no. 812	**Jean Kent**
	2 Dec.	Vol. 20, no. 813	**Stewart Granger**
	9 Dec.	Vol. 20, no. 814	**MontgomeryClift**
	16 Dec.	Vol. 20, no. 815	**Arlene Dahl**
	23 Dec.	Vol. 20, no. 816	**Derek Bond**
			Hazel Cherry
			Joan Greenwood
			Richard Todd
			Audrey Hepburn
			Phyllis Calvert
	30 Dec.	Vol. 20, no. 817	**Petula Clark**
1951	6 Jan.	Vol. 21, no. 818	**Margaret Lockwood**
	13 Jan.	Vol. 21, no. 819	**Lisa Daniely**
	20 Jan.	Vol. 21, no. 820	**Anne Baxter**
	27 Jan.	Vol. 21, no. 821	**Dirk Bogarde**
	3 Feb.	Vol. 21, no. 822	**Claudette Colbert**
	10 Feb.	Vol. 21, no. 823	**Joan Fontaine**

YEAR	MONTH	REF. No.	COVER STAR
	17 Feb.	Vol. 21, no. 824	**Ava Gardner James Mason**
	24 Feb.	Vol. 21, no. 825	**Alan Ladd**
	3 March	Vol. 21, no. 826	**Van Heflin**
	10 March	Vol. 21, no. 827	**Susan Hayward**
	17 March	Vol. 21, no. 828	**Yolande Donlan**
	24 March	Vol. 21, no. 829	**Constance Smith**
	31 March	Vol. 21, no. 830	**Judy Garland**
	7 April	Vol. 21, no. 831	**Ann Blyth**
	14 April	Vol. 21, no. 832	**Gregory Peck**
	21 April	Vol. 21, no. 833	**Peggy Dow**
	28 April	Vol. 21, no. 834	**Esther Williams Howard Keel**
	5 May	Vol. 21, no. 835	**Audrey Hepburn**
	12 May	Vol. 21, no. 836	**Nadia Gray**
	19 May	Vol. 21, no. 837	**George Sanders**
	26 May	Vol. 21, no. 838	**Jane Greer Gary Cooper**
	2 June	Vol. 21, no. 839	**Vera-Ellen**
	9 June	Vol. 21, no. 840	**Michael Rennie**
	16 June	Vol. 21, no. 841	**Kathryn Grayson**
	23 June	Vol. 21, no. 842	**Corinne Calvet**
	30 June	Vol. 21, no. 843	**Marta Toren**
	7 July	Vol. 22, no. 844	**Yvonne De Carlo**
	14 July	Vol. 22, no. 845	**Rhonda Fleming**
	21 July	Vol. 22, no. 846	**Piper Laurie**
	28 July	Vol. 22, no. 847	**Danny Kaye**
	4 Aug.	Vol. 22, no. 848	**Debra Paget**
	11 Aug.	Vol. 22, no. 849	**Errol Flynn Patrice Wymore**
	18 Aug.	Vol. 22, no. 850	**Eleanor Parker Anthony Dexter**
	25 Aug.	Vol. 22, no. 851	**Glynis Johns Anthony Darnborough**
	1 Sept.	Vol. 22, no. 852	**Ingrid Bergman**
	8 Sept.	Vol. 22, no. 853	**Leslie Caron Gene Kelly**
	15 Sept.	Vol. 22, no. 854	**Farley Granger Ruth Roman**
	22 Sept.	Vol. 22, no. 855	**Howard Keel**
	29 Sept.	Vol. 22, no. 856	**Loretta Young**
	6 Oct.	Vol. 22, no. 857	**Alastair Sim**
	13 Oct.	Vol. 22, no. 858	**Robert Beatty Zachary Scott**
	20 Oct.	Vol. 22, no. 859	**Clark Gable**
	27 Oct.	Vol. 22, no. 860	**Van Johnson and wife**
	3 Nov.	Vol. 22, no. 861	**Diana Lynn Corinne Calvet**
	10 Nov.	Vol. 22, no. 862	**Kirk Douglas**
	17 Nov.	Vol. 22, no. 863	**Doris Day**
	24 Nov.	Vol. 22, no. 864	**Jane Wyman**
	1 Dec.	Vol. 22, no. 865	**Shelley Winters**
	8 Dec.	Vol. 22, no. 866	**Betty Grable**
	15 Dec.	Vol. 22, no. 867	**Anthony Steel**
	22 Dec.	Vol. 22, no. 868	**Jack Warner**

YEAR	MONTH	REF. No.	COVER STAR
	29 Dec.	Vol. 22, no. 869	**Peggy Dow**
1952	5 Jan.	Vol. 23, no. 870	**Jane Russell**
	12 Jan.	Vol. 23, no. 871	**Pier Angeli Stewart Granger**
	19 Jan.	Vol. 23, no. 872	**Kerima**
	26 Jan.	Vol. 23, no. 873	**Robert Taylor**
	2 Feb.	Vol. 23, no. 874	**Elizabeth Taylor**
	9 Feb.	Vol. 23, no. 875	**Gloria Grahame**
	16 Feb.	Vol. 23, no. 876	**Jean Peters**
	23 Feb.	Vol. 23, no. 877	**Alec Guinness Glynis Johns**
	1 March	Vol. 23, no. 878	**Ava Gardner**
	8 March	Vol. 23, no. 879	**Kirk Douglas Jane Wyman**
	15 March	Vol. 23, no. 880	**Richard Todd Joan Rice**
	22 March	Vol. 23, no. 881	**Linda Darnell**
	29 March	Vol. 23, no. 882	**Janet Leigh**
	5 April	Vol. 23, no. 883	**Marlon Brando**
	12 April	Vol. 23, no. 884	**Vera-Ellen**
	19 April	Vol. 23, no. 885	**Claudette Colbert**
	26 April	Vol. 23, no. 886	**Rita Hayworth**
	3 May	Vol. 23, no. 887	**James Mason**
	10 May	Vol. 23, no. 888	**Mel Ferrer**
	17 May	Vol. 23, no. 889	**Susan Hayward**
	24 May	Vol. 23, no. 890	**Dale Robertson**
	31 May	Vol. 23, no. 891	**Martin and Lewis**
	7 June	Vol. 23, no. 892	**Piper Laurie**
	14 June	Vol. 23, no. 893	**Mona Freeman**
	21 June	Vol. 23, no. 894	**Dawn Addams**
	28 June	Vol. 23, no. 895	**Ann Sheridan**
	5 July	Vol. 24, no. 896	**Anne Baxter**
	12 July	Vol. 24, no. 897	**Betty Hutton**
	19 July	Vol. 24, no. 898	**Joan Rice**
	26 July	Vol. 24, no. 899	**Esther Williams Vivian Blaine Joan Evans**
	2 Aug.	Vol. 24, no. 900	**David Hutchinson Anthony Steel**
	9 Aug.	Vol. 24, no. 901	**Marilyn Monroe**
	16 Aug.	Vol. 24, no. 902	**Leslie Caron**
	23 Aug.	Vol. 24, no. 903	**Jane Wyman**
	30 Aug.	Vol. 24, no. 904	**Eva Bartok**
	6 Sept.	Vol. 24, no. 905	**Patrice Wymore Virginia Mayo**
	13 Sept.	Vol. 24, no. 906	**Ronald Shiner**
	20 Sept.	Vol. 24, no. 907	**Barbara Payton**
	27 Sept.	Vol. 24, no. 908	**Doris Day**
	4 Oct.	Vol. 24, no. 909	**Ted Ray Kay Walsh**
	11 Oct.	Vol. 24, no. 910	**Audrey Hepburn Gregory Peck**
	18 Oct.	Vol. 24, no. 911	**Claire Bloom Charlie Chaplin**
	25 Oct.	Vol. 24, no. 912	**Marge and Gower Champion**

YEAR	MONTH	REF. No.	COVER STAR
	1 Nov.	Vol. 24, no. 913	**Virginia Gibson**
			Gordon MacRae
	8 Nov.	Vol. 24, no. 914	**Linda Christian**
	15 Nov.	Vol. 24, no. 915	**Janet Leigh**
	22 Nov.	Vol. 24, no. 916	**Pier Angeli**
	29 Nov.	Vol. 24, no. 917	**Bing Crosby**
			Bob Hope
			Dorothy Lamour
	6 Dec.	Vol. 24, no. 918	**Jeanmaire**
	13 Dec.	Vol. 24, no. 919	**Rita Gam**
	20 Dec.	Vol. 24, no. 920	**Jill Melford**
			Norman Wisdom
			Margaret Lockwood
			Diana Decker
	27 Dec.	Vol. 24, no. 921	**Mitzi Gaynor**
			Richard Allan
1953	3 Jan.	Vol. 25, no. 922	**Corinne Calvet**
	10 Jan.	Vol. 25, no. 923	**Ava Gardner**
	17 Jan.	Vol. 25, no. 924	**Marta Toren**
	24 Jan.	Vol. 25, no. 925	**Esther Williams**
	31 Jan.	Vol. 25, no. 926	**Jean Peters**
	7 Feb.	Vol. 25, no. 927	**Gregory Peck**
	14 Feb.	Vol. 25, no. 928	**Burt Lancaster**
			Eva Bartok
	21 Feb.	Vol. 25, no. 929	**Eva Bergh**
	28 Feb.	Vol. 25, no. 930	**Richard Burton**
			Olivia De Havilland
	7 March	Vol. 25, no. 931	**Robert Newton**
			Linda Darnell
			Keith Andes
	14 March	Vol. 25, no. 932	**Colette Marchand**
			José Ferrer
	21 March	Vol. 25, no. 933	**Jack Hawkins**
	28 March	Vol. 25, no. 934	**Piper Laurie**
	4 April	Vol. 25, no. 935	**Bob Hope**
			Marilyn Maxwell
			Eddie Mayehoff
			Mickey Rooney
	11 April	Vol. 25, no. 936	**Kirk Douglas**
			Lana Turner
	18 April	Vol. 25, no. 937	**Joan Collins**
	25 April	Vol. 25, no. 938	**Arlene Dahl**
	2 May	Vol. 25, no. 939	**Queen Elizabeth II**
	9 May	Vol. 25, no. 940	**Marilyn Monroe**
	16 May	Vol. 25, no. 941	**Barbara Ruick**
	23 May	Vol. 25, no. 942	**Leslie Caron**
	30 May	Vol. 25, no. 943	**Marge Champion**
	6 June	Vol. 25, no. 944	**Kathleen Hughes**
	13 June	Vol. 25, no. 945	**Kay Kendall**
			Kenneth More
	20 June	Vol. 25, no. 946	**Jane Powell**
	27 June	Vol. 25, no. 947	**Jan Sterling**

YEAR	MONTH	REF. No.	COVER STAR
	4 July	Vol. 26, no. 948	**Debbie Reynolds**
	11 July	Vol. 26, no. 949	**Rita Hayworth**
	18 July	Vol. 26, no. 950	**Jean Peters**
	25 July	Vol. 26, no. 951	**Eva Bartok**
	1 Aug.	Vol. 26, no. 952	**Alec Guinness**
			Yvonne De Carlo
	8 Aug.	Vol. 26, no. 953	**Ronald Shiner**
			Gaby Bruyere
	15 Aug.	Vol. 26, no. 954	**Adrienne Corri**
	22 Aug.	Vol. 26, no. 955	**Jill Melford**
	29 Aug.	Vol. 26, no. 956	**Ruth Hampton**
	5 Sept.	Vol. 26, no. 957	**Gloria Grahame**
	12 Sept.	Vol. 26, no. 958	**Jane Wyman**
	19 Sept.	Vol. 26, no. 959	**Debra Paget**
	26 Sept.	Vol. 26, no. 960	**Susan Cabot**
	3 Oct.	Vol. 26, no. 961	**Elaine Stewart**
	10 Oct.	Vol. 26, no. 962	**Vittorio Gassman**
			Yvonne De Carlo
	17 Oct.	Vol. 26, no. 963	**Denise Darcel**
			Jack Carson
	24 Oct.	Vol. 26, no. 964	**Glynis Johns**
			Richard Todd
	31 Oct.	Vol. 26, no. 965	**Janet Leigh**
			Donald O'Connor
	7 Nov.	Vol. 26, no. 966	**Ava Gardner**
	14 Nov.	Vol. 26, no. 967	**Jeanne Crain**
	21 Nov.	Vol. 26, no. 968	**Tony Curtis**
			Lori Nelson
	28 Nov.	Vol. 26, no. 969	**Abbe Lane**
	5 Dec.	Vol. 26, no. 970	**Ruth Roman**
	12 Dec.	Vol. 26, no. 971	**Norman Wisdom**
	19 Dec.	Vol. 26, no. 972	**Bob Hope**
	26 Dec.	Vol. 26, no. 973	**Shelley Winters**
1954	2 Jan.	Vol. 27, no. 974	**Jane Griffiths**
			Gregory Peck
	9 Jan.	Vol. 27, no. 975	**Gina Lollobrigida**
	16 Jan.	Vol. 27, no. 976	**Marilyn Monroe**
	23 Jan.	Vol. 27, no. 977	**Kay Kendall**
	30 Jan.	Vol. 27, no. 978	**Terry Moore**
	6 Feb.	Vol. 27, no. 979	**Allyn McLerie**
			Dick Wesson
	13 Feb.	Vol. 27, no. 980	**Fred Astaire**
			Cyd Charisse
	20 Feb.	Vol. 27, no. 981	**Esther Williams**
			John Bromfield
	27 Feb.	Vol. 27, no. 982	**Peggy Cummins**
			David Niven
	6 March	Vol. 27, no. 983	**Ann Miller**
			Kathryn Grayson
	13 March	Vol. 27, no. 984	**Maureen O'Hara**
			Jeff Chandler

YEAR	MONTH	REF. No.	COVER STAR
	20 March	Vol. 27, no. 985	**Deborah Kerr James Mason**
	27 March	Vol. 27, no. 986	**Debra Paget**
	3 April	Vol. 27, no. 987	**Jean Peters**
	10 April	Vol. 27, no. 988	**Kenneth More Suzanne Cloutier**
	17 April	Vol. 27, no. 989	**Piper Laurie**
	24 April	Vol. 27, no. 990	**Martine Carol**
	1 May	Vol. 27, no. 991	**Anne Baxter Steve Cochran**
	8 May	Vol. 27, no. 992	**Julia Adams**
	15 May	Vol. 27, no. 993	**Ludmilla Tcherina**
	22 May	Vol. 27, no. 994	**Jane Russell**
	29 May	Vol. 27, no. 995	**Edmund Purdom Ann Blyth**
	5 June	Vol. 27, no. 996	**Jean Simmons**
	12 June	Vol. 27, no. 997	**Ava Gardner Robert Taylor**
	19 June	Vol. 27, no. 998	**Laya Raki**
	26 June	Vol. 27, no. 999	**Marge and Gower Champion**
	3 July	Vol. 28, no. 1000	**Maggie McNamara**
	10 July	Vol. 28, no. 1001	**Grace Kelly**
	17 July	Vol. 28, no. 1002	**Mari Aldon**
	24 July	Vol. 28, no. 1003	**Mara Corday**
	31 July	Vol. 28, no. 1004	**Yvonne De Carlo**
	7 Aug.	Vol. 28, no. 1005	**Sheree North**
	14 Aug.	Vol. 28, no. 1006	**Martha Hyer**
	21 Aug.	Vol. 28, no. 1007	**Debbie Reynolds**
	28 Aug.	Vol. 28, no. 1008	**Gloria Grahame**
	4 Sept.	Vol. 28, no. 1009	**Janet Leigh**
	11 Sept.	Vol. 28, no. 1010	**Sara Shane**
	18 Sept.	Vol. 28, no. 1011	**Anne Baxter**
	25 Sept.	Vol. 28, no. 1012	**Jill Adams**
	2 Oct.	Vol. 28, no. 1013	**Jackie Lane**
	9 Oct.	Vol. 28, no. 1014	**Cyd Charisse**
	16 Oct.	Vol. 28, no. 1015	**Hedda Lynton**
	23 Oct.	Vol. 28, no. 1016	**Marilyn Monroe**
	30 Oct.	Vol. 28, no. 1017	**Kathleen Hughes**
	6 Nov.	Vol. 28, no. 1018	**Marla English**
	13 Nov.	Vol. 28, no. 1019	**Allison Hayes**
	20 Nov.	Vol. 28, no. 1020	**Vera-Ellen**
	27 Nov.	Vol. 28, no. 1021	**Cleo Moore**
	4 Dec.	Vol. 28, no. 1022	**Rita Moreno**
	11 Dec.	Vol. 28, no. 1023	**Debra Paget**
	18 Dec.	Vol. 28, no. 1024	**Jane Russell**
	25 Dec.	Vol. 28, no. 1025	**Shirley Eaton**
1955	1 Jan.	Vol. 29, no. 1026	**Jana Mason**
	8 Jan.	Vol. 29, no. 1027	**Kim Novak**
	15 Jan.	Vol. 29, no. 1028	**Gloria De Haven**
	22 Jan.	Vol. 29, no. 1029	**Anne Baxter**
	29 Jan.	Vol. 29, no. 1030	**Elisa Lotti**
	5 Feb.	Vol. 29, no. 1031	**Dorothy Malone**
	12 Feb.	Vol. 29, no. 1032	**Dani Crayne**
	19 Feb.	Vol. 29, no. 1033	**Mamie Van Doren**
	26 Feb.	Vol. 29, no. 1034	**Myrna Hansen**
	5 March	Vol. 29, no. 1035	**Shawn Smith**
	12 March	Vol. 29, no. 1036	**Betty Grable**
	19 March	Vol. 29, no. 1037	**Mitzi Gaynor**
	26 March	Vol. 29, no. 1038	**Marjorie Hellen**
	2 April	Vol. 29, no. 1039	**Colleen Miller**
	9 April	Vol. 29, no. 1040	**Joyce Van Der Veen**
	16 April	Vol. 29, no. 1041	**Martha Hyer**
	23 April	Vol. 29, no. 1042	**Nicole Maurey**
	30 April	Vol. 29, no. 1043	**Belinda Lee**
	7 May	Vol. 29, no. 1044	**Jill Ireland**
	14 May	Vol. 29, no. 1045	**Jill Adams**
	21 May	Vol. 29, no. 1046	**Jacqueline Curtis**
	28 May	Vol. 29, no. 1047	**Julia Arnall**
	4 June	Vol. 29, no. 1048	**Maureen Swanson**
	11 June	Vol. 29, no. 1049	**Piper Laurie**
	18 June	Vol. 29, no. 1050	**Eunice Gayson**
	25 June	Vol. 29, no. 1051	**Aleta Morrison**
	2 July	Vol. 30, no. 1052	**Jayne Mansfield**
	9 July	Vol. 30, no. 1053	**Susan Beaumont**
	16 July	Vol. 30, no. 1054	**Diane Foster**
	23 July	Vol. 30, no. 1055	**Brigitte Bardot**
	30 July	Vol. 30, no. 1056	**Doreen Dawne**
	6 Aug.	Vol. 30, no. 1057	**Pamela Devis**
	13 Aug.	Vol. 30, no. 1058	**Gilda Russell**
	20 Aug.	Vol. 30, no. 1059	**Sally Forrest**
	27 Aug.	Vol. 30, no. 1060	**Joyce Cooke**
	3 Sept.	Vol. 30, no. 1061	**Gloria De Haven**
	10 Sept.	Vol. 30, no. 1062	**Mamie Van Doren**
	17 Sept.	Vol. 30, no. 1063	**Esther Williams**
	24 Sept.	Vol. 30, no. 1064	**Mara Corday**
	1 Oct.	Vol. 30, no. 1065	**Jeanne Crain Jane Russell**
	8 Oct.	Vol. 30, no. 1066	**Anita Ekberg**
	15 Oct.	Vol. 30, no. 1067	**Lisa Gastoni**
	22 Oct.	Vol. 30, no. 1068	**Belinda Lee**
	29 Oct.	Vol. 30, no. 1069	**Jill Day**
	5 Nov.	Vol. 30, no. 1070	**Maureen Becok**
	12 Nov.	Vol. 30, no. 1071	**Shirley Ann Field**
	19 Nov.	Vol. 30, no. 1072	**Ava Gardner**
	26 Nov.	Vol. 30, no. 1073	**Marianne Brauns**
	3 Dec.	Vol. 30, no. 1074	**Sophia Loren**
	10 Dec.	Vol. 30, no. 1075	**Cyd Charisse**
	17 Dec.	Vol. 30, no. 1076	**Jackie Lane**
	24 Dec.	Vol. 30, no. 1077	**Magda Miller**
	31 Dec.	Vol. 30, no. 1078	**Diana Dors**
1956	7 Jan.	Vol. 31, no. 1079	**Kathleen Hughes**
	14 Jan.	Vol. 31, no. 1080	**Julia Arnall**

YEAR	MONTH	REF. No.	COVER STAR
	21 Jan.	Vol. 31, no. 1081	**Mary Murphy**
	28 Jan.	Vol. 31, no. 1082	**Jackie Collins**
	4 Feb.	Vol. 31, no. 1083	**Lita Baron**
	11 Feb.	Vol. 31, no. 1084	**Dani Crayne**
	18 Feb.	Vol. 31, no. 1085	**Rita Moreno**
	25 Feb.	Vol. 31, no. 1086	**Simon McQueen**
	3 March	Vol. 31, no. 1087	**Joy Webster**
	10 March	Vol. 31, no. 1088	**Rosalina Neri**
	17 March	Vol. 31, no. 1089	**Ann Talbot**
	24 March	Vol. 31, no. 1090	**Shirley Deane**
	31 March	Vol. 31, no. 1091	**April Olrich**
	7 April	Vol. 31, no. 1092	**Brigitte Bardot**
	14 April	Vol. 31, no. 1093	**Aleta Morrison**
	21 April	Vol. 31, no. 1094	**Gina Lollobrigida**
	28 April	Vol. 31, no. 1095	**Joan Collins**
	5 May	Vol. 31, no. 1096	**Lola Albright**
	12 May	Vol. 31, no. 1097	**Mitzi Gaynor**
	19 May	Vol. 31, no. 1098	**Tonia Bern**
	26 May	Vol. 31, no. 1099	**Belinda Lee**
	2 June	Vol. 31, no. 1100	**Dany Carrel**
	9 June	Vol. 31, no. 1101	**Elsa Martinelli**
	16 June	Vol. 31, no. 1102	**Jane Russell**
	23 June	Vol. 31, no. 1103	**Shane Cordell**
	30 June	Vol. 31, no. 1104	**Valerie Allen**
	7 July	Vol. 32, no. 1105	**Colleen Miller**
	14 July	Vol. 32, no. 1106	**Victoria Shaw**
	21 July	Vol. 32, no. 1107	**Kim Novak**
	28 July	Vol. 32, no. 1108	**Sabrina**
	4 Aug.	Vol. 32, no. 1109	**Vera Miles**
	11 Aug.	Vol. 32, no. 1110	**Yana**
	18 Aug.	Vol. 32, no. 1111	**Una Pearl**
	25 Aug.	Vol. 32, no. 1112	**Natalie Wood**
	1 Sept.	Vol. 32, no. 1113	**Nilda Terrace**
	8 Sept.	Vol. 32, no. 1114	**Barbara Roscoe**
	15 Sept.	Vol. 32, no. 1115	**Sheena Marshe**
	22 Sept.	Vol. 32, no. 1116	**Leslie Carol***
	29 Sept.	Vol. 32, no. 1117	**Dorothy Malone**
	6 Oct.	Vol. 32, no. 1118	**Karen Steele**
	13 Oct.	Vol. 32, no. 1119	**Lucy Marlow**
	20 Oct.	Vol. 32, no. 1120	**Anita Ekberg**
	27 Oct.	Vol. 32, no. 1121	**Sarita Montiel**
	3 Nov.	Vol. 32, no. 1122	**Kim Parker**
	10 Nov.	Vol. 32, no. 1123	**Eileen Elton**
	17 Nov.	Vol. 32, no. 1124	**Marilyn Monroe**
	24 Nov.	Vol. 32, no. 1125	**Jacqueline Curtis**
	1 Dec.	Vol. 32, no. 1126	**Barbara Lang**
	8 Dec.	Vol. 32, no. 1127	**Martha Hyer**
	15 Dec.	Vol. 32, no. 1128	**Sheree North**
	22 Dec.	Vol. 32, no. 1129	**Hazel Sutton**
	29 Dec.	Vol. 32, no. 1130	**Vera-Ellen**
1957	5 Jan.	Vol. 33, no. 1131	**Barbara Pinney**
	12 Jan.	Vol. 33, no. 1132	**Marjorie Hellen**
	19 Jan.	Vol. 33, no. 1133	**June Cunningham**

*Later known as Carole Lesley.

YEAR	MONTH	REF. No.	COVER STAR
	26 Jan.	Vol. 33, no. 1134	**Diane Brewster**
	2 Feb.	Vol. 33, no. 1135	**Lynn Tracey**
	9 Feb.	Vol. 33, no. 1136	**Rhonda Fleming**
	16 Feb.	Vol. 33, no. 1137	**Janette Scott**
	23 Feb.	Vol. 33, no. 1138	**Adele Collins** **Zoe Newton**
	2 March	Vol. 33, no. 1139	**Valerie Allen**
	9 March	Vol. 33, no. 1140	**Jane Rieger**
	16 March	Vol. 33, no. 1141	**Jayne Mansfield**
	23 March	Vol. 33, no. 1142	**Anna Maria Alberghetti**
	30 March	Vol. 33, no. 1143	**Marigold Russell**
	6 April	Vol. 33, no. 1144	**June Ramsey**
	13 April	Vol. 33, no. 1145	**Elsa Martinelli**
	20 April	Vol. 33, no. 1146	**Jackie Lane**
	27 April	Vol. 33, no. 1147	**Taina Elg**
	4 May	Vol. 33, no. 1148	**Diana Dors**
	11 May	Vol. 33, no. 1149	**Lisa Gastoni**
	18 May	Vol. 33, no. 1150	**Gia Scala**
	25 May	Vol. 33, no. 1151	**Elaine Stewart**
	1 June	Vol. 33, no. 1152	**Hazel Court**
	8 June	Vol. 33, no. 1153	**Sheree North**
	15 June	Vol. 33, no. 1154	**Anne Heywood**
	22 June	Vol. 33, no. 1155	**Marisa Allasio**
	29 June	Vol. 33, no. 1156	**Shirley Eaton**
	6 July	Vol. 34, no. 1157	**Luana Lee**
	13 July	Vol. 34, no. 1158	**Kim Novak**
	20 July	Vol. 34, no. 1159	**Mitzi Gaynor**
	27 July	Vol. 34, no. 1160	**Neile Adams**
	3 Aug.	Vol. 34, no. 1161	**Carol Morris**
	10 Aug.	Vol. 34, no. 1162	**Lisa Davis**
	17 Aug.	Vol. 34, no. 1163	**Esther Williams**
	24 Aug.	Vol. 34, no. 1164	**June Laverick**
	31 Aug.	Vol. 34, no. 1165	**Rita Moreno**
	7 Sept.	Vol. 34, no. 1166	**Mara Corday**
	14 Sept.	Vol. 34, no. 1167	**Shirley Deane**
	21 Sept.	Vol. 34, no. 1168	**Shirley Ann Field**
	28 Sept.	Vol. 34, no. 1169	**Belinda Lee**
	5 Oct.	Vol. 34, no. 1170	**Kay Kendall**
	12 Oct.	Vol. 34, no. 1171	**Mamie Van Doren**
	19 Oct.	Vol. 34, no. 1172	**Andra Martin**
	26 Oct.	Vol. 34, no. 1173	**Jayne Mansfield**
	2 Nov.	Vol. 34, no. 1174	**Anne Aubrey**
	9 Nov.	Vol. 34, no. 1175	**Benice Swanson**
	16 Nov.	Vol. 34, no. 1176	**Christine Carere**
	23 Nov.	Vol. 34, no. 1177	**Merry Anders**
	30 Nov.	Vol. 34, no. 1178	**Barbara Nichols**
	7 Dec.	Vol. 34, no. 1179	**Martha Hyer**
	14 Dec.	Vol. 34, no. 1180	**Joan Collins**
	21 Dec.	Vol. 34, no. 1181	**Beverly Garland**
	28 Dec.	Vol. 34, no. 1182	**Mitzi Gaynor**
1958	4 Jan.	Vol. 35, no. 1183	**Jill Ireland**
	11 Jan.	Vol. 35, no. 1184	**Dorrie Butlin**
	18 Jan.	Vol. 35, no. 1185	**Gia Scala**
	25 Jan.	Vol. 35, no. 1186	**Gillian Vaughan**
	1 Feb.	Vol. 35, no. 1187	**Julie London**
	8 Feb.	Vol. 35, no. 1188	**Jill St John**

YEAR	MONTH	REF. No.	COVER STAR
	15 Feb.	Vol. 35, no. 1189	**Janice Venneear**
	22 Feb.	Vol. 35, no. 1190	**Debbie Reynolds**
	1 March	Vol. 35, no. 1191	**Brigitte Bardot**
			Frank Sinatra
			Tommy Sands
	8 March	Vol. 35, no. 1192	**Anne Heywood**
			Anthony Perkins
			Terry Dene
	15 March	Vol. 35, no. 1193	**Dominique Boschero**
	22 March	Vol. 35, no. 1194	**Jane Powell**
			Tony Franciosa
			Russ Tamblyn
	29 March	Vol. 35, no. 1195	**Carole Lesley**
	5 April	Vol. 35, no. 1196	**Tommy Steele**
			Anita Ekberg
			Dirk Bogarde
	12 April	Vol. 35, no. 1197	**Leila Williams**
			David McCallum
			Jerry Lewis
	19 April	Vol. 35, no. 1198	**Janet Leigh**
	26 April	Vol. 35, no. 1199	**Rosanna Schiaffino**
	3 May	Vol. 35, no. 1200	**John Saxon**
			Yvonne Warren
			John Derek
	10 May	Vol. 35, no. 1201	**Nadine Tallier**
			Charlton Heston
			George Nader
	17 May,	Vol. 35, no. 1202	**Mamie Van Doren**
	24 May	Vol. 35, no. 1203	**Sandra Francis**
	31 May	Vol. 35, no. 1204	**Barbara Lang**
	7 June	Vol. 35, no. 1205	**Claire Kelly**
	14 June	Vol. 35, no. 1206	**Kim Novak**
	21 June	Vol. 35, no. 1207	**Joanna Moore**
	28 June	Vol. 35, no. 1208	**Venetia Stevenson**
	5 July	Vol. 36, no. 1209	**Christine Carere**
	12 July	Vol. 36, no. 1210	**Merry Anders**
	19 July	Vol. 36, no. 1211	**Susan Oliver**
	26 July	Vol. 36, no. 1212	**Barbara Nichols**
	2 Aug.	Vol. 36, no. 1213	**Jayne Mansfield**
			Elvis Presley
			Andy Griffith
	9 Aug.	Vol. 36, no. 1214	**Vanda**
	16 Aug.	Vol. 36, no. 1215	**Jean Moorehead**
	23 Aug.	Vol. 36, no. 1216	**Linda Cristal**
	30 Aug.	Vol. 36, no. 1217	**Luciana Lovello***
	6 Sept.	Vol. 36, no. 1218	**Barbara Joyce**
	13 Sept.	Vol. 36, no. 1219	**Perin Lewis**
	20 Sept.	Vol. 36, no. 1220	**Virginia Maskell**
	27 Sept.	Vol. 36, no. 1221	**Rita Moreno**
	4 Oct.	Vol. 36, no. 1222	**Lucette Marimar**
	11 Oct.	Vol. 36, no. 1223	**Sheree Winton**
	18 Oct.	Vol. 36, no. 1224	**Sandra Dee**
	25 Oct.	Vol. 36, no. 1225	**Nina Shipman**
	1 Nov.	Vol. 36, no. 1226	**Judi Moyens**
	8 Nov.	Vol. 36, no. 1227	**Tony Curtis**
	15 Nov.	Vol. 36, no. 1228	**Sophia Loren**
	22 Nov.	Vol. 36, no. 1229	**Claire Gordon**
	29 Nov.	Vol. 36, no. 1230	**Beth Rogan**
	6 Dec.	Vol. 36, no. 1231	**John Saxon**
	13 Dec.	Vol. 36, no. 1232	**Jose Read**
	20 Dec.	Vol. 36, no. 1233	**Pat Laurence**
	27 Dec.	Vol. 36, no. 1234	**Anne Heywood**
1959	3 Jan.	Vol. 37, no. 1235	**Norma Parnell**
	10 Jan.	Vol. 37, no. 1236	**Rita Royce**
	17 Jan.	Vol. 37, no. 1237	**Margaret Clews**
	24 Jan.	Vol. 37, no. 1238	**Sal Mineo**
	31 Jan.	Vol. 37, no. 1239	**Tommy Sands**
	7 Feb.	Vol. 37, no. 1240	**Shirley Ann Field**
	14 Feb.	Vol. 37, no. 1241	**Rosalie Ashley**
	21 Feb.	Vol. 37, no. 1242	**Yul Brynner**
	28 Feb.	Vol. 37, no. 1243	**Joan Collins**
	7 March	Vol. 37, no. 1244	**Wendy Peters**
	14 March	Vol. 37, no. 1245	**Margaret Simons**
	21 March	Vol. 37, no. 1246	**Janet Munro**
	28 March	Vol. 37, no. 1247	**Cliff Richard**
	4 April	Vol. 37, no. 1248	**Anne Aubrey**
	11 April	Vol. 37, no. 1249	**Frank Sinatra**
	18 April	Vol. 37, no. 1250	**Noelle Adam**
	25 April	Vol. 37, no. 1251	**Pamela Searle**
	2 May	Vol. 37, no. 1252	**Gordon Scott**
	9 May	Vol. 37, no. 1253	**Susan Kohner**
	16 May	Vol. 37, no. 1254	**Mary Ann Bourne**
	23 May	Vol. 37, no. 1255	**Marty Wilde**
	30 May	Vol. 37, no. 1256	**Julie Glenville**
	6 June	Vol. 37, no. 1257	**Vivi Bak**
	13 June	Vol. 37, no. 1258	**Nadja Tiller**
	20 June	Vol. 37, no. 1259	**Anthony Perkins**
	27 June	Vol. 37, no. 1260	**Eve Eden**
	22 Aug.	Vol. 38, no. 1261	**Claudia Cardinale**
	29 Aug.	Vol. 38, no. 1262	**Dirk Bogarde**
	5 Sept.	Vol. 38, no. 1263	**Veronica Gray**
	12 Sept.	Vol. 38, no. 1264	**Leila Williams**
	19 Sept.	Vol. 38, no. 1265	**Elke Sommer**
	26 Sept.	Vol. 38, no. 1266	**Mylene Demongeot**
	3 Oct.	Vol. 38, no. 1267	**Nadja Regin**
	10 Oct.	Vol. 38, no. 1268	**Yvonne Monlaur**
	17 Oct.	Vol. 38, no. 1269	**May Britt**
	24 Oct.	Vol. 38, no. 1270	**Pauline Shepherd**
	31 Oct.	Vol. 38, no. 1271	**Jackie Lane**
	7 Nov.	Vol. 38, no. 1272	**Doris Day**
	14 Nov.	Vol. 38, no. 1273	**Gina Lollobrigida**
	21 Nov.	Vol. 38, no. 1274	**Joan Collins**
	28 Nov.	Vol. 38, no. 1275	**Joy Gibson**
	5 Dec.	Vol. 38, no. 1276	**Belinda Lee**
	12 Dec.	Vol. 38, no. 1277	**Brigitte Bardot**
	19 Dec.	Vol. 38, no. 1278	**Pat Boone**
	26 Dec.	Vol. 38, no. 1279	**Julie Shearing**
1960	2 Jan.	Vol. 39, no. 1280	**Delyse Humphreys**
	9 Jan.	Vol. 39, no. 1281	**Constance Towers**
	16 Jan.	Vol. 39, no. 1282	**Paul Newman**
	23 Jan.	Vol. 39, no. 1283	**Kim Parker**

*Italian actress credited in films as Luciana Paluzzi.

YEAR	MONTH	REF. No.	COVER STAR
	30 Jan.	Vol. 39, no. 1284	**Jo Waring**
	6 Feb.	Vol. 39, no. 1285	**Margo Mayne**
	13 Feb.	Vol. 39, no. 1286	**Adam Faith**
	20 Feb.	Vol. 39, no. 1287	**Debbie Reynolds**
	27 Feb.	Vol. 39, no. 1288	**Leslie Parrish**
	5 March	Vol. 39, no. 1289	**Charlton Heston**
	12 March	Vol. 39, no. 1290	**Robert Wagner**
			Natalie Wood
	19 March	Vol. 39, no. 1291	**Sal Mineo**
	26 March	Vol. 39, no. 1292	**Elizabeth Taylor**
	2 April	Vol. 39, no. 1293	**Billy Fury**
	9 April	Vol. 39, no. 1294	**Anthony Perkins**
			Tuesday Weld
	16 April	Vol. 39, no. 1295	**Yvette Mimieux**
	23 April	Vol. 39, no. 1296	**Jackie Rae**
			Janette Scott

PREMIERE 1987 –

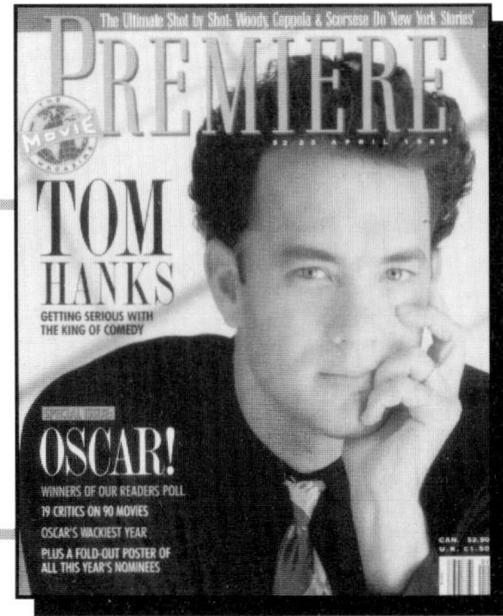

An American film monthly written in the style of *Rolling Stone* with similar format. Fine photographic covers, good articles and regular filmographies. Edited by Susan Lyne and published by K – III, USA.

YEAR	MONTH	REF. No.	COVER STAR
1987	July/ Aug.	Vol. 1, no. 1	**Dan Aykroyd** **Tom Hanks**
	Oct.	Vol. 1, no. 2	**Diane Keaton**
	Nov.	Vol. 1, no. 3	**William Hurt**
	Dec.	Vol. 1, no. 4	**Charlie Sheen**
			Michael Douglas
1988	Jan.	Vol. 1, no. 5	**Robin Williams**
	Feb.	Vol. 1, no. 6	**Cher**
			Nicholas Cage
	March	Vol. 1, no. 7	**Harrison Ford**
	April	Vol. 1, no. 8	**Robert Duvall**
			Dennis Hopper
			Sean Penn
	May	Vol. 1, no. 9	**Kevin Costner**
			Susan Sarandon
	June	Vol. 1, no. 10	**Lily Tomlin**
			Bette Midler
	July	Vol. 1, no. 11	**Tom Cruise**
	Aug.	Vol. 1, no. 12	**Charlie Sheen**
			Emilio Estevez
			Kiefer Sutherland
			Lou Diamond Phillips
	Sept.	Vol. 2, no. 1	**Mel Gibson**
	Oct.	Vol. 2, no. 2	**Sigourney Weaver**
	Nov.	Vol. 2, no. 3	**U2**
	Dec.	Vol. 2, no. 4	**Michelle Pfeiffer**
1989	Jan.	Vol. 2, no. 5	**Arnold Schwarzenegger**
	Feb.	Vol. 2, no. 6	**Dustin Hoffman**
	March	Vol. 2, no. 7	**Nick Nolte**
	April	Vol. 2, no. 8	**Tom Hanks**
	May	Vol. 2, no. 9	**Sean Young**
	June	Vol. 2, no. 10	**Steven Spielberg**
			Harrison Ford
	July	Vol. 2, no. 11	**Michael Keaton**
	Aug.	Vol. 2, no. 12	**Dennis Quaid**
	Sept.	Vol. 3, no. 1	**Kim Basinger**
	Oct.	Vol. 3, no. 2	**Michael J. Fox**
	Nov.	Vol. 3, no. 3	**Kathleen Turner**
	Dec.	Vol. 3, no. 4	**Meryl Streep**
			Roseanne Barr

TIME 1923 –

For many an individual, to appear on the cover of *Time* is to receive the ultimate accolade. It has been written about in plays and novels, sung about in songs, and in *Meet John Doe* John Doe, played by Gary Cooper, realizes his success only when he sees his face on *Time*'s front page. Today it is still the world's foremost and most respected news magazine. It was founded in 1923 by Henry Luce and Briton Hadden with a working title of 'Facts'; the name *Time* was inspired by a nineteenth-century English magazine.

Time was first published on 3 March 1923, as a weekly. Joseph G. Cannon was on its very first cover and the first film star cover was of Ethel Barrymore, an established actress in films, though the cover story actually concerned her work in the theatre. Early *Time* covers worth noting: 15 August 1932, a rare cover of the Marx Brothers; 31 August 1936, a fine portrait of Clark Gable by Clarence Bull; 30 November 1936, studio portrait of Marlene Dietrich; 3 March 1941, Gary Cooper as John Doe; 10 November 1941, an artist-drawn cover of Rita Hayworth by George Petty. The general guide for collectors is that one *Time* cover is worth ten covers of any other magazine. There are exceptions to this, notably the Shirley Temple cover of 27 April 1936, which is worth little, because she is partially hidden. Further, American editions of *Time* are worth twice as much as international editions.

Listed below are film orientated covers only.

YEAR	MONTH	REF. No.	COVER STAR
1924	10 Nov.	Vol. 4, no. 19	**Ethel Barrymore**
1925	6 July	Vol. 6, no. 1	**Charlie Chaplin**
1926	19 July	Vol. 8, no. 3	**Will Rogers**
1929	14 Jan.	Vol. 13, no. 2	**Adoph Zukor**
	30 Sept.	Vol. 14, no. 14	**Ina Claire**
1931	9 Feb.	Vol. 17, no. 6	**Charlie Chaplin**
1932	7 March	Vol. 19, no. 10	**Lionel and John Barrymore**
	15 Aug.	Vol. 20, no. 7	**Marx Brothers**
1933	7 Aug.	Vol. 22, no. 6	**Marie Dressler**
	25 Dec.	Vol. 22, no. 26	**Charlotte Henry**
1934	26 March	Vol. 23, no. 13	**George Arliss**
	27 Aug.	Vol. 24, no. 9	**Cecil B. De Mille**
1935	27 May	Vol. 25, no. 21	**Miriam Hopkins**
	19 Aug.	Vol. 26, no. 8	**Jean Harlow**
	30 Dec.	Vol. 26, no. 27	**Helen Hayes**
1936	27 April	Vol. 27, no. 17	**Shirley Temple**
	31 Aug.	Vol. 28, no. 9	**Clark Gable**
	30 Nov.	Vol. 28, no. 22	**Marlene Dietrich**
1937	16 Aug.	Vol. 30, no. 7	**Paul Muni**
	27 Dec.	Vol. 30, no. 26	**Walt Disney**
1938	28 March	Vol. 31, no. 13	**Bette Davis**
	9 May	Vol. 31, no. 19	**Orson Welles**
	8 Aug.	Vol. 32, no. 6	**Frank Capra**

YEAR	MONTH	REF. No.	COVER STAR
1939	10 April	Vol. 33, no. 15	**Ginger Rogers**
	17 July	Vol. 34, no. 3	**Sonja Henie**
	25 Dec.	Vol. 34, no. 26	**Vivien Leigh**
1940	18 March	Vol. 35, no. 12	**Mickey Rooney**
	28 Oct.	Vol. 36, no. 18	**Ethel Merman**
1941	3 March	Vol. 37, no. 9	**Gary Cooper**
	7 April	Vol. 37, no. 14	**Bing Crosby**
	10 Nov.	Vol. 38, no. 19	**Rita Hayworth**
1943	2 Aug.	Vol. 42, no. 5	**Ingrid Bergman**
	20 Sept.	Vol. 42, no. 12	**Bob Hope**
	20 Dec.	Vol. 42, no. 25	**Greer Garson**
1944	24 Jan.	Vol. 43, no. 4	**Jimmy Durante**
1946	11 March	Vol. 47, no. 10	**Danny Kaye**
	8 April	Vol. 47, no. 14	**Laurence Olivier**
	11 Nov.	Vol. 48, no. 20	**Helen Traubel**
1947	10 Feb.	Vol. 49, no. 6	**Deborah Kerr**
	7 April	Vol. 49, no. 14	**Fred Allen**
	19 May	Vol. 49, no. 20	**J. Arthur Rank**
	28 July	Vol. 50. no. 4	**Hedda Hopper**
1948	12 Jan.	Vol. 51, no. 2	**Gregory Peck**
	28 June	Vol. 51, no. 26	**Jean Simmons**
	19 July	Vol. 52, no. 3	**Howard Hughes**
	23 Aug.	Vol. 52, no. 8	**Betty Grable**
	22 Nov.	Vol. 52, no. 21	**Tallulah Bankhead**
	20 Dec.	Vol. 52, no. 25	**Olivia De Havilland**
1949	21 Feb.	Vol. 53, no. 8	**Louis Armstrong**
	16 May	Vol. 53, no. 20	**Milton Berle**
	25 July	Vol. 54, no. 4	**Harold Lloyd**
	22 Aug.	Vol. 54, no. 8	**Elizabeth Taylor**
1950	9 Jan.	Vol. 55, no. 2	**Carol Channing**
	24 April	Vol. 55, no. 17	**Betty Hutton**
	12 June	Vol. 55, no. 24	**Darryl F. Zanuck**
	27 Nov.	Vol. 56, no. 22	**William Boyd**
1951	9 April	Vol. 57, no. 15	**Barbara Bel Geddes**
	6 Aug.	Vol. 58, no. 6	**Mario Lanza**
	3 Sept.	Vol. 58, no. 10	**Ava Gardner**
	1 Oct.	Vol. 58, no. 14	**Bert Lahr**
	3 Dec.	Vol. 58, no. 23	**Patrice Munsel**
	31 Dec.	Vol. 58, no. 27	**Groucho Marx**
1952	3 March	Vol. 59, no. 9	**John Wayne**
	31 March	Vol. 59, no. 13	**Charles Laughton**
	26 May	Vol. 59, no. 21	**Lucille Ball**

YEAR	MONTH	REF. No.	COVER STAR
	1 Sept.	Vol. 60, no. 9	**Katharine Hepburn**
	17 Nov.	Vol. 60, no. 20	**Claire Bloom**
1953	23 Feb.	Vol. 61, no. 8	**Rosemary Clooney**
	30 March	Vol. 61, no. 13	**Rosalind Russell**
	8 June	Vol. 61, no. 23	**3-D movies**
	10 Aug.	Vol. 62, no. 6	**Shirley Booth**
	7 Sept.	Vol. 62, no. 10	**Audrey Hepburn**
1954	15 March	Vol. 63, no. 11	**Jack Webb**
	7 June	Vol. 63, no. 23	**Humphrey Bogart**
	16 Aug.	Vol. 64, no. 7	**Gina Lollobrigida**
	11 Oct.	Vol. 64, no. 15	**Marlon Brando**
	27 Dec.	Vol. 64, no. 26	**Walt Disney**
1955	31 Jan.	Vol. 65, no. 5	**Grace Kelly**
	13 June	Vol. 65, no. 24	**Gwen Verdon**
	29 Aug.	Vol. 66, no. 9	**Frank Sinatra**
	28 Nov.	Vol. 66, no. 22	**Julie Harris**
1956	27 Feb.	Vol. 67, no. 9	**William Holden**
	14 May	Vol. 67, no. 20	**Marilyn Monroe**
	23 July	Vol. 68, no. 4	**Rex Harrison**
1957	29 July	Vol. 70, no. 5	**Kim Novak**
	30 Dec.	Vol. 70, no. 27	**Maria Schell**
1958	21 April	Vol. 71, no. 16	**Alec Guinness**
	21 July	Vol. 72, no. 3	**Robert Preston**
1959	2 March	Vol. 73, no. 9	**Harry Belafonte**
	22 June	Vol. 73, no. 25	**Shirley MacLaine**
	21 Dec.	Vol. 74, no. 25	**Anne Bancroft**
1960	14 March	Vol. 75, no. 11	**Ingmar Bergman**
1961	29 Dec.	Vol. 78, no. 26	**Jackie Gleason**
1962	6 April	Vol. 79, no. 14	**Sophia Loren**
1963	26 April	Vol. 81, no. 17	**Richard Burton**
	20 Sept.	Vol. 82, no. 12	**International cinema**
1964	10 April	Vol. 83, no. 15	**Barbra Streisand**
1965	5 March	Vol. 85, no. 10	**Jeanne Moreau**
1966	29 July	Vol. 88, no. 5	**Lauren Bacall**
	23 Dec.	Vol. 88, no. 26	**Julie Andrews**
1967	17 March	Vol. 89, no. 11	**Lynn & Vanessa Redgrave**

YEAR	MONTH	REF. No.	COVER STAR
	1 Sept.	Vol. 90, no. 9	**Sandy Dennis**
	22 Sept.	Vol. 90, no. 12	**The Beatles**
	8 Dec.	Vol. 90, no. 23	***Bonnie and Clyde***
	22 Dec.	Vol. 90, no. 25	**Bob Hope**
1969	7 Feb.	Vol. 93, no. 6	**Dustin Hoffman** **Mia Farrow**
	8 Aug.	Vol. 94, no. 6	**John Wayne**
	28 Nov.	Vol. 94, no. 22	**Raquel Welch**
1970	16 Feb.	Vol. 95, no. 7	**Jane, Henry and Peter Fonda**
	15 June	Vol. 95, no. 24	**Mike Nichols**
	7 Sept.	Vol. 96, no. 10	**Elliott Gould**
1971	11 Jan.	Vol. 97, no. 2	**Ali MacGraw**
	22 March	Vol. 97, no. 12	**George C. Scott**
	3 May	Vol. 97, no. 18	**Alexis Smith**
1972	28 Feb.	Vol. 99, no. 9	**Liza Minnelli**
	3 July	Vol. 100, no. 1	**Woody Allen**
	4 Dec.	Vol. 100, no. 23	**Liv Ullmann**
1973	22 Jan	Vol. 101, no. 4	**Marlon Brando**
	16 July	Vol. 102, no. 3	**Marilyn Monroe** **Norman Mailer**
	26 Nov.	Vol. 102, no. 22	**Peter Falk**
1974	18 March	Vol. 103, no. 11	**Robert Redford** **Mia Farrow**
	12 Aug.	Vol. 104, no. 7	**Jack Nicholson**
1975	17 March	Vol. 105, no. 11	**Cher**
	19 May	Vol. 105, no. 21	**Mikhail Baryshnikov**
	16 June	Vol. 105, no. 25	**Margaux Hemingway**
	23 June	Vol. 105, no. 26	***Jaws***
	15 Dec.	Vol. 106, no. 24	**Marisa Berenson**
1976	29 March	Vol. 107, no. 13	**Dustin Hoffman** **Robert Redford**
	31 May	Vol. 107, no. 23	**Paul McCartney**
	25 Oct.	Vol. 108, no. 17	***King Kong***
	22 Nov.	Vol. 108 no. 21	**Kate Jackson** **Farrah Fawcett** **Jaclyn Smith**
1977	28 March	Vol. 109, no. 13	**Lily Tomlin**
	26 Sept.	Vol. 110, no. 13	**Diane Keaton**
1978	9 Jan	Vol. 111, no. 2	**Burt Reynolds** **Clint Eastwood**
	3 April	Vol. 111, no. 14	**John Travolta**
	3 July	Vol. 112, no. 1	**Warren Beatty**

YEAR	MONTH	REF. No.	COVER STAR
1979	12 March	Vol. 113, no. 11	**Robin Williams**
	30 April	Vol. 113, no. 18	**Woody Allen**
	13 Aug.	Vol. 114, no. 7	**Diane Lane**
1980	3 March	Vol. 115, no. 9	**Peter Sellers**
	19 May	Vol. 115, no. 20	***Star Wars***
	22 Dec.	Vol. 116, no. 25	**John Lennon**
1981	9 Feb.	Vol. 117, no. 6	**Brooke Shields**
	7 Sept.	Vol. 118, no. 10	**Meryl Streep**
	16 Nov.	Vol. 118, no. 20	**Katharine Hepburn** **Henry Fonda**
1982	22 Feb.	Vol. 119, no. 8	**Jaclyn Smith**
	14 June	Vol. 119, no. 24	**Gerry Cooney** **Sylvester Stallone**
	6 Dec.	Vol. 120, no. 23	**Paul Newman**
1983	7 Feb.	Vol. 121, no. 6	**Robert Mitchum**
	2 May	Vol. 121, no. 18	**Nastassja Kinski**
	23 May	Vol. 121, no. 21	**George Lucas**
	18 July	Vol. 122, no. 3	**David Bowie**
1984	19 March	Vol. 123, no. 12	**Michael Jackson**
	14 May	Vol. 123, no. 20	**Shirley MacLaine**
	31 Dec.	Vol. 124, no. 27	**David Lean**
1985	27 May	Vol. 125, no. 21	**Madonna**
	15 July	Vol. 126, no. 2	**Steven Spielberg**
	16 Sept.	Vol. 126, no. 11	**Philip Michael Thomas** **Don Johnson**
1986	26 May	Vol. 127, no. 21	**Molly Ringwald**
	28 July	Vol. 128, no. 4	**Sigourney Weaver**
1987	26 Jan.	Vol. 129, no. 4	**Willem Dafoe** **Charlie Sheen** **Tom Berenger**
	2 March	Vol. 129, no. 9	**Bette Midler**
	24 Aug.	Vol. 130, no. 8	**Steve Martin**
	28 Sept.	Vol. 130, no. 13	**Bill Cosby**
	16 Nov.	Vol. 130, no. 20	**Glenn Close** **Michael Douglas**
	7 Dec.	Vol. 130, no. 23	**Shirley MacLaine**
1988	25 April	Vol. 131, no. 17	**Mickey Mouse**
	11 July	Vol. 132, no. 2	**James Olmos**
1989	9 Jan.	Vol. 133, no. 2	**Gene Hackman** **Willem Dafoe**
	26 June	Vol. 133, no. 26	**Kevin Costner**
	25 Dec.	Vol. 134, no. 26	**Tom Cruise**

CHAPTER THREE

ANNUALS

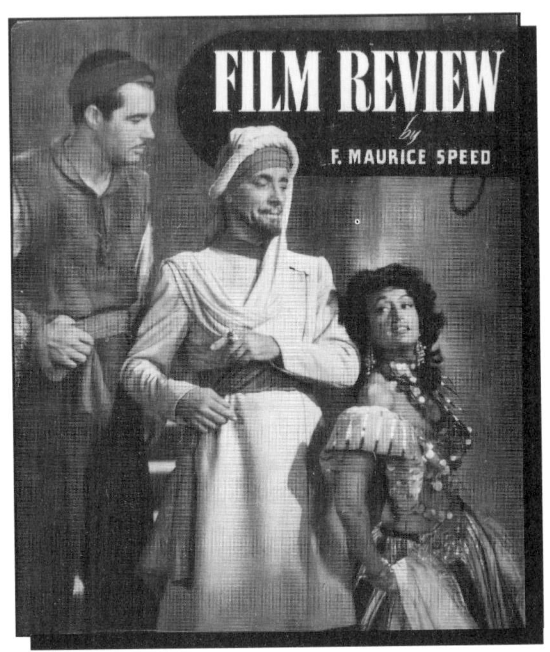

The first *Film Review* jacket from 1944.

Early film annuals were of the fanzine variety: *Filmgoers*, *Film Lovers*, *Film Pictorial*, *Picture Show*, *Picturegoer* annuals all had their gossip, fashion articles and portraits of the current stars. Later came titles such as *Film Parade* and *Hollywood Album*, which generally followed the same pattern. So in 1944, when F. Maurice Speed edited and compiled *Film Review*, which attempted to record the year's films, giving relevant details of casts, credits, and release dates, it was the first annual to offer a complete record in words and pictures of movies, illustrated throughout with star portraits and film stills in black and white and Kodachrome. Published by MacDonald & Company until 1968 when W.H. Allen took over as publishers, it is still running today and is the most collectable of all film annuals. F. Maurice Speed still edits the book along with James Cameron-Wilson. The most valuable are the early editions complete with their original dust jackets. Listed below are the stars (in bold type) and/or films appearing on the dust jackets to date followed by all the full-page colour plates of the stars that appeared inside the book until 1965.

1944 **James Craig**, **Ronald Colman**, **Carmen D'Antonio** in *Kismet*. Gloria Jean. Linda Darnell. Carmen Miranda. Greer Garson. Gene Tierney. Betty Grable. Maria Montez. Carole Landis. Ginger Rogers and Dan Lopez in *Lady In The Dark*. Jon Hall in *Ali Baba And The Forty Thieves*. Danny Kaye and Dinah Shore in *Up In Arms*. Marlene Dietrich in *Kismet*. Hedy Lamarr. Virginia Wilson. Phil Silvers and Rita Hayworth in *Cover Girl*. Susanna Foster and Claude Rains in *The Phantom Of The Opera*. Rita Hayworth in *Cover Girl*. Nelson Eddy in *The Phantom Of The Opera*. Don Ameche. Martha Raye. Deanna Durbin. Linda Darnell. Rosalind Russell. Sonja Henie. Ann Rutherford. Jane Frazee. Trudy Marshall. Anne Gwynne. Ann Sothern.

1945 – 6 **Donna Reed**. Loretta Young. Gloria De Haven. Louise Allbritton. Virginia Mayo. The Diamond Horseshoe Girls. Vivian Blaine. Joan Fontaine. Eddie Bracken. Alice Faye.

1946 – 7 **Larry Parks** and **Evelyn Keyes** in *The Jolson Story*. Maureen O'Hara and Paul Henreid in *Spanish Main*. Vivian Blaine. Marsha Hunt. Ava Gardner. Hedy Lamarr. Gary Cooper. Greer Garson. Laraine Day and Robert Young in *Those Endearing Young Charms*. James Craig. Joan Leslie. Beverly Tyler. June Haver. Joan Lorring. Lana Turner. Richard Greene. Ida Lupino. Gloria De Haven. Cornel Wilde. Anne Baxter. Claudette Colbert. Pat Kirkwood. Rita Hayworth. Margaret O'Brien. June Allyson. Ginger Rogers. Jane Wyman. Lucille Bremer. Ann Blyth. Ann Miller.

1947 – 8 **Cyd Charisse** and **Ricardo Montalban** in *Fiesta*. Dennis Price and Margaret Lockwood in *Hungry Hill*. John Mills in *So Well Remembered*. James Stewart and Donna Reed in *It's A Wonderful Life*. James Mason. Bette Davis. Danny Kaye. Jennifer Jones. Arlene Dahl and Dennis Morgan in *My Wild Irish Rose*. Van Heflin. Gloria De Haven. Mickey Rooney and Marilyn Maxwell in *Summer Holiday*. Janis Paige. Robert Mitchum and Greer Garson in *Desire Me*. Zachary Scott. Gregory Peck, Claude Jarman Jr and Jane Wyman in *The Yearling*. Linda Darnell in *Forever Amber*. Deborah Kerr in *Black Narcissus*. Van Johnson and Janet Leigh. Yvonne De Carlo and Jean-Pierre Aumont in *Song Of Scheherazade*. Virginia Mayo. Joanne Dru. John Hodiak. Barbara Stanwyck. Hedy Lamarr. Claire Trevor. Lois Maxwell. Lana Turner. Kathryn Grayson.

1948 – 9 **Alexis Smith**. Laurence Olivier. Danny Kaye and Virginia Mayo in *Kid From Brooklyn*. Susan Peters and Alexander Knox in *Sign Of The Ram*. William Powell and Myrna Loy. Larry Parks and Ellen Drew in *The Swordsman*. Valerie Hobson. George Sanders and Angela Lansbury in *The Affairs Of Bel Ami*. Lizabeth Scott. Scene from *Unconquered*. Kay Walsh in *Vice Versa*. George Brent and Frances Gifford in *Luxury Liner*. Esther Williams and Peter Lawford in *On An Island With You*. Gregory Peck and Valli in *The Paradine Case*. Margaret O'Brien in *The Unfinished Dance*. Ingrid Bergman in *Joan Of Arc*. Cathy O'Donnell. Alan Ladd and Brenda Marshall in *Whispering Smith*. Frank Sinatra and J. Carrol Naish in *The Kissing Bandit*. Clark Gable and Lana Turner. Olga San Juan. Stewart Granger in *Blanche Fury*. Jane Wyman. Jane Powell. Robert Young and Marguerite Chapman in *Relentless*. Jon Hall. Michael Dunane. Patricia Morison and Adele Jergens in *Prince Of Thieves*. John Wayne and Laraine Day in *Tycoon*. Rita Hayworth. Maureen O'Hara.

1949 – 50 **Trevor Howard** and **Anouk** in *The Golden Salamander*. Olivia De Havilland. Anna Neagle and Michael Wilding in *Maytime In Mayfair*. Robert Montgomery. Susan Hayward. Jean Simmons, Donald Houston and Peter Wood in *The Blue Lagoon*. Humphrey Bogart and Lauren Bacall in *Key Largo*. Fredric March and Derek Bond in *Christopher Columbus*. Ava Gardner in *One Touch Of Venus*. Cyd Charisse. Shirley Temple. Trevor Howard and Anouk in *The Golden Salamander*. Dennis Morgan. Dorothy Malone. Don Defore and Janis Paige in *One Sunday Afternoon*. Robert Barrat and Ingrid Bergman in *Joan Of Arc*. Lizabeth Scott and Dan Duryea in *Too Late For Tears*. Kathryn Grayson and Johnnie Johnston. John Derek. Gig Young, Robert Coote, Gene Kelly and Van Heflin in *The Three Musketeers*. Barbara Stanwyck. Errol Flynn in *Adventures Of Don Juan*. Alan Ladd. Jeanne Crain in *Lady Windermere's Fan*. James Donald and Jean Kent in *Trottie True*. Mickey Rooney and Betty Garrett in *Words And Music*. Anne Baxter. Spencer Tracy and Deborah Kerr.

1950 – 1 **Arlene Dahl**, **Red Skelton**, **Fred Astaire** and **Vera-Ellen** in *Three Little Words*. Dan Dailey and Betty Grable in *My Blue Heaven*. Doris Day. Alan Ladd. Jean Simmons. Bobby Driscoll and Andrew Blackett in *Treasure Island*. Janet Leigh. Ava Gardner. William Powell. Richard Widmark and Barbara Bel Geddes in *Panic In The Streets*. Betty Garrett. Esther Williams and Red Skelton. Elizabeth Taylor, Janet Leigh, June Allyson and Margaret O'Brien in *Little Women*. Claude Rains and Valli in *The White Tower*. Dane Clark and Margaret Lockwood. Richard Carlson, Deborah Kerr and Stewart Granger in *King Solomon's Mines*. David Niven and Kathryn Grayson in *Toast Of New Orleans*. Fred Astaire and Vera-Ellen in *Three Little Words*. Greer Garson in *The Miniver Story*. Paul Douglas and Jean Peters in *Love That Brute*. James Barton and June Haver in *The Daughter Of Rosie O'Grady*. Gary Cooper and Patricia Neal in *Bright Leaf*. Howard Keel. Ann Miller. Betty Hutton. *Three Musketeers*. Greer Garson and Errol Flynn in *The Forsyte Saga*. Danny Kaye, Alan Hale, Lew and Sam Hearn in *The Inspector General*. Dennis Morgan. Lana Turner.

1951 – 2 **Debra Paget** and **Louis Jourdan** in *Bird Of Paradise*. Judy Holliday in *Born Yesterday*. Debra Paget. Bob Hope. Anthony Dexter and Eleanor Parker in *Valentino*. Elizabeth Taylor. Yvonne De Carlo in *Hotel Sahara*. Dan Dailey. Ann Blyth. Evelyn Keyes. Anne Baxter. Janet Leigh and John Wayne in *Jet Pilot*. Ava Gardner and Robert Mitchum in *My Forbidden Past*. James Cagney and Virginia Mayo in *Fine & Dandy*. Gregory Peck and Susan Hayward in *David And Bathsheba*. Ricardo Montalban and Jane Powell in *Two Weeks With Love*. Barbara Hale and Bill Williams in *The Clay Pigeon*. Farley Granger and Joan Evans in *Roseanna McCoy*. Gloria Grahame.

Richard Widmark. Patricia Neal. William Lundigan and Susan Hayward in *I'd Climb The Highest Mountain*. Ann Doran. Irene Dunne. Fred MacMurray and William Demarest in *Never A Dull Moment*. Donald O'Connor. Gregory Peck and Barbara Payton in *Only The Valiant*. Gale Storm. Robert Mitchum and Jane Russell in *His Kind Of Woman*.

1952 – 3 **Gregory Peck** and **Ann Blyth** in *The World In His Arms*. Jeanne Crain. Debbie Reynolds. Corinne Calvet. Janet Leigh. Betty Hutton. Esther Williams. Shelley Winters. Nadia Gray. Burt Lancaster in *The Crimson Pirate*. Peggy Dow. Joan Rice. Lana Turner in *The Merry Widow*. Elizabeth Taylor and Robert Taylor in *Ivanhoe*. Gordon MacRae and Doris Day. Mel Ferrer and Stewart Granger in *Scaramouche*. Gary Cooper and Mari Aldon in *Distant Drums*. Allyn McLerie and Ray Bolger in *Where's Charley?* Julia Adams and James Stewart in *Where The River Bends*. Glynis Johns in *Encore*. Piper Laurie and Tony Curtis in *Son Of Ali Baba*. Barry Fitzgerald. Maureen O'Hara and John Wayne in *The Quiet Man*. Robert Taylor and Deborah Kerr in *Quo Vadis*. Yvonne Donlan and Dirk Bogarde in *Penny Princess*. Michael Redgrave and Joan Greenwood in *The Importance Of Being Earnest*. Virginia Mayo in *Painting The Clouds With Sunshine*. Ann Sheridan. Cary Grant. Betsy Drake and George Winslow in *Room For One More*. Richard Todd. Merle Oberon and Leo Genn in *24 Hours Of A Woman's Life*.

1953 – 4 **Jean Simmons** and **Richard Burton** in *The Robe*. Zsa Zsa Gabor in *Moulin Rouge*. Jane Wyman. Janet Leigh. Danny Thomas and Peggy Lee in *The Jazz Singer*. James Mason. Rhonda Fleming. Errol Flynn. Jean Peters. John Wayne and Janet Leigh in *Jet Pilot*. Dale Robertson. Farley Granger and Jeanmaire in *Hans Christian Andersen*. Murray Matheson, Barry Jones, Leo Genn, Lowell Gilmore and Spencer Tracy in *Plymouth Adventure*. Ava Gardner. Elizabeth Taylor. Robert Mitchum. Susan Hayward. Martin and Lewis. Milly Vitale. Marilyn Monroe. Mario Lanza and Doretta Morrow in *Because You're Mine*. Jan Sterling. Doris Day and Ray Bolger in *April In Paris*. Cyd Charisse. Dinah Sheridan, John Gregson, Kenneth More and Kay Kendall in *Genevieve*. George Cole in *Will Any Gentleman?* Richard Todd and Glynis Johns in *The Sword And The Rose*. Richard Todd. Abbe Lane. Alan Ladd. Ruth Hampton and Russell Johnson in *Law & Order*.

1954 – 5 **Marilyn Monroe** and **Robert Mitchum** in *River Of No Return*. Tony Curtis and Janet Leigh in *The Black Shield Of Falworth*. Marlon Brando and Mary Murphy. Ann Blyth and Stewart Granger in *All The Brothers Were Valiant*. Glynis Johns. John Wayne. Mitzi Gaynor. Burt Lancaster. Howard Keel. Ava Gardner. Laurence Harvey and Susan Shentall in *Romeo and Juliet*. Jane Powell in *Three Sailors And A Girl*. Sterling Hayden and Jane Wyman in *So Big*. Doris Day and Howard Keel in *Calamity Jane*. James Stewart and June Allyson in *The Glenn Miller Story*. Alan Ladd in *The Black Knight*. Maureen O'Hara and Jeff Chandler in *War Arrow*. Deborah Kerr. Gina Lollobrigida. Pier Angeli. Noelle Middleton. Maggie McNamara. Mamie Van Doren. Kay Kendall. Guy Mitchell and Teresa Brewer in *Those Redheads From Seattle*. David Farrar, Jeanne Crain and Dana Andrews in *Duel In The Jungle*. Van Heflin and Ruth Roman in *Tanganyika*. Elaine Stewart. Susan Hayward in *Demetrius And The Gladiators*. Jean Peters. Nancy Olson and Will Rogers Jr in *The Boy From Oklahoma*. James Stewart and Ruth Roman in *The Far Country*.

1955 – 6 **Dirk Bogarde**, **Jill Adams** and **Belinda Lee**. Gregory Peck in *Moby Dick*. Edmund Purdom. James Mason. Rock Hudson. Dirk Bogarde, Jill Adams and Belinda Lee. Norman Wisdom in *The Man Of The Moment*. Van Johnson. Alan Ladd. Cyd Charisse. Debbie Reynolds. Lucy Marlow. Kathleen Hughes. Jean Simmons and Stewart Granger in *Footsteps In The Fog*. John Mills in *Above Us The Waves*. Howard Keel and Esther Williams in *Jupiter's Darling*. Glenn Ford and Eleanor Powell in *Interrupted Melody*. Pier Angeli and Vic Damone. Ludmilla Tcherina and Mel Ferrer in *Oh Rosalinda*. Alec Guinness and Jack Hawkins in *The Prisoner*. Peter Finch, Michael Craig, Anthony Steel and Diane Cilento in *Passage Home*. Jonathan Ashmore in *A Kid For Two Farthings*. Mandy Miller and Kenneth More in *Raising A Riot*. Rex Harrison, Kay Kendall and Cecil Parker in *The Constant Husband*. Brigitte Bardot and Dirk Bogarde in *Doctor In The House*. Marlon Brando and Jean Simmons in *Guys & Dolls*. Ann Blyth and Howard Keel in *Kismet*. Esther Williams. Janette Scott. Janet Leigh. Diana Dors.

1956 – 7 **Janet Leigh**. Grace Kelly. *Carousel*. Cyd Charisse. George Nader. Belinda Lee. Shirley Jones. Tony Curtis. Anna Magnani. Anna Maria Sandri. Kim Novak. Dana Wynter. Julia Arnall. Susan Hayward. Clark Gable. Cary Grant. James Stewart. Richard Burton in *Alexander The Great*. Grace Kelly and Louis Jourdan in *The Swan*. John Wayne and Lauren Bacall in *Blood Alley*. Frank Sinatra and Debbie Reynolds in *The Tender Trap*. Kay Kendall and Robert Taylor in *The Adventures Of Quentin Durward*. Jacques Sernas, Rossana Podesta and Brigitte Bardot in *Helen Of Troy*. Edmond O'Brien and Jan Sterling in *1984*. Janette Scott. Howard Keel and Dolores Gray in

Kismet. Rory Calhoun. Donna Reed. Virginia Mayo. Gia Scala. Rhonda Fleming. Marlon Brando and Frank Sinatra in *Guys & Dolls*. Kirk Douglas in *Lust For Life*.

1957 – 8 **Carole Lesley**. Yul Brynner in *The Ten Commandments*. Barbara Lang. Audie Murphy. Natalie Wood. Anthony Steel. Marjorie Hellen. Gregory Peck. Kim Novak. George Baker. Rock Hudson. Gordon MacRae. Dean Martin, Anna Maria Alberghetti, Eva Bartok and Dewey Martin in *Ten Thousand Bedrooms*. Joan Collins, Dolores Gray, Ann Sheridan, Ann Miller, Joan Blondell, Agnes Moorehead. Jeff Richards in *The Opposite Sex*. Stewart Granger and Ava Gardner in *Bhowani Junction*. Janette Scott and John Fraser in *The Good Companions*. Julie Adams. Barbara Nichols. Victoria Shaw. Colleen Miller. Zena Marshall, Tony Martin, Vera-Ellen and Robert Flemyng in *Let's Be Happy*. Virginia McKenna and Richard Todd. Doris Day. Rita Moreno. Patricia Owens and James Mason in *Island In The Sun*. David Niven. Elizabeth Mueller. Donna Reed. George Nader. Jayne Mansfield. Deborah Kerr. Ann Heywood.

1958 – 9 **Jackie Lane**. Joanne Woodward. Rossano Brazzi and Mitzi Gaynor in *South Pacific*. Ava Gardner, Tyrone Power, Robert Evans, Eddie Albert, Errol Flynn and Mel Ferrer in *The Sun Also Rises*. Suzy Parker. Christine Carere. Danny Kaye. June Allyson and David Niven in *My Man Godfrey*. William Holden. Claire Bloom. Kay Kendall. Sylvia Syms. Yul Brynner and Maria Schell in *The Brothers Karamazov*. Gena Rowlands. Anne Baxter. Jennifer Jones and Rock Hudson in *A Farewell To Arms*. Jackie Lane and Jeremy Spenser in *Wonderful Things*. Janet Leigh and Tony Curtis in *The Vikings*. Mylene Demongeot. Richard Todd and Juliette Greco. Frankie Vaughan. Elvis Presley. John Carradine and Charlton Heston in *The Ten Commandments*. Anthony Perkins. Sophia Loren. Fernandel. June Laverick. Carole Lesley. Cary Grant and Ingrid Bergman. Jack Hawkins. Harry Andrews. John Mills and Sylvia Syms in *Ice Cold In Alex*. Anne Heywood. Michael Craig and Belinda Lee in *Nor The Moon By Night*.

1959 – 60 **James MacArthur** and **Janet Munro** in *Third Man On The Mountain*. Jean Simmons and Gregory Peck in *The Big Country*. Janet Munro. Ingrid Bergman and Curt Jurgens in *Inn Of The Sixth Happiness*. Shirley MacLaine. Barbara Lang. Claire Kelly. Mickey Shaughnessy. Trevor Howard, Errol Flynn and Juliette Greco in *The Roots Of Heaven*. Clifton Webb and Dorothy McGuire in *The Remarkable Mr Pennypacker*. Kenneth More in *The Sheriff Of Fractured Jaw*. Paul Newman and Joanne Woodward in *Rally Round The Flag, Boys*. Christine Carere and Rossano Brazzi in *A Certain Smile*. Ava Gardner. Maurice Chevalier. Myrna Hansen. Donald Sinden, Margaret Simons and Marigold Russell.

1960 – 1 **Kirk Douglas** in *Spartacus*. Charlton Heston and Haya Harareet in *Ben Hur*. David Ladd in *The Sad Horse*. Kenneth More and Dana Wynter in *Sink The Bismark!* Leslie Parrish. Marie Devereux. Frank Sinatra and Gina Lollobrigida in *Never So Few*. Frank Sinatra, Shirley MacLaine and Maurice Chevalier in *Can Can*. Anthony Quinn and Dolores Michael. Eva Marie Saint, James Mason and Cary Grant in *North By Northwest*. Pat Boone and Diane Baker in *Journey To The Centre Of The Earth*. Barbara Eden. Dennis Holmes, Susan Hayward and Stephen Boyd in *Woman Obsessed*. Gary Crosby, Carol Lynley, Clifton Webb and Jane Wyman in *Holiday For Lovers*. Debbie Reynolds and Robert Wagner. Herbert Lom and Martha Hyer* in *The Big Fisherman*. Dorothy McGuire and John Mills in *Swiss Family Robinson*.

*Erroneously credited as Susan Kohner.

1961 – 2 **Mel Ferrer** and **Annette Vadim** in *Blood And Roses*. Elvis Presley and Juliet Prowse in *GI Blues*. Tony Hancock. Elke Sommer. Mel Ferrer and Annette Vadim. Lee Remick in *Sanctuary*. Nancy Kwan in *World Of Suzie Wong*. Peter Finch. *Cleopatra*. Julie Newmar. Yves Montand. Marlon Brando and Pina Pellicer in *One-Eyed Jacks*. Judy Holliday, Dean Martin, Nancy Walters and Fred Clark in *Bells Are Ringing*. Dirk Bogarde and Mylene Demongeot. Steve Forrest and Barbara Eden in *Flaming Star*. Juliette Greco and Stephen Boyd in *The Big Gamble*. Debbie Reynolds and Tony Curtis in *The Rat Race*. Ralph Bellamy and Greer Garson in *Sunrise At Campobello*.

1962 – 3 **Hayley Mills**. Cliff Richard. Elizabeth Taylor in *Cleopatra*. Dany Robin, John Fraser and Peter Sellers in *The Waltz Of The Toreadors*. Christine Kaufman. Marlon Brando and Tarita in *Mutiny On The Bounty*. Leslie Caron. Hayley Mills. Elvis Presley and Joan Blackman. Audrey Hepburn and George Peppard in *Breakfast At Tiffany's*. Natalie Wood, George Chakiris and Rita Moreno in *West Side Story*. Jill St John. Paul Newman. Debbie Reynolds and Steve Forrest in *The Second Time Around*. Stephen Boyd and Dolores Hart. Stella Stevens. Joan Staley.

1963 – 4 **Sandra Dee**. Richard Burton and Elizabeth Taylor in *The VIPs*. Robert Taylor in *The Flight Of The White Stallions*. Rex Harrison and Elizabeth Taylor in *Cleopatra*.

1964 – 5 **Audrey Hepburn** in *My Fair Lady*. Sean Connery and Honor Blackman.

1965 – 6 **Sean Connery** and **Claudine Auger** in *Thunderball.*

1966 – 8 **Richard Burton** and **Elizabeth Taylor** in *The Taming Of The Shrew.*

1968 – 9 *Oliver.*

1969 – 70 **Petula Clark** and **Peter O'Toole** in *Goodbye Mr Chips.*

1970 – 1 *Waterloo.*

1971 – 2 *Nicholas and Alexandra.*

1972 – 3 *Young Winston.*

1973 – 4 *Godspell.*

1974 – 5 **Jon Voight** in *The Odessa File.*

1975 – 6 *The Jungle Book.*

1976 – 7 **Peter Sellers**, *The Pink Panther Strikes Again.*

1977 – 8 *Valentino.*

1978 – 9 **Olivia Newton-John** and **John Travolta** in *Grease.*

1979 – 80 **Donald Sutherland** and **Vanessa Redgrave** in *Bear Island.*

1980 – 1 **Sam J. Jones** in *Flash Gordon.*

1981 – 2 **Dudley Moore** and **Liza Minnelli** in *Arthur.*

1982 – 3 **Dyan Cannon** and **Michael Caine** in *Deathtrap.*

1983 – 4 **Roger Moore** in *Octopussy.*

1984 – 5 *The Wizard of Oz.*

1985 – 6 *Revolution.*

1986 – 7 **David Bowie** in *Labyrinth.*

1987 – 8 *The Witches Of Eastwick.*

1988 – 9 *The Last Emperor.*

1989 – 90 **Jack Nicholson** in *Batman.*

Another annual popular with collectors is *Screen World*, which was first published in 1949, by Greenberg in New York, and edited by Daniel Blum. Today it is edited by John Willis and published by Crown Publishers Inc., New York. It offers a complete pictorial and statistical record of the current movie season with full cast lists. Each annual is dedicated to a star, Clara Kimball Young being the first.

Finally a word about the *International Motion Picture Almanac* which has been published regularly since 1929. The longest continually published reference book on the movie industry, this outstanding work is the most treasured of all film books and early editions are hard to find. Each almanac reviews the year's films, awards, film festivals, and lists: a who's who, major studios, personnel, theatre circuits, and trade publications. In short, it is the film buff's bible. Originally edited by Terry Ramsaye, author of *A Million And One Nights*, the classic history of the silent cinema, it was edited until 1970 by Charles Aaronson who was then succeeded by Richard Getner. Editor-in-chief and publisher was Martin Quigley; today it is edited by Jane Klain and published by Quigley Publishing Company Inc., New York.

CHAPTER FOUR

CIGARETTE CARDS AND POSTCARDS

CIGARETTE CARDS

Cigarette cards generally came in sets of 50 and were inserted in packets of cigarettes as early as 1870. They were either colour, black and white or sepiatone pictures on small cards which had on the reverse side a brief biography of a personality or a description of the subject. One of the earliest cinema cigarette card sets was issued by Major Drapkin & Co., London, in 1913 – 'Cinematograph Actors', a series of 96. One of the last cinema cigarette card sets to be issued was Turf Cigarettes' '50 Film Stars' in the 1950s; they were bluetone and formed the back part of the pushout packet, having to be cut out by the collector.

Cards should be in pristine condition and in complete sets. Below are listed the British tobacco manufacturers who issued cinema cigarette cards, including those in the Channel Islands, Eire, and overseas issues by British-based firms. In some cases complete sets are identified and some examples of the jottings on the reverse sides of the cards have been highlighted. Prices quoted refer to complete sets in undamaged condition.

ABDULLA & CO.

YEAR	TITLE	NO. IN SERIES	PRICE
1932	**Cinema Stars, Set 1**	52 (Photographic production)	
1932	**Cinema Stars, Set 2**	30	
1933	**Cinema Stars, Set 3**	30	
1933	**Cinema Stars, Set 4**	32	£50.00
1934	**Cinema Stars, Set 5**	32	£50.00
1934	**Cinema Stars, Set 6**	30	
1934	**Film Favourites**	50	
1934	**Film Stars**	50	
1934	**Film Stars**	24 (Postcard size)	
1934	**Film Stars**	24 (Postcard size)	
1939	**Screen Stars**	40	£30.00
1939	**Screen Stars**	40	£60.00
1935	**Stage and Cinema Beauties**	50	
1934	**Stars of The Stage and Screen**	30	

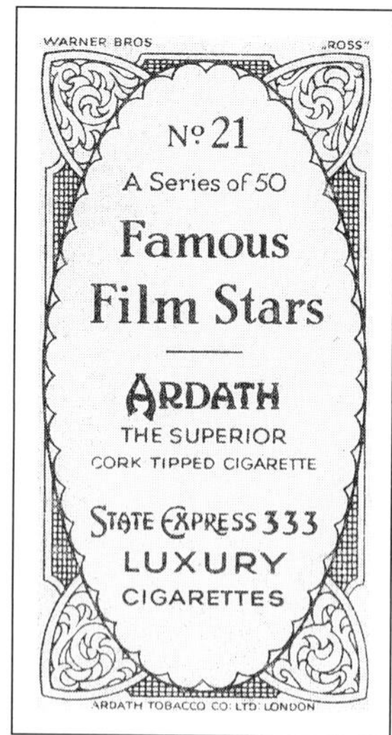

ARDATH TOBACCO CO. LTD.

YEAR	TITLE	NO. IN SERIES	PRICE
1934	**British-Born Film Stars**	50	£50.00
1934	**British-Born Film Stars**	50 (Medium size)	
1934	**Famous Film Stars**	50	£25.00
1935	**Film, Stage and Radio Stars**	50	£32.50
1935	**Film, Stage and Radio Stars**	25 (Different)	£18.75
1938	**Film Stars** (State Express)		
1938	**Film Stars** (Straight Cut)		

YEAR	TITLE	NO. IN SERIES	PRICE
1936	**From Screen and Stage**	50 (Extra large size)	£25.00
1939	**Photocards Group 'N' (Films)**	45 (Photographic)	£28.00
1939	**Photocards Group 'N' (Films)**	45 (Large photographic)	£22.50
1939	**Real Photographs Group 'O' (Films)**	45 (Photographic)	£22.50
1935	**Scenes From Big Films**	100	
1935	**Scenes From Big Films**	100 (Medium size)	

ASSOCIATED TOBACCO MANUFACTURERS

YEAR	TITLE	NO. IN SERIES	PRICE
1926	**Cinema Stars**	25 (5 Brands)	

THOMAS BEAR & SONS LTD

YEAR	TITLE	NO. IN SERIES	PRICE
1936	**Cinema Artistes, Set 2**	50	
1937	**Cinema Artistes, Set 4**	50	
1928	**Cinema Stars 'BAMT'**	50	
1926	**Stage and Film Stars**	50	

BUCKTROUT & CO. LTD (Channel Isles)

YEAR	TITLE	NO. IN SERIES	PRICE
1926	**Cinema Stars, 1st**	50	£62.50
1927	**Cinema Stars, 2nd**	50	£75.00

CARRERAS LTD

YEAR	TITLE	NO. IN SERIES	PRICE
1935	**Famous Film Stars**	96	£48.00
1939	**Film and Stage Beauties**	54 (Photographic)	£8.75
1939	**Film and Stage Beauties**	54 (Large photographic)	£16.50
1939	**Film and Stage Beauties**	36 (Large photographic)	£14.00
1939	**Film and Stage Beauties**	36 (Extra large, photographic)	£23.50
1938	**Film Favourites**	50	£32.50
1937	**Film Stars, A series**	54 (Photographic)	£27.00
1938	**Film Stars, 2nd series**	54 (Photographic)	£16.50

A SERIES OF 50

Described by FLORENCE DESMOND

No. 41

CLARK GABLE

(Metro-Goldwyn-Mayer)

Clark Gable is one of the most natural and unaffected film stars one could wish to meet. I met him for the first time at a dinner-party given by Joan Crawford. After dinner, Joan showed a film in which Clark Gable was appearing. No one could have been more embarrassed than Clark. He begged us not to make rude remarks about it. He possesses a grand sense of humour, and has a most attractive speaking voice. He had a very varied career, before he finally became an actor. When he can get away from Hollywood, he leads an out-door life.

CARRERAS LTD

(ESTD 1788)

ARCADIA WORKS, LONDON, ENGLAND

KEEP THIS ATTRACTIVE SERIES OF ART PICTURES IN THE CARRERAS "SLIP-IN" ALBUM OBTAINABLE FROM ALL TOBACCONISTS (PRICE ONE PENNY)

YEAR	TITLE	NO. IN SERIES	PRICE
1938	**Film Stars (As 2nd series)**	54 (Large photographic)	£35.00
1936	**Film Stars**	36 Different (extra large photographic)	£63.00
1936	**Film Stars, 2nd series**	36 Different (extra large)	£63.00
1937	**Film Stars, 3rd series**	36 (Extra large photographic)	£63.00
1938	**Film Stars 4th series**	36 (Extra large photographic)	£63.00
1936	**Film Stars**	50 (By Florence Desmond)	£25.00
1934	**Film Stars** (Oval)	72	£54.00
1934	**Film Stars** (Oval) **'Real Photos'**	(Photographic production)	
1939	**Glamour Girls of Stage and Films**	54 (Photographic)	£10.00
1939	**Glamour Girls of Stage and Films**	54 (Large)	£11.00
1939	**Glamour Girls of Stage and Films**	36 (Large)	£11.00
1939	**Glamour Girls of Stage and Films**	36 (Extra large)	£16.00
1929	**Paramount Stars**	27 (Photographic production)	£20.00

TURF SLIDES (Cut to size)

YEAR	TITLE	NO. IN SERIES	PRICE
1949	**Famous Film Stars**	50	£25.00
1948	**Film Favourites**	50	£35.00
1947	**Film Stars**	50	£30.00

AUSTRALIAN ISSUES

YEAR	TITLE	NO. IN SERIES	PRICE
1933	**Film Stars Series**	72 (Smile Away)	
1933	**Film Stars Series**	72 (Standard)	£65.00
1933	**Personality Series, Film Stars**	72	£57.50

CAVANDERS LTD

YEAR	TITLE	NO. IN SERIES	PRICE
1934	**Cinema Stars**	30	£22.50

W.A. & A.C. CHURCHMAN

YEAR	TITLE	NO. IN SERIES	PRICE
1934	**British Film Stars**	25	£31.25

MAJOR DRAPKIN & CO.

YEAR	TITLE	NO. IN SERIES	PRICE
1913	**Cinematograph Actors**	96 (Bigger than standard)	

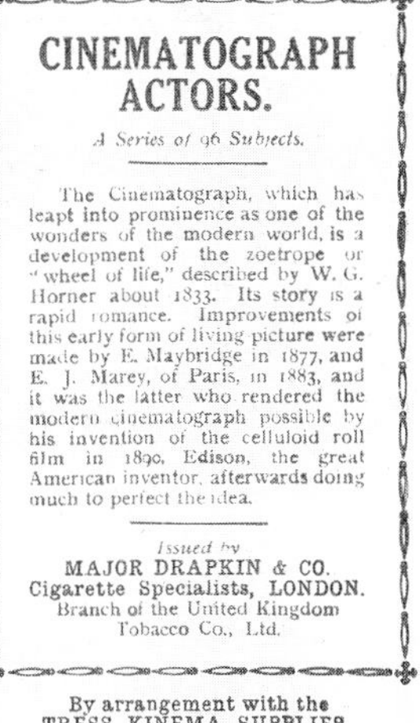
CINEMATOGRAPH ACTORS.

A Series of 96 Subjects.

The Cinematograph, which has leapt into prominence as one of the wonders of the modern world, is a development of the zoetrope or "wheel of life," described by W. G. Horner about 1833. Its story is a rapid romance. Improvements of this early form of living picture were made by E. Maybridge in 1877, and E. J. Marey, of Paris, in 1883, and it was the latter who rendered the modern cinematograph possible by his invention of the celluloid roll film in 1890. Edison, the great American inventor, afterwards doing much to perfect the idea.

Issued by

MAJOR DRAPKIN & CO.
Cigarette Specialists, LONDON.
Branch of the United Kingdom Tobacco Co., Ltd.

By arrangement with the TRESS KINEMA SUPPLIES.

STARS OF SCREEN & STAGE
A SERIES OF 48. Nº 14

GINGER ROGERS

Ginger Rogers was born in 1911 in Missouri. As a child dancer, at 14, she won medals and cups for the Charleston. She went on the New York stage, and after some time there made her talkie debut in "42nd Street." This was followed by "Gold Diggers of 1933." She has recently appeared in "Finishing School" with Frances Dee (No. 22 in this series), "Rafter Romance" and "Change of Heart." Two more Radio stars in this series are Wheeler and Woolsey (No. 6).

PARK DRIVE
CIGARETTES
Gallaher Ltd.
VIRGINIA HOUSE, LONDON & BELFAST

EDWARDS RINGER & BIGG

YEAR	TITLE	NO. IN SERIES	PRICE
1923	**Cinema Stars**	50	£37.50
1923	**Cinema Stars**	25 (Large size)	£25.00

GALLAHER LTD

YEAR	TITLE	NO. IN SERIES	PRICE
1934	**Champions of Screen & Stage**	48 (Red back)	£15.00
1934	**Champions of Screen & Stage**	48 (Blue back)	£36.00
1934	**Champions of Screen & Stage**	48 (Blue back)	£31.50
1926	**Cinema Stars**	100	£100.00
1935	**Famous Film Scenes**	48	£20.00
1936	**Film Episodes**	48	£20.00
1935	**Film Partners**	48	£20.00
1939	**My Favourite Part**	48	£20.00

1. **Luise Rainer** 2. **Nova Pilbeam**
3. **Lilli Palmer** 4. **Jessie Matthews**
5. **Glenda Farrell** 6. **Florence Desmond**
7. **Raymond Massey**
8. **Sir Cedric Hardwicke** 9. **Kay Francis**
10. **Valerie Hobson** 11. **Leslie Banks**
12. **Errol Flynn** 13. **Judy Garland**
14. **Eleanor Powell** 15. **Vivien Leigh**
16. **Greta Garbo** 17. **Spencer Tracy**
18. **Joan Crawford** 19. **Myrna Loy**
20. **Edna Best** 21. **Diana Churchill**
22. **Laurence Olivier** 23. **Flora Robson**
24. **Clark Gable** 25. **Norma Shearer**
26. **Olivia De Havilland** 27. **René Ray**
28. **Florence Rice** 29. **Paul Muni**
30. **Jean Parker** 31. **Gracie Fields**
32. **Joan Blondell** 33. **Virginia Bruce**
34. **Gordon Harker** 35. **Margaret Sullavan**
36. **Sally Eilers** 37. **Jeanette MacDonald**
38. **Yvonne Arnaud**
39. **Margaret Lockwood**
40. **Rosalind Russell** 41. **Margaretta Scott**
42. **Ruth Chatterton** 43. **Wallace Beery**
44. **Elizabeth Allan**
45. **Robert Montgomery** 46. **Bette Davis**
47. **William Powell** 48. **Maureen O'Sullivan.**

YEAR	TITLE	NO. IN SERIES	PRICE
1935	**Portraits of Famous Stars**	48	£24.00
1935	**Shots from Famous Films**	48	£15.00
1936	**Shots from the Films**	24 (Medium size. Photographic)	
1935	**Signed Portraits of Famous Stars**	48	£48.00
1935	**Stars of Screen & Stage**	48 (Brown back)	£48.00
1935	**Stars of Screen & Stage**	48 (Green back)	£20.00

LOUIS GERARD LTD

YEAR	TITLE	NO. IN SERIES	PRICE
1937	**Screen Favourites**	24	
1937	**Screen Favourites**	24	
1937	**Screen Favourites and Dancers**	48	£75.00

HIGNETT BROS & CO.

YEAR	TITLE	NO. IN SERIES	PRICE
1936	**Shots from the Films**	50	£62.50

MY FAVOURITE PART
SERIES OF 48. Nº 16

GRETA GARBO
M-G-M STAR

Making "Marie Walewska" is the happiest memory I have in connection with films. Playing opposite so great an actor as Charles Boyer, assisting in bringing to the screen so important an episode, and having, once again, my great friend Clarence Brown as director, made production of this film a most delightful experience.

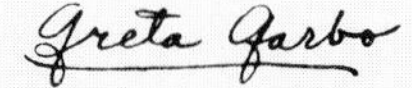

Born Stockholm, Sweden. Films include: Queen Christina, Anna Karenina, Camille, Marie Walewska.

ISSUED BY
GALLAHER LTD
VIRGINIA HOUSE, LONDON & BELFAST

R. & J. HILL LTD

YEAR	TITLE	NO. IN SERIES	PRICE
1936	**Cinema Celebrities**	35 (Spinet House)	£15.75
1936	**Cinema Celebrities**	35	£15.75
1931	**Famous Cinema Celebrities**	48 (Spinet) (Photographic)	
1931	**Famous Cinema Celebrities**	48 (Photographic)	
1931	**Famous Cinema Celebrities**	48 (Kadi) (Large. Photographic)	
1931	**Famous Cinema Celebrities, Series A**	48 (Large. Photographic)	
1932	**Famous Cinema Celebrities**	50 (Devon) (Photographic)	
1932	**Famous Cinema Celebrities**	50 (Toucan) (Photographic)	
1932	**Famous Cinema Celebrities, Series C**	50 (Photographic)	
1932	**Famous Cinema Celebrities**	50 (Kadi) (Large. Photographic)	
1932	**Famous Cinema Celebrities, Series D**	50 (Large. Photographic)	
1938	**Famous Film Stars**	40	£26.00
1938	**Famous Film Stars**	40 (Arabic text)	£32.00
1935	**Film Stars and Celebrity Dancers**	48	£60.00
1934	**Scenes from the Films**	50 (Photographic production)	£95.00
1938	**Scenes from the Films**	40	£12.00
1927	**Who's Who in British Films**	50	£37.50
1927	**Who's Who in British Films**	50 (Large size)	£45.00

JAMES ILLINGWORTH LTD

YEAR	TITLE	NO. IN SERIES	PRICE
1937	**Shots from the Films**	24 (Medium size. Photographic)	

INTERNATIONAL TOBACCO CO. LTD

YEAR	TITLE	NO. IN SERIES	PRICE
1937	**Film Favourites**	100 (Black backs)	
1937	**Film Favourites**	100 (Brown backs)	
Unissued.	**Screen Lovers**	48 (Summit)	£84.00

PETER JACKSON

YEAR	TITLE	NO. IN SERIES	PRICE
1935	**Famous Film Stars**	28 (Photographic production)	£53.00
1934	**Famous Films**	27 (Photographic production)	£51.25
1936	**Film Scenes**	28 (Photographic production)	£50.00
1936	**Film Scenes**	28 (Different) (Large. Photographic)	£70.00
1937	**Shots from the Films**	28 (Photographic production)	£35.00
1937	**Shots from the Films**	24 (Medium size. Photographic)	£45.00
1934	**Stars in Famous Films**	28 (Photographic production)	£56.00

SOCIÉTÉ JOB

YEAR	TITLE	NO. IN SERIES	PRICE
1926	**Cinema Stars**	48 (Numbered) (Bigger than standard)	
1926	**Cinema Stars**	48 (Unnumbered) (Bigger than standard)	£32.50
1926	**Cinema Stars**	48 (Numbered)	
1926	**Cinema Stars**	48 (Unnumbered)	

LAMBERT & BUTLER
OVERSEAS ISSUES

YEAR	TITLE	NO. IN SERIES	PRICE
1925	**Popular Film Stars**	50 (Photographic production)	£45.00
1925	**Popular Film Stars**	50 (Photographic production)	£40.00
1925	**Popular Film Stars**	50 (Varsity) (Photographic)	

R.J. LEA LTD

YEAR	TITLE	NO. IN SERIES	PRICE
1939	**Famous Film Stars**	54 (Photographic production)	£51.50
1934	**Film Stars, 1st series**	36 (Photographic)	£62.50
1934	**Film Stars, 2nd Series**	36 (Photographic)	£56.00

RICHARD LLOYD & SONS

YEAR	TITLE	NO. IN SERIES	PRICE
1935	**Cinema Stars (1 – 27)**	27 (Photographic production)	
1935	**Cinema Stars (28 – 54)**	27 (Photographic production)	£13.50
1936	**Cinema Stars (55 – 81)**	27 (Photographic production)	
1937	**Cinema Stars**	25 (Matt)	£18.75

J. MILLHOFF & CO. LTD

YEAR	TITLE	NO. IN SERIES	PRICE
1934	**Film Stars**	24 (Postcard size)	

DUTCH ISSUES

YEAR	TITLE	NO. IN SERIES	PRICE
1924	**Film Series 1**	40 (Large size)	
1924	**Film Series 1**	60 (2 Printings) (Large size)	
1925	**Film Series 2**	60 (Large size)	

STARS OF SCREEN & HISTORY
A SERIES OF 25
10
MARLENE DIETRICH AS "PRINCESS SOPHIA FREDERICA"
(Paramount)

Princess Sophia Frederica, who later became Catherine the Great of Russia, was born at Stettin on May 2nd, 1729. Married to the Grand Duke Peter in 1745, the marriage proved most unhappy, the future Czar being as stupid and dull as his wife was clever. Shortly after his accession to the throne, he was deposed and Catherine became Empress in July 1762. She ruled her country with great firmness, and during her 34 years' reign the frontiers of Russia were greatly extended. In *The Scarlet Empress*, the rôle of Sophia Frederica (afterwards Catherine) was played by Marlene Dietrich, whose dramatic genius gives delight to film audiences the world over. Her films include *Knight without Armour* and *Angel*.

STEPHEN MITCHELL & SON
BRANCH OF THE IMPERIAL TOBACCO CO. (OF GREAT BRITAIN & IRELAND), LTD.

YEAR	TITLE	NO. IN SERIES	PRICE
1925	**Film Series 3**	25 (Large size)	
1926	**Film Series 4**	105 (Medium size. Photographic production)	
1926	**Film Series 4**	206 (Medium size. Photographic production)	

STEPHEN MITCHELL

YEAR	TITLE	NO. IN SERIES	PRICE
1939	**Stars of Screen and History**	25	£25.00

B. MORRIS & SONS LTD

YEAR	TITLE	NO. IN SERIES	PRICE
1923	**Film Star Series**	50	£100.00
1934	**How Films Are Made**	25	£16.25

MOUSTAFA LTD

YEAR	TITLE	NO. IN SERIES	PRICE
1924	**Cinema Stars**	25	

B. MURATTI SONS & CO. LTD
GERMAN ISSUES

YEAR	TITLE	NO. IN SERIES	PRICE
1932	**Cinema Stars Series No. 2**	30	

31

CHARLES LAUGHTON

as Rembrandt Van Ryn in "Rembrandt"

Charles Laughton rarely attempts disguise, but he is a master of make-up for all that. He goes to immense pains to adapt his own very individual appearance to that of the part he is to play. In two pictures that he made for London Films, particularly, this thoroughness is seen. The beard he wore as Henry VIII owed its effectiveness to the fact that he grew every hair of it himself. So also with the moustache that he wears in this portrait as Rembrandt. Notice how the actor has trained this straggling growth so that it exactly suggests the devil-may-care character of the great painter.

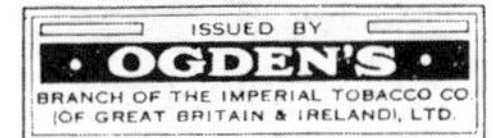

MURRAY, SONS & CO.

YEAR	TITLE	NO. IN SERIES	PRICE
1929	**Cinema Scenes**	22 (Photographic production)	
1926	**Stage and Film Stars**	50	£100.00

OGDENS LTD

YEAR	TITLE	NO. IN SERIES	PRICE
1938	**Actors, Natural and Character Studies**	50	£30.00
1936	**Shots from the Films**	50	£50.00

GODFREY PHILLIPS LTD

YEAR	TITLE	NO. IN SERIES	PRICE
1924	**Cinema Stars**	25 (Circular) (Medium size)	£43.75
1923	**Cinema Stars, Set 1**	52 (Photographic production)	£104.00
1924	**Cinema Stars**	30 (Brown)	£52.50
1925	**Cinema Stars**	30 (Black and white)	£30.00
1930	**Cinema Stars**	32 (Black and white)	£32.00
1934	**Cinema Stars**	32 (Brown, Hand coloured)	£30.50
1935	**Cinema Stars**	30 (Plain back)	£13.50
1939	**Famous Love Scenes**	36 (Medium size)	£7.25

YEAR	TITLE	NO. IN SERIES	PRICE
1934	**Film Favourites**	50	£12.50
1934	**Film Stars**	50	£12.00
1934	**Film Stars**	24 (Postcard size)	£18.00
1934	**Film Stars**	24 (Postcard size)	
1934	**Film Stars**	24 (Postcard size)	£30.00
1934	**Film Stars**	24 (Postcard size)	
1934	**Film Stars 2nd (25 – 48)**	24 (Postcard size)	£60.00
1934	**Film Stars 2nd (25 – 48)**	24 (Postcard size. Non-postcard)	
1936	**Screen Stars A**	48 (Embossed)	£24.00

1. **Franchot Tone** 2. **Margaret Lindsay**
3. **Irene Dunne** 4. **Robert Taylor**
5. **Elizabeth Allan** 6. **Anita Louise**
7. **Errol Flynn** 8. **Rosalind Russell**
9. **Jeanette MacDonald**
10. **Douglas Fairbanks Jr** 11. **Jean Gillie**

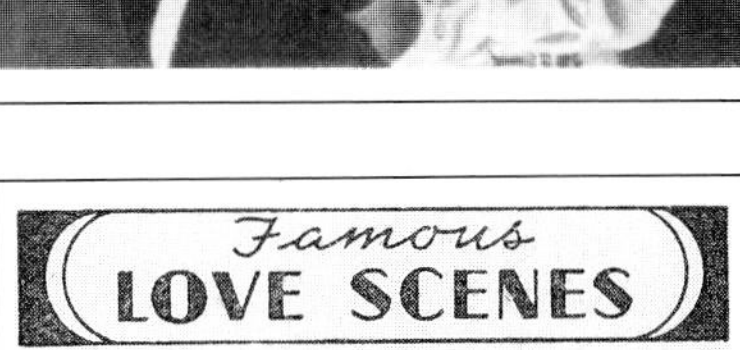

NO. 10 A SERIES OF 36

"FIRE OVER ENGLAND".

Laurence Olivier as Michael Ingolby.
Vivien Leigh as Cynthia Burleigh.

Tudor England provided many great romances, and a war between England and Spain added tempestuous hope and anxiety to the love affair between Michael and Cynthia. The lovers were parted when Michael adventured into Spain as a spy. He was caught, but fought his way out of the Escurial and returned to England to lead the fire ships which turned the Armada into a blazing inferno. With troublesome times ended the pair consummated their happiness in marriage.

(By courtesy of London Film Productions.)

GODFREY PHILLIPS LTD.
AND ASSOCIATED COMPANIES

12. **Myrna Loy** 13. **Robert Montgomery**
14. **Jean Harlow** 15. **William Powell**
16. **Merle Oberon** 17. **Jean Parker**
18. **Clive Brook** 19. **Margaret Sullavan**
20. **Ann Harding** 21. **Warren William**
22. **Olivia De Havilland** 23. **Bette Davis**
24. **Freddie Bartholomew**
25. **Carole Lombard** 26. **Clark Gable**
27. **Greta Garbo** 28. **Helen Vinson**
29. **Wallace Beery** 30. **Norma Shearer**
31. **Genevieve Tobin** 32. **Robert Young**
33. **Kay Francis** 34. **Eleanor Powell**
35. **Robert Donat** 36. **Constance Cummings**
37. **Jessie Matthews** 38. **George Brent**
39. **Luise Rainer** 40. **Josephine Hutchinson**
41. **Dick Powell** 42. **Jean Muir**
43. **Leslie Howard** 44. **Joan Crawford**
45. **Lionel Barrymore** 46. **Gloria Stuart**
47. **Joan Blondell** 48. **Maureen O'Sullivan.**

1936	**Screen Stars A**	48 (Not embossed)	£48.00
1936	**Screen Stars B**	48 (Different)	£24.00
1934	**Shots from the Films**	48 (Medium size)	£8.50
1933	**Stage and Cinema Beauties A**	35	£28.00
1933	**Stage and Cinema Beauties B**	35 (Different)	£22.75
1935	**Stage and Cinema Beauties**	50 (Different)	£40.00
1934	**Stars of the Screen**	54	£43.25
1936	**Stars of the Screen**	48 (Embossed)	£19.25
1936	**Stars of the Screen**	48 (Not embossed)	£19.25
1936	**Stars of the Screen**	16 (Strips of 3) (Extra large size)	£20.00

BDV PACKAGE ISSUES

YEAR	TITLE	NO. IN SERIES	PRICE
1932	**Film Stars**	67	

OVERSEAS ISSUES

YEAR	TITLE	NO. IN SERIES	PRICE
1934	**Film Stars**	50	£62.50
1934	**Stars of British Films**	50 (BDV)	£62.50
1934	**Stars of British Films**	50 (De Reszke)	£62.50
1934	**Stars of British Films**	50 (Greys)	£62.50
1934	**Stars of British Films**	50 (No brand)	£62.50

THIS SURFACE IS ADHESIVE. ASK YOUR TOBACCONIST FOR THE ATTRACTIVE ALBUM (PRICE ONE PENNY) SPECIALLY PREPARED TO HOLD THE COMPLETE SERIES

FILM STARS

THIRD SERIES

10

BETTE DAVIS

(Warner-First National)

Bette Davis was born on April 5th, 1908, in Boston, Massachusetts, and christened Ruth Elizabeth. School dramatics gave way to dramatic and dancing training, and Bette Davis began to make her way on the stage. Given a Hollywood contract, she made no great sensation. The contract lapsed, and she had her bags packed to return to New York when George Arliss asked her to play a leading role in "The Silent Voice." Since then she has acted in thirty-one films, winning the American Academy Award in 1935 for her work in "Of Human Bondage." Her latest films are "Kid Galahad," "It's Love I'm After," "That Certain Woman," "Jezebel" and "The Sisters."

JOHN PLAYER & SONS

BRANCH OF THE IMPERIAL TOBACCO CO. (OF GREAT BRITAIN & IRELAND) LTD.

JOHN PLAYER & SONS

YEAR	TITLE	NO. IN SERIES	PRICE
1934	**Film Stars**	50	£37.50
1934	**Film Stars (2nd series)**	50	£25.00
1934	**Film Stars (2nd series)**	50	
1938	**Film Stars (3rd series)**	50	£20.00
1934	**Film Stars**	25 (Large size)	£50.00
1934	**Film Stars**	25 (Eire) (Large size)	
1938	**Screen Celebrities**	50 (Eire)	

OVERSEAS ISSUES

YEAR	TITLE	NO. IN SERIES	PRICE
1938	**Film Stars (3rd series)**	50	

PREMIER TOBACCO MFRS LTD

YEAR	TITLE	NO. IN SERIES	PRICE
1936	**Stage and Screen Personalities**	50 (Brown)	
1936	**Stage and Screen Personalities**	100 (Grey)	£100.00

RELIANCE TOBACCO MFG CO

YEAR	TITLE	NO. IN SERIES	PRICE
1934	**Famous Stars**	35	£120.00

RICHMOND CAVENDISH CO. LTD

YEAR	TITLE	NO. IN SERIES	PRICE
1927	**Cinema Stars**	50 (Photographic production)	

ROTHMANS LTD

YEAR	TITLE	NO. IN SERIES	PRICE
1939	**Beauties of the Cinema**	40	£32.00
1939	**Beauties of the Cinema**	24 (Circular, matt) (Large size)	£60.00
1939	**Beauties of the Cinema**	24 (Varnished) (Large)	£60.00
1925	**Cinema Stars**	24	£12.50
1925	**Cinema Stars**	24 (Large size)	£16.25
1934	**Prominent Screen Favourites**	24	£15.50

W. SANDORIDES & CO. LTD

YEAR	TITLE	NO. IN SERIES	PRICE
1924	**Cinema Celebrities**	25	£50.00
1924	**Cinema Celebrities**	25 (Extra large size)	
1924	**Cinema Stars**	25 (With firm's name)	
1924	**Cinema Stars**	25 (Big Gun)	
1924	**Cinema Stars**	25 (Lucana)	
1924	**Cinema Stars**	25 (Big Gun) (Extra large size)	£43.75
1924	**Cinema Stars**	25 (Lucana 66) (Extra large size)	
1924	**Cinema Stars**	25 (Sandorides) (Extra large size)	£50.00

NICHOLAS SARONY & CO.

YEAR	TITLE	NO. IN SERIES	PRICE
1933	**Cinema Stars**	50	£37.50
1930	**Cinema Stars**	38 (Postcard size)	
1930	**Cinema Stars (2nd series)**	42 (Postcard size)	
1930	**Cinema Stars (3rd series)**	50 (Postcard size)	
1930	**Cinema Stars (4th series)**	42 (Postcard size)	
1930	**Cinema Stars (5th series)**	25 (Postcard size)	£93.75
1929	**Cinema Studies**	25	£16.25

SIMONETS LTD (Channel Islands)

YEAR	TITLE	NO. IN SERIES	PRICE
1926	**Cinema Scenes Series**	24 (Photographic production)	

JOHN SINCLAIR LTD

YEAR	TITLE	NO. IN SERIES	PRICE
1934	**Film Stars**	54 (Real photos)	£54.00
1937	**Film Stars**	54 (Real photos)	£48.50
1937	**Film Stars (55 – 108)**	54 (Photographic)	£40.00

SINGLETON & COLE LTD

YEAR	TITLE	NO. IN SERIES	PRICE
1930	**Famous Film Stars**	25	

F. & J. SMITH

YEAR	TITLE	NO. IN SERIES	PRICE
1920	**Cinema Stars**	25 (8 brands)	£125.00

SMITH'S PINEWOOD CIGARETTES

1. **Gerald Ames** 2. **Roscoe (Fatty) Arbuckle**
3. **John Barrymore** 4. **Charles Chaplin**
5. **Charles Chaplin** 6. **Marguerite Clark**
7. **Arnold Daly** 8. **Hazel Dawn**
9. **Gaby Deslys** 10. **Marie Doro**
11. **Tom Mix** 12. **Victor Moore**

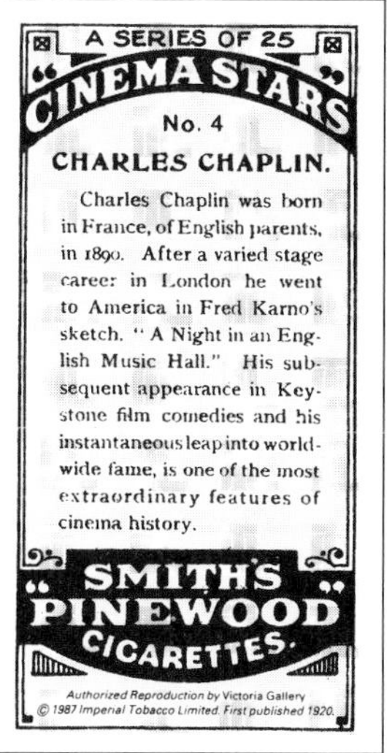

13. **Marshall Neilan** 14. **Mabel Normand**
15. **House Peters** 16. **Mary Pickford**
17. **Elizabeth Risdon** 18. **Ford Sterling**
19. **Blanche Sweet** 20. **Alma Taylor**
21. **Florence Turner** 22. **Charlotte Walker**
23. **Fannie Ward** 24. **Pearl White**
25. **Kathlyn Williams.**

TEOFANI & CO LTD

YEAR	TITLE	NO. IN SERIES	PRICE
1926	**Cinema Celebrities**	50 (Broadway novelties)	
1926	**Cinema Celebrities**	50 (Anonymous)	
1924	**Cinema Stars**	25 (Blue Band cigarettes)	
1924	**Cinema Stars**	25 ('Favourites' printed)	
1924	**Cinema Stars**	25 ('Favourites' stamped)	
1924	**Cinema Stars**	25 (Three Star cigarettes)	
1924	**Cinema Stars**	25 (Three Star magnums)	
1924	**Cinema Stars**	25 (Extra large size)	
1936	**Film Actors and Actresses**	12 (Plain back)	£3.00
1934	**Modern Movie Stars and Cinema Celebrities**	48	£19.25

THEMANS & CO.

YEAR	TITLE	NO. IN SERIES	PRICE
SILK ISSUES		(Mainly anonymous)	
1914	**Film Stars (Series B6)**	48 (Medium size)	
1914	**Film Stars (Series D6)**	14 (Postcard size)	

UNITED KINGDOM TOBACCO CO. LTD

YEAR	TITLE	NO. IN SERIES	PRICE
1933	**Cinema Stars**	32	£30.00
1934	**Cinema Stars**	50	£45.00
1934	**Cinema Stars**	50 (Anonymous)	£45.00

UNITED SERVICES MGF. CO. LTD

YEAR	TITLE	NO. IN SERIES	PRICE
1937	**Popular Screen Stars**	50	£100.00

WALKERS TOBACCO CO. LTD (W.T.C.)

YEAR	TITLE	NO. IN SERIES	PRICE
1936	**Film Stars**	32 (Tatleys) (Photographic production)	£30.00
1935	**Film Stars**	48 (Walkers) (Photographic production)	

WESTMINSTER TOBACCO CO. LTD

YEAR	TITLE	NO. IN SERIES	PRICE
1928	**Cinema Artistes**	100 (Green back)	
1931	**Cinema Artistes**	50 (Grey back)	
1935	**Cinema Celebrities**	48	
1927	**Cinema Stars**	50 (Photographic production)	
1926	**Cinema Stars**	50 (Coloured) (Medium size. Photographic)	
1930	**Cinema Stars**	50 (Uncoloured) (Medium size. Photographic)	
1927	**Film Favourites**	52 (Coloured) (Medium size. Photographic)	
1927	**Film Favourites**	52 (Uncoloured) (Medium size. Photographic)	
1931	**Film Personalities**	50 (Medium size)	
1925	**Movie Stars**	52 (Medium size. Photographic)	
1926	**Popular Film Stars**	50 (Photographic)	
1921	**Stage and Cinema Stars**	100 (Black caption) (Medium)	
1921	**Stage and Cinema Stars**	100 (Grey caption) (Medium)	£100.00
1927	**Stars of Filmland**	50 (Firm in brown) (Medium. Photographic)	
1927	**Stars of Filmland**	50 (Firm in white) (Medium. Photographic)	

W.D. & H.O. WILLS LTD

YEAR	TITLE	NO. IN SERIES	PRICE
1928	**Cinema Stars (1st series)**	25	£25.00
1928	**Cinema Stars (2nd series)**	25	£18.75
1931	**Cinema Stars (3rd series)**	50	£50.00
AUSTRALIAN ISSUES			
1930	**Famous Film Stars**	100	£50.00
1933	**Famous Film Stars**	100 (Medium size)	
1933	**Famous Film Stars**	100 (Medium size. Photographic)	
BRAND ISSUES			
Four Aces Cigarettes			
1928	**Film Favourites**	75	£75.00
1926	**Stage and Film Stars**	50 (Numbered)	£62.50
1926	**Stage and Film Stars**	50 (Unnumbered)	£75.00
1926	**Stars of the Cinema**	52 (Photographic production.	
Scissors Cigarettes			
1916	**Cinema Stars**	25	£47.50
1926	**Cinema Stars**	50 (Photographic production)	
OTHER OVERSEAS ISSUES			
1927	**Movie Stars**	48 (Photographic production.	
1936	**Stars of the Cinema**	52 (Photographic production)	

A. & M. WIX

YEAR	TITLE	NO. IN SERIES	PRICE
1940	**Cinema Cavalcade**	250 (More than one size)	£100.00

YEAR	TITLE	NO. IN SERIES	PRICE
1940	**Cinema Cavalcade, Vol. 2**	250 (More than one size)	£100.00
1930	**Film Favourites**	100	
1931	**Film Favourites (2nd series)**	100	
1932	**Film Favourites (3rd series)**	100	£65.00

CINEMA CAVALCADE

A series of 250 'n Reeks van 250

No. 166. IN THE STILL OF THE NIGHT—

A Marxian Serenade.

(*Courtesy of Metro-Goldwyn-Mayer.*)

"Cinema Cavalcade", 132 page book, with 5 colour plates, to contain this series, obtainable for sixpence from **MAX, P.O. Box 5764, Johannesburg** State whether English or Afrikaans edition is preferred.

No. 166. IN DIE STILTE VAN DIE NAG—

A Marxis-tiese Serenade.

„Rolprent-Skou", 'n Voortreflike boek waarin hierdie reeks prentjies geplak kan word, is verkrygbaar teen betaling van ses pennies in posseels van **MAX, Posbus 5764, Johannesburg** Meld asseblief of u Engelse of Afrikaanse uitgaaf verkies.

Issued with **MAX** Cigarettes
Uitgereik met **MAX** Sigarette

J. WIX & SONS LTD

YEAR	TITLE	NO. IN SERIES	PRICE
1932	**Love Scenes From Famous Films (1st series)**	25	£50.00
1932	**Love Scenes From Famous Films (1st series)**	25 (Large)	£50.00
1932	**Love Scenes From Famous Films (1st series)**	25 (Postcard)	
1932	**Love Scenes From Famous Films (2nd series)**	25	£40.00
1932	**Love Scenes From Famous Films (2nd series)**	25 (Large size)	
1932	**Love Scenes From Famous Films (2nd series)**	25 (Postcard)	
1932	**Scenes From Famous Films (3rd series)**	25	£50.00
1932	**Scenes From Famous Films (3rd series)**	25 (Postcard size)	

POSTCARDS

The world's first postcard was issued in 1869, in Austria. Picture postcards did not appear until 1882, when an official card for the Nuremberg Exhibition was made by an artist named Zrenner. Some of the earliest film-star portrait postcards were issued by the film studios: Biograph, Essanay, Imperial, Metro Mayer, Pathé, Transatlantic, Vitagraph. Then there were those issued by the portrait specialists: Beagles, Lilywhite, 'Milton', Rotary, Valentine's, and by the film fan magazines: *Film Pictorial*, *Film Weekly*, *Picture Show*, *Picturegoer*. Postcards are divided into seven periods:

1. 1869 – 99
2. 1900 – 14
3. 4 August 1914 – 11 November 1918.
4. 12 November 1918 – 2 September 1939.
5. 3 September 1939 – 7 May 1945.
6. 8 May 1945 – 1 October 1969.
7. 2 October 1969 – onwards.

Listed below are examples of film-star portrait postcards. The first is a series of 33 souvenir postal cards of Vitagraph Players, issued by the film company in 1912. These are followed by a selection of *Picturegoer* sepia portrait postcards, issued by the film magazine during the forties and fifties. Note that each series number represents a different pose.

GARY COOPER

VITAGRAPH PLAYERS

1. Florence Turner
2. Maurice Costello
3. Leo Delaney
4. Edith Halleren
5. Hal Reid
6. Kenneth Casey
7. Edith Storey
8. Rose E. Tapley
9. Maurice Costello
10. Earle Williams
11. John Bunny
12. 'Eagle Eye'
13. Charles Kent
14. Lottie Pickford
15. Adele De Garde
16. 'Eagle Eye'
17. Anne Schafer
18. Helen Gardner
19. Tom Powers
20. William Shea
21. Norma Talmadge
22. Wallace Reid
23. Van Dyke Brooke
24. Julia Swayne Gordon
25. Lillian Walker
26. James W. Morrison
27. Ralph Ince
28. Florence Turner
29. John Bunny
30. Zena Kiefe
31. 'Jean' (Vitagraph dog)
32. Mary Maurice
33. Tefft Johnson

PICTUREGOER SERIES
(In alphabetical order)

Abbott and Costello W 698
Julia Adams D139
John Agar W 825
June Allyson W923, D 326
Don Ameche W 298
Keith Andes D 315
Dana Andrews D 455
Pier Angeli W 981, D 156
Anouk D 306
Eve Arden W 813
Fred Astaire W 449
Richard Attenborough W 475
Cecile Aubry W 922
Jean-Pierre Aumont D 336
Gene Autry W 369, W 601
Lauren Bacall D 409
Stanley Baker D 499
Lucille Ball W 911
Suzan Ball D 393
Lex Barker W 898, D 265
Gene Barry D 438
Lionel Barrymore W 733
Eva Bartok D 235
Richard Basehart W 884
Anne Baxter D106
Robert Beatty W 591
Barbara Bel Geddes W 696
William Bendix W 574
Joan Bennett W 323
Ingrid Bergman W 269
Lyle Bettger D 351
Marie Blanchard D 432
Ann Blyth D 51, D 208
Claire Bloom D 313
Dirk Bogarde W 994, D 290, D 334
Humphrey Bogart W 271
Ray Bolger D 227
Shirley Booth D 478
William Boyd W 270
Charles Boyer W 640
Scott Brady W 819
Marlon Brando D 128
Keefe Brasselle W 959
George Brent W 517
David Brian W 881
Lloyd Bridges W 951
Richard Burton D 459

CHAPTER FIVE

FRONT-OF-HOUSE SETS AND POSTERS

FRONT-OF-HOUSE SETS

Front-of-house sets, as the name suggests, are sets of movie stills originally designed to be displayed in showcases located outside the movie theatre, at the front of the house. Their purpose was to attract the audience into the theatre by showing – generally eight – scenes from the movie, each one carefully chosen to convey the mood of that particular movie. Early stills were matt sepia. Later came glossy black and white stills and colour. All were 10 × 8 in. in size. Today fewer and fewer of these sets are being produced for theatre display, television having already shown the best scenes of the current releases to millions of homes.

Collectors should note that the original front-of-house sets will be mounted on a white border with the title of the movie and the stars on the bottom margin. Further proof of authenticity will be found on the reverse side of the still, which should bear the studio or photographer's stamp. Examine stills for signs of cracking, as this would be further proof of an original: glossy surfaces are sensitive to light. Reproductions often look too good to be true. Below is a list of front-of-house sets that are greatly sought after by collectors.

Gentlemen Prefer Blondes (1953), Marilyn Monroe and Jane Russell
Rebel Without A Cause (1955), James Dean and Natalie Wood
Love Me Tender (1956), Elvis Presley and Debra Paget
The Wizard Of Oz (1939), Judy Garland and Ray Bolger
Casablanca (1942), Humphrey Bogart and Ingrid Bergman
Citizen Kane (1941), Orson Welles and Joseph Cotten
Dracula (1931), Bela Lugosi and Helen Chandler
The Third Man (1949), Joseph Cotten, Trevor Howard, Alida Valli and Orson Welles
The Maltese Falcon (1941), Humphrey Bogart and Mary Astor
Gone With The Wind (1939), Clark Gable and Vivien Leigh
King Kong (1933), Robert Armstrong and Fay Wray
Camille (1936), Greta Garbo and Robert Taylor
The Bride Of Frankenstein (1935), Boris Karloff and Colin Clive
Sons Of The Desert (1933), Laurel and Hardy
The Adventures of Robin Hood (1938), Errol Flynn and Olivia De Havilland
Some Like It Hot (1959), Marilyn Monroe, Jack Lemmon and Tony Curtis
The Searchers (1956), John Wayne and Jeffrey Hunter
Star Wars (1977), Mark Hamill, Harrison Ford and Carrie Fisher
Dr No (1962), Sean Connery and Ursula Andress
Raiders Of The Lost Ark (1981), Harrison Ford and Karen Allen

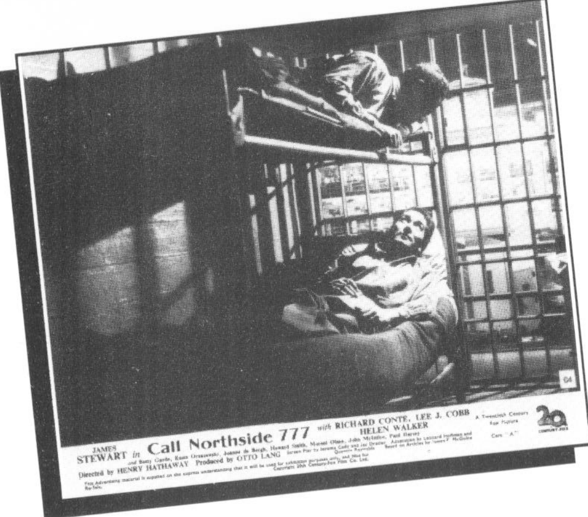
JAMES
STEWART in Call Northside 777 with RICHARD CONTE, LEE J. COBB
HELEN WALKER
Directed by HENRY HATHAWAY Produced by OTTO LANG

JAMES
STEWART in Call Northside 777 with RICHARD CONTE, LEE J. COBB
HELEN WALKER
Directed by HENRY HATHAWAY Produced by OTTO LANG

JAMES
STEWART in Call Northside 777 with RICHARD CONTE, LEE J. COBB
HELEN WALKER
Directed by HENRY HATHAWAY Produced by OTTO LANG

JAMES
STEWART in Call Northside 777 with RICHARD CONTE, LEE J. COBB
HELEN WALKER
Directed by HENRY HATHAWAY Produced by OTTO LANG

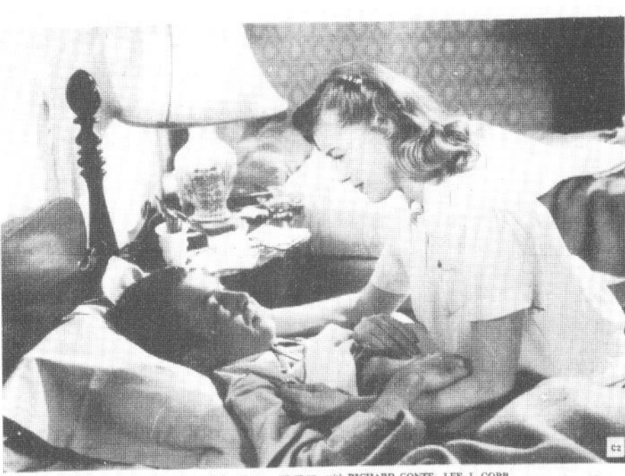
JAMES
STEWART in Call Northside 777 with RICHARD CONTE, LEE J. COBB
HELEN WALKER
Directed by HENRY HATHAWAY Produced by OTTO LANG

JAMES
STEWART in Call Northside 777 with RICHARD CONTE, LEE J. COBB
HELEN WALKER
Directed by HENRY HATHAWAY Produced by OTTO LANG

JAMES
STEWART in Call Northside 777 with RICHARD CONTE, LEE J. COBB
HELEN WALKER
Directed by HENRY HATHAWAY Produced by OTTO LANG

JAMES
STEWART in Call Northside 777 with RICHARD CONTE, LEE J. COBB
HELEN WALKER
Directed by HENRY HATHAWAY Produced by OTTO LANG

POSTERS

Movie posters come in varying sizes: one-sheets (27 × 41 in.), three-sheets (41 × 81 in.), six-sheets (81 × 81 in.), twenty-four sheets (246 × 108 in.). In addition to these sizes there are half-sheets (22 × 28 in.), quads (30 × 40 in.), and the varying sizes adopted by the various European countries. All of these posters were designed to be used for specific purposes in a theatre's publicity for a movie. The theatre manager would make a selection from a campaign or press book. For example, he might choose one twenty-four sheet, which would be displayed on the billboard located above the canopy outside his theatre; two three-sheets for display in frames on exterior walls; one one-sheet to be exhibited on a stand or in a case in the foyer or lobby.

For the poster collector, the most popular sizes are the one-sheet and the quad, which can easily be framed and hung on a wall in their home. There are four points to be considered when purchasing a movie poster: 1) style; 2) origin; 3) artwork; 4) price.

Posters are often issued in more than one style of design. You will find that these are marked at the bottom of the poster: 'Style A' or 'Style B' or whatever letters the film studio used. A 'Style A' poster would generally show an illustration of the leading star, but not necessarily the co-star.

The best way to identify an original poster is to study the original press book that was issued with the film's release. The book will illustrate the various designs and sizes that were available to the exhibitor. If the poster shows a different design to those illustrated in the book, then you are looking at a re-issue or reproduction. Re-issue posters will have an R in the bottom margin, followed by a number signifying a date. A further guide to the buyer would be if newspaper quotes from critics, or Academy Award winning notices, appear on the poster, in which case it is most definitely a re-issue.

Prices for one-sheets or quads will vary enormously from a few pounds to a few hundred, depending on rarity, condition, popularity and whether it is the work of a notable illustrator.

Poster artwork determines the true value of a poster. Although poster artwork is a collaborative enterprise, generally one illustrator dominates. Since movie posters first appeared, in 1890 in Paris, they have attracted some of the world's finest illustrators from Norman Rockwell to William Rose, from Al Hirschfeld to Ted Ireland, from Sam Berman to Saul Bass. Leading illustrators of movie posters are listed below along with the titles of the films for which they contributed poster artwork.

CONSTANTIN ALAJALOV
The Cabinet Of Dr Caligari Werner Krauss, Conrad Veidt
Monkey Business Marx Brothers
Horse Feathers Marx Brothers
Love Me Tonight Maurice Chevalier, Jeanette MacDonald

SAUL BASS
Carmen Jones Dorothy Dandridge, Harry Belafonte
The Big Knife Jack Palance, Ida Lupino
The Man With The Golden Arm Frank Sinatra, Kim Novak
The Racers Kirk Douglas, Bella Darvi
The Seven Year Itch Marilyn Monroe, Tom Ewell
The Shrike José Ferrer, June Allyson
Attack! Jack Palance, Eddie Albert
Storm Center Bette Davis, Brian Keith
Saint Joan Jean Seberg, Anton Walbrook
Edge Of The City John Cassavetes, Sidney Poitier
Around The World In Eighty Days David Niven, Cantinflas
Bonjour Tristesse David Niven, Deborah Kerr
The Pride And The Passion Cary Grant, Sophia Loren
The Young Stranger James MacArthur, Kim Hunter
The Big Country Gregory Peck, Jean Simmons
Cowboy Jack Lemmon, Glenn Ford
Vertigo James Stewart, Kim Novak
Anatomy Of A Murder James Stewart, Ben Gazzara
North By Northwest Cary Grant, Eva Marie Saint

SAM BERMAN
Million Dollar Legs W.C. Fields, Jack Oakie
Duck Soup Marx Brothers
Klondike Annie Mae West, Victor McLaglen
Poppy W.C. Fields, Rochelle Hudson
The Big Broadcast Of 1937 Jack Benny, George Burns, Gracie Allen

WILLIAM GALBRAITH CRAWFORD
The Big Parade John Gilbert, Renée Adorée
Ben Hur Ramon Novarro, Francis X. Bushman
A Woman Of Affairs Greta Garbo, Lewis Stone
Anna Christie Greta Garbo, Charles Bickford
Red Dust Clark Gable, Jean Harlow
Grand Hotel Greta Garbo, John Barrymore, Lionel Barrymore, Joan Crawford
Dancing Lady Joan Crawford, Clark Gable
Dinner At Eight Marie Dressler, John Barrymore, Jean Harlow

The Painted Veil Greta Garbo, George Brent
Tarzan And His Mate Johnny Weissmuller, Maureen O'Sullivan
The Thin Man William Powell, Myrna Loy
Mutiny On The Bounty Charles Laughton, Clark Gable
Naughty Marietta Jeanette MacDonald, Nelson Eddy
Reckless Jean Harlow, William Powell
Riff Raff Jean Harlow, Spencer Tracy
The Shop Around The Corner James Stewart, Margaret Sullavan
For Me And My Gal Judy Garland, Gene Kelly
Meet Me In St Louis Judy Garland, Margaret O'Brien

JAMES MONTGOMERY FLAGG
Lost Horizon Ronald Colman, H.B. Warner, Thomas Mitchell
Small Town Girl Janet Gaynor, Robert Taylor
The Case Against Mrs Ames Madeleine Carroll, George Brent

HANS FLATO
Blonde Venus Marlene Dietrich, Herbert Marshall
The Scarlet Empress Marlene Dietrich, John Lodge
Angel Marlene Dietrich, Herbert Marshall
Bitter Sweet Anna Neagle, Fernand Gravet

KAROLY GROSZ
Dracula Bela Lugosi, Helen Chandler
Frankenstein Boris Karloff, Colin Clive
The Old Dark House Melvyn Douglas, Charles Laughton
The Invisible Man Gloria Stuart, Claude Rains
The Mummy Boris Karloff, Zita Johann, David Manners
Murders In The Rue Morgue Bela Lugosi, Sidney Fox
The Bride Of Frankenstein Boris Karloff, Colin Clive

ALVAN CORDELL HADLEY
The General Buster Keaton, Marion Mack
The Navigator Buster Keaton, Kathryn McGuire
College Buster Keaton
The Jazz Singer Al Jolson, May McAvoy
The Circus Charlie Chaplin, Merna Kennedy
Whoopee! Eddie Cantor, Eleanor Hunt
Hell's Angels Ben Lyon, James Hall, Jean Harlow
City Lights Charlie Chaplin, Virginia Cherrill

ALBERT HIRSCHFELD
Broadway Melody Charles King, Anita Page
Hallelujah! Daniel Haynes, Nina Mae McKinney
Spite Marriage Buster Keaton, Dorothy Sebastian
Bacon Grabbers Laurel and Hardy
Min And Bill Marie Dressler, Wallace Beery
Pardon Us Laurel and Hardy
Sidewalks Of New York Buster Keaton, Anita Page
Pack Up Your Troubles Laurel and Hardy
The Devil's Brother Laurel and Hardy
Sons Of The Desert Laurel and Hardy
A Night At The Opera Marx Brothers
A Day At The Races Marx Brothers
At The Circus Marx Brothers
Go West Marx Brothers
The Sunshine Boys Walter Matthau, George Burns
New York, New York Liza Minnelli, Robert De Niro

TED IRELAND (Vincentini)
A Tale Of Two Cities Ronald Colman, Elizabeth Allan
The Painted Veil Greta Garbo, Herbert Marshall
No More Ladies Joan Crawford, Robert Montgomery
Rose Marie Jeanette MacDonald, Nelson Eddy
San Francisco Clark Gable, Jeanette MacDonald
Captains Courageous Spencer Tracy, Lionel Barrymore
I Take This Woman Spencer Tracy, Hedy Lamarr
Ninotchka Greta Garbo, Melvyn Douglas
The Women Norma Shearer, Joan Crawford, Rosalind Russell
Northwest Passage Spencer Tracy, Robert Young
Tortilla Flat Spencer Tracy, Hedy Lamarr
White Cargo Hedy Lamarr, Walter Pidgeon
Journey For Margaret Robert Young, Laraine Day, Margaret O'Brien
Easter Parade Judy Garland, Fred Astaire

FREDERIC C. MADAN
Check And Double Check Freeman F. Gosden, Charles V. Correll
Cimarron Richard Dix, Irene Dunne
Bird Of Paradise Joel McCrea, John Halliday
The Informer Victor McLaglen, Heather Angel
She Randolph Scott, Nigel Bruce, Helen Gahagen
Footlight Parade James Cagney, Joan Blondell, Ruby Keeler, Dick Powell

NORMAN ROCKWELL
The Magnificent Ambersons Joseph Cotten, Dolores Costello
The Song Of Bernadette Jennifer Jones, William Eythe, Charles Bickford
Along Came Jones Gary Cooper, Loretta Young
The Razor's Edge Tyrone Power, Gene Tierney, Clifton Webb
Cinderfella Jerry Lewis, Ed Wynn
Stagecoach Ann-Margret, Alex Cord, Bing Crosby

ARMANDO SEGUSO
Goodbye Mr Chips Robert Donat, Greer Garson
Gone With The Wind Clark Gable, Vivien Leigh
The Shop Around The Corner Margaret Sullavan, James Stewart
The Philadelphia Story Cary Grant, Katharine Hepburn, James Stewart
Mrs Miniver Greer Garson, Walter Pidgeon
Random Harvest Ronald Colman, Greer Garson
Crossroads William Powell, Hedy Lamarr
The Human Comedy Mickey Rooney, Frank Morgan, James Craig
Kismet Ronald Colman, Marlene Dietrich
Mrs Parkington Greer Garson, Walter Pidgeon
Thirty Seconds Over Tokyo Spencer Tracy, Van Johnson, Robert Walker
The Cat And The Canary Bob Hope, Paulette Goddard
For Whom The Bell Tolls Gary Cooper, Ingrid Bergman

ALBERTO VARGAS
Ladies They Talk About Barbara Stanwyck, Lyle Talbot
Nana Anna Sten, Lionel Atwill
Moon Over Miami Don Ameche, Betty Grable
Flame Of New Orleans Marlene Dietrich, Roland Young
Dubarry Was A Lady Gene Kelly, Lucille Ball

CHAPTER SIX

SIGNED PHOTOGRAPHS

Betty Grable

Signed photographs of movie stars can be the most fascinating and rewarding memorabilia of all, or they can be the most frustrating of collectables. The autograph collector is faced with a bewildering amount of signed photographs, some genuine, some not. So there are a few ground rules to heed if you wish to build a bona fide collection of autographs, rather than a heap of worthless facsimiles. 1. You should buy only from reputable dealers. 2. You should join an international autograph organization and get the advice of experts. 3. The signature will be worth more if signed during the period of the photograph, rather than years later. 4. The signature should be ink signed. 5. Learn as much as you can about the star whose autograph you are seeking: how does she or he sign, do they sign using their first name only; do they use white, green, red, blue or black ink?

The price of an autographed photo will depend also on condition and rarity. Garbo, Dean, Monroe, Presley, Laurel and Hardy, will be the most expensive. An ink-signed picture of Garbo would be a rare jewel indeed as she kept her signature for documents. Dean was not alive long enough to sign many photos. Monroe's signature will fetch over a thousand pounds, while Presley and Laurel and Hardy signed photos will be worth a few hundred.

For first leaguers you can expect to pay, for genuine 'period' signed photographs, the following prices: Fred Astaire and Ginger Rogers – £200; Humphrey Bogart – £500; Charlie Chaplin – £400; Gary Cooper – £150; Judy Garland – £80; Jean Harlow – £100; Jayne Mansfield – £50; Elizabeth Taylor – £100.

Many stars would send signed photographs of themselves to film magazines and these would be published with the star's inscribed greeting. Some of the best examples of these are those printed in *Picture Show*. See list below.

DATE	STAR
1949	
30 July	**Gregory Peck**
6 Aug.	**Jean Simmons**
13 Aug.	**Michael Wilding**
20 Aug.	**Margaret Lockwood**
27 Aug.	**Stewart Granger**
10 Sept.	**Linda Darnell**
17 Sept.	**Cary Grant**
24 Sept.	**Anna Neagle**
8 Oct.	**Dennis Price**
15 Oct.	**Valerie Hobson**
22 Oct.	**Trevor Howard**
29 Oct.	**Ingrid Bergman**
5 Nov.	**Alan Ladd**
12 Nov.	**Greer Garson**
19 Nov.	**Richard Todd**
26 Nov.	**Judy Garland**
3 Dec.	**Van Johnson**
17 Dec.	**Betty Grable**
24 Dec.	**Ann Todd**
31 Dec.	**Richard Conte**
1950	
7 Jan.	**Patricia Medina**
14 Jan.	**Errol Flynn**
21 Jan.	**Dan Dailey**
28 Jan.	**Yvonne De Carlo**
4 Feb.	**Glenn Ford**
11 Feb.	**Jeanne Crain**
18 Feb.	**Richard Widmark**
25 Feb.	**Janet Leigh**
4 March	**Robert Mitchum**
11 March	**Jean Kent**
18 March	**Montgomery Clift**
25 March	**Anne Baxter**
1 April	**Joseph Cotten**
8 April	**Barbara Hale**
15 April	**Bing Crosby**
22 April	**Lizabeth Scott**
29 April	**John Wayne**
6 May	**Ava Gardner**
13 May	**Peter Lawford**
20 May	**June Haver**
27 May	**Larry Parks**
3 June	**Marta Toren**
10 June	**Jimmy Hanley**
17 June	**Kathryn Grayson**
24 June	**Guy Rolfe**
1 July	**Vera-Ellen**
8 July	**William Holden**
15 July	**Evelyn Keyes**
22 July	**Roy Rogers**
29 July	**Ginger Rogers**
5 Aug.	**Fred Astaire**
12 Aug.	**Virginia Mayo**
19 Aug.	**Nigel Patrick**
26 Aug.	**Betty Garrett**
2 Sept.	**Gene Autry**

DATE	STAR
9 Sept.	**Diana Lynn**
16 Sept.	**Douglas Fairbanks Jr**
23 Sept.	**Elizabeth Taylor**
30 Sept.	**Dirk Bogarde**
7 Oct.	**Jean Simmons**
14 Oct./4 Nov.	**James Stewart**
11 Nov.	**June Allyson**
18 Nov.	**Dick Powell**
25 Nov.	**Valentina Cortesa**
9 Dec.	**Betty Hutton**
16 Dec.	**David Farrar**
23/30 Dec.	**Joan Crawford**
1951	
6 Jan.	**Ray Milland**
13 Jan.	**Audrey Totter**
20 Jan.	**Robert Taylor**
27 Jan.	**Margaret Leighton**
3 Feb.	**MacDonald Carey**
17 Feb.	**Wendell Corey**
24 Feb.	**Nancy Olson**
3 March	**Gene Kelly**
10 March	**Ruth Roman**
17 March	**Ricardo Montalban**
24 March	**Eleanor Parker**
31 March	**Van Heflin**
7 April	**Deborah Kerr**
14 April	**Burt Lancaster**
21 April	**Joan Fontaine**
28 April	**John Lund**
5 May	**Ann Blyth**
12 May	**Dennis Morgan**
19 May	**Jane Wyman**
26 May	**Howard Keel**
2 June	**Jane Powell**
9 June	**David Brian**
16 June	**Arlene Dahl**
23 June	**Victor Mature**
30 June	**Dan Dailey and Betty Grable**
7 July	**Barry Sullivan**
14 July	**Betsy Drake**
21 July	**Gary Cooper**
28 July	**Lauren Bacall**
4 Aug.	**Mario Lanza**
11 Aug.	**Jane Russell**
18 Aug.	**Dana Andrews**
1 Sept.	**Jeff Chandler**
8 Sept.	**Gene Tierney**
15 Sept.	**Laurence Harvey**
22 Sept.	**Viveca Lindfors**
29 Sept.	**Robert Walker**
6 Oct.	**Glynis Johns**
13 Oct.	**Farley Granger**
20 Oct.	**Shelley Winters**
27 Oct.	**Alec Guinness**
3 Nov.	**Petula Clark**
10 Nov.	**Spencer Tracy**

DATE	STAR
17 Nov.	**Doris Day**
24 Nov.	**David Tomlinson**
1 Dec.	**Moira Shearer**
8 Dec.	**John Hodiak**
15 Dec.	**Corinne Calvet**
22 Dec.	**Fernando Lamas**
1952	
5 Jan.	**Zachary Scott**
12 Jan.	**Rhonda Fleming**
19 Jan.	**Gary Merrill**
26 Jan.	**Pier Angeli**
2 Feb.	**Gordon MacRae**
9 Feb.	**Mona Freeman**
16 Feb.	**Frank Sinatra**
23 Feb.	**Jean Peters**
1 March	**Gene Nelson**
8 March	**Adele Mara**
15 March	**Kirk Douglas**
22 March	**Patricia Neal**
29 March	**Anthony Steel**
5 April	**Esther Williams**
12 April	**Louis Jourdan**
19 April	**Margaret Johnston**
26 April	**Forrest Tucker**
3 May	**Lucille Ball**
10 May	**John Derek**
17 May	**Patrice Wymore**
24 May	**Arthur Kennedy**
31 May	**Maria Schell**
7 June	**Tony Curtis**
14 June	**Joan Evans**
21 June	**John McCallum and Googie Withers**
28 June	**Dinah Shore**
5 July	**Paul Henreid**
12 July	**Cyd Charisse**
26 July	**Mitzi Gaynor**
2 Aug.	**James Mason**
16 Aug.	**Lloyd Bridges**
23 Aug.	**Susan Cabot**
30 Aug.	**Dale Robertson**
6 Sept.	**Joanne Dru**
20 Sept.	**Cathy O'Donnell**
27 Sept.	**Louis Hayward**
4 Oct.	**Mai Zetterling**
11 Oct.	**Jody Lawrance**
25 Oct.	**Rita Hayworth**
1 Nov.	**Mario Lanza**
8 Nov.	**Sally Forrest**
15 Nov.	**David Wayne**
22 Nov.	**Lana Turner**
29 Nov.	**Cornel Wilde**
6 Dec.	**Merle Oberon**
13 Dec.	**Marlon Brando**
27 Dec.	**Robert Taylor**

DATE	STAR
1953	
3 Jan.	**Piper Laurie**
10 Jan.	**Randolph Scott**
17 Jan.	**Debra Paget**
24 Jan.	**Rory Calhoun**
31 Jan.	**Debbie Reynolds**
7 Feb.	**Charlie Chaplin**
14 Feb.	**Jean Hagen**
21 Feb.	**Mel Ferrer**
28 Feb.	**Maureen O'Hara**
7 March	**Dane Clark**
14 March	**Dinah Sheridan**
21 March	**Richard Denning**
28 March	**Constance Smith**
4 April	**Rock Hudson**
11 April	**Shirley Booth**
18 April	**Sterling Hayden**
25 April	**Loretta Young**
2 May	**Terence Morgan**
9 May	**Peggy Cummins**
16 May	**Jack Hawkins**
23 May	**Marilyn Monroe**
30 May	**Richard Burton**
6 June	**Leslie Caron**
13 June	**Maxwell Reed**
20 June	**Helen Hayes**
4 July	**Barbara Stanwyck**
11 July	**George Cole**
18 July	**Suzan Ball**
25 July	**Herbert Lom**
1 Aug.	**Gail Davis**
8 Aug.	**Dan Duryea**
15 Aug.	**Coleen Gray**
22 Aug.	**Ralph Meeker**
29 Aug.	**Celia Johnson**
5 Sept.	**Ronald Shiner**
12 Sept.	**Eileen Herlie**
19 Sept.	**Audie Murphy**
26 Sept.	**Jan Sterling**
3 Oct.	**Dennis O'Keefe**
10 Oct.	**Donna Reed**
17 Oct.	**Vittorio Gassman**
24 Oct.	**Margaret Lockwood**
7 Nov.	**Gregory Peck**
14 Nov.	**Ava Gardner**
21 Nov.	**Errol Flynn**
5 Dec.	**Jeff Chandler**
12 Dec.	**Richard Basehart**
19 Dec.	**Ursula Thiess**
26 Dec.	**Bob Hope**
1954	
2 Jan.	**Ginger Rogers**
9 Jan.	**Donald Sinden**
16 Jan.	**Hildegarde Neff**
23 Jan.	**Gene Barry**
30 Jan.	**Paula Raymond**
6 Feb.	**Red Skelton**

DATE	STAR
27 Feb.	**Scott Brady**
6 March	**Alex Nicol**
13 March	**Lori Nelson**
27 March	**Julia Adams**
3 April	**David Niven**
10 April	**Jane Russell**
17 April	**John Bentley**
24 April	**Allyn McLerie**
1 May	**Laurence Harvey**
15 May	**William Holden**
22 May	**Polly Bergen**
29 May	**Keefe Brasselle**
5 June	**Elizabeth Sellars**
12 June	**Dirk Bogarde**
19 June	**Veronica Hurst**
26 June	**Tyrone Power**
3 July	**Joan Rice**
10 July	**Dennis O'Keefe**
17 July	**Lucille Ball and Desi Arnaz**
24 July	**Charlton Heston**
31 July	**Muriel Pavlow**
7 Aug.	**Peter Finch**
21 Aug.	**Derek De Marney**
28 Aug.	**Rita Gam**
4 Sept.	**Robert Wagner**
11 Sept.	**Laya Raki**
18 Sept.	**Van Johnson**
25 Sept.	**Yvonne De Carlo**
16 Oct.	**Robert Cummings**
23 Oct.	**Odile Versois**
6 Nov.	**Audrey Hepburn**
13 Nov.	**Robert Mitchum**
27 Nov.	**David Knight**
11 Dec.	**John Gregson**
18 Dec.	**Virginia McKenna**
25 Dec.	**Kenneth More**
1955	
1 Jan.	**Mamie Van Doren**
8 Jan.	**Jack Palance**
15 Jan.	**Glynis Johns**
22 Jan.	**Humphrey Bogart**
29 Jan.	**Noelle Middleton**
5 Feb.	**Norman Wisdom**
12 Feb.	**Petula Clark**
19 Feb.	**Steve Forrest**
26 Feb.	**Moira Shearer**
19 March	**John Justin**
26 March	**Gloria De Haven**
2 April	**Eric Portman**
9 April	**Grace Kelly**
16 April	**John Ericson**
23 April	**Doris Day**
30 April	**Richard Widmark**
7 May	**Jeanne Crain**
14 May	**Denholm Elliott**
21 May	**Elaine Stewart**

DATE	STAR
11 June	**George Nader**
18 June	**Bella Darvi**
25 June	**Richard Basehart**
2 July	**Colleen Miller**
9 July	**Jacques Sernas**
30 July	**Belinda Lee**
6 Aug.	**Tommy Trinder**
13 Aug.	**Eva Bartok**
20 Aug.	**Frankie Laine**
27 Aug.	**Rosemary Clooney**
3 Sept.	**Tab Hunter**
17 Sept.	**Edmund Purdom**
24 Sept.	**Ann Miller**
1 Oct.	**John Derek**
8 Oct.	**Diana Dors**
15 Oct.	**Bill Travers**
22 Oct.	**Diane Cilento**
29 Oct.	**Jack Lemmon**
5 Nov.	**Faith Domergue**
19 Nov.	**Julie Harris**
26 Nov.	**Lex Barker**
17 Dec.	**Diana Lynn**
31 Dec.	**June Allyson**
1956	
14 Jan.	**Marilyn Monroe**
21 Jan.	**Michael Redgrave**
28 Jan.	**Patrice Wymore**
4 Feb.	**Audie Murphy**

Leslie Caron

Alan Ladd

DATE	STAR
11 Feb.	**Ida Lupino**
18 Feb.	**Henry Fonda**
25 Feb.	**Shelley Winters**
5 May	**Howard Keel**
12 May	**Glenn Ford**
19 May	**Jennifer Jones**
26 May	**Vernon Gray**
9 June	**Robert Stack**
16 June	**Joanne Dru**
23 June	**Alan Ladd**
30 June	**Dorothy Malone**
7 July	**Cameron Mitchell**
14 July	**Kim Novak**
21 July	**Dennis Lotis**
28 July	**Gina Lollobrigida**
4 Aug.	**Guy Rolfe**
11 Aug.	**Anne Francis**
18 Aug.	**Susan Stephen**
25 Aug.	**Jeff Chandler**

DATE	STAR
1 Sept.	**John Mills**
22 Sept.	**Debbie Reynolds**
29 Sept.	**Jeremy Spenser**
6 Oct.	**Marisa Pavan**
20 Oct.	**Yul Brynner**
27 Oct.	**Liberace**
3 Nov.	**Anita Ekberg**
10 Nov.	**Richard Lewis**
17 Nov.	**Dana Wynter**
24 Nov.	**Bryan Forbes**
1 Dec.	**Lauren Bacall**
8 Dec.	**Steve Cochran**
29 Dec.	**Eva Marie Saint**
1957	
5 Jan.	**Stanley Baker**
12 Jan.	**James Dean**
19 Jan.	**Gordon MacRae**
26 Jan.	**Jimmy Edwards**
2 Feb.	**Lee Patterson**
9 Feb.	**Jean Simmons**
16 Feb.	**Tom Conway**
2 March	**Betty Hutton**
9 March	**John Forsythe**
16 March	**Fess Parker**
23 March	**Terry Moore**
30 March	**Sal Mineo**
6 April	**Martha Hyer**
13 April	**Ian Carmichael**
27 April	**Richard Attenborough**
4 May	**Lilli Palmer**
11 May	**John Fraser**
18 May	**Betta St John**
25 May	**Henry Fonda**
1 June	**Laraine Day**
8 June	**Michael Medwin**
15 June	**Barbara Rush**
22 June	**Brian Donlevy**
29 June	**Tommy Steele**
6 July	**Rod Steiger**
13 July	**Lois Maxwell**
20 July	**Donald O'Connor**
3 Aug.	**Anthony Perkins**
10 Aug.	**Shirley MacLaine**
17 Aug.	**John Gregson**
24 Aug.	**Vera Miles**

DATE	STAR
14 Sept.	**Pat Boone**
21 Sept.	**Frankie Vaughan**
28 Sept.	**George Baker**
19 Oct.	**Elsa Martinelli**
2 Nov.	**Martine Carol**
9 Nov.	**Don Murray**
23 Nov.	**Tony Randall**
14 Dec.	**Jayne Mansfield**
1958	
1 Feb.	**Taina Elg**
1 March	**Keith Michell**
8 March	**Teresa Wright**
29 March	**Lisa Gastoni**
19 April	**Shirley Jones**
3 May	**Anne Heywood**
10 May	**Russ Tamblyn**
17 May	**Mylene Demongeot**
24 May	**Diane Varsi**
7 June	**Elizabeth Taylor**
14 June	**Mario Lanza**
5 July	**Gordon Scott**
12 July	**Peter Arne**
30 Aug.	**Claire Bloom**
6 Sept.	**Vera Day**
13 Sept.	**Max Bygraves**
20 Sept.	**Anna Gaylor**
4 Oct.	**Pier Angeli**
29 Nov.	**Hope Lange**
13 Dec.	**Virginia Maskell**
27 Dec.	**Nicole Maurey**
1959	
3 Jan.	**Terry Thomas**
10 Jan.	**June Thorburn**
24 Jan.	**Ingrid Bergman**
31 Jan.	**Hardy Kruger**
7 Feb.	**Christine Carere**
21 Feb.	**Eartha Kitt**
14 March	**Trevor Howard**
4 April	**Rosalind Russell**
18 April	**Heather Sears**
25 April	**Tony Curtis**
2 May	**Luciana Paluzzi**

CHAPTER SEVEN

PROPS AND SOUVENIRS

PROPS

Dancing. Astaire and Kelly up there on the big screen. The movie is *Ziegfeld Follies*, the dance number is 'The Babbit And The Bromide', and that straw boater with a rose silk hatband worn by Astaire, was auctioned for £3,410 in 1988.

Robert Taylor and Kay Kendall in a sensitive scene from *The Adventures Of Quentin Durward*. The moss-green velvet dress worn by Kay was bought in auction in 1989, price – £286.

Marilyn Monroe is leaning on a bar, being consoled by Don Murray. Of course the movie is *Bus Stop*. Marilyn's blouse is green, overlaid with black lace. It looks good on Marilyn. In 1988 it fetched over £6,000 in auction. That same blouse was a star souvenir prize offered to readers of *Picture Show* on 24 November 1956. It was eventually won by a Mrs Fulcher.

A memorable moment from Hitchcock's *Rear Window*, James Stewart being nursed by Grace Kelly. Stewart's green-checked pyjamas and Kelly's ivory-coloured halter blouse were *Picture Show's* star souvenir prizes for the week of 4 December 1954.

Here is a selected list of some of the souvenir prizes that were given away by *Picture Show*:

Shoes worn by **Vivien Leigh** in *Caesar and Cleopatra.*
Suede gauntlets worn by **Errol Flynn** in *The New Adventures Of Don Juan.*
Shirt worn by **James Cagney** in *White Heat.*
Sequinned tiara worn by **June Haver** in *Look For The Silver Lining.*
A figured bow tie worn by **Humphrey Bogart** in *Tokyo Joe.*
Sailor hat worn by **Frank Sinatra** in *On The Town.*
Sword used by **Tyrone Power** in *The Black Rose.*
Hat worn by **James Stewart** in *Broken Arrow.*
White gloves worn by **Erich Von Stroheim** in *Sunset Boulevard.*
Net evening gloves worn by **Deanna Durbin** in *For The Love Of Mary.*
Headband worn by **Victor Mature** in *Samson and Delilah.*
Uniform cap worn by **Clark Gable** in *Command Decision.*
White hand-stitched gloves worn by **Elizabeth Taylor** in *Father's Little Dividend.*
Red and white silk tie worn by **William Holden** in *Born Yesterday.*
Soft straw hat worn by **Kirk Douglas** in *Ace In The Hole.*
Cap worn by **Danny Kaye** in *On The Riviera.*
Black dancing sandals worn by **Vera-Ellen** in *Happy Go Lovely.*
Gloves worn by **Mario Lanza** in *The Great Caruso.*
Underwater compass used by **Richard Widmark** in *The Frogmen.*
Black straw bonnet worn by **Kathryn Grayson** in *Show Boat.*
Cream ruffled shirt worn by **Howard Keel** in *Show Boat.*
Silk scarf, with red squirrel and black leaf design, worn by **Virginia Mayo** in *Fine And Dandy.*
Cap worn by **Gene Kelly** in *An American In Paris.*
Blue satin ballet shoes worn by **Leslie Caron** in *An American in Paris.*
Oyster silk evening shoes worn by **Betty Grable** in *Meet Me After The Show.*

Decorated belt, from Saks, Fifth Avenue, New York, worn by **Doris Day** in *It's A Great Feeling.*

Silk bandanna worn by **James Stewart** in *Where The River Bends.*

Yellow sou'wester worn by **Debbie Reynolds** in *Singin' In The Rain.*

Lilac coloured shirt worn by **Jeff Chandler** in *Battle At Apache Pass.*

Red and black checked shirt worn by **Stewart Granger** in *The Wild North.*

Blackberry coloured suede gloves worn by **Jennifer Jones** in *Carrie.*

Black and white silk tie worn by **Laurence Olivier** in *Carrie.*

An embroidered blouse worn by **Jeanne Crain** in *Belles On Their Toes.*

Long black net stockings worn by **Susan Hayward** in *With A Song In My Heart.*

Mask worn by **Stewart Granger** in *Scaramouche.*

Brown bowler hat worn by **Lou Costello** in *Abbott and Costello Lost In Alaska.*

Bowler hat and cravat worn by **Charlie Chaplin** in *Limelight.*

A multi-coloured striped sash worn by **Mario Lanza** in *Because You're Mine.*

Hat worn by **John Mills** in *The Gentle Gunman.*

Red, blue, cream patterned shirt worn by **Bob Hope** in *Road To Bali.*

Blue straw hat worn by **Lana Turner** in *The Merry Widow.*

Long, white kid gloves worn by **Deborah Kerr** in *The Prisoner Of Zenda.*

Navy blue beret worn by **Gregory Peck** in *Snows Of Kilimanjaro.*

Trigger's horseshoe mounted on a wooden shield.

Iron cross worn by **James Mason** in *The Desert Rats.*

Coffee mug presented to a member of the cast of *The Quiet Man* by **John Wayne**.

Sanforized khaki shirt worn by **James Stewart** in *Thunder Road.*

Champagne satin cap worn by **Jean Simmons** in *Young Bess.*

Cream cap worn by **Jerry Lewis** and a shirt worn by **Dean Martin** in *The Caddy.*

Onyx and rhinestone earrings worn by **Janet Leigh** in *Walking My Baby Back Home.*

Red silk scarf worn by **Grace Kelly** in *Mogambo.*

Pearl and crystal earrings worn by **Donna Reed** in *From Here To Eternity.*

Black dress tie worn by **Fred Astaire** in *The Band Wagon.*

Gilt earrings, with a blue stone set on a cream background, worn by **Greer Garson** in *Julius Caesar.*

Leopardskin-patterned swimsuit with matching turban, gilt earrings attached, worn by **Esther Williams** in *Easy To Love.*

Brown, yellow, red and black checked blouse, worn by **Ava Gardner** in *Ride Vaquero.*

Cream batiste blouse worn by **Rita Hayworth** in *Miss Sadie Thompson.*

Two sets of army insignia, US initials and crossed pistols worn on revers and lapels, by **Gregory Peck** in *Night People.*

Two blouses, one yellow with a red tie, the other black with a green tie, worn by **Joan Crawford** in *Johnny Guitar.*

Large bracelet, diamanté stones and pearls set round a black centre on which is a single pearl, worn by **Marilyn Monroe** in *River Of No Return.*

Diaphanous gold-spotted scarf worn by **Elizabeth Taylor** in *Elephant Walk.*

Black velvet and net cocktail hat, trimmed with diamanté and silver beads, worn by **Audrey Hepburn** in *Sabrina Fair.*

Navy blue knit tie worn by **William Holden** in *Sabrina Fair.*

Burgundy coloured pure silk bow tie worn by **Humphrey Bogart** in *Sabrina Fair.*

A red and white checked gingham blouse and a salmon pink terry cloth jumper, both items worn by **Debbie Reynolds** in *Athena.*

Royal Flying Corps tie worn by **Errol Flynn** in *Lilacs In The Spring.*

Green shirt worn by **Howard Keel** in *Seven Brides For Seven Brothers.*

Pipe with a carved Indian head used by **Bing Crosby** in *The Country Girl.*

Mushroom coloured silk blouse worn by **Grace Kelly** in *The Country Girl.*

Lace-edged cravat worn by **Stewart Granger** in *Moonfleet.*

Rhinestone earrings worn by **Marilyn Monroe** in *The Seven Year Itch.*

Pearl choker necklace worn by **Jane Russell** in *Foxfire.*

Cream and red playsuit and chiffon scarf worn by **Debbie Reynolds** in *Hit The Deck.*

Black and white cravat and tie-pin worn by **Fred Astaire** in *Daddy Long Legs.*

Striped silk blouse and rhinestone earrings worn by **Doris Day** in *Love Me Or Leave Me.*

Gold, maroon and red striped tie worn by **Frank Sinatra** in *The Tender Trap.*

Grey alpaca shorts worn by **William Holden** in *Love Is A Many Splendored Thing.*

Pearl necklace and earrings worn by **Grace Kelly** in *The Swan.*

Dean Martin's velour hat from his own wardrobe.

Cap worn by **Henry Fonda** in *Mister Roberts.*

Corduroy cap worn by **Gordon MacRae** in *Carousel.*

Yellow and rust coloured pantaloons worn by **Danny Kaye** in *The Court Jester.*

Martin and Lewis pen, inscribed: 'Stolen from Martin and Lewis'.

Blue and white cotton sweater worn by **Paul Newman** in *Somebody Up There Likes Me.*

Dice used by **Marlon Brando** in *Guys And Dolls.*

Felt hat worn by **Elvis Presley** in *Love Me Tender.*

One earring, nylons, pink kid gloves, worn by **Grace Kelly** in *High Society.*

Red bandanna worn by **Burt Lancaster** in *The Rainmaker.*

Handkerchief embroidered with the name 'Lizzie', character played by **Katharine Hepburn** in *The Rainmaker.*

Yellow satin shoes worn by **Audrey Hepburn** in *Funny Face.*

Silk kimono jacket with brown sash worn by **Marlon Brando** in *Teahouse Of The August Moon.*

Top hat worn by **David Niven** in *Around The World In Eighty Days.*

Pale blue georgette headscarf worn by **Joan Collins** in *The Wayward Bus.*

Shirt worn by **Elvis Presley** in *Loving You.*

Grey short-sleeved sports shirt worn by **Elvis Presley** in *Jailhouse Rock.*

Checked shirt-blouse worn by **Shirley Jones** in *April Love.*

Gilt earrings worn by **Elizabeth Taylor** in *Cat On A Hot Tin Roof.*

These props and souvenirs would now fetch high prices if sold. I hope that you find the list as fascinating as I did and enjoy spotting these items the next time you see the films that they appeared in.

SOUVENIRS

In 1984 Royal Doulton produced a celebrity series of character jugs: **Louis Armstrong**, **Jimmy Durante**, **W.C. Fields**, **Groucho Marx**, **Mae West**. Each handle was symbolic of the star: trumpet, piano keys, cane, cigar, parasol respectively. You might still be able to obtain these jugs at £35 each from stockists of Royal Doulton. Even more interesting is that one of the stars selected for the series was Clark Gable. Approximately 2,000 of the Gable jug were distributed in the United States when suddenly Royal Doulton had to withdraw them from dealers because the Gable estate did not approve the design. Consequently they were returned and destroyed except for at least 80 jugs that had already been sold to jubilant collectors. That jug now, with its movie camera and tripod handle, is worth over £2,000. Even rarer would be the prototypes that did not go into full production for the series: **Humphrey Bogart**, **Elvis Presley** and **Marilyn Monroe**. One of the Monroe jugs found its way on to the open market, exchanging hands for £9,000.

Royal Doulton commissioned the sculptor William K. Harper to capture Charlie Chaplin and Laurel and Hardy images in fine china figures, to commemorate the centenary of the births of Chaplin and Stan Laurel. The figures are hand-made and hand-decorated; limited editions of 5,000 of Chaplin, and of Laurel and Hardy 9,500 of each. The Chaplin figure stands 9 in. tall and each detail has been sensitively re-created from his tilted bowler to his turned-up shoes. Likewise the Laurel and Hardy figures are expertly lifelike from the tie-twiddling Hardy to the head-scratching Laurel. Priced at £99.50 for the Chaplin, and £195 for the Laurel and Hardy, the figures are available only from Lawleys By Post. A further figure of Groucho Marx is planned for the summer of 1991.

ADDRESSES OF DEALERS AND MOVIE CONVENTIONS

MAGAZINES

Ken's, 29 High Street, Newport Pagnell, Bucks MK16 8AR. 0908 610003.
Monday to Saturday, 9.30 a.m. to 5.00 p.m. Closed: Thursday. Mail order. No catalogue. Nearest railway station: Milton Keynes.

Joyce and Ken Graham's shop has an excellent stock of magazines, each one carefully placed in a see-through cover. If ever a store enticed you to browse, this is it. Also offers a good selection of signed photographs, sheet music, picture postcards, and other ephemera.

Jay-Bee Magazines, 134 West Street, New York, NY 10001. 212 675–1600.

Henry Greenbaum's establishment is a treasure-trove basement of magazines from 1885 to 1987, with over two million back issues. Mail order. Send dates of wanted magazines with international reply coupons or self-addressed envelope for quote.

Tilleys Bookshops, 29/31 South Street, New Whittington, Chesterfield, Derbyshire, S43 2AA and at 281 Shoreham Street, Sheffield 1 (located opposite Sheffield United Football Ground). 0742 752 442.
Mail order from the Chesterfield address. Shop hours of Sheffield branch: Tuesday, Friday and Saturday, 9.30 to 1.30, 3 to 5 p.m.

The Tilley brothers offer a warm welcome and an extensive stock of magazines. Will keep an index card on your wants. Advisable to ring before calling.

BOOKS

The Cinema Bookshop, 13–14 Great Russell Street, London WC1. 071 637 0206.
Monday to Saturday, 10.30 a.m. to 5.30 p.m. Mail order. No catalogue.

Well-established business with a fine range of titles. Fred Zentner carries a huge stock in his basement, so if you do not see what you want . . .

Larry Edmund's Book Shop, 6658 Hollywood Boulevard, Hollywood, California, CA 90028.
Mail order. Catalogue. Good general stock of movie memorabilia.

Momi Bookshop, South Bank, London SE1 8XT. 071 928 3535.
Tuesday to Saturday, 10.00 a.m. to 9.00 p.m. Sunday, 10.00 a.m. to 7.00 p.m. Monday, 12.00 noon to 7.00 p.m. Mail order available.

In the Museum of the Moving Image. It offers an excellent selection of titles from biographies to reference works, screenplays to annuals.

A. Zwemmer, 80 Charing Cross Road, London WC2. 071 836 4710.
Monday to Friday, 9.30 a.m. to 6.00 p.m. Saturday, 10.00 a.m. to 5.30 p.m. Mail order and catalogue available.

Excellent display of film books, often titles unobtainable elsewhere.

CIGARETTE CARDS

Murray Cards (International) Ltd, 51 Watford Way, Hendon Central, London NW4 3JH. 081 202 5688 and Cecil Court Collectors Centre, 20 Cecil Court, Charing Cross Road, London WC2.
Monday to Saturday, 10.30 a.m. to 5.30 p.m. Hendon branch, Monday to Friday 9.00 a.m. to 5.00 p.m. Mail order and catalogue available.

It is a joy to behold a dealer who is both knowledgeable and obviously enjoys his work. Besides a superb stock of cigarette cards, there are fine examples of bubblegum cards and tea cards, etc.

POSTCARDS

Golden Age Postcards (Tony Bryatt), 28 St Peter's Road, Malvern, Worcs. WR14 1QS. Mail order.

Reflections of a Bygone Age (Brian and Mary Lund), 27 Walton Drive, Keyworth, Notts. NG12 5FN. 06077 4087.
Mail order. Also publish *Picture Postcard Annual.*

FRONT-OF-HOUSE SETS AND POSTERS

Flashbacks, 6 Silver Place, Beak Street, London W1R 3LJ. 071 437 8562.
Monday to Saturday, 10.30 a.m. to 7.00 p.m. Mail order.

Well stocked with a wide range of posters and stills.

Jagarts, Jeff Gordon, PO Box 6114, Yorkville Station, New York, NY 10128.
Poster City, Tod Fiertag, 3 Henry Street, Box 94, Orangeburg, New York, NY 10962.

Excellent selection of original one-sheets. Catalogue available. Knowledgeable and respected dealer.

Peter Woodland, 38 Verney Walk, Aylesbury, Bucks. HP21 8ED. 0296 415722.
Mail order.

Stills, posters. Film material bought and sold. Excellent range of movie star portraits.

SIGNED PHOTOGRAPHS

Ken's (See under magazines.)

Nate's Autographs, PO Box 459, Stevenson, Maryland, MD 21153, USA.

Robert L. Polk, 4728 North LaVergne Avenue, Chicago, Ill. 60630, USA. 312 286–4543.
Free monthly price lists.

Lee Lacy, 13a Willow Road, Hampstead, London NW3 1TJ. 071 794 6078.
Mail order and monthly list.

Specializing in show business autographs. Offers an excellent and efficient service.

Universal Autograph Collectors Club, Chris Wilson, Secretary, PO Box 6181, Washington, DC 20044–6181, USA.

Founded in 1965, UACC has over 1,500 members. Members are sent a bimonthly journal, *The Pen and Quill*, which has informative articles on all forms of autographic material. To join costs $18 per annum for US, Canada, Mexico; $24 for other areas.

PROPS AND SOUVENIRS

Christie's South Kensington Ltd, 85 Old Brompton Road, London SW7 3LD. 071 581 7611.

Hold auctions approximately twice a year for

film and entertainment sales. Frequented by dealers and serious collectors.

Phillips, Blenstock House, 7 Blenheim Street, New Bond Street, W1Y 0AS. 071 629 6602.
Fine art auctioneers.

Sotheby's, New Bond Street, London W1A 2AA. 071 493 8080.

They hold two auctions a year on Rock 'n' Roll and Film Memorabilia.

ROYAL DOULTON

Lawleys By Post, Minton House, London Road, Stoke-on-Trent ST4 7QD. 0782 744 787.
Figures of Chaplin and Laurel and Hardy were specially commissioned by Lawleys By Post, which is the direct marketing division of Royal Doulton, and so are available by mail order only and are not sold in any shops.

GENERAL

Dave and Patrick Cutts, 129 Huthwaite Road, Sutton-in-Ashfield, Notts. NG17 2GY. 0623 553443.
Mail order. Posters, front-of-house sets, magazines, postcards, books, stills.

You will receive a friendly and efficient service from the brothers Cutts.

D.C. East, 17 Dove Close, Basingstoke, Hants.
Mail order. Postcards, stills, posters, books, magazines.

Teddy Green, 2 Laurel Walk, Juniper Close, St Leonards on Sea, East Sussex TN38 9RH.
Mail order. Catalogues available.

Movie star portraits and posters.

S. and P. Parker's Movie Market, The Medlycott Centre, Milborne Port, Sherborne, Dorset DT9 5BA.
Mail order. Send stamped addressed envelope for free illustrated catalogue.

Photographs, video cassettes, film posters, lobby sets, front-of-house sets.

The Vintage Magazine Shop, 39 Brewer Street, London. 071 439 8525.

MOVIE CONVENTIONS

'Atlantique City' Indoor Antiques & Collectables Market, Atlantic City Convention Center, Atlantic City, New Jersey, USA.
9 a.m. to 8 p.m. on Saturday, 10 a.m. to 6 p.m. on Sunday. Held annually in March. Write to Brimfield Associates, Box 1519, Pleasantville, New Jersey 08232, USA.

Film Fair, Westminster Central Hall, Storey's Gate, London SW1. Opposite Westminster Abbey.
10.00 a.m. to 5.00 p.m. Held six times a year in January, March, May, July, September and November.

Autographs, books, 8mm films, magazines, postcards, posters, programmes, projectors, records, stills. Postal information from Don Walker, 21 Bronsart Road, Fulham, London SW6 6AJ. 071 385 6468. 7 p.m. to 10 p.m. Telephone information from Ed Mason, Chelsea Antiques Market, Shop 5, 253 Kings Road, London SW3. Monday to Saturday, 10 a.m. to 6 p.m. 071 352 9695.

Movie Jumble, Woluwe Shopping Center, Boulevard de la Woluwe and Avenue Paul Hyman, Woluwe Saint Lambert, Brussels, Belgium.
Annual film fair. Held on a Sunday in November, 9 a.m. to 2.30 p.m. Contact: 'Count' Coune & Sons, Ch. de Waterloo, 336 B 1060 Brussels, Belgium.

BIBLIOGRAPHY

Besides the obvious use of the magazines referred to in this book, I have also consulted copies of *Film Dope*, *Magazines of the Movies* and the following books.

BEGO, MARK. *The Best of Modern Screen*, Columbus Books, London, 1986.

BRODE, DOUGLAS. *Woody Allen, His Films and Career*, Columbus Books, London, 1986.

CHANELES, SOL. *Collecting Movie Memorabilia*, Arco Publishing Co., New York, 1977.

CONWAY, MICHAEL, and RICCI, MARK. *The Films of Marilyn Monroe*, Citadel Press, New Jersey, 1966.

HALLIWELL, LESLIE. *The Filmgoer's Companion*, Granada Publishing, London, 1983.

HALLIWELL, LESLIE. *Film Guide*, 7th edn, Grafton Books, London, 1989.

HEIDE, ROBERT, and GILMAN, JOHN. *Starstruck, The Wonderful World of Movie Memorabilia*, Doubleday & Co., New York, 1986.

HENRY, MARILYN, and DeSOURDIS, RON. *The Films of Alan Ladd*, Citadel Press, New Jersey, 1981.

KERY, PATRICIA FRANZ. *Great Magazine Covers of the World*, Abbeville Press Inc., New York, 1982.

KLAIN, JANE. *International Motion Picture Almanac*, Quigley Publishing Co., New York, 1990.

KUNHARDT, Jr, PHILIP B. *Life, The First 50 Years 1936–1986*. Little, Brown & Co. (Canada) Ltd, 1986.

McCARTHY, CLIFFORD. *Bogey, The Films of Humphrey Bogart*, Citadel Press, New Jersey, 1965.

MURRAY, MARTIN. *Cigarette Card Values* (1991). Murray Cards (International) Ltd, London.

QUINLAN, DAVID. *Quinlan's Illustrated Directory of Film Stars*, B.T. Batsford Ltd, London, 1986, 1991.

REBELLO, STEPHEN, and ALLEN, RICHARD. *Reel Art: Great Posters from the Golden Age of the Silver Screen*, Abbeville Press Inc., New York, 1988.

ROBERTSON, PATRICK. *The Guinness Book of Film Facts and Feats*, Guinness Superlatives Ltd, Enfield, Middlesex, 1980.

SHIPMAN, DAVID. *The Great Movie Stars: The Golden Years*, Angus & Robertson, London, 1970, 1979.

SLIDE, ANTHONY. *International Film, Radio and Television Journals*, Greenwood Press, Westport, Connecticut, 1985.

SPEED, F. MAURICE. *Film Review*, all edns, 1944–89. MacDonald & Co./W.H. Allen, London.

STEINBERG, COBBETT. *Reel Facts*, Vintage Books, New York, 1978.

SWANBERG, W.A. *Luce and His Empire*, Charles Scribner's Sons, New York, 1972.

THOMAS, TONY. *A Wonderful Life: The Films and Career of James Stewart*, Citadel Press, New Jersey, 1988.

WILLIS, JOHN. *Screen World*, various edns to 1989, Crown Publishers Inc., New York.

WINCHESTER, CLARENCE. *The World Film Encyclopedia*, Amalgamated Press Ltd, London, 1933.

WINCHESTER, CLARENCE. *Winchester's Screen Encyclopedia*, Winchester Publications Ltd, London, 1948.

INDEX TO THE MOST POPULAR STARS

INDEX OF MAGAZINES